WI                                    N

# World Geography

*Edited by*

## OTIS W. FREEMAN
*and* **JOHN W. MORRIS**

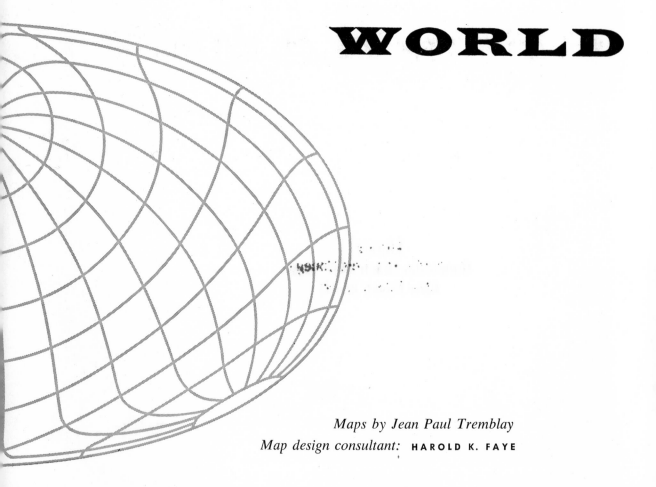

# WORLD

*Maps by Jean Paul Tremblay*
*Map design consultant:* HAROLD K. FAYE

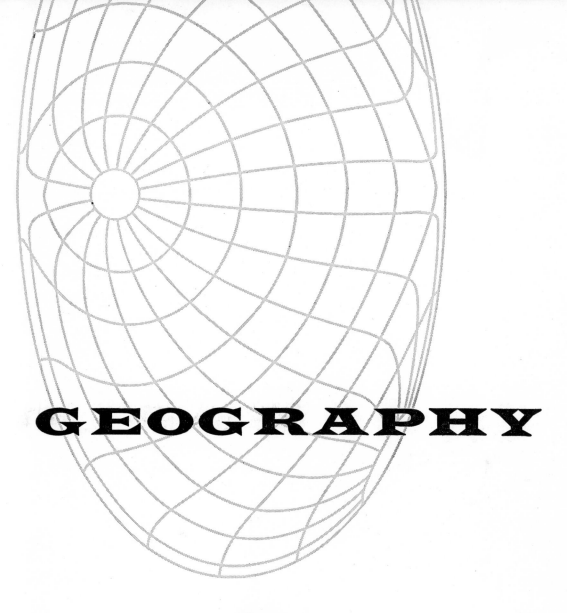

# GEOGRAPHY

*McGraw-Hill Book Company, Inc.*    **1958**

NEW YORK  TORONTO  LONDON

*This book is set in*
*Times Roman, which was*
*originally designed by*
*Stanley Morison for*
*The Times of London.*
*The headings are Spartan Heavy.*
*The chapter titles are*
*Latin Wide. The world maps*
*on binding and part titles*
*are based on the Briesemeister*
*elliptical equal-area*
*projection, American*
*Geographical Society*
*of New York.*

# Preface

THIS CENTURY has seen two world wars and many minor wars, revolutions, and "police actions." Since World War I several empires have disintegrated and many countries have changed their form of government. European nations have lost numerous colonies. Between 1941 and 1957, 25 new nations have come into existence. The boundaries of many countries have been changed. A new international body, the United Nations, has been created to maintain world peace and improve relations among nations.

*World Geography* is planned to give college and university students information about nations and continents to help them in their understanding of world affairs and the applications of geography in general. The study of familiar geographic areas has been chosen as the primary approach to world geography because we believe that this organization will help the students learn and remember essential facts and basic principles. The book proceeds, after a general introductory chapter, from areas close at hand to those more distant. Part One, the Western Hemisphere, includes (in order) the United States, Canada, Middle America, and South America. Part Two, the Eastern Hemisphere, is divided into areas selected for convenience and location. Each chapter describes a region which has unity, although the factors which account for this are not always the same. The detail in which an area is studied depends upon its relative importance in world affairs. Some continents, such as South America and Australia, are considered as a whole, but others, like Europe and North America, are divided into groups of related countries and studied in more detail. Because of the need for much greater knowledge of the United States, three chapters have been devoted to the study of the home country.

Throughout the text human activities are related to the earth's relief features, climatic regions, and natural resources—soils, vegetation, supplies of water, and mineral deposits. After studying the physical environment, each area description considers significant aspects of the cultural environment such as cities, industries, and other economic and cultural activities. Man succeeds most easily when he

*v*

acts in harmony with nature, but modern man is not inevitably dominated by his environment, because he can overcome many natural handicaps. For example, man can produce power from fuels, build dams and bring water to irrigate deserts, fertilize and reclaim poor or worn-out soil, extract raw materials and transport them great distances to industrial centers where they are manufactured for local use and for distribution all over the world. World geography gives the student a conception of the broad patterns of human occupations, the distribution of population, and the important areas of commodity production. Its study contributes greatly to knowledge which will help students understand, evaluate, and reach decisions about current world problems.

The text is intended to meet several needs. One is a survey of the countries and areas of the world to be included in the general education curriculum, especially where such a course is the only one the student will take. Another is a second course following that on principles of geography. Institutions which offer two terms of geography, one on the Eastern Hemisphere and the other on the Western Hemisphere, will find the volume adapted to their requirements. The book will also serve as a text for courses in world regional geography.

Questions at the end of each chapter supplement the text and provide discussion material to help increase student interest in the subject. Geography is such a dynamic subject that there are daily occurrences which show how current events and human relationships are affected by geographic factors. Maps, photographs, and clippings which deal with such happenings, when posted on a bulletin board or made the basis for class discussions, will help to arouse class interest in geography. The use of films and slides will enrich the course.

Geography has many words or terms which are not commonly used. In general, such words or phrases are defined when first used in the text. To supplement these definitions, and to aid in understanding many of the more common terms, a glossary has been added at the close of the book.

A "Study Guide" has been prepared for student use with *World Geography*. Each unit in the manual correlates with a text chapter. An outline study guide, a map exercise, a series of completion review statements, a list of important terms, suggested discussion questions and projects, and a self-test of multiple-choice and true-false exercises will enable the student to check his progress.

In preparing *World Geography,* the editors have called upon a team of specialists, all experienced teachers who combine comprehensive knowledge about the regions they describe with awareness of what information is most essential for students. Most of the authors have done original research on the regions about which they write, and many have made outstanding contributions in these fields.

Many public agencies, representatives from foreign lands, corporations, and individuals have supplied photographs and information used in the book, and the sincere thanks of the authors and editors is extended for such assistance. Numerous individuals have read portions of the volume and offered suggestions which the editors deeply appreciate. Special acknowledgment is due Alan P. Mewha and Norah E. Zink, both of the State Teachers College, Indiana, Pennsylvania, for such help, and also to Harold Faye, map consultant, and Jean Tremblay, cartographer, who have done excellent work in preparing the maps used in the text.

*Otis W. Freeman*
*John W. Morris*
EDITORS

# Contents

# Introduction:

# World Geography

A knowledge of geography is fundamental to understanding human activities in the modern world. Scanning a daily paper, reading a news magazine, or viewing a newscast on television all indicate our interest in national and international situations. All parts of the world are within a few hours' travel time of each other. Most are only minutes apart in communication time. The activities of any one group of people may greatly affect the work and life of numerous other groups. Thus, there is a definite interrelationship between all the groups of peoples, or nations, of the world. To understand why certain groups act as they do, why people prosper in some areas and are poor or stagnant in others, we need a knowledge of the various environments—both cultural and physical—which produce these differences.

For an exceedingly long time the earth has been undergoing changes. There have been upheavals of mountains, vast outpourings of molten rock, downwarps to form inland seas, and reduction, by erosion, of entire mountain chains to plains. Large areas of some land masses have been covered by glaciers while other areas have been inundated by the oceans. These and other changes, such as the development and spread of plants and animals, the formation of soils, the deposition of minerals, and the changes of climate which are constantly in progress, are some of the factors affecting occupancy of the earth. In addition, man's historic and cultural inheritance affects his activities, particularly his utilization of available resources.

The surface area of the earth is 196,950,000 square miles, of which 139,440,000 is water and 57,510,000 is land. Although the land area is but one-fourth the total surface of the earth, to man who lives on the land the continents and islands are of far more importance than the oceans that occupy the remaining three-fourths of the surface. Actually the huge masses of land called continents include about one-third of the earth's surface, and the ocean basins account for about two-thirds. The volume of water exceeds the capacity of the basins, however, with the result that ocean water has encroached upon the margins of the continents, thereby reducing the exposed land area to approximately one-quarter of the earth's surface. Encircling both the land and water masses is the vast layer of atmosphere which not only extends out into space but penetrates both the land and water.

Developments in aerial transportation, of intercontinental missiles, and of earth satellites have led to increased interest in the atmosphere and the growth of knowledge about it. Next can be expected the hurling of objects into space beyond the earth's atmosphere to the moon or possibly to a planet.

## THE LITHOSPHERE

The land areas, or solid portions of the earth's surface, are called the "lithosphere." Within the lithosphere are seven recognized continents. Asia, Africa, and Europe, sometimes called the Eastern Hemsphere or the Old World, form one continuous land mass. Australia, which lies to the southeast of this mass, is also a part of the Eastern Hemisphere. The Western Hemisphere, or New World, consists of North and South America, the two continents being connected by a narrow isthmus. Antarctica, which surrounds the South Pole, is isolated from the other continents.

The earth is also divided by the equator into a Northern and a Southern Hemisphere. The land masses of Europe, Asia, and North America are completely within the Northern Hemisphere, whereas Australia and Antarctica are entirely within the Southern Hemisphere. Both South America and Africa are crossed by the equator; thus each is partly in both hemispheres. Since much more of the land area, about 75 per cent, is in the Northern Hemisphere than in the Southern, the Northern Hemisphere is frequently referred to as the land hemisphere.

### Location and Shape

The shape and latitudinal location are more important and have greater influence upon human activities than does the size of the continent. North America, South America, and Africa all have triangular shapes with the base of the triangle to the north. South America, having its greatest expanse in the equatorial belt, has much territory with a sensible temperature and humidity not conducive to the highest types of human development under present conditions. The continent narrows considerably in the latitudes of Argentina and Uruguay. Africa is a desert land at its greatest width since, at that latitude, it is crossed by the subtropical high-pressure belt in which the air is descending so that moisture is absorbed rather than liberated. The central part of Africa, like the northern part of South America, is in the humid equa-

torial area. Only where highlands offset the lowland climatic conditions, and along the northern and southern edges of the continent, has much development taken place. North America is more advantageously situated than the other two. Although it reaches its greatest width along the edges of the Arctic Ocean, much of its land is in the productive temperate areas between 30° to 55°40′ north latitude.

The Eurasian land mass must be considered as a single unit. It, too, has somewhat of a triangular shape, with the base along the east side. From this triangular core project many peninsulas including Malaya, India, Arabia, Italy, and Iberia. In some respects the continent of Europe is but a peninsula extending westward from Asia. Although Eurasia has its greatest east-west extension from about 35° to 50° north latitude, the very size of the land mass counteracts this desirable location. High mountains and distances so great that rain-bearing winds lose most of their moisture before reaching the continental heartland result in large areas of dry lands. Thus, most of the people live along the margins of the land mass.

Australia has somewhat of a rectangular shape. Antarctica almost forms a circle. Australia, in the southern trade wind and subtropical high-pressure belts, is largely a region of arid and semiarid lands. The mountains along its eastern coast prevent much rain reaching the central and western interior. Antarctica, encircling the South Pole, is a land of snow and ice too cold for human habitation except under certain conditions which have been developed for scientific expeditions.

### Continental Topography

Each continent has its areas of mountains, hills, plains, and plateaus. Frequently the continental shape is determined by the location of the younger mountains or the older, more resistant rock masses. Both North and South America have high mountain ranges along their western sides. Each also has older, worn-down mountains near its eastern borders. Wide plains fill the spaces between the mountain masses. Only narrow coastal plains are adjacent to the western mountains of the American continents. In many places, however, fertile coastal plains are near the eastern border of the land masses.

A long mountain axis extends across south central Eurasia. South from this axis extend such plateaus as Iberia, the Balkans, Anatolia, Arabia, Iran, and the Deccan. To the north and northwest of this mountain core lies the great lowland plain of Europe and Asia; to the east are the densely populated coastal plains of China and Vietnam. Within the heart of this land mass are the high and dry Tibet Plateau and the Gobi. Because numerous peninsulas extend from the European part of the land mass the coast line of Europe is longer than that of any other continent.

Africa is frequently referred to as a plateau continent since much of its interior is a great central plateau. With the exception of the Atlas Mountains in the northwest, most of the highlands are scattered along the eastern side of the continent from the Red Sea to the Cape of Good Hope. Large plains are found only in the borderlands of the Sahara. For the most part the coastal plains are narrow. The abrupt changes in elevation between the coastal plains and the central plateau, along with tropical climates, diseases, and unfriendly natives, deterred the exploration of Africa for many decades.

Australia has three dominant landforms, the Eastern Highlands, the plains area in the east central part of the continent, and the western plateaus. The continent has a lower average elevation than any of the other land masses. Narrow coastal plains, south and east of the highlands, are the principal populated regions.

Little is definitely known about the detailed topography of Antarctica since most of the surface is continually covered by snow and glaciers. It is a rugged mass with several mountain ranges and peaks.

## Nations of the World

Except for Australia and Antarctica, the continents are divided into independent nations and dependencies. There are approximately 170 such political units, about 90 of which are independent. Independent countries range in size from the 8.6 million square miles in the Soviet Union to the 100 acres in Vatican City. The United States, the fifth largest country, is considerably above the average in area. Europe has more independent countries than any other continent, but except for the European part of the U.S.S.R., the countries are small. France, the largest, is smaller than the state of Texas. Many new independent countries—Libya, Sudan, Tunis, Morocco, and Ghana (Gold Coast)—are in Africa. Malaya, the youngest of all, is in Asia.

### TABLE I-1. THE CONTINENTS

| Continent | Area, sq miles | Population * | Highest peak, ft |
| --- | --- | --- | --- |
| Africa | 11,635,000 | 208,000,000 | Mt. Kilimanjaro—19,565 |
| Antarctica | 5,250,000 | 0 | Mt. Markham—15,100 |
| Asia | 17,035,000 | 1,350,000,000 | Mt. Everest—29,002 |
| Australia | 2,975,000 | 9,000,000 | Mt. Kosciusko—7,305 |
| Europe | 3,850,000 | 545,000,000 | Mt. Elbrus—18,481 |
| North America | 7,435,000 | 230,000,000 | Mt. McKinley—20,270 |
| South America | 6,860,000 | 118,000,000 | Mt. Aconcagua—22,835 |

* Areas and populations of continents vary with authorities depending on whether or not certain islands are included in their calculations.

## THE HYDROSPHERE

The water parts of the earth—oceans, seas, bays, gulfs, lakes, and others—are called the "hydrosphere." The most important of these water bodies, because of their great size, are the oceans. There are three major oceans, the Pacific, Atlantic, and Indian, and one minor ocean, the Arctic. Some maps may show an Antarctic Ocean but this so-called ocean is essentially only the southern parts of the three major oceans.

### Location and Shape

The Pacific Ocean is shaped like a huge inverted U, with the closed part at the north where the continents of Asia and North America almost meet. The eastern part of the Pacific, adjacent to the Americas, is almost free of islands. Westward from the central part of the ocean, islands both large and small are numerous. The Pacific attains its greatest width, 10,000 miles, near the equator. In area this huge body of water is greater than all the land masses of the world combined.

The Atlantic Ocean, shaped somewhat like the letter S, is east of the American continents but west of Europe and Africa. The narrowest part of the Atlantic is between Cape São Roque, Brazil, and the African coast near Dakar, French West Africa, where it is only about 1,850 miles in width. Except near the continental masses the ocean is relatively free of islands. The Atlantic and Pacific join between South America and Antarctica.

The Indian Ocean, south of Asia, east of Africa, and west of Australia, is dominantly a tropical ocean. It connects with the Atlantic at the southern tip of Africa and with the Pacific through the East Indian islands and south of Australia. Like the Pacific it has a shape rather like an inverted U. The Indian Ocean is the only ocean that does not touch North America.

The Arctic Ocean, because of its location in the north polar region, is of little importance in world trade. It is the counterpart of Antarctica and has almost the same size and shape. Most of the surface of the Arctic is covered by heavy, shifting masses of ice throughout the year. Usually near the shores of Eurasia and North America the Arctic sea lanes are open for a brief period during the short summer. The Arctic's position between Europe and North America gives it strategic importance. Air routes from North America to Eastern Europe over the Arctic Ocean are much shorter than those that follow parallels of latitude. On the direct route over the Arctic, the flying distance of about 6,000 miles across Siberia from Fairbanks, Alaska, to Moscow, U.S.S.R., is shortened to 4,200 miles. By flying over Greenland, the approximately 6,000 air miles from Chicago to Moscow can be cut nearly 2,000 miles.

### Oceans and Man

The oceans, like the land, influence man and his activities in many ways. From the oceans man secures food, furs, minerals, and many other useful items. The oceans are the primary source of one of man's chief needs—water. It is from the oceans that the atmosphere secures most of the moisture which eventually falls as rain or some other form of precipitation.

Because of differences in temperature, variations in salinity, the rotation of the earth, and winds, the ocean waters have definite movements called drifts and currents. Warm currents are streams of water which are warmer than the water through which they are flowing. For the most part warm currents flow generally toward the polar areas. In the Atlantic the warm Gulf Stream, flowing northward along the east coast of the United States, crosses the ocean under the influence of the westerly winds and moves northward along the northwest coast of Europe. Here the warmed waters help produce a more moderate climate much farther north than is found on the east sides of continental masses. The Japanese Current in the north Pacific warms the western coast of North America. Cold currents are, in many ways, the opposite of the warm currents. They are colder than the water through which they are flowing, usually flow equatorward, and often affect ad-

TABLE I-2. OCEANS

| Ocean | Area, sq miles * | Average depth, ft † | Greatest known depth, ft |
|-------|------------------|---------------------|--------------------------|
| Arctic | 5,440,000 | 4,200 | 17,850 (400 miles north of Herald Island) |
| Atlantic | 31,000,000 plus 10,000,000 in adjoining seas | 12,900 | 30,246 (Milwaukee Deep) |
| Indian | 28,350,000 | 13,000 | 24,440 (Java Trench) |
| Pacific | 64,000,000 plus 4,600,000 in adjoining seas | 14,000 | 35,640 (Marianas Trench) |

\* Areas vary with authorities depending on whether or not adjacent seas and bays are included.

† No complete ocean survey exists, therefore this figure will change as research progresses.

versely the continental area past which they move. The Labrador Current flowing south along the eastern Canadian coast, the Humboldt (Peruvian) Current moving north along the west coast of South America, and the California Current, which flows along the California coast south from San Francisco, are typical examples.

During past ages the oceans have served nations as defensive barriers, but with the air age their importance as barriers has diminished. The oceans continue, however, to furnish the cheapest means for the transportation of goods between nations. The world's greatest sea lane connects industrial Europe with industrial North America across the North Atlantic.

### THE ATMOSPHERE

The layer of the atmosphere which rests on and penetrates the land and water surfaces is called the "troposphere." In this layer temperatures change, pressures vary, clouds form, moisture condenses, winds develop, and weather originates. Weather is the constant change in the atmospheric conditions. When these conditions are observed for a period of years, however, fairly definite patterns of occurrence can be identified. Averaging weather data within a specified area gives climatic types as shown on the back end paper and in Table I-3.

### Climatic Zones

The climate of any particular place results from a combination of factors—location, topography, relative position of high- and low-pressure areas, temperature averages, and many other conditions. Mountains especially influence the amount of rainfall a place may receive depending upon its location on the windward or leeward side. Storms can advance more easily over plains than in areas of rugged relief.

Climatic regions must be areas of generalizations. The boundaries of climatic regions are seldom well-defined lines as shown on maps but rather are zones of increasing variation in rainfall, temperature, cloudiness, number of storms, and other factors. A place in western Iowa, which is in a climate boundary zone, might have a dry continental steppe climate one year and a humid continental interior climate the following year.

The pattern of climates is fairly regular, as can be determined by a study of the map. Mediterranean climates, for example, always occur on the west coasts of continents in latitudes of approximately 30° to 40° in both the Northern

**TABLE I-3. CLIMATIC REGIONS**

| Climate | Type Locations | Characteristics |
|---|---|---|
| **Rainy tropical** | Amazon Basin<br>Congo Basin<br>Indonesia | Heavy rainfall all seasons, average temperature about 80°F. Average annual temperature range usually not more than 5 or 6°F. High humidity. All-year growing season |
| **Wet-and-dry tropical**<br>Savanna | Caribbean area<br>Northern Australia<br>East Central Africa<br>Sudan<br>Llanos, Campos | Annual rainfall 30–60 in., uneven distribution. Hot wet season during period of greatest rainfall. Length of wet and dry seasons variable with distance from equator |
| Monsoon | India<br>Burma<br>Southeast China | Heavy summer rainfall, dry winters. Annual temperatures usually average above 60°F |
| **Semiarid tropical steppe** | Northern Mexico<br>Iran<br>Syria | Undependable, meager rainfall of 10–20 in. yearly. Low humidity. Temperatures range from below freezing in coldest months to an average of 60°F or higher during summer |
| **Tropical desert** | Interior Saudi Arabia<br>Sahara<br>Australian Desert | Rainfall over much of area less than 4 in. annually. Large daily temperature ranges. Very low humidity |
| **Mediterranean** | Mediterranean Basin<br>Southwestern California<br>Central Chile | Maximum rainfall during winter season with very little or no rainfall during summer. Semiarid to subhumid. Average yearly temperature about 60°F |
| **Marine west-coast** | Northwestern coast of United States<br>British Isles—West Central Europe<br>Southern Chile | Temperate humid climate. Temperatures usually between 40–60°F. Great variation in rainfall depending on altitude. Rain all seasons, maximum winter |

and Southern Hemispheres. In each case these regions have a pattern of winter rainfall, summer dryness, and moderate temperatures throughout the year. In like manner the humid continental climates appear within the interior or along the east coasts of the continents. In these areas the range of temperature increases and rainfall decreases toward the interior from the coast. The characteristics of each of the other climatic regions are summarized in Table I-3.

| Climate | Type Locations | Characteristics |
|---|---|---|
| **Humid subtropical** | Southeastern United States<br>East Central China<br>Pampa of Argentina<br>Southern Brazil | Average hot month temperatures about 75°F. Winters usually mild. Yearly rainfall varies from 30 to 65 in. depending on distance inland |
| **Humid continental**<br>Long summer | Corn Belt, United States<br>Hungary<br>Korea | Warm to hot summers, cold winters. Rainfall varies, decreasing toward interior of continent and with increasing latitude. Usually an early summer maximum |
| Short summer | Northeast United States<br>Southeast Siberia<br>Central Russia | Mild to cool summers. Long, cold winters. Annual rainfall about 30–40 in., fairly evenly distributed throughout the year |
| **Continental or mid-latitude steppe** | Great Plains, United States<br>Chaco, Argentina | Large variation in annual rainfall. Average 16–22 in. Hot summers, cool to cold winters |
| **Continental or mid-latitude desert** | Mohave Desert, Great Basin<br>Gobi<br>Turkestan | Marked temperature extremes, hottest month averages 90°F. Rainfall usually less than 7 in. |
| **Subpolar continental or taiga** | Central and east central Canada<br>Central part of Soviet Union | Long, cold winters. At least one month has temperature above 50°F. In summer long periods of daylight during each 24 hr. Much of area receives less than 15 in. of rainfall |
| **Tundra or polar** | Arctic coast of Asia, Europe, and North America | Very short, cool summers. Long, cold winters. Average temperature warmest month between 32–50°F. Annual rainfall usually 10–12 in. |
| **Polar icecap** | Antarctica<br>Northern Greenland | No month with average temperature above 32°F |
| **High altitude** | Himalayas<br>Andes<br>Rockies | Conditions vary with altitude in a particular latitude |

## Climate and Man

The climate of an area affects, at least to some extent, what man may do to make a living. Most of the grasslands or steppes of the world are used for grazing. Humid continental interior areas are usually good farmlands; the marine west coast is, in many respects, ideal for forests. Where minerals are found, where good harbors exist, where manufacturing has been developed, climate has less influence upon the activities of man. In the not too distant future, technological advances may enable man to bring water for irrigation from the oceans, seed clouds for rainfall when and where needed, track and dissipate tornadoes, and in numerous other ways adjust the climate to fit human needs better.

## GEOGRAPHY AND MAPS

To understand the location and distribution of various physical and cultural elements, the geography student is constantly confronted with the problem of visualizing an area considerably more extensive than his maximum range of vision. Ancient man recognized this and made crude drawings, or maps, to show relative locations. As knowledge about the earth increased, and man realized the problems of showing all or part of the curved surface of the earth on a flat surface, many different map projections were developed.

Maps are the essential tool for the study of geography. Users of maps must understand that no map, unless it is one of an unusually small area, is absolutely accurate. The map, since it is a representation of a curved surface upon a flat surface, will be distorted in either area, direction, or shape depending upon the factors which the cartographer wishes to emphasize, and upon the type of projection used in the construction of the map. Nevertheless, maps are the principal visual means of explaining areal and directional relationships.

The color atlas section that starts on the facing page includes a World Physical Map, a World Land Use Map, a map of the United States, a map of each continent, and maps of the Polar areas. All maps in the atlas are made on equal-area projections except the two maps of the polar regions which are made on stereographic projections. In the limited areas shown, however, these are close enough to areal equivalence to serve the same purpose. The world and continental maps are also based on an interrupted projection which permits greater accuracy in the shape of the larger land masses. A study of the World Physical Map will reveal certain specific features. The projection has been interrupted, or broken, along meridans which cross only land areas of very sparse population. For example, the interruption be-

tween North America and Europe is along the 40 degree west longitude line, or near the center of the Atlantic Ocean, and divides only the glacier-covered island of Greenland. Note that there are three interruptions in the Southern Hemisphere, one between each of the land masses.

On an equal-area projection all points equally distant from the center of the projection are also equally distant from the center of the map, and all places equally distant from the center have the same distortion. Except for Antarctica, the projection for each continent is based along a meridian which extends as a straight line north or south from the equator. Thus, the projection of North America is centered on the 100th meridian west, South America on the 60th meridian west, Africa on the 20th meridian east, Australia on the 140th meridian east, and the great Eurasian land mass on the 40th meridian east. Since distortions in the projection are relative, and since it is an equal-area projection, the continents can be compared with each other with some accuracy as to size and shape.

On an equal-area projection all areas bear a correct proportional relationship to each other. Each map contains a scale statement relating the size of a given area on the map to its corresponding area on the earth. Since all projections are equal area, it is possible to make a size comparison of any area on a map with any other area on the same map or with areas on other maps with the same scale. In this atlas it is also possible by calculation to compare areas on other maps at different scales.

The last plate in the atlas section shows the Polar areas. Although both maps are practically equal area, they are made on a considerably different grid. Either the North or South Pole is used as the center for the map. The lines of latitude are all circles and the meridians

The maps in this atlas contain two kinds of information important in the study of geography. They picture the physical aspects of our planet—continents and islands, seas and lakes, peaks and plains—in correct relationship to each other. They present features of human culture, such as the names of countries and cities and the location of political boundaries.

One map is a general view of the earth. Another indicates by special color coding what use man makes of the land. The balance of the atlas is devoted to specific regions on a larger scale. A dramatic contrast between the areas of vegetation and the barren deserts is apparent, as is the way plant life is distributed in relation to the world's oceans, rivers, mountain chains, and plateaus.

In all the maps except the one for land use, the artist-cartographer, Hal Shelton, has shown the color differences of the surface that would be seen by an imaginary observer out in space. Summer, the chief season of growth, is represented as prevailing everywhere at the same time.

The key at the right explains the colors to be found in the maps: snow and ice, dominant types of natural vegetation, and desert. Its coloring and relief illustrate in miniature the wide variety of physical features in the maps themselves.

# WORLD ATLAS

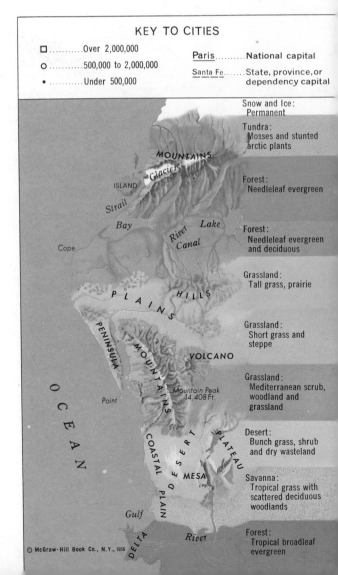

KEY TO CITIES

▫..........Over 2,000,000

○..........500,000 to 2,000,000

•..........Under 500,000

Paris..........National capital

Santa Fe......State, province, or dependency capital

Snow and Ice: Permanent

Tundra: Mosses and stunted arctic plants

Forest: Needleleaf evergreen

Forest: Needleleaf evergreen and deciduous

Grassland: Tall grass, prairie

Grassland: Short grass and steppe

Grassland: Mediterranean scrub, woodland and grassland

Desert: Bunch grass, shrub and dry wasteland

Savanna: Tropical grass with scattered deciduous woodlands

Forest: Tropical broadleaf evergreen

MOUNTAINS
Glacier
ISLAND
Strait
Bay
Cape
River
Lake
Canal
PLAINS
HILLS
PENINSULA
MOUNTAINS
VOLCANO
Point
Mountain Peak 14,408 Ft.
COASTAL PLAIN
DESERT
MESA
PLATEAU
OCEAN
Gulf
DELTA
River

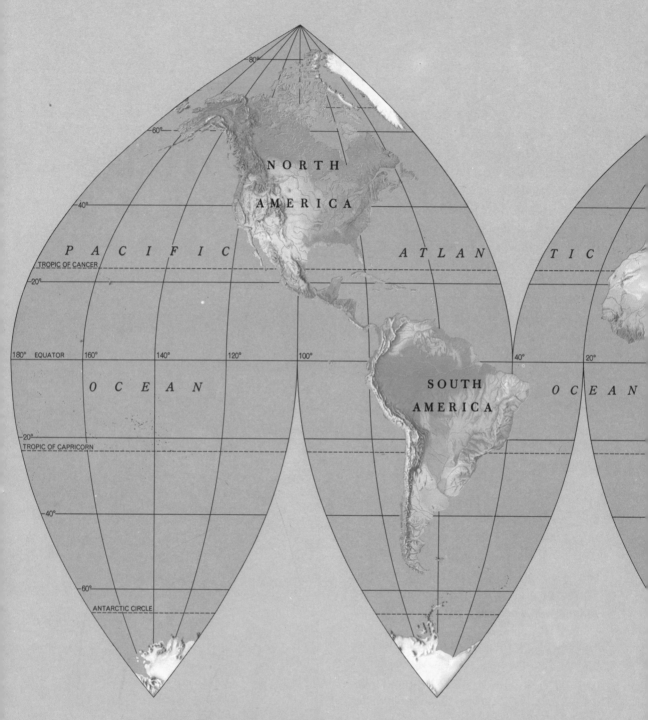

# PHYSICAL MAP OF THE WORLD

Parabolic Equal-area Projection
1 square inch = 3,168,400 square miles

Linear scale 1780 miles to one inch at the Equator

| 0 | 1000 | 2000 | 3000 |

Statute miles

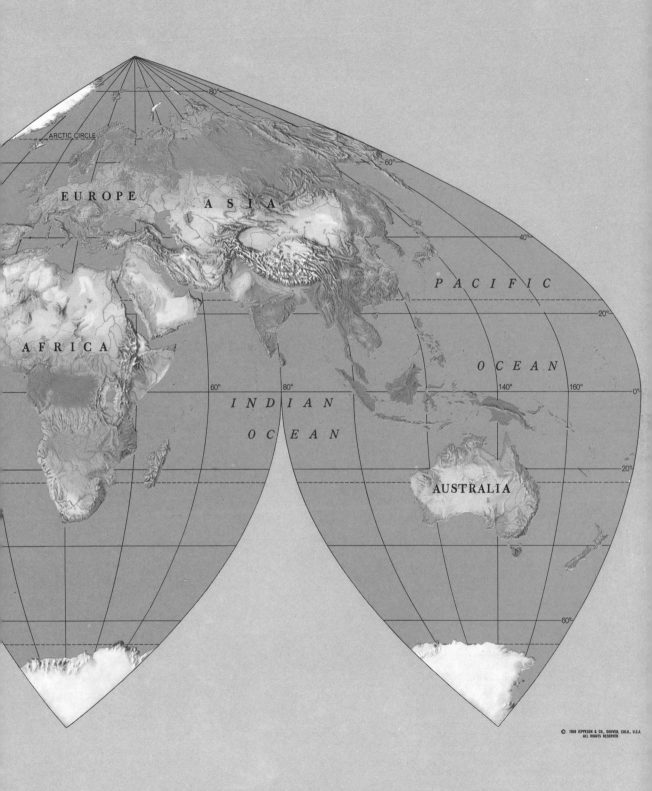

EUROPE

ASIA

AFRICA

PACIFIC

OCEAN

INDIAN

OCEAN

AUSTRALIA

ARCTIC CIRCLE

80°

60°

40°

20°

60°

80°

140°

160°

0°

20°

60°

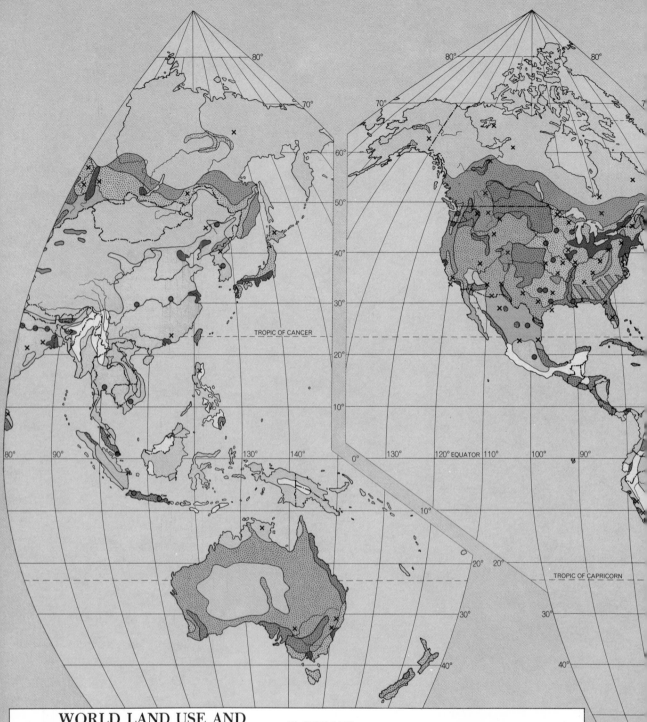

# WORLD LAND USE AND ECONOMIC DEVELOPMENT

The land of the world is used variously as shown by the colors below. Superimposed on the map is the pattern of the world's economies: those that are technically advanced are indicated by a dot symbol and those that are underdeveloped are shown without this overprint. Technically advanced lands have less than 45% of their labor forces in agriculture. Considered by per capita gross national product, Chile and Japan would be removed from, and Venezuela added to, technically advanced countries. Plantations are considered technically advanced.

**I. SUBMERGED LAND** — (Developmental stage not shown)
See inset map

**II. URBAN AND MANUFACT- URING LAND** — (Developmental stage as in country of location)

**III. RURAL LAND**

A. Unused, or very primitively used

B. Forest Exploitation

C. Grazing

D. Agriculture
1. Predominantly subsistence agriculture
2. Mixed commercial and subsistence agriculture, diversified crops and animals
3. Predominantly commercial agriculture or horticulture

E. Major Mineral Extraction

— (Developmental stage of economies not shown)
— Underdeveloped economies
— Technically advanced economies
— Underdeveloped economies
— Technically advanced economies
— (Entirely in underdeveloped economies)
— Underdeveloped economies
— Technically advanced economies
— Underdeveloped economies
— Technically advanced economies
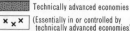 (Essentially in or controlled by technically advanced economies)

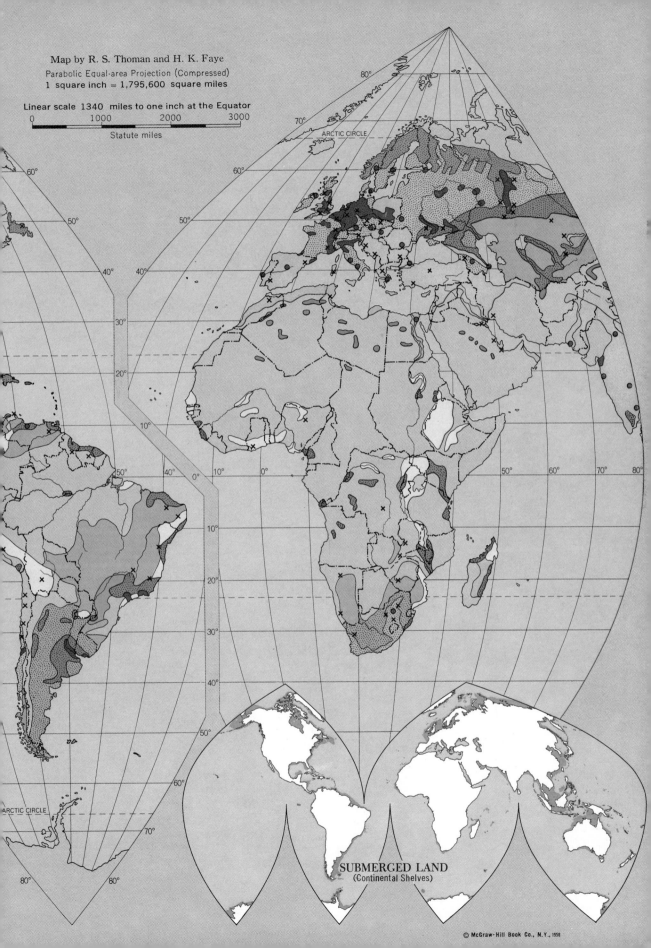

Map by R. S. Thoman and H. K. Faye

Parabolic Equal-area Projection (Compressed)

1 square inch = 1,795,600 square miles

Linear scale 1340 miles to one inch at the Equator

0    1000    2000    3000

Statute miles

ARCTIC CIRCLE

SUBMERGED LAND
(Continental Shelves)

# THE UNITED STATES OF AMERICA

Lambert Conformal Conic Projection

National capitols underlined: Ottawa

State and province capitols underlined: Atlanta

SOUTH AMERICA

Parabolic Equal-area Projection

1 square inch = 360,000 square miles

Linear scale 600 miles to one inch at the Equator

0      500      1000      1500

Statute miles

**EUROPE**

Lambert Azimuthal Equal-area Projection
1 square inch = 72,900 square miles

Linear scale 270 miles to one inch

| 0 | 100 | 200 | 300 | 400 | 500 | 600 |

Statute miles

ICELAND

Reykjavik

ARCTIC CIRCLE

NORWEGIAN SEA

LOFOTEN IS.

FAEROES

Trondheim

SHETLAND IS.

Bergen

NORTH
ATLANTIC
OCEAN

HEBRIDES

ORKNEY IS.

NORTH
SEA

Oslo

Lake Vänern

Göteborg

SCOTLAND

Aberdeen

Glasgow    Dundee

NORTHERN
IRELAND   Belfast   Edinburgh

Skagerrak

Aarhus

Copenhagen    Malmö

DENMARK

Kiel

Newcastle

IRELAND
Dublin

Manchester    Leeds

Liverpool    Sheffield

Birmingham    ENGLAND

WALES

Lübeck

Hamburg

EAST

Bremen

EUR

Hannover    Berlin

Amsterdam

The Hague

NETHERLANDS

Rotterdam    Dortmund

Antwerp    NORTH

Essen    Cologne

GERMANY

Leipzig

Dresden

SILESIA

Pozn

Cork

Cardiff    London

Brighton

Lands End

English Channel

CHANNEL IS.

Le Havre

Brussels    BELGIUM    Bonn    WEST

LUX.

Frankfurt

Karl Marx

Prague

CZECHOSL

Paris    R.

Seine

Loire

FRANCE

Nantes

Tours

Strasbourg    SAAR    GERMANY

Stuttgart

BAVARIA

Danube

Brno

Vienna

Linz

AUSTRIA

Graz

Cape Finisterre

Bordeaux

Bay of
Biscay

Bilbao

Saint Étienne
AUVERGNE
MTS.

Lyons

Zurich

Bern

SWITZERLAND

LIECH.

Rhine River

Rhône R.

Milan

Po River

Turin

Genoa

Ljubljana

Trieste

Venice

Bologna

DINARIC ALP

YUG

Zagre

Oporto

SPANISH

PYRENEES

ANDORRA

Toulouse

Saragossa

Marseille    Nice

MONACO    Florence

ADRIATIC

SEA

Lisbon

PORTUGAL

SPAIN

Ebro River

Madrid

Tagus River

Barcelona

CORSICA

Rome

ITALY

TYRRHENIAN SEA

Cape St. Vincent

PLATEAU

Guadalquivir River

Valencia

Murcia

BALEARIC IS.

SARDINIA

Naples

SA. NEVADA

Seville

Cádiz

Málaga

MEDITERRA

Cagliari

Palermo

SICILY

Catania

Tangier    Strait of Gibraltar

Tetuán

Oran

Algiers

Bizerte

Bône

Cape Bon

Casablanca    Rabat

Meknes    Fès

BN E A N

Constantine

Tunis

TUNISIA

MOROCCO

Marrakech

ATLAS    MTS.

ALGERIA

Sfax

20° North Cape
Hammerfest

BARENTS SEA

30°    40°    70°    50°    60°    70°

Murmansk

KOLA PENIN.

Narvik

U R A L

S I B E R I A

Ob River

Pechora River

Irtysh River

70°

Nizhni Tagil

Sverdlovsk

Chelyabinsk

WHITE SEA

Arkhangelsk

N. Dvina River

FINLAND

LAKE REGION

Petrozavodsk

Lake Onega

Tampere

Lake Ladoga

Gulf of Bothnia

Turku

Helsinki

Leningrad

Rybinsk Reservoir

Molotov

U R A L   M T S.

Ufa

Magnitogorsk

ÅLAND IS.

Gulf of Finland

Stockholm

SAREMA

Tallin

Lake Peipus

Riga

GOTLAND

Kaliningrad

Vilnyus

Minsk

B A L T I C   S E A

Kalinin

Ivanovo

Rybinsk Reservoir

Moscow

Gorki

Volga River

Kazan

Kuibyshev

Chkalov

60°

50°

U N I O N   O F   S O V I E T

S O C I A L I S T   R E P U B L I C S

Tula

Don

Saratov

Ural River

Voronezh

Volga River

Stalingrad

Astrakhan

CASPIAN DEPRESSION

ARAL SEA

Gdansk

PLAIN

Vistula River

Warsaw

Łódź

POLAND

Kraków

Brest Litovsk

PRIPET MARSHES

Kiev

Dnieper River

Kharkov

DONETS BASIN

Makeevka

Don

Rostov

CASPIAN SEA

Lvov

Dniester River

UKRAINE

Dnepropetrovsk

Krivoi Rog

Zaporoshe

Stalino

Zhdanov

CARPATHIAN MTS.

KIA

Budapest

HUNGARIAN PLAIN

GARY

Cluj

Iași

Odessa

Sea of Azov

Kerch

Krasnodar

Mt. Elbrus 18,564

zeged

ROMANIA

Timișoara

Brăila

CRIMEA

Sevastopol

Yalta

C A U C A S U S   M T S.

Batum

Tiflis

Baku

botica

elgrade

Bucharest

Constanta

B L A C K   S E A

Kars

Yerevan

E L B U R Z

arajevo

Danube River

Stalin

Kerch

40°

LAVIA

BULGARIA

Sofia

BALKAN MTS.

Istanbul

Bosporus

Tabriz

I R A N

MTS.

ALBANIA

rane

Plovdiv

Sea of Marmara

Tehran

Salonika

GREECE

AEGEAN SEA

Izmit

Ankara

ANATOLIAN PLATEAU

T U R K E Y

ZAGROS MTS.

IONIAN IS.

Patras

Athens

Izmir

TAURUS MTS.

Adana

Aleppo

Orontes R.

SYRIA

A S S Y

Mosul

Tigris

Euphrates

Baghdad

River

CYPRUS

Nicosia

Candia

CRETE

SEA

Beirut

LEBANON

Sidon

Damascus

I R A Q

River

Basra

20°    30°    40°    30°

© 1958 JEPPESEN & CO., DENVER, COLO., U.S.A.
ALL RIGHTS RESERVED

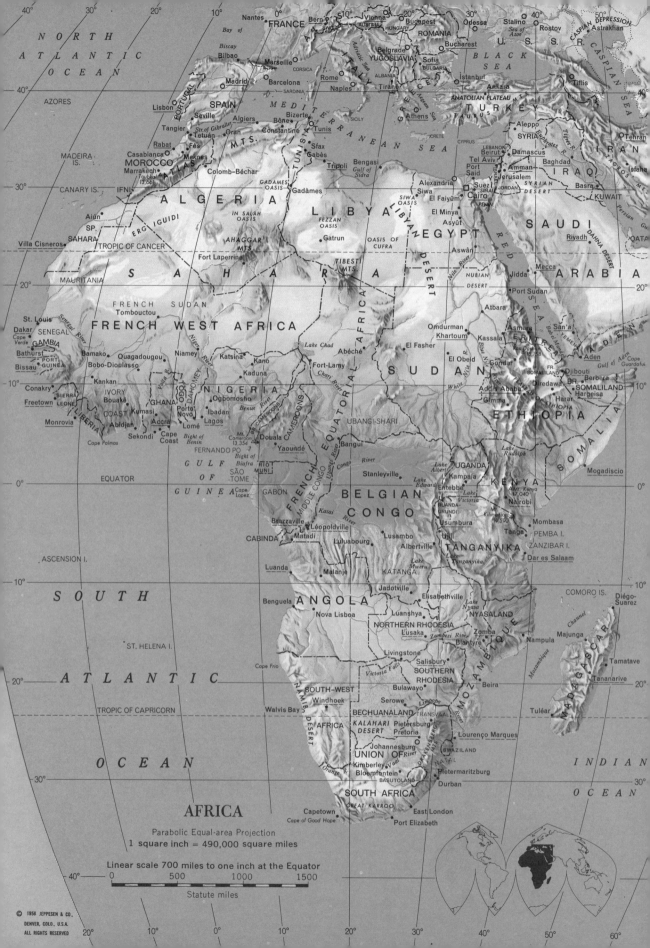

# AFRICA

Parabolic Equal-area Projection
1 square inch = 490,000 square miles

Linear scale 700 miles to one inch at the Equator

Statute miles

# AUSTRALIA, NEW ZEALAND AND THE EAST INDIES

Parabolic Equal-area Projection
1 square inch = 490,000 square miles

Linear scale 700 miles to one inch at the Equator

| 0 | 500 | 1000 | 1500 |

Statute miles

# NORTH POLAR REGION

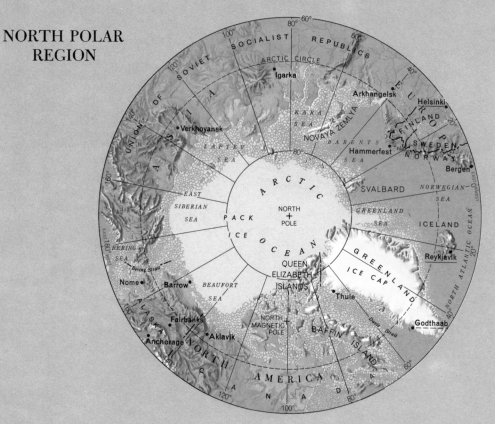

Polar Stereographic Projection
1 square inch = 1,440,000 square miles (approx.)

Linear scale 1200 miles to one inch

| | | | | |
|---|---|---|---|---|
| 0 | 500 | 1000 | 1500 | 2000 |

Statute miles

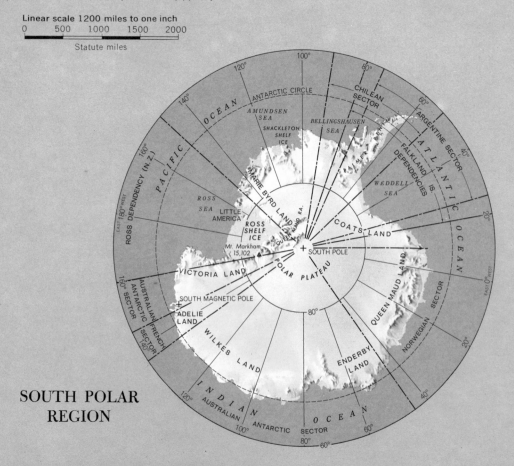

# SOUTH POLAR REGION

are all straight lines extending from the center to the edge of the map. On the North-Pole-centered projection the entire outer edge of the map is south; on the South-Pole-centered map the outer edge is north. To read directions on any map one must carefully follow longitude and latitude lines.

Numerous black-and-white maps can be found in this book. Various symbols and shadings have been used to show distributions. For example, Figures 6-7,* 14-2, and 15-1 show

* First numeral(s) refers to the chapter, second numeral(s) to the number of the illustration within the chapter.

the distribution of population by the dot method; Figures 14-3 and 15-2 show concentrations of population in cities by using circles. Figures 7-2 and 9-5 show the distribution of population by shading. The key with the map explains the symbol used. The maps in each chapter have been designed to show certain specific locations and distributions for the region being discussed.

Frequent reference to the atlas, and to the specific maps in each chapter, will aid in orienting the material being studied.

# Part I. Western

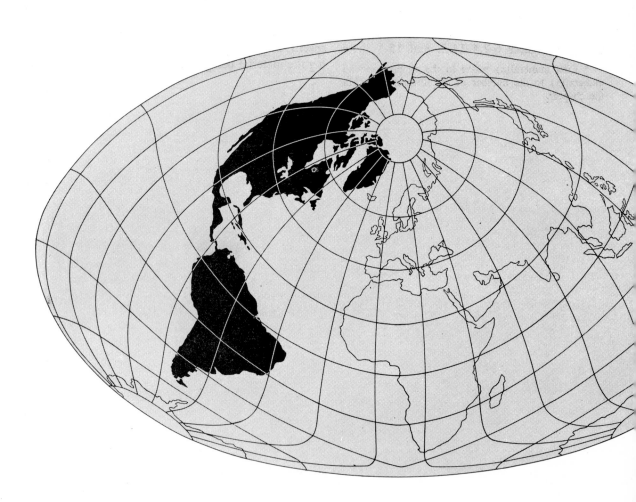

# Hemisphere

North and South America are sizable continents, their combined area totaling more than 14 million square miles. When compared with Asia they are small, however, since that largest of all continents is over 2 million square miles greater in area than the New World. South America is southeast of its northern neighbor, with most of its west coast lying east of the meridian of New York City. Cape São Roque, the easternmost point in Brazil, is on the mid-meridian between New York and London; Cape Prince of Wales, the most western point of the Alaskan mainland, is only 60 miles from Asia. The American continents extend between Cape Morris Jesup at the northern tip of Greenland, only 440 miles from the North Pole, and Cape Horn, at 56° south latitude, the southern tip of South America.

## PHYSICAL SETTING

### Climate

Climatically the continents have many differences. All of North America is north of the equator and only its narrowest part has a rainy tropical climate. In contrast the equator crosses South America at almost its greatest width, much of that continent having a wet, tropical climate. With cold climates the reverse is true. The Arctic Circle crosses northern North America at near its maximum width. Thus, the far north of this continent has such a severe climate that there is little agriculture and inhabitants are few. On the other hand, all of South America is well north of the Antarctic Circle, only stormy Tierra del Fuego and the high mountain areas having climates too cold for farming. In general the middle latitudes have the most favorable climates for man, but South America is narrow in the temperature areas. In some measure this handicap is rendered less serious because a considerable amount of tropical South America has such a high elevation.

### Relief Features

The relief features of North and South America are somewhat similar. Each continent has a mountain chain parelleling the Pacific, that in South America being much higher. East of the mountain barrier vast plains extend north-south through the continental interiors. The plains of North America are well populated in the mid-

dle latitudes but settlement rapidly declines toward the north. In South America, the widest plains are in the tropics and are poorly developed when compared with the mid-latitude plains of Argentina and Uruguay. Unfortunately, these countries are located where the continent is rapidly narrowing so that areas of productive land and favorable climate are smaller than similar areas in the United States. Highlands, older geologically and more reduced in height by erosion than the western cordilleras, are located near much of the Atlantic coast in both continents. In general they are considerably less of a barrier than the younger, higher, and more rugged western mountains, and have less effect on climate.

## PEOPLE OF THE NEW WORLD

The first people to occupy the New World were the American Indians whose ancestors came from Asia. They eventually occupied both continents although the Indian population in neither was ever very great. Their culture, to a great extent, depended upon their physical environments. Where conditions were favorable, several wild plants—beans, squash, maize (corn), pumpkins, white potatoes, manioc (cassava), bananas, yams—were domesticated. Besides the dog, the llama of Peru was the only domestic animal kept by the Indians. Some groups, such as the Incas of the Andean plateaus and the Aztecs of Mexico, attained high stages of civilization by becoming both farmers and craftsmen. The Iroquoian and the Muskhogean groups, living in what is now the eastern part of the United States, developed a somewhat sedentary agricultural civilization. On the Western plains, however, the Sioux, Arapaho, Cheyenne, Comanche, Osage, and others, lived a migratory life by following the buffalo herds as they roamed the plains. Some of the Indians living in the Pacific Northwest were fishermen whereas many of those in California were gatherers who depended on roots and fruits.

At present North America has almost double the population of its southern neighbor. The Spanish, who settled much of the area south of

the Rio Grande, came seeking riches in the form of gold and other scarce minerals. The English, who eventually dominated settlement north of the Rio Grande, came seeking places to build homes and to develop agriculture and other resources. Finally they produced manufactured goods for the markets of the world. Independence for the Colonies and the development of the United States as it expanded across the continent helped attract thousands of migrants to the New World. Even in proportion to population, North America produces more raw materials and manufactured goods than South America. Reasons for this greater production in North America are the large areas of soil and climate suitable for growing wheat, cotton, corn, and other agricultural products, far greater resources of coal, and the development of other minerals and of water power. In addition there are the less tangible but equally important factors of inventiveness, skill in all forms of production, and political stability.

During the last century there have been great shifts in population of the United States. From the 1860s into the 1890s most of the public land of the West passed into private ownership and the population was predominantly rural. Thereafter industries expanded and the cities grew until now the population is largely urban.

## GEOGRAPHICAL RELATIONSHIPS

### North America

The western part of North America is dominated by high, rugged mountains. The western Cordillera extends southward from the Alaskan and Brooks Ranges in Alaska and is separated in Canada into the Pacific Coast Range and the Rocky Mountains. The Coast Range, trending south and southeast, has determined much of the shape of the western edge of the continent. The Rocky Mountains in many places parallel the Coast Range, the eastern edge being about 600 miles inland. However, at approximately the 49th parallel—the United States–Canadian boundary—the Rockies form a large curve, swinging eastward into the central parts of Colorado and New Mexico, and in places are more than 1,000 miles east of the Coast Range.

In the United States, between these two mountain groups, other large mountain ranges and plateaus have developed. The Columbia Intermontane province in Washington, Oregon, and Idaho was formed mainly as a result of volcanic activity; the Colorado Plateau of Utah, Colorado, New Mexico, and Arizona has resulted from a gradual uplifting of the land. Inland from the coast, the Sierra Nevada of eastern California and the Cascades of Washington and Oregon are both higher than the Coast Range. The largest area of North America without drainage to the oceans is that part of Nevada and Utah which is trapped between the Rockies and the Sierra Nevada.

In northern Mexico the various ranges come together forming the Sierra Madre and the Central Plateau of Mexico. South of the Isthmus of Tehuantepec the mountains form a low, broken ridge to the South American border. The western Cordillera has its greatest elevations in the north, Mt. McKinley in southern Alaska reaching 20,270 feet. The highest point in the United States proper is Mt. Whitney, of the Sierra Nevada in California, with an elevation of 14,996 feet.

The effect of these western mountains upon the activities of man is very distinct. Since their elevations cause the prevailing westerly winds to be cooled and thus to lose their moisture, the area between the mountains and even for some distance east of the Rockies is too dry for most types of agriculture. Grazing and irrigation farming are the dominant occupations except where mining or some specialized activity has developed. Population density over most of the area is sparse.

In the eastern part of the continent old, worn-down mountains, such as the Laurentian Highlands of Canada and the Appalachians of the United States, are bordered by low plateaus or plains. Although these mountains formed transportation barriers during the colonial period, they present only minor difficulties to modern engineering. The mountains have contributed to the growth of manufacturing since they are the source of much water power and many minerals. Much of the area, already highly industrialized and densely populated, will be greatly aided by the improvement of the St. Lawrence–Great Lakes Seaway.

The central part of North America is a vast plain. Fertile soils, moderate rainfall, and agricultural skill have made it the most productive food-supplying region in the world. American farms or ranches are highly mechanized. With careful farm management more wheat, cotton, corn, hogs, cattle, and some other farm products are grown than in any other comparable area. Highways, railways, airways, and waterways connect all parts of this highly productive area with the Eastern industrial region. Good harbors along the eastern coast give its output easy access to world markets.

Three large groups of islands—the Aleutians, the Canadian Arctic Archipelago, and the West Indies—are also part of North America. Southwest of Greenland, the world's largest island, and north of Canada lie Victoria, Baffin, Ellesmere, and many other islands, which form the Canadian Arctic Archipelago. Some have never been completely explored. Because of their high latitude and cold climate, most are uninhabited. Greenland is nearly covered by an icecap, and most of its population lives along the southern and southwestern shore. Its chief importance is as a military site. Extending westward from the Alaskan Peninsula toward Asia are the Aleutians, a group of volcanic islands of relatively little importance. Between the United States and South America are the Greater Antilles and other productive islands that make up the West Indies. Since many of these mountainous islands are greatly overpopulated, the standard of living in most instances leaves much to be desired. (See Atlas maps of North America.)

## South America

South America, like North America, also has a region of high, rugged, young mountains along its west coast, old, low, and worn-down mountains to the east, and large plains between the two. The Andes, a formidable barrier between eastern and western South America, rise abruptly from the Pacific and Caribbean shores of the continent. Starting with three distinct ridges in Venezuela and Colombia they extend for 4,000 miles along the western edge of the continent to Cape Horn. In the southern part of Colombia the three ridges come together. From this point southward they separate, as in Ecuador, southern Peru, and Bolivia, leaving high intermontane plateaus between the ridges. South from central Chile they form a long, high, continuous range. The Andes attain their greatest elevation on the Chilean–Argentine border in Mt. Aconcagua, 22,835 feet, which is the highest point in the Americas. Since much of South America is in the tropics, the intermontane plateaus, here about 4,000 to 7,000 feet in elevation, are among the more desirable places for human habitation. It was in these plateau basins that the Indians reached their highest stage of civilization.

In the eastern part of the continent, the older highlands and plateaus of Brazil and the Guiana Highlands of Venezuela are somewhat comparable to the highlands in eastern North America. On the plateaus and highlands of eastern Brazil that country has its greatest agricultural, mineral, and manufacturing development and its greatest population density.

Except for part of the Pampa, the large plains areas of South America are poorly developed. The Llanos of Venezuela and Colombia, the Amazon Basin of Brazil, and the Gran Chaco of Paraguay and Argentina are all sparsely settled. Climatic conditions, which vary seasonally from droughts to periods of excessive rainfall, and an all-year high temperature tend to retard settlement. The Pampa of Argentina and Uruguay, in an area of temperate climate, is one of the world's leading producers of cattle, sheep, and wheat. Again with the exception of the Pampa, which has a well-developed railway network, the South American plains lack transportation systems other than their rivers. The Amazon River, which carries more water than any other in the world, drains the large Amazon Basin. The Orinoco serves the Llanos, and the Gran Chaco depends upon the Paraná and its tributaries for a part of its transportation.

The coast line of South America, except for the southern third of Chile, is very regular; hence the continent has few good harbors. Southern Chile has many islands but none of importance. The large island of Tierra del Fuego is at the southern end of the continent from which it is separated by the Strait of Magellan. The Falkland Islands, controlled by Britain but claimed by Argentina, are about 300 miles east of the Strait of Magellan; the Galapagos Islands, owned by Ecuador, are approximately 600 miles west of that country. Neither group contributes much to the world economy. (See Atlas maps of South America.)

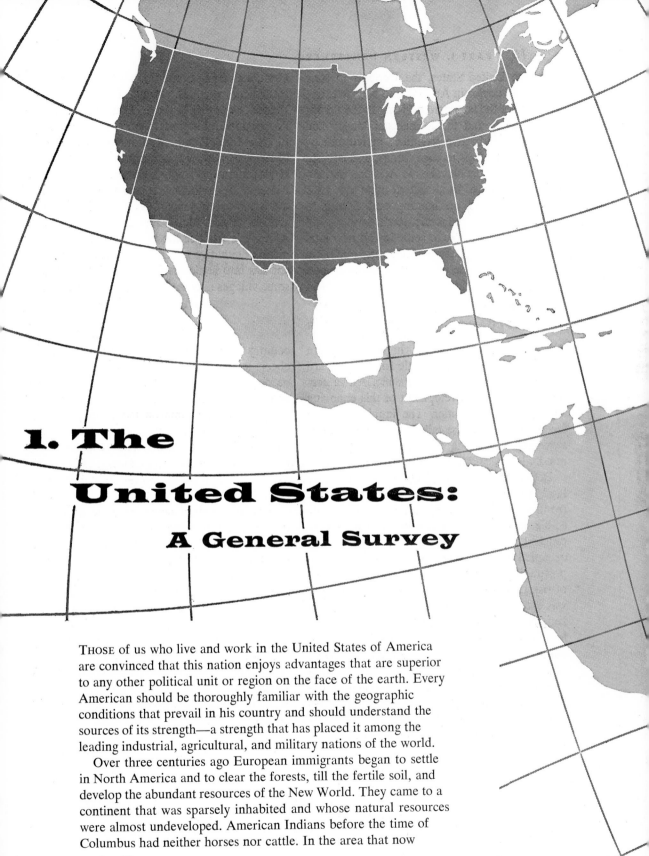

# 1. The
# United States:
## A General Survey

THOSE of us who live and work in the United States of America
are convinced that this nation enjoys advantages that are superior
to any other political unit or region on the face of the earth. Every
American should be thoroughly familiar with the geographic
conditions that prevail in his country and should understand the
sources of its strength—a strength that has placed it among the
leading industrial, agricultural, and military nations of the world.

Over three centuries ago European immigrants began to settle
in North America and to clear the forests, till the fertile soil, and
develop the abundant resources of the New World. They came to a
continent that was sparsely inhabited and whose natural resources
were almost undeveloped. American Indians before the time of
Columbus had neither horses nor cattle. In the area that now

15

forms the United States, the Iroquois in New York, the Pueblos in Arizona and New Mexico, and some of the larger tribes living in the South-eastern states and the Mississippi Valley had developed a primitive sedentary agriculture by planting such crops as corn, beans, and squash. A few, such as the Navahos in Arizona, had developed irrigation. In almost all other areas the natives depended on hunting and fishing to meet their simple economic needs.

The first Europeans to settle in this new land were the Spanish. Before 1550, their explorers and colonizers made an effort to establish forts and towns in Florida and north along the Rio Grande as far as Santa Fe. The first permanent settlement was St. Augustine, 1565. The French, exploring in the St. Lawrence area, had no permanent settlements on the mainland until after 1590. The first permanent English settlement, Jamestown, was not made until 1607. It was from the English settlements along the fringe of the Atlantic seaboard, however, that the westward movement began which took new settlers inland along an advancing frontier. Along this frontier the migrants gradually displaced the native tribes, thus transforming wilderness into settled and cultivated land, where some villages later grew into large cities.

### INFLUENCE OF THE FRONTIER

American society evolved during the expansion of settlement from the Atlantic fringe westward across the continent to the Pacific. An important factor in the development of this changing society was the frontier. The immigrants first faced a million square miles of primeval forest, swarming with game and populated by a few hundred thousand natives.

Before a nation could come into existence the land had to be transformed. In America the frontier was a zone between a comparatively stable and well-settled region and one hardly touched by civilization. This was an area thinly occupied by Indians and offering abundant opportunities for development although at the cost of risk and hardship. As the zone of settlement was extended, forests were cleared, the sod broken, crops and orchards planted, homes and villages built, railroads and highways constructed, and a savage wilderness transformed into farms and cities.

The century following Independence saw territorial gains that extended the United States across the continent to the Pacific. Frontier settlements spread across empty areas until the country became a united whole. Abundant cheap land gave poor men an opportunity to become landowners quickly. Although the chance to acquire good free homestead land virtually ended early in the twentieth century, the human characteristics developed on the frontier still affect the American people and their way of life. The experience of overcoming natural difficulties and the thrill of taking part in the settlement and expansion of the country colored and shaped the thinking and culture of Americans. Great and untouched natural resources and the economic needs of both the new land and the Old World furthered the development of lumbering, mining, and manufacturing. Men who tilled their own land, however, often did not want to work for wages in industry. This led to a shortage of labor, high wages, immigration up to a million persons per year, and invention of laborsaving machinery. So, descendants of migrants from the Old World developed the peculiar culture of the United States in the New, while the power and production of the country expanded beyond the most optimistic forecasts.

### PHYSICAL REGIONS

Located in the United States, either in whole or in part, are eight major physical regions (Figure 1-1). Within each region there is considerable unity but variations are great enough so that several subregions can be recognized. Mountains or plains are usually the dominant land-

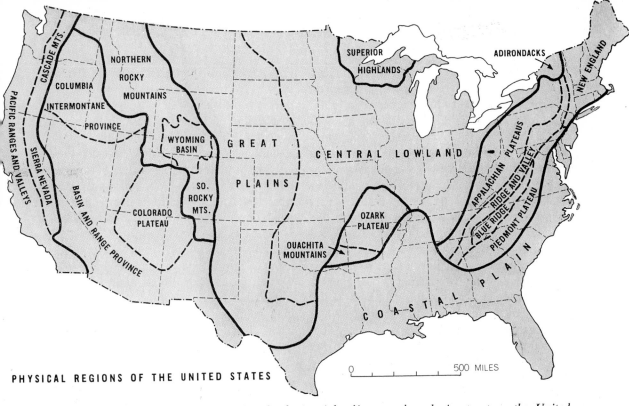

PHYSICAL REGIONS OF THE UNITED STATES

0       500 MILES

*Figure 1-1   On the basis of landform and geologic structure the United States is divided into eight physical regions. Where adjacent to Canada or Mexico the regions extend into those countries.*

| | |
|---|---|
| *Appalachian Highlands* | *Canadian Shield* |
|   *New England* |   *Adirondack Mountains* |
|   *Piedmont Plateau* |   *Superior Highlands* |
|   *Blue Ridge* | *Rocky Mountains* |
|   *Ridge and Valley* |   *Northern Rockies* |
|   *Appalachian Plateaus* |   *Wyoming Basin* |
| *Coastal Plain* |   *Southern Rockies* |
| *Interior Highlands* | *Intermontane Region* |
|   *Ozark Plateau* |   *Columbia Intermontane province* |
|   *Ouachita Mountains* |   *Basin and Range province* |
| *Interior Plains* |   *Colorado Plateau* |
|   *Central Lowlands* | *Pacific Region* |
|   *Great Plains* |   *Sierra Nevada–Cascade Mountains* |
| |   *Pacific Ranges and Valleys* |

forms, although in certain areas hills or plateaus may be more prominent. Most of the physical regions found in the United States are coextensive with those of Canada or Mexico. In the eastern half of the nation, the regions do not have the extremes in elevations that are to be noted in the West. In most of the regions, because of differences in underlying rocks and variations in landforms, boundaries are fairly definite.

The Appalachian System, extending southwestward from New England to northern Alabama, is characterized by numerous mountain ranges and ridges interlocked with a series of elongated valleys and bordered, in part, by plateaus. In New England the highland areas are continuous with those of eastern Canada. After being formed they were eroded to a peneplain (almost a plain). Since then they have been uplifted, extensively dissected by erosion, and glaciated. The upland areas of rough, irregular topography are inland, at no point extending to the sea. The western edge of the New England Upland borders the Lake Champlain–Hudson Valley Lowland; to the east is a narrow, indented coastal plain. The Piedmont, the southeastern division of the Appalachians, extends from the Hudson River into Alabama. It is underlain by hard, old crystalline rock and is much like a rolling plain. The Fall Line, which forms the eastern edge of the Piedmont, is determined by the numerous rapids and small waterfalls which are formed where streams flow from the harder rock of the plateau onto the weaker materials of the coastal plain. Along the western edge of the Piedmont is the Blue Ridge, which attains its greatest height and width along the Tennessee–North Carolina boundary and narrows and decreases in elevation toward the northeast. West of the Blue Ridge is the steeply folded Ridge and Valley area. Noted for its long and nearly parallel even-crested ridges, this subregion presented a major obstacle to the pioneers moving westward. The western edge of the Ridge and Valley area is marked by the steep escarpment known as the Cumberland Escarpment in the South and the Allegheny Front in Pennsylvania. Beyond the Front is the Appalachian Plateau area. Numerous local names have been given to various parts of this subregion. In southern New York, it is known as the Catskill Mountains; in western Pennsylvania and a part of West Virginia, it is called the Allegheny Plateau; and in Kentucky and Tennessee it forms the Cumberland Plateau. Drainage in the Appalachian region varies with location. In New England and across the northern and central part of the Piedmont, the rivers flow toward the Atlantic. Rivers cutting across the southern edge of the Piedmont flow into the Gulf of Mexico. West of the Blue Ridge, the course of the streams was determined largely by the trends of the folds. In many instances, however, the

rivers cut through the ridges and form water gaps as is the case with the Delaware and Susquehanna Rivers.

The Coastal Plain, beginning with Cape Cod and Long Island, extends the full length of the Atlantic and Gulf coasts into Mexico. Varying in width from less than a few miles to approximately 500 miles where it follows the Mississippi River northward to southern Illinois, the plain is a region of relatively recent deposits. Near the shore are great swamps like the Dismal Swamp in Virginia and North Carolina, Okefenokee in Georgia, the Everglades in Florida, and much of the lower Mississippi Delta in Louisiana. Just offshore, in many locations, long, narrow sand islands have been formed. The Mississippi Embayment, which separates the East Gulf Coastal Plain from the West Gulf Coastal Plain, has been filled by river sediments. In this lowland the Mississippi meanders over a wide alluvial floodplain. Along each side of the river are low bluffs. Because of the vast amount of sediment which the river carries, it is constantly extending its large delta, making it hard to tell where land ends and the sea begins.

The Adirondacks of northern New York and the Superior Highlands of Minnesota, Michigan, and Wisconsin are outliers of the Canadian Upland. The Adirondacks, lying between Lakes Champlain and Ontario and north of the Mohawk Valley, are separated from the Canadian section by the St. Lawrence Lowland. During the glacial period the ice sheets removed the surface materials, smoothed and rounded the bedrock, and deepened the valleys. As the ice retreated, the area was left covered with till (glacial debris) which deranged many of the streams, forming waterfalls, rapids, and lakes. Although some of the lakes have disappeared as a result of filling or draining, the Adirondacks are still a region of lakes. The Superior Highlands do not attain the elevations of the Adirondacks. The surface of the ancient crystalline rocks ranges from about 1,300 to 1,600 feet although a few places exceed 2,000 feet. Like the Adirondacks, this area has also been glaciated. When the ice sheet melted, it left a thick layer of glacial till. As a result the drainage was greatly disturbed, causing numerous lakes and extensive swamps.

The Interior Highland region, located in the southern half of Missouri, the western part of Arkansas, and along the eastern edge of Oklahoma, is made up of the Ozark Plateau and the Ouachita Mountains with the intervening Arkansas River Valley. The Ozark Plateau, situated north of the Arkansas River, is a broad, flat-topped uplift that has been widely dissected by stream erosion. The southern edge of the Ozarks, known as the Boston Mountains, is higher and rougher than the rest of the plateau. The Ouachita Mountains, which attain elevations of almost 3,000 feet, are a series of folded sandstone beds extending generally in an east–west direction. The Arkansas Valley varies in width from five to twenty miles.

The Interior Plains, extending from the Appalachians to the Rockies, and from Canada to the Interior Highlands and the Coastal Plain, form the largest physical region in the United States. The area between the Appalachians and the Mississippi River slopes gently westward; that between the Rockies and the Mississippi slopes eastward. The two chief tributaries of the Mississippi, the Ohio and Missouri Rivers, mark the approximate southern boundary of the area once covered by the continental glaciers. The region is usually divided into two large subregions, the Central Lowland and the Great Plains, both of which generally have a moderately rolling surface. Originally much of it was forested or covered with tall prairie grass. That part of the Central Lowland in middle Tennessee and central Kentucky contains the famous Bluegrass section and the Nashville Basin, the latter being surrounded by the Highland Rim.

The Great Plains slope eastward from an elevation of 4,000 to 6,000 feet to about 500 to 1,600 feet where they merge with the Central Lowland. In this subregion of fertile soil, frequently deficient in moisture, the plant life of the Great Plains is dominated by short-grass and other subhumid vegetation. Numerous sectional names are applied to parts of this area. The northern section, in Montana, North Dakota, and South Dakota, is frequently referred to as the Missouri Plateau since its drainage is entirely into the Missouri River. The southern section, extending southward from about the South Dakota–Nebraska boundary into central Texas and generally west of the 101st meridian, is called the High Plains. In this area, alluvial materials washed from the Rockies were deposited on top of an old surface, causing a greater elevation. South of the Canadian River, the High Plains are called the Llano Estacado or Staked Plains; the southern part is known as the Edwards Plateau. In general the surface of all the High Plains appears almost flat, being broken only by the streams that cross it. The eastern edge, however, is a narrow zone of rough topography known as the Break of the Plains.

The Rocky Mountain System, between the Great Plains and the Intermontane Plateaus, extends north from about Santa Fe, New Mexico, to central Wyoming, thence west and northwest to the United States–Canadian boundary. The system can be divided into the Northern and Southern Rocky Mountain provinces, which are separated by the Wyoming Basin. Included in this region are hundreds of ranges and basins. Some have been formed by faulting (movements along breaks in the earth's crust), some by folds, and others by severe dissection of the uplands. The ranges vary greatly in length, width, and height. Steep cliffs, snow-capped peaks, glaciers, waterfalls, deep gorges, swift-flowing streams, and even geysers are among the characteristics of the mountains.

The Intermontane region is divided into three large subregions, Columbia Intermontane province, Basin and Range province, and Colorado Plateaus. The Columbia province, largely in southern Idaho and the eastern parts of Washington and Oregon, covers approximately 225,-000 square miles, which during past geologic ages became largely covered by numerous lava flows. Both the Columbia and the Snake Rivers have eroded deep canyons into the bedrock. The Colorado Plateaus form a roughly circular area west and south of the Rocky Mountains in Colorado, Utah, Arizona, and New Mexico. The strata are nearly horizontal even though the region has been lifted to elevations ranging from 5,000 to 10,000 feet. Many canyons, the most noted of which is the Grand Canyon, have been cut to great depths, making the plateaus very rugged in spite of their original level surfaces. Between the Columbia and Colorado subregions is the Basin and Range province. Within this are many north–south-trending mountain ranges with elevations up to 10,000 feet. The northern part of this province is frequently referred to as the Great Basin since all drainage is to the interior, no stream flowing out to the ocean. Most of the Intermontane region is arid.

The Pacific region groups together the Cascade Mountains and Sierra Nevada on the east, the Coast Range on the west, and the intervening Willamette Valley–Puget Lowland and the Great Valley of California. On the basis of differences in formation and location, each of these subdivisions might be classed as an individual region. The Sierra Nevada and Cascades form a continuous system of mountains between the Great Basin and the Pacific province. The division between these two mountain groups lies just south of the volcano, Lassen Peak. In the Cascades are several inactive volcanic cones having elevations of 10,000 to over 14,000 feet. The Sierra Nevada is the result of a great block fault which has its steepest slopes facing east. The Coast Range mostly parallels the Pacific Coast from Canada to Mexico. The crest of the Coast Ranges is lower than that of either the Sierra Nevada or Cascades. The Willamette Valley–Puget Lowland is between the Cascades and the Coast Ranges; the Great Valley of California separates the Sierra Nevada from the Coast Ranges. Drainage basins in the Pacific region are generally small. Largest is that of the Columbia River, which crosses the Cascades—the only one cutting through this region from the east. This Columbia Gorge is used by railroads and highways.

## CLIMATE

The mid-latitude location of the United States gives the country a wide range of climates, with the eastern half of the nation generally receiving enough precipitation for successful agriculture (Figures 1-2 and 1-3). Except in the far Northwest (and the higher mountains), the western half of the continental United States receives insufficient precipitation to grow satisfactory field crops unless special methods of dry-farming or irrigation are used. Westerly winds dominate most of the nation, and cyclonic storms commonly associated with this wind zone cause most of the rainfall and snowfall as well as the widely variable seasonal and daily temperatures that are characteristic of middle latitudes.

The generally favorable climate is a great advantage to the eastern part of the United States. Almost all this half of the country is humid, having 25 to 60 inches or more of annual rainfall, with the total precipitation declining westward toward the Great Plains. The principal climates of the Eastern states are classified as humid subtropical and humid continental. The latter has two phases, a continental long summer and a continental short summer. The southernmost tip of Florida is classified as humid tropical. Mean temperatures and rainfall generally decline northward from the Gulf of Mexico. The temperature range between winter and summer increases inland, as is customary in continents in the middle latitudes. In the Corn Belt and winter-wheat-growing areas the summers are long, but farther north, around the Great Lakes and in the spring-wheat-growing region, the summers are short. This difference in length of summer affects the species of forest trees and the crops grown, thereby making a natural boundary between the two continental interior climates of the East. Throughout the interior lowlands, rainfall comes largely from humid air masses moving inland from the Gulf of Mexico and is at its maximum in summer, a fact which is favorable for farming. Thunderstorms account for much of the rainfall in the warm season. In winter, snowfall may be heavy in the northern half of the region. Prolonged droughts seldom occur. The Atlantic

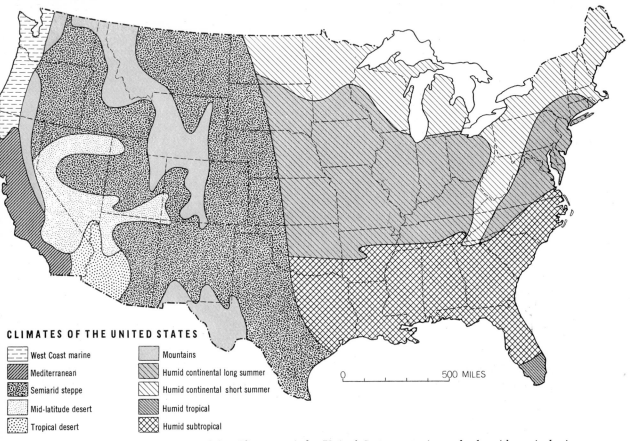

*Figure 1-2   Climates of the United States vary from the humid tropical of southern Florida to the mixed climates of mountain areas. In the mountain areas of the western part of the United States the climatic regions trend north and south with the higher elevations, but in the eastern part of the country the regions extend east and west across the lower lands and change more with latitude.*

coastal areas have a large seasonal range in temperature because of the effect of the west winds from the interior, but the presence of the ocean causes a lag in time for both the coldest and warmest periods, January and February having almost the same temperatures. The same is true of July and August. On the east coast, the distribution of rainfall is nearly even throughout the year.

Chief climates of the Western United States, in addition to large mountain areas with un-classified climates, are the marine west-coast, Mediterranean or subtropical dry summer, con-tinental steppe and desert, and subtropical and desert (Figure 1-2). A "steppe" is a semiarid grassland, which differs from the desert in hav-

ing rainfall enough to support forage sufficient for grazing. Deserts, with five inches or less of rainfall per year, have only a few drought-resistant plants. The winds and the north–south-extending mountain systems are important fac-tors affecting Western climates. The onshore winds and closeness of the northwest moun-tains to the Pacific cause abundant rainfall in the rather narrow zone of the marine west-coast climate. Temperatures are mild and the heavy rainfall has a winter maximum. The Mediter-ranean climate is found in central and south-western California. It has very mild, somewhat rainy winters and long, dry summers. The grow-ing season is long, nearly frost-free, and excel-lent for subtropical fruits and crops, although

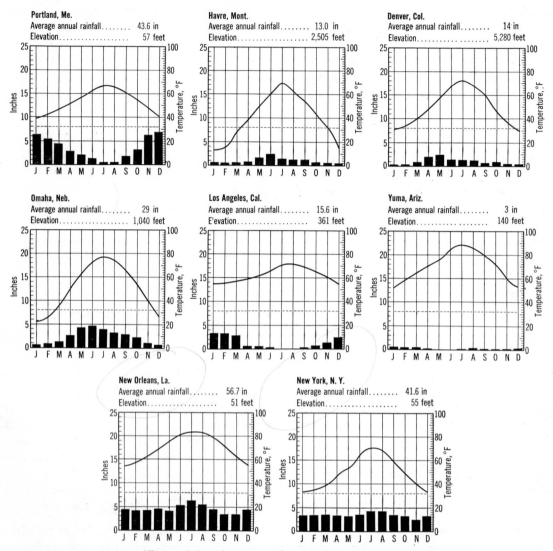

*Figure 1-3   Climate graphs for selected cities of the United States.*

irrigation is usually necessary. Rainfall decreases from north to south. Inland, the windward (west) side of the Sierra Nevada and other mountains has much rainfall, but on the leeward (east) side of the ranges a rapid decline in precipitation occurs. East of the mountains, the semiarid grasslands or steppes have intermediate rainfall between the deserts and the more humid regions. The subtropical and continental steppes and deserts differ chiefly in severity of winter weather. In the west-wind belt, the steppes and deserts are on the leeward side of the mountains. Grazing and irrigated farming are the most important land uses. Inland, continental influences are shown by the extreme range of temperatures. In part of Nevada and south central Oregon, a contributory cause for cold winters of the continental steppe and desert is the considerable elevation of the desert areas. The Columbia Basin farther north has milder winters and a longer growing season because of its lower elevation. The Great Plains have a continental steppe climate; the temperature range is great and the rainfall, though slight, has a summer maximum that is beneficial to wheat and other hardy crops. Grazing and irrigated farming are also widely practiced. The subtropical deserts and steppes in the Southwest are both in low latitudes and at low altitudes. Furthermore, a high-pressure belt of dry de- scending air generally covers the area. Rainfall is small and always uncertain. Summer is very hot and the winters warm to mild. Here sub- tropical products and even dates can be grown where water for irrigation is available on land convenient to transportation.

## NATURAL VEGETATION

Forests originally covered most of the humid sections of the United States. The semiarid Great Plains, the steppes, and desert lands be- tween the forested mountains of the West sup- ported only grass or a scant cover of desert plants. In its original state, the eastern half of the nation was almost completely covered by trees.

There were three main types of forests in the Eastern and Central states (Figure 1-4). The southern forest consisted mainly of pines on the broad sandy plains and of cypress and various hardwoods, such as gum, oak, sycamore, and elm, in the swamps and river bottomlands. The hills and the Piedmont area supported a mixed forest of pines and hardwoods. Large parts of

*Figure 1-4   The natural vegetation regions of the United States are closely related to the landforms and climates. Trees dominate in the eastern part of the country and in the western mountains where there is sufficient rainfall. Grass of varying kinds is characteristic of the central part of the nation. Short-grass and desert vegetation are found in the semiarid and arid parts.*

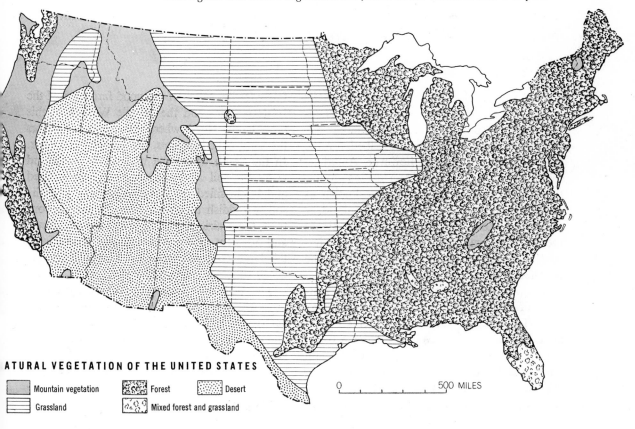

NATURAL VEGETATION OF THE UNITED STATES

Mountain vegetation    Forest    Desert

Grassland    Mixed forest and grassland

0          500 MILES

the original forest land are now cleared and in productive farms. The central hardwood forest covered the country from the Middle Atlantic region to the prairies. The forest was of mixed hardwoods, including oak, ash, elm, beech, maple, walnut, and hickory, with minor stands of pine and hemlock. Much of this forest has been cleared for agriculture. The northern forest consisted of white pine, spruce, fir, and other conifers, with some hardwoods, especially maple, oak, birch, and aspen. This forest was found around the upper Great Lakes, in Maine, and in the Adirondacks. It also extended west from the upper Great Lakes and south throughout the higher parts of the Appalachian Mountains. Although most of the white pine has been cut and great inroads made on other species, the larger proportion of the northern region is not farmed and can best be used for recreation and the growing of new forests.

In the western half of the country, the Great Plains, interior basins, and deserts were treeless except for groves of cottonwoods along the rivers. Where there was sufficient rainfall, the Rocky Mountains and Basin Ranges supported a forest of pines, fir, spruce, and other conifers. The lower limit of the forest was determined by decreased rainfall, the upper tree line by decreased temperature at high elevations. Most of the mountains remain in forests, but much of the saw timber has been cut. In the Pacific Northwest the magnificent Douglas fir grows along with spruce, fir, hemlock, and cedar. This region has the largest remaining stands of timber in the nation. Along the coast of northern California is the home of the giant redwood. Conifers flourish on the Sierra Nevada and on the Klamath Mountains, but in southern California there is a lack of commercial forests. The land there supports only live oak, thickets of chaparral brush, and grass or herbage of little value except for protecting slopes against erosion.

The grasslands of the Great Plains and interior basins are generally located in regions of low rainfall and support a widespread livestock industry. These grazing lands are supplemented by mountain pastures during the summer. Even sagebrush and bushes afford some browse to sheep and goats.

## SOILS

Since the physical characteristics of most soils are closely related to the climatic conditions under which the soils were formed, numerous different soil types have been described for the United States. In general, however, American soil types can be classified in two leading groups, those that occur in humid regions, known as pedalfers, and soils formed under semiarid or desert conditions, called pedocals. The names are derived from the chemical symbols of important elements, aluminum and iron in the pedalfer, and calcium (lime) in the pedocal.

The pedalfers are characteristic of the eastern half of the United States and other rainy areas, for example, parts of the Pacific Northwest. These soils are developed under a forest cover, and soluble salts like those of calcium have been leached out. Where the trees were deciduous hardwoods with broad leaves, the soils are usually red to yellow in color and are fairly fertile. Much of the good farmland of the Eastern states and the Middle West is of this type. In the North where the trees are conifers the soils, called podsols, are leached and poor. In the South where the weather is warm and rainy, the soil of the pinelands is also leached and is classified as a red-and-yellow podsolic soil, a reddish to gray sand or loam. In contrast, the prairie soils of Indiana, Illinois, Iowa, and adjacent areas are black and fertile from the large content of humus derived from the decay of grass stems and roots.

The pedocals developed under dry conditions where the vegetation was mostly grass and herbage. These soils are relatively unleached and contain a zone of lime carbonate. Pedocals are excellent for raising wheat whenever the rainfall is adequate. The chernozem soil is formed between the arid and humid lands under subhumid conditions that favor growth of

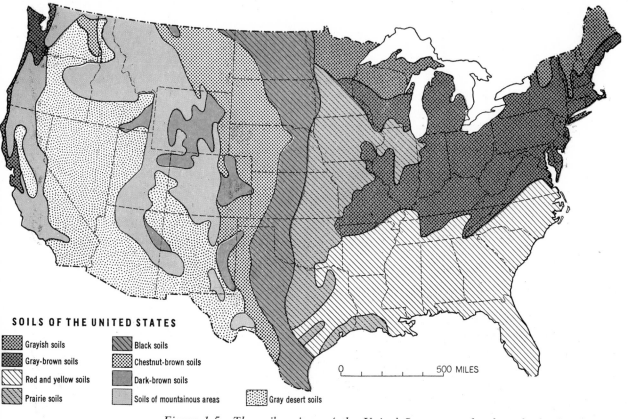

*Figure 1-5 The soil regions of the United States are related to the landforms, climates, and vegetation of the area in which they exist. In many places the boundaries of the soil regions are almost the same as the boundaries of the other regions.*

tall grasses. The decay of the grasses furnishes much humus, which causes the soil to have a dark chocolate color and makes it very fertile. In the drier sections the grass becomes shorter and finally, when the desert is reached, grows only in clumps. The color of the soils changes from chocolate to chestnut, then to light-brown, and finally to the gray desert type, with the re- duction in humus content that results from the decline in rainfall and amount of vegetation. Pedocal soils are fertile because they occur in places where the rainfall is too low to cause the leaching of the soluble salts on which plants feed. They are productive, however, only if there is adequate water, whether supplied by rain or irrigation.

## AGRICULTURE

For over two centuries most of the people of the United States were farmers. Until after the 1880s, about 80 per cent of the American population was rural. Cereals, meat, cotton, and other farm products were the largest exports until after 1900. Even today there are many foreign markets for American farm products. In the past the agricultural advantages were vast tillable areas of virgin, productive soil with adequate rainfall and growing season and lands that lay level to gently rolling so that machinery could be used to advantage. Approximately 350 million of the nearly 2,000 million acres in the United States are now tilled. Other hundreds of millions of acres are used for grazing land. It has been estimated that as many as 455 million acres are arable. Important to the growth of American agriculture was the invention of tractors, trucks, and other machinery that replaced animal power and reduced the need for man-

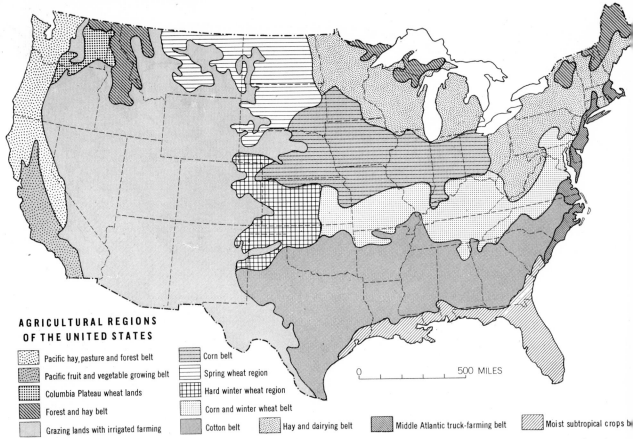

AGRICULTURAL REGIONS
OF THE UNITED STATES

- Pacific hay, pasture and forest belt
- Pacific fruit and vegetable growing belt
- Columbia Plateau wheat lands
- Forest and hay belt
- Grazing lands with irrigated farming
- Corn belt
- Spring wheat region
- Hard winter wheat region
- Corn and winter wheat belt
- Cotton belt
- Hay and dairying belt
- Middle Atlantic truck-farming belt
- Moist subtropical crops b

*Figure 1-6   The agricultural regions of the United States are the result of both the physical and cultural activities of the areas. Although a region may have one or two principal crops, there are many crops grown in each. Each has a large variety of land uses.*

power. Land once used to grow feed for draft animals now is available to produce food for people. No country in the world grows as much farm produce per manpower-hour as the United States. Today about one-sixth of the population are farmers, yet they feed the 170 million inhabitants well and have a surplus to export. Part of this productivity results from use of fertilizers, such improvements in plants as hybrid corn, improved breeds of livestock, and efficient handling of crops that reduces waste and loss. Transportation is adequate; nearly every farm is on a good-to-passable road, and few farms in the East are farther than 5 or 10 miles from a railroad. Refrigeration is available to preserve perishable produce during shipment. American farm homes are typically modern, with electricity, radio, television, telephone service, and mail delivery. A large portion of them, espe-

cially those in the North, have plumbing and central heating. Cows are commonly milked by machines; and pigs and poultry are raised under efficient and sanitary conditions. In a few regions, conditions for farming are unfavorable because of poor soil, drought, erosion, or remoteness from market. In such areas, some farmers live in substandard housing and have an inferior diet. But on the whole, farming in no other country is more prosperous than in the United States.

The many types of farming that occur in the United States are the result of such natural factors as soil, climate, and surface features and such human factors as the skill and experience of farmers and variable market conditions (Figure 1-6).

Dairying is the dominant farm system in the Northeastern United States. Here pastures thrive, for hay and other fodder crops grow well in the humid climate. Closeness to the manufacturing belt and the major cities of the country provides a never-failing market for animal and dairy products. Specialty crops also are grown here; for example, orchard fruits and grapes in western Michigan and along the shores of Lakes Erie and Ontario; potatoes in Maine, sugar beets in Michigan, and tobacco and onions in the Connecticut Valley. The dairy farms with their large barns for hay storage and stable room for stock, towering silos, poultry houses, and many outbuildings epitomize the region.

The Corn Belt extends from middle Ohio to central Nebraska and Kansas and is the heart of agricultural United States. This region has deep, fertile soils, a level to slightly hilly surface, and a hot summer which usually has sufficient rainfall. On the farms, corn and fodder crops are fed to animals and turned into pork, eggs, poultry, milk, and beef. This is the region of the country most important for output of cereals and animal products. Big barns and silos, houses for smaller animals such as hogs and chickens, and sheds for larger animals and the many kinds of machinery are characteristic buildings.

Vegetables, fruits, and specialty crops like tobacco are typical of the Middle Atlantic coastal region. Inland is a transition belt between the Dairy and Corn Belts to the north and the Cotton Belt to the south. The transition belt extends from southern Pennsylvania and Virginia west through Missouri. Crops include corn and winter wheat, with tobacco and orchard fruits locally important. Farms vary widely in size and productivity. Some are large and prosperous. Others are small subsistence places on which the farmers earn a bare existence. The poorest parts of this belt are in the hills and mountains.

The Southeast comprises the old Cotton Belt. Besides this chief money crop, areas are devoted to rice, fruit, including citrus fruits in central Florida, sugar cane, winter vegetables, peanuts, and tobacco. Corn is the chief cereal. The production of livestock and poultry is increasing. The winters are short and there is little need for hay and shelter, so barns are small compared with those in the North.

The Winter-Wheat Belt is on the eastern slopes of the Great Plains west of the Corn Belt and north of the Cotton Belt. Here the annual rainfall is under 25 inches and the farms are large—from a half section to more than a section (640 acres). Some farms cover several sections. Wheat is planted and harvested by power-drawn or self-propelled machinery. On drier lands, wheat is planted only once in two years or twice in three years; the land is left fallow (uncropped) in the off years to allow moisture to accumulate for the next crop. The soil moisture is conserved by cultivation which leaves the surface of the ground cloddy and breaks the underground openings through which water would evaporate. Livestock is often raised by being grazed on the fall-sown (winter) wheat but a few farms have nothing but wheat—not a horse, cow, or chicken. Wheat storage bins and towering elevators along the railroads break the monotony of the landscape. Farm buildings are generally few, and machinery is sometimes exposed in the open all winter.

The Spring-Wheat Belt is located in the northern Great Plains from western Minnesota across the Dakotas to central Montana. Here the winters are often too severe for growing fall-sown (winter) wheat. Farms may be several sections in size, and the land is alternately in wheat and fallow. Frequently, plantings are made in strips at right angles to the wind. The rougher land is used for livestock; alfalfa and sugar beets are raised by irrigation of the level bottomlands of rivers.

Although irrigation is practiced in some localities, the grazing of cattle and sheep is the chief farm activity carried on in the western mountain, plateau, and semidesert areas from the western Great Plains to the Pacific valleys. The hot, dry lands in parts of Arizona, southeast California, and the Rio Grande Valley produce citrus fruit, winter vegetables, cotton, alfalfa, and a variety of other irrigated crops. Parts of eastern Washington and Oregon are good for growing wheat. The southern California valleys are nearly frost-free, and some are famous for Mediterranean crops such as citrus and soft fruits, cotton, alfalfa, and vegetables. Central California is noted for its vineyards, orchards, rice, barley, and alfalfa; dairying is also important and livestock graze on the hilly coast ranges. The lowlands of the Willamette-Puget Depression have a long growing season and abundant rainfall which results in excellent pastures. Here is much dairying, mixed farming, and cultivation of small fruits.

## MINERALS

The industrial empire of the United States is built upon a wealth and variety of minerals and fuels—coal, petroleum, copper, natural gas, and many others (Figure 1-7). Coal reserves are estimated at 3,500 billion tons, with an annual output of about 500 million tons, the largest production of any nation. The high quality of the coal and accessibility to markets have placed the Appalachian Plateaus (both the Allegheny Plateau section and the Cumberland Plateau) in the lead in mining coal, which is shipped to consumers by rail, highway, river, and sea as well as the Great Lakes. Other extensive deposits occur in the Middle West, in the Great Plains, and in the Rocky Mountains. Petroleum and natural gas reach markets by pipeline—a method of shipment that has greatly increased both demand and output. Texas,

*Figure 1-7    The eastern half of the United States is well supplied with mineral fuels. In many places in the nation the coal and petroleum fields overlap. Metals are found largely in mountain or highland areas.*

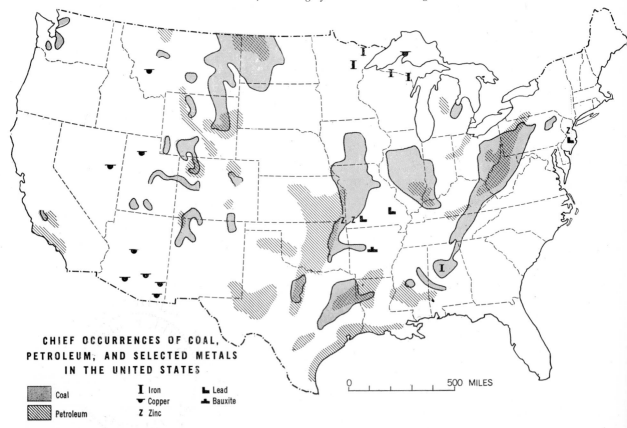

CHIEF OCCURRENCES OF COAL, PETROLEUM, AND SELECTED METALS IN THE UNITED STATES

Coal
Petroleum
I  Iron
▼ Copper
Z  Zinc
L  Lead
▲ Bauxite

0                    500 MILES

California, Louisiana, and Oklahoma are the principal gas and petroleum producers, but other Southern, Middle Western, and Central states are also important. Modern transportation and machinery depend mainly on oil products, and the industrial progress of the nation is directly related to this abundance of fuels and lubricants.

Iron, the most important metal in our modern civilization, is mined chiefly in the upper Great Lakes region and in the Appalachian Highlands from New York southwest to Alabama. Known Western deposits in Utah and other states are of minor significance. The occurrence of great iron deposits near coal supplies or cheap water transport helped the United States become a first-rank nation in iron and steel production. Among other metals, copper is mined mainly in the Western states (Ari-

zona, Utah, Montana) and Michigan. New Jersey mines zinc, but most lead and zinc come from the Ozarks and Rockies. Bauxite, the ore of aluminum, is mined in Arkansas. Minor metals such as gold, silver, and uranium are obtained chiefly in the western third of the country.

Nonmetallic minerals such as clay, and limestone for cement, are widely distributed, and their commercial development depends largely upon their proximity to large markets for building materials. Texas and Louisiana lead in the production of sulfur, used in many chemical processes. The United States once exported large quantities of minerals, but since 1945 consumption of some minerals has overtaken production; the nation now imports about as much as it exports, including petroleum.

## MANUFACTURING

Stretching in a broad belt across the varied surface of the Northeastern United States is the country's chief manufacturing region (Figure 1-8). For the most part the belt forms a quadrangle with the cities of Minneapolis, St. Louis, Baltimore, and Portland, Maine, as the corners. There is, however, one large extension southward from this quadrangle along the Piedmont Plateau to Atlanta.

This region has many advantages for manufacturing activities. It has superior transport facilities for both foreign and domestic commerce, including excellent harbors and seaports tapped by railways and highways forming a close net. Its climate is neither too hot nor too cold for industrial workers. It has a growing season advantageous for most midlatitude crops and sufficient precipitation for nonirrigated agriculture. Some forest resources are available. It has water power, too, and large mineral resources, including coal, petroleum, natural gas, metallic minerals such as iron, lead, zinc, and copper, and nonmetallic substances such as clay and cement.

This industrial zone was settled in the last three centuries by energetic people with the

"know-how" and leadership needed for industrial development. More than half the country's population lives in this area, which includes the larger number of the nation's urban centers. The leading manufactures include iron and steel products, machinery, and metal wares of all types; cotton, woolen, and synthetic textiles; clothing and shoes; chemicals, meat packing, fruit and vegetable processing; agricultural implements, automobiles, tires and other rubber goods; cement, glass, and clay products; flour and baked goods; railway cars and supplies; shipbuilding, woodworking, and the manufacture of furniture; paper and publishing, optical goods, and many small articles and specialty products.

Outside the principal manufacturing zone, smaller scattered centers have developed near Birmingham and along the Gulf Coast in Louisiana and Texas. The Kansas City–Omaha–Wichita area is a factory center in the Corn Belt. Other important industrial centers are in California near Los Angeles and San Francisco Bay and in Portland, Oregon, and the district around Seattle and Tacoma in the state of Washington.

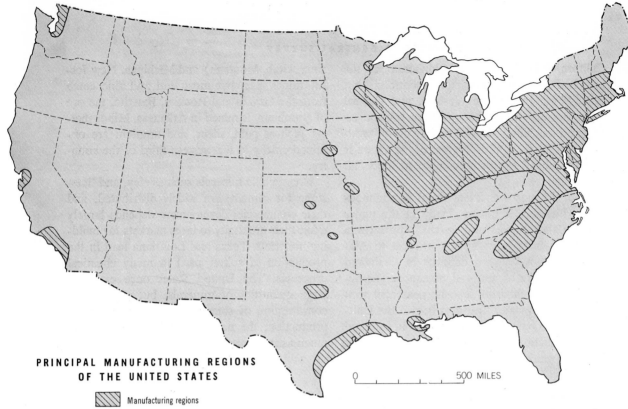

PRINCIPAL MANUFACTURING REGIONS
OF THE UNITED STATES

0 ____ 500 MILES

▨ Manufacturing regions

*Figure 1-8   The principal manufacturing region of the United States is lo-
cated in the northeastern quarter of the nation. An ample supply of fuel, large
reserves of iron ore nearby, natural deep-water transportation, and industrious people combine to make this the world's most productive area. Smaller
regions are to be found in other areas that have certain specific advantages.*

## POPULATION DISTRIBUTION

The 170 million inhabitants of the United
States are unevenly distributed over its 3 million square miles, principally because of the
varying geographical conditions that prevail
throughout the country (Figure 1-9). Factors
that affect land use, and thus the density and
distribution of population, are climates, soils,
forests, and grasslands, inland water resources,
location of harbors, and natural outlets from
the hinterlands. All these factors operate to support a larger population in the Eastern than in
the Western part of the nation. Areas having
good level land with rainfall and growing seasons suitable for most crops, such as those
found east of the 97th meridian, have many
cities and, in general, an evenly distributed rural population. In contrast, few people live in
rugged mountains and plateaus, deserts, alkali
flats, or uncleared forests.

During the past half century not only has the
population increased from 92 million to 170
million, but it has also shifted from a rural to
an urban situation. In 1910, 45 per cent of the
people lived in urban areas; by 1950, the urban
population had increased to 59 per cent. In
those forty years, the number of cities with
populations of 100,000 or more increased from
38 to 107. Since 1950 this trend toward urbanization has continued. It is now estimated that
between 63 and 65 per cent of the total population are residents of urban communities.

The growth of large cities during the past
twenty-five years has been almost phenomenal.
Five cities—New York, Chicago, Philadelphia,
Los Angeles, and Detroit—each had populations of more than 1.8 million in 1950. Since
that date it is very probable that Baltimore, St.
Louis, Cleveland, and Washington have passed

the million mark. New York and Chicago are among the 10 largest cities in the world.

More than 75 per cent of the American people live east of the 97th meridian, which almost divides the United States into two equal parts. Of the 41 cities in the nation having a population of 250,000 or more in 1950, 32 are in the Eastern, 9 in the Western half of the country. The greatest concentration of population is in the vicinity of New York City. New York State, although ranking twenty-ninth in area, has a larger total population than any other state. Rhode Island has the greatest population density, 673 per square mile. For all the area east of the 97th meridian, the average population density is about 140 per square mile.

In the area west of the 97th meridian, where many factors do not favor the support of a large population, the density per square mile is about 16. Nevada, with a smaller population than any other state, averages only 1.6 persons per square mile. California has the largest total population of any Western state, yet its density per square mile of 72 is exceeded by that of 17 Eastern states. The largest concentration of population in the West is the Los Angeles area.

*Figure 1-9    The northeastern part of the United States is the most densely populated part of the Western Hemisphere. Industrial activities create large cities and intensive land use results in an exceedingly dense rural population. Population density in general reflects the landforms, climate, and soils of the area.*

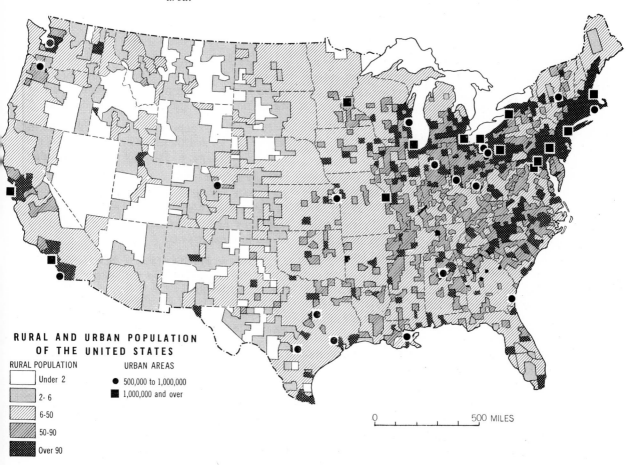

RURAL AND URBAN POPULATION
OF THE UNITED STATES

RURAL POPULATION
Under 2
2- 6
6-50
50-90
Over 90

URBAN AREAS
● 500,000 to 1,000,000
■ 1,000,000 and over

0          500 MILES

## EASTERN AND WESTERN UNITED STATES

In the chapters that follow, the United States has been divided into two parts so that it may be studied in greater detail. The boundary between these two parts is not a definite line, but rather a zone extending from about the 95th to the 100th meridian. Within or bordering these five degrees is most of the recognized boundary between the Great Plains and the Central Lowland, the area across which the 20-inch annual rainfall line fluctuates, the zone of change between short-grass and tall-grass vegetation, and the place of contact between pedocal and pedalfer soils. Since the 97th meridian is also near the center of this zone it has been taken, arbitrarily, as the boundary between the Eastern and Western United States. East of the 97th meridian, the population is moderate to dense.

Much of the area is plains or low plateaus. Here, highway and railway networks are well developed and inland waterways have many miles of navigable channels. Much agricultural land is fairly intensively used, and manufacturing is highly developed. West of the 97th meridian, mountains, plateaus, and rough topography dominate the landscape. Over most of the area population is sparse. Rainfall, except on the western sides of some mountains, is generally deficient, and most agricultural land is used extensively. In several areas, however, especially in the Far West, manufacturing is important and is rapidly expanding. Mining of different kinds is common to both the Eastern and Western United States.

### EXERCISES

*1.* What are the four largest agricultural regions in area? In production? What are the relationships between these regions and the physical and climatic regions of the United States?

*2.* What factors have aided the growth of population east of the 97th meridian? What factors have hindered it west of the 97th?

*3.* What physical regions are wholly or partly east of the Mississippi River? Why was the Appalachian region such a barrier to the early colonists?

*4.* Where are the principal grassland areas of the United States? What is the relationship between the vegetation and use of these areas and the climatic conditions that prevail in them?

*5.* What are the two great soil classes? Where, in general, is the chief location of each in the United States? What is the dominant vegetation composing each?

*6.* What are the mineral fuels? Where are the principal areas of production? Why do the Pacific Coast states not feel the lack of coal?

*7.* Which physical regions are entirely west of the 100th meridian? What are the principal occupations in these regions? What are the chief minerals mined?

*8.* Where is the largest manufacturing region of the United States? How do you account for its location in this area instead of some other part of the nation? Where are smaller centers developing?

*9.* How does the population density in the eastern part of the United States differ from that in the western? What geographic factors aid in causing these differences?

*10.* Where are the wettest and driest parts of the United States? What is the relationship between landforms and the amount of precipitation received in these regions?

*11.* What geographic factors have aided the United States in its development as the leading nation in the world?

*12.* What are the principal geographic differences between the area east of the 97th meridian and the area west of it?

*13.* What geographic factors helped determine the routes of exploration followed by the pioneers? In what ways did these factors later influence the location of transportation routes?

*14.* How do you account for the uneven distribution of population in the Rocky Mountain states?

## SELECTED REFERENCES

Alexander, John W.: "Industrial Expansion in the United States 1939–1947," *Economic Geography,* 28:128–142, April, 1952.

Atwood, Wallace: *The Physiographic Provinces of North America,* Ginn & Company, Boston, 1940.

Brown, Ralph: *Historical Geography of the United States,* Harcourt, Brace and Company, Inc., New York, 1948.

Haystead, Ladd, and Gilbert Fite: *The Agricultural Regions of the United States,* University of Oklahoma Press, Norman, 1955.

Miller, George J., Almond E. Parkins, and Bert Hudgins: *Geography of North America,* 3d ed., John Wiley & Sons, Inc., New York, 1954.

Murphy, Raymond E., and J. E. Vance: "Delimiting the CBD," *Economic Geography,* 30:189–222, July, 1954.

————: "A Comparative Study of Nine Central Business Districts," *Economic Geography,* 30:301–336, October, 1954.

————: "Internal Structure of the CBD," *Economic Geography,* 31:21–46, January, 1955.

Philbrick, Allen K.: "Principles of Areal Functional Organization in Regional Human Geography," *Economic Geography,* 33:299–336, October, 1957.

Smith, J. Russell, and M. Ogden Phillips: *North America,* Harcourt, Brace and Company, Inc., New York, 1942.

White, C. Langdon, and Edwin J. Foscue: *Regional Geography of Anglo-America,* Prentice-Hall, Inc., Englewood Cliffs, N.J., 1953.

Wright, Alfred J.: *United States and Canada,* 2d ed., Appleton-Century-Crofts, Inc., New York, 1956.

# 2. Eastern United States

THE United States occupies the most valuable and productive part of North America. Location, relief features, climate, and natural resources have all furthered development of the country. Located primarily between the 25th and 49th parallels of north latitude, this region lies almost midway between the tropics and the Arctic. Here is a mixture of landforms from mountains to rolling plains, a variety of climates ranging from humid subtropical to cold and moist, a variation in vegetation extending from grasslands to forests. Abundant natural resources—water, forests, minerals, animals— are to be found. Into this land of great wealth came the energetic, intelligent people of Western Europe seeking homes and a new way of life.

When Western Europeans, with their varied cultural

backgrounds, made their first settlements along the Atlantic coast of North America they did not anticipate future greatness for the nation they were helping to found. Dense forests, semi-savage tribes of Indians, poor, sandy soil and swamps in the coastal lands confronted the settlers of Jamestown. The Pilgrims coming to New England a few years later found conditions even worse. Besides forests and Indians, they soon discovered that the soil was stony and poor, and that New England weather could, at times, be very disagreeable. Fortunately, better land was found in the Middle Atlantic region and back from the coast of Virginia on which successful farming could be based. Development of timber, fish, water power, and other resources stimulated industry. From these beginnings, some 350 years ago, has grown a most prosperous and powerful nation.

Although the Spanish made settlements in the present states of Florida and New Mexico, explored vast territories in the Southeastern states, crossed parts of Texas, Oklahoma, and Kansas, and traded in the Southwestern states long before the first English settlement, it was from the English Atlantic seaboard colonies that the nation received most of its heritage. Since these early beginnings the eastern half of the United States has, in most respects, been the most important part of the nation (Figure 2-1). In this part of the country today live over 75 per cent of the people, who produce about 75 per cent of the agricultural products and 80 per cent of the manufactured goods. From its ports are shipped yearly almost 90 per cent of the nation's exports and through these same ports come 85 per cent of its imports. Within the Eastern half of the nation are over two-thirds of its railroads and three-fifths of its highways.

## NEW ENGLAND

In area, New England is only a small part of the United States, but it has long been a leader in the culture, commerce, and skilled manufactures of the nation. New England's first settlers came from Great Britain. Forests covered the entire region, so that the land had to be cleared of trees before settlers could begin farming. Moreover, glaciers had deposited stones that had to be picked off the fields before tillage could begin. The climate was severe; much of the land was hilly, and the soil was generally poor. Constant hard work was necessary to make even a scant living on the small farms. As a result of these conditions, some New Englanders turned to the sea and engaged in fishing and ocean commerce. Often, men became traders and dealt with the settlements developing to the westward. Others began the manufacture of articles from wood, metals, and leather. Some of these small enterprises have expanded into great industries and corporations that now employ thousands of workers. With the development of industry, immigrants were drawn from Canada and many of the countries of Europe. These have blended into the present complex of racial stocks living in the region.

## *Physical Setting*

New England has diverse relief, with hills predominating. There are large areas of highlands and smaller areas of lowlands. The major uplands are the Green Mountains of Vermont, the White Mountains of New Hampshire, the Berkshire Hills in Massachusetts, and the Maine Uplands. In general, these upland surfaces exceed 2,000 feet in elevation with a few peaks attaining heights in excess of 5,000 feet. This entire area has been peneplained, tilted, warped, again dissected and, during a still later geologic period, glaciated. Many of the lowlands are located where the least resistant rocks occur. Lowlands include the Housatonic, Connecticut, and Merrimac Valleys, the Lake Champlain Trench, the Narragansett, Portland, and Boston Basins, and the Aroostook area in northeast Maine. Most of the agriculture in New England is carried on in these valleys and basins. They are also the location of a great majority of the important New England cities.

All of New England has been glaciated. The tops of many hills and mountains were scraped

*Figure 2-1  Cities and towns of varying sizes are scattered throughout the
eastern part of the nation. Note their location in relation to the landforms and
waterways.*

off; weak rocks were gouged out. In some instances rivers were dammed; in other places
glacial till, or moraines, were spread over large
areas. Glacial lakes are numerous; only a few,
however, are large enough to serve as sources
of municipal and industrial water supply. On
the other hand, they do regulate stream flow,
serve as recreation sites, and add beauty to the
landscape. Glaciers and glacial deposits often
changed the course of rivers, causing waterfalls
or rapids to form at outcrops of resistant rocks.
Many factory towns were founded at such power sites. Along the ocean shore, the glaciers dug
deep troughs below sea level in the river valleys
that permit the sea to penetrate far inland.

The climate of interior New England is of a

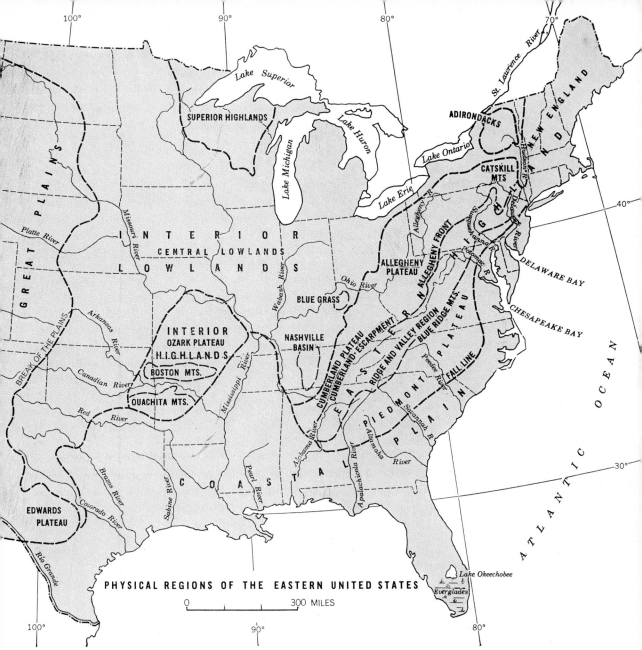

*Figure 2-2   The regions of the eastern part of the United States are a result of both physical and cultural factors. Each has definite characteristics which make its chief activities different from those of the other regions.*

continental type, but near the coast it is somewhat modified by the winds which blow from the sea a part of the time. Away from the coast, toward the interior, the length of the growing season decreases markedly and rapidly, being only 159 days in length at Burlington, Vermont, as compared with 199 days at Boston.

## Agriculture

Early New England settlers came seeking a living from the land. Farming, although handicapped by cold winters, short, cool summers, thin, stony soils, poor transportation, and a limited market survived as a major activity until the opening of the Erie Canal, the building of railroads, and the development of manufacturing. Importation of cheap wheat and other farm products from the interior caused the abandonment of many farms, especially those at higher elevation. Fields reverted to scrub and forest; houses settled into ruin. A part of this erstwhile farmland is now in state and national forests. Some abandoned farms, however, have been reoccupied by European immigrants and by city folk desiring to own land or a country home.

In many sections of New England, specialized farming prevails. Dairy farming is highly developed, and dairy products normally account for one-third of the cash income from agriculture. During the cool, wet summers, hay and pasture grasses grow well even on steep slopes with poor, leached soils. From 80 to 90 per cent of the cropland harvested in the Vermont and New Hampshire uplands is devoted to hay. Corn is grown for grain and silage and, near the great industrial cities, the dairy industry uses large quantities of imported feed concentrates. Improved handling of fresh milk and the large urban demand for milk products has enabled dairy farms remote from markets to operate successfully. The Lake Champlain Lowland of western Vermont ships milk and cream to Boston, southern New England cities, and New York.

Specialty crops are locally important. Sumatra leaf tobacco, which is used for cigar wrappers, is grown on the terraces of the lower Connecticut River. The crop is shielded from the sun by cloth netting supported by poles and wire. Tobacco for cigar fillers is grown in the open. In the Aroostook Valley of Maine the sandy, porous soils and the cool, rainy summers delimit an area where potatoes are grown. Because of their superior quality, and the care used in production and grading, many of these potatoes are sold for seed. Another Maine specialty is sweet corn for canning, the climate keeping the corn at just the right degree of succulence for a considerable period. Onions and a variety of market vegetables come from suitable land near the cities. Many hardy fruits, especially apples, are grown. On Cape Cod,

cranberries improved from the wild variety are planted in swampy mucklands. Maine harvests and cans large quantities of wild blueberries. Maple syrup is also a specialty product, especially in Vermont. The long, cool springs with freezing nights and thawing days result in a flow of sap sufficiently prolonged to justify the labor and expense of tapping the sugarbush.

*Forests*

Viewing the New England landscape from an airplane or mountain peak gives the impression of extensive forests broken by small cultivated areas and settlements. Often small communities are half hidden by the tall shade trees that give an added charm to the fine old dwellings. About 76 per cent of New England is under some sort of forest cover. These forests are the recreation playgrounds and sports areas for the large urban communities of the Northeastern United States. Besides the wood lot found on nearly every farm, commercial forests cover large areas.

For over two hundred years the region supplied lumber for building, wood manufactures, ships, and fuel. During many decades, Bangor, on the Penobscot River, was the preeminent sawmill center of the nation. After the virgin forests had been cut, the new growth was useful chiefly for pulpwood and cordwood. Today the pulp and paper industry is the largest consumer, although the forests still produce other materials in reduced amounts. Improved forest management is a definite regional need, although some of the paper companies manage their large forest holdings so efficiently that their pulpwood requirements can be supplied permanently. National, state, and community forests, along with some privately owned land, are being developed for growing timber. Usually pulp and paper mills locate along rivers, which can be used for power, log storage, and manufacturing needs, just as the sawmills sought similar sites before the saw timber was largely exhausted. New England, today, has less standing saw timber than any other forested region in the nation.

Along the irregular coast line of New England are many harbors useful to both local fishermen and ocean commerce. The abundance of excellent timber—white pine for masts, spruce for spars, and oak for framework and planking —helped make shipbuilding profitable in the days of wooden sailing vessels. Pine trees also provided tar, pitch, and turpentine—the so-called naval stores. There are still many small boat and shipbuilding establishments.

## Fisheries

In the shallow waters adjacent to New England is one of the major fishing grounds of the world. Here the banks, which are usually less than 100 fathoms in depth, are important feeding grounds for cod, halibut, haddock, mackerel, and herring. Fisheries have been an important source of income since colonial days. Although the catch varies, it is approximately a billion pounds annually, and two-thirds of it enters through Massachusetts ports, especially Gloucester and Boston. Fish are sold fresh in local markets, quick-frozen, canned, salted, dried, or smoked. Shore fisheries supply clams, oysters, crabs, and lobsters. Some by-products of the industry are fish meal, fertilizer, and vitamin oil. During the century preceding the 1870s New England dominated the whaling industry. The whalers, together with the commercial trading fleet, carried the American flag to all shores of the world. Profits from the whaling industry furnished some of the capital for construction of textile mills such as those in New Bedford and Fall River.

## Industries and Cities

A large majority of the people of New England live in cities. There they work in factories, engage in commerce, trade, and service occupations, or follow some craft or profession. Also important are financial businesses such as investments and banking, insurance, importing and exporting, and the management of large corporations. The region is a hive of industry, producing nearly 10 per cent of all manufactures of the United States with only about 6 per cent of the country's population. This is the more noteworthy since few raw materials are secured locally.

New England contains no coal or petroleum, and deposits of metals are of small importance. Building stone, however, is quarried extensively. Barre, Vermont, is famed for granite, and marble is produced in several localities. Stone is now used mostly for decorative purposes and monuments. It has been largely replaced by concrete, steel, and glass in large structures because these materials cost less, use less labor, and so make buildings more economical.

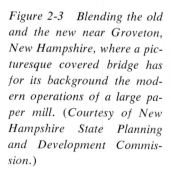

*Figure 2-3 Blending the old and the new near Groveton, New Hampshire, where a picturesque covered bridge has for its background the modern operations of a large paper mill. (Courtesy of New Hampshire State Planning and Development Commission.)*

New England produces little wool and no cotton yet it leads the country in the fabrication of woolens, and manufactures much cotton cloth. Concord, Manchester, Nashua, Lowell, Lawrence, Fall River, New Bedford, Providence, and numerous other cities are important for textiles. Although low in production of hides and leather, the region leads in making women's shoes and ranks high in the production of men's shoes. Brockton, Haverhill, and Lynn are noted for manufacturing footwear. There is also a large production of machinery, household equipment, tools, hardware, wire, and other steel products. Among the cities known for these items are Springfield, Worcester, New Haven, Hartford, and Bridgeport. Ships are built at Quincy and other port cities. Hundreds of factories make specialty products such as watches at Waltham, optical goods at Southbridge, jewelry and emblems at Attleboro, hats at Danbury, canoes at Oldtown, fine paper at Holyoke, and all kinds of grinding equipment at Worcester. Boston is noted for its textile processing and book publishing. Few parts of the world make so much, so well, with so few local resources. Among the factors accounting for New England's industrial importance are an early start and a reputation for producing excellent goods, skilled labor, efficient management, proximity to large markets, and capital for investment.

Coal, oil, and natural gas are imported but the region has much water power. Before the development of electric power transmission, mills and factories were located at falls and dams where machinery could be run directly by water wheels. As a result many towns were crowded into narrow valleys where water power was available. There is much concentration of manufactures. An industry succeeds and competitors follow, favored by the skilled labor that has been trained for certain methods of production. Concentration, however, also has disadvantages. If a factory, which is the main support of a community, ceases operations, moves to some other site, or works on a part-time basis, the entire community suffers. Competition from Southern textile mills, which have expanded until they now surpass New England mills in output of cottons, has caused many New England mills to close. Some affected cities have been able to secure new industries, but in others there is unemployment and loss of population.

Southern New England is a land of cities; 29 urban areas have populations of 50,000 or more. Boston, the largest of these, is frequently called the "hub of New England." This city has an excellent harbor with deep entrance channels and an extensive frontage for berthing ships. Its sea-borne imports are largely coal and petroleum products together with a variety of raw materials and commodities that are either consumed in New England or manufactured there. Imports far exceed exports both in tonnage and value. Like many of its old colonial neighbors, Boston is a city of narrow, crooked streets, historical landmarks, noted educational institutions, fine old residential districts, and cultural tradition.

*Recreation*

Recreation in the New England region is favored by the beauty and variety of the landscapes, inland resorts, and the nearness of the playgrounds to New York, Boston, and other large cities. The area offers mountains, hills, forests, lakes and rivers, irregular coasts varying from sandy beaches to rock-girt harbors, hunting, fishing, and boating facilities, deep, long-lying snows for winter sports, interesting historical sites and architectural gems, national, state, and community parks, and a closely woven net of highways and railroads. There are varied accommodations for people of different means. An increasing appreciation of the importance of the industry has heightened willingness to cater to various wants and tastes. Thousands of people are supported by the recreation industry which brings New England an estimated income of more than half a billion dollars annually. The development of recreation and summer residence in localities once hard to reach was made possible by the automobile and paved highways along the ocean shores, to inland waters and mountain views.

## NEW YORK CITY AND UPPER NEW YORK STATE

From Portland, Maine, to Norfolk, Virginia, stretches an almost continuous series of cities that function as seaports and railroad terminals, or as manufacturing, financial, and political centers. The focal point of the cities in this strip is New York. Between the major cities of this urbanized zone are situated mills, factories, and refineries at spacious sites convenient to transportation, great numbers of suburban communities, and thousands of country homes. Transportation by private automobile, trucks, buses, and commuter trains makes it as convenient to live in the country or the suburbs as in the big cities. So many people prefer homes outside of city limits that, since 1920, the suburbs have grown much faster than the cities themselves.

Because the Appalachian Highlands separate this urbanized zone from the populous and productive Ohio Valley and southern Great Lakes region, the corridors that connect the coastal and interior cities are of major importance. Railroads and highways cross the mountain barrier from Norfolk, Washington, Baltimore, and Philadelphia, but the lowest route, and one that is without steep grades, is the Hudson-Mohawk Lowland between New York and Buffalo. This route extends north from New York to Albany and then west to Lake Erie. Indians and fur traders first used the route, and wagon roads followed. In 1825 the Erie Canal, now the New York State Barge Canal, was opened and New York became the seaboard terminus of the only low-level water route from the rich and rapidly developing Interior Lowlands. In 1851, a through railroad was completed between Buffalo and New York. The combination of canal and rail services so stimulated commerce and settlement that New York quickly outgrew its former rivals Boston, Baltimore, and Philadelphia, in trade and population. Along the Hudson-Mohawk route, an urbanized belt, containing scores of cities, has developed. The excellent transportation has led to the establishment of many manufacturing plants which provide employment.

*The City of New York*

New York, the largest city in the Western Hemisphere, has developed from the settlement made as New Amsterdam in 1626 at the southern end of Manhattan Island. Now covering about 300 square miles and having a population of approximately 8,000,000, the city is the core of the Greater New York metropolitan area. Within this metropolitan area of over 2,600 square miles live some 13,500,000 persons who reside in approximately 370 different municipalities. The metropolitan area includes such cities as Newark, Hoboken, and Paterson in New Jersey, Stamford in Connecticut, and Yonkers and New Rochelle in New York. New York City alone now covers Manhattan and Staten Islands, part of Long Island, and some territory on the mainland. Politically, the city is divided into the five boroughs of the Bronx, Brooklyn, Manhattan, Queens, and Richmond.

Manhattan Island is the heart of the New York business district. Upon this island has been built the greatest group of skyscrapers in the world, many buildings exceeding 50 stories in height. Within these great buildings are housed the headquarters of the leading commercial, industrial, and financial enterprises of the United States. The density of population in all of New York City exceeds 25,000 per square mile. During the daytime working period, in many of the Manhattan business districts the density is greater than 100,000 persons per square mile.

The intermingling of land and water hampers the movement of goods and people. Vehicular and railroad tunnels plunge under the water; enormous and costly bridges stretch high above while tugs, barges, lighters, and ferryboats plying on the surface facilitate the movement of both people and goods. Twelve major railroads serve the port area, though only three of them have terminals on Manhattan Island. Since most of the streets are narrow and sometimes winding, traffic congestion makes delivery by truck slow and costly. Most New York residents do not try to drive cars to work. Even so, vehicular tunnels, subways, and throughways for automobiles have relieved the traffic only in part. Hundreds of thousands of office workers, professional persons, and laborers commute daily to Manhattan Island from Long Island, New Jersey, Connecticut, and Hudson River points. At the rush hours the subways, suburban trains, ferries, and buses are filled to capacity in transporting suburbanites into or out of the metropolis.

One of the principal problems faced by New York is that of water supply. Each day, 1,200 million gallons of water are used by its industries and its people. The cost of constructing aqueducts and tunnels to bring the city water from sources east of the Hudson and from the

Catskills, west of the river, exceeds the cost of the Panama Canal or the Grand Coulee Project.

Housing such a large population is also a problem of great concern. The population is polyglot, for people move into the metropolis from every country on earth. Examples of special homogeneous groups include Negro and Spanish Harlem and Chinatown. Unfortunately, many New Yorkers live in crowded and often unhealthful apartments. Parks for playgrounds are inadequate, although progress is being made in providing recreation areas, especially on Long Island. The movement of many residents into the suburbs, in order to secure more favorable living conditions, lessens the number of taxpayers and increases the financial problems of the city.

Most of the world's great business firms maintain offices in New York, and large corporations are usually managed from there. As the nation's financial center New York dominates banking, investment, and insurance. Industries such as garment and jewelry manufacturing which produce high-value, high-style items in relatively small space remain in midtown Manhattan where buyers congregate. The city leads in the styling and production of clothes. It makes or controls the manufacture of most toys, novelties, pharmaceuticals, books, and periodicals. New York managers present the country's major concerts, plays, and musical attractions and staff most of those sent on tour.

As a result of congestion and high land values, industries requiring large space for their operations have sought sites in neighboring areas (Figure 2-5). Many of these cities have other complementary and supplementary functions in the metropolitan area. Among these are providing residential sections for people who work in New York, terminals and freight yards for railroads that do not go into Manhattan, dockage for coastal vessels and tramp ships, and storage facilities. Several cities sharing the environmental advantages of New York have become centers of commerce and industry in their own right. Among such cities are Bayonne, an oil-refining center; Perth Amboy, noted for the refining of metals and the importation of coal; Jersey City and Hoboken, the location of many huge factories, shipyards, and docks; Elizabeth, famous for petroleum refining and manufacturing sewing machines; Newark, with

*Figure 2-4 Manhattan Island as seen from the air over the East River. Note the concentration of towering office buildings on the lower part of the island, and the wharves, warehouses, and ships on both sides of the waterway. The first bridge is Manhattan Bridge with the famous Brooklyn Bridge just beyond. (Courtesy of New York State Department of Commerce.)*

a wide diversity of manufactures; and Paterson, a textile center.

One of the principal reasons for the great development in the New York vicinity is the excellent harbor. A marvelous system of protected and interconnected waterways, well sheltered from, but easily accessible to, the sea, is the focus of routes to and from the ocean and the continental interior. Eight bays and six rivers afford more than 700 miles of water frontage. Along these extend 200 piers equipped to service ocean-going vessels; in addition, there are hundreds of smaller docks and piers. The Hudson River has a channel deep enough to accommodate the largest ships, and tides and currents are strong enough to help keep it scoured out. There are no natural obstacles to shipping since the tidal range is small and the waters are ice-free during all the year. Ten thousand or more vessels utilize the port facilities annually. The New York area normally handles 40 to 50 per cent of the nation's imports and 30 to 40

per cent of its exports. Its total of well over 150 million short tons yearly is more than twice that of any other United States port.

### Hudson-Mohawk Lowland

New York State is crossed by two lowland areas. Along its eastern side the state is separated from New England by the Hudson River–Lake Champlain Lowland. Extending east-west across the state, and separating the Adirondacks from the Appalachian Plateaus, is the Mohawk Lowland. The two lowlands, which are at right angles to each other, form the most used land and water transportation route from New York to Buffalo and the interior of the United States. The Hudson River is so deep that ocean-going ships can go upstream as far as Albany. Smaller ships can navigate to Troy or through a canal to Lake Champlain and then through the Richelieu River to the St. Lawrence.

The chief tributary to the Hudson River is the Mohawk, which flows east to join the ma-

*Figure 2-5 Sketch map of the New York harbor area showing major rivers, bays, and ship canals. (Adapted from a map of the Corps of Engineers, United States Army.)*

jor stream at Cohoes. Through the Mohawk Valley, and the lowland to its west, was built the Erie Canal. Between 1905 and 1918 the Erie Canal and the canalized Mohawk River were deepened and widened to form the New York State Barge Canal. It extends from Troy on the Hudson River to Tonawanda on the Niagara River, from which it connects with Lake Erie. Branch canals connect with Lake Ontario ports. Along this same route has also developed an extensive system of railways and highways.

Within these lowland areas, especially the Mohawk, many industrial cities have developed. Started because of some particular advantage of site, the cities have continued to grow because of improved transportation and their concentration upon producing industrial specialties. Albany, the state capital, is near the intersection of the Barge Canal and the Hudson River with the Lake Champlain Lowland route to Montreal. Rochester, at the falls of the Gen-

esee River, early developed water power resources. Syracuse exploited local salt deposits to build a significant chemical industry. Some cities profited through utilizing the skills of early settlers. Gloversville was settled by immigrants skilled in glovemaking, Utica by those skilled in the knitting industry. The important industries of other cities capitalize inventiveness or commercial acumen. Troy is noted for its manufacturing of shirts, Schenectady for electrical goods, and Rochester for the production of photographic equipment and scientific instruments.

Buffalo, the second largest city in New York, is located at the eastern terminus of water-borne traffic on the four western Great Lakes and at the western end of the Mohawk Lowland. This situation is excellent for receiving iron ore, limestone, and grains from upper lake ports. Coal comes from the Allegheny Plateau. The harbor has been extended and improved to accommodate large lake vessels, and docks and

*Figure 2-6   Air view of Buffalo. Lake steamers are unloading wheat at the big flour mills and iron ore that will be shipped to blast furnaces. Note the connections between water and rail routes and the overhead throughway for automobiles. (Courtesy of Buffalo Chamber of Commerce.)*

wharves are mechanized to speed loading and unloading. The western terminus of the New York State Barge Canal is an integral part of the waterfront. Originally primarily a transshipment point, Buffalo is today a great manufacturing city utilizing power from both coal and Niagara Falls for flour and cereal manufacture, steel fabrication, and chemical, electrical, and other industries.

## Adirondacks

Upper New York State, north of the Mohawk Valley, is a rugged, mountainous country. A region of peaks, forests, lakes, and scenic beauty, the Adirondacks serve as a recreation area for the densely populated parts of the northeastern section of the United States. Many hunters and fishermen are attracted to the region. The Adirondack Forest Preserve covers much of the area. The forests supply pulpwood to nearby mills. Resort hotels have been built along the shores of such lakes as Placid and George. During the winter season the resorts remain open for such activities as skiing, sledding, and ice skating. Transportation routes by both rail and highway cross or penetrate the region. Iron mining has been active since 1940, after a period when production was small.

## THE MIDDLE ATLANTIC COASTAL PLAIN

The Middle Atlantic Coastal Plain has a nearly level surface and rises toward the interior in a series of low terraces. Poorly drained areas or swamps are common. The coast line is very irregular because of drowning of river mouths by the invasion of ocean water. The resulting estuaries, or tidewater bays, include Delaware and Chesapeake Bays, the lower Potomac, James, and York Rivers, and Albemarle Sound. Inland a scarp (low cliff) marks the contact of the Coastal Plain with the Piedmont. Where streams cross this scarp, there are rapids or falls because of the differences in the hardness of the rocks. The resulting feature, known as the Fall Line, determines the head of navigation on most major rivers of the region as well as the site of numerous water power developments. Many cities, including Trenton, Baltimore, Washington, and Richmond are located along this Fall Line, and their elevations vary from near sea level to over 400 feet.

The climate of the region is humid. The temperature range is continental in type, although milder than farther inland. The growing season increases in length toward the south, in part because the wide bays of warm water help to prevent late frosts in spring and early frosts in fall. These conditions produce a climate favorable for most crops, and healthful and pleasant for the millions of people who live in this region.

## Agriculture

Agriculture has long been an important activity. The earliest settlements in tidewater Maryland and Virginia were generally rural. Towns, like Williamsburg and Yorktown, were few because most plantations had frontage on tidewater. Planters shipped tobacco directly to England and received imports from the mother country at their own landings. The wide-spreading bays, an advantage for commerce in colonial days, became a liability in later times when land routes largely replaced waterways. As a result parts of peninsular Maryland and Virginia east of Chesapeake Bay became isolated, and a quiet rural life survives there in contrast with the more common suburban developments around the many cities near the inner margin of the Coastal Plain.

Much of the region is covered with light sandy soils. The ground is easily tilled, and many truck farmers produce early and late-season vegetables and fruits for the urban markets. On drained swampland and loam soils in northern New Jersey, the truck farms are meticulously tended and yield abundantly. Other sections in northern New Jersey, peninsular Maryland, and areas near Norfolk are also intensively farmed, much fertilizer being used to increase production. In the Delmarva Peninsula poultry raising is of prime importance, for the area is one of the nation's leaders in the broiler industry. Besides the fruit, vegetables, and poultry that are sped by railroad or truck to the cities, great quantities are canned or frozen. Over four hundred canneries and other food processing plants operate in and around Baltimore. Other hundreds operate in the Camden and Philadelphia district.

## Fisheries

Fish have always been an important source of food in the area. Chesapeake and Delaware Bays lead the United States in the production of shellfish. Oysters grow well in the warm, shallow water that is relatively free from silt and mud. Overexploitation of the beds has led to the development of oyster farms where the oysters are propagated scientifically. Locally, herring, shad, flounder, mackerel, and bluefish are taken by offshore fishermen. Quantities of menhaden are netted and though inedible are used in the fertilizer industry. Owners of small craft often take parties of vacationers "deep-sea fishing" on the shallow waters of the Continental Shelf.

## Industries

Although truck farming, fishing, and the tourist industry are important, the great bulk of the population on the Atlantic Coastal Plain resides in cities and is employed in manufacturing, commerce, retail trade, and various service occupations. Situated on the eastern edge of the manufacturing belt, the area makes at least some of almost every product manufactured in the United States. Iron and steel, oil products, chemicals, transportation equipment, clothing, textiles, electrical goods, and thousands of other articles are manufactured. Most large cities of the Atlantic Coastal Plain developed along the Fall Line where water power, protection from storms and open sea, and the necessity for bulk-breaking and transshipment led to early settlement and continued growth. Several of these cities have become major seaports, and nearly all are manufacturing centers. The large population of the region provides a huge market for all kinds of goods.

The low relief of the plain further aided manufacturing by permitting easy construction of railroads and highways, but the broad tidewater bays, in many places, prevent construction of routes along the coast. This has led to the building of great highway bridges over several of the bays. The bridges rise so high above the water that ocean ships pass freely underneath the spans. Examples of these include the Delaware, Chesapeake Bay, Potomac, York, and James bridges in addition to those across the Hudson River. Combined with the turnpikes (toll roads) the bridges have greatly reduced travel time from New York to other Northern cities and to the South. In addition, numerous railroads and many highways connect the in-

*Figure 2-7 Much of the land in southern New Jersey is in truck farms. Here, near Riverton, a field is being planted with carrots. (Courtesy of News and Views, Riverton, New Jersey.)*

dustrial and seaport cities with the mineralized uplands and interior plains.

Cities in the region can be divided into three large groups, manufacturing and commercial, resort and vacation, and political. Philadelphia, third largest city in the nation, is located at the junction of the Delaware and Schuylkill Rivers. This city, founded by William Penn in 1682, has continued to develop according to the plan he approved. City Hall Square forms the heart of the business district, and a gridiron pattern of streets extends from there to all parts of the city. The city contains many historical places: Independence Hall, where the Declaration of Independence was signed, still stands; nearby are such buildings as Betsy Ross House, Carpenters' Hall, where the first Congress met, and Christ Church, where many of the nation's founders worshiped. Modern Philadelphia is among the top-ranking seaports of the nation. The Delaware River, which is navigable for ocean-going ships as far as Trenton, ranks second to New York City in commercial tonnage. Proximity to coal and other resources has furthered the growth of Philadelphia. The city has a great diversity of industrial enterprises—chemicals, printing, tobacco, hats, rugs, foodstuffs, and radios—which have benefited from excellent transportation, access to markets both at home and abroad, and the early start of the city. Just across the Delaware River, in New Jersey, is Camden which is an important producer of food and electronic products. Nearby, in Delaware, is Wilmington, the center for chemical industries.

Baltimore, on the west shore of Chesapeake Bay, is one of the region's larger cities and one of the chief seaports of the nation. Like Philadelphia, Baltimore is an old, historic city as well as a modern commercial and manufacturing center. Along its waterfront are numerous shipbuilding and dry docks, grain elevators, oil storage facilities, and ore piers. Sparrows Point, a suburb, has one of the largest steel mills in the world and enormous shipyards. Transportation in the Baltimore area is excellent. Chesapeake Bay is connected to Delaware Bay by a canal. Other centers for transportation, industry,

and commerce include Trenton, Richmond, and Norfolk–Newport News–Hampton Roads. This latter port is a great naval base. It leads the nation in shipbuilding and also is a center for exporting and shipping coal from the Appalachian field.

In the Middle Atlantic states the tourist and recreation industry is big business amounting to several hundred millions of dollars annually. Summer resorts have grown along the seashore, where sandy beaches are within easy reach of the larger cities. Among these resorts Atlantic City, with its famed 7-mile-long boardwalk, and Asbury Park are perhaps the best known. Restored Williamsburg, Yorktown battlefield, numerous Civil War battle sites, Mount Vernon, and other mansions of plantation days attract tourists to the tidewater parts of Virginia and Maryland.

Washington, D.C., the nation's capital, is unique among the cities of the region. Although its population exceeds 1,000,000 persons, manufacturing is of minor importance. The city has just one important industry—government. Many varied service enterprises care for the thousands of government workers and the numerous tourists and visitors. For the most part, the city is a place of beauty. The site was selected by Washington and the city plan designed by L'Enfant. Wide avenues radiate from the Capitol somewhat like the spokes of a wheel. In addition, the city is overlaid by a gridiron pattern. Trees shade many of the main avenues as well as residential areas. Government buildings, many built of light-colored stone, are located along Constitution, Pennsylvania, and other avenues. Large parks, the Mall, various monuments and shrines, museums, and archives are all places of interest. The present city has outgrown the District of Columbia, and expanded into Maryland and across the Potomac into Virginia. Washington and especially its suburbs are rapidly increasing in population with the South supplying many of the newcomers. Most wage earners and "white-collar" workers are employed by the government or are in service occupations.

## EASTERN UPLANDS

The Eastern Uplands contrast greatly with the adjacent regions in density of population, number of cities, and intensity of land use. The region, extending southwest from the Hudson-Mohawk Depression to Alabama, rises above the surrounding lowlands from which it differs in elevation, ruggedness of relief, and hardness of the bedrock. To the east and south are the Atlantic and Gulf Coastal Plains, to the west the Central Lowland. Because of extreme variations in soils, relief, and mineral resources the distribution of population is very irregular. Compared with the adjacent lowlands there are few large cities, since the factors favoring urban growth are seldom present. Forests and woodlands occupy half the region, and many of the higher ridges or more rugged slopes are uninhabited. In some areas deer, bear, and other wild game are common.

The Uplands have had marked effects on transportation, since railroads and highways had to be built in the valleys and over the passes that afford the lowest or easiest routes. Until roads were constructed, travel was so slow and difficult that settlement was restricted to the coastal lowlands and the Piedmont. The eighteenth century was half gone before frontiersmen searched out the gaps in the mountain barrier and began settling in Tennessee, the fertile Bluegrass region of Kentucky, and the Ohio Valley. These early settlers were generally farmers. Today there are some highly productive farming regions but most of the farms are small and income from them is often considerably below the national average. Exploitation of the forest and mineral resources had small significance until after the mid-1800s when railroads, the development of industry, and the growth of lowland cities provided markets.

### Piedmont

South from the Hudson River, and extending eastward from the Blue Ridge or other front ranges of the Appalachian Mountains to the Fall Line, is a hilly belt or low plateau, known as the Piedmont, whose rolling surface is underlain by hard, crystalline bedrock. The region is approximately 50 miles wide in the north, increasing to 120 miles in South Carolina. On the east, at the Fall Line, elevation of the Piedmont is generally 200 to 400 feet, rising to 1,400 feet near the Blue Ridge. Many streams cross the region, and the valleys which have been eroded into the bedrock offer numerous sites for generating electricity.

The Piedmont is very productive. Its wooded hills and broad cultivated slopes are attractive to both residents and visitors. Agriculture was originally favored by the generally fertile, reddish loam soils, an abundant rainfall of 40 to 50 inches annually, and a long growing season ranging from 180 to 240 days. After the forests had been cleared and row crops of corn, cotton, and tobacco raised, erosion of the hilly land became a problem. This is especially true in the Carolinas. In some areas, because of the long frost-free and rainy season, three-fourths of the topsoil has been removed and great gullies have been formed, thus hindering farming operations on the sloping land. Many upland farms have been abandoned. Damage by floods has increased, and reservoirs built for the storage of water for hydroelectric plants are being filled with silt. Some owners are now rehabilitating gullied land by seeding permanent pastures. This has resulted in a shift from tilled crops to the raising of beef and dairy cattle. In the north, especially near York and Lancaster, Pennsylvania, careful rotation of crops and the practice of mixed farming with livestock production have prevented erosion and even increased the original fertility of the soil. Here the farmers are prosperous and population is increasing. The big barns, houses, and other farm buildings are evidence of good farming practices. Grass and hay crops thrive. The Piedmont in Virginia also has long been important for the raising of livestock, especially cattle.

Tobacco is a leading cash crop in North Carolina, Virginia, and eastern Pennsylvania. Tobacco culture requires careful preparation of the soil, transplanting of seedlings from seed beds, cultivation, spraying, removal of worms, topping, and curing. Need for hand labor in this work limits the amount of land planted to the crop as much as does the soil or climate. On an average farm usually tobacco is planted on only 8 to 12 acres. If tobacco is raised steadily on a piece of land, the fertility of the soil is exhausted in a few years. Some farmers, especially those in the southern Piedmont, then abandon the field and clear new land for tobacco; others add commercial fertilizers to maintain production. The most successful farmers, especially those in the northern Piedmont, rotate crops, plant tobacco on the same field only once in four or five years, and build up the soil by fertilizing with animal manure and green manure crops.

Much of the Piedmont is included in the manufacturing belt of the United States. Coal can be secured from the Appalachian Plateaus and much water power has been developed, especially in North Carolina. The northern Piedmont is near many of the largest cities and markets of the Middle Atlantic Lowland. Harrisburg, Pennsylvania, and Charlottesville and Lynchburg in Virginia are among the urban communities. In western North Carolina are numerous manufacturing centers. High Point is famous as a producer of furniture. Greensboro, Raleigh, and Charlotte are cotton and synthetic fiber mill towns. Winston-Salem and Durham also produce textiles but are better known for their manufactures of tobacco, especially cigarettes. Besides Greenville, Columbia, and Spartanburg, South Carolina has many small textile towns. In Georgia, the cities of Augusta, Macon, and Columbus are noteworthy for manufacturing textiles, chemicals, and other products. Atlanta, near the southern end of a high mountain barrier, is the inland railroad and distributing center of the South. It also has a large variety of manufactures. Cheap water power, an abundant labor supply, and raw materials available nearby are among the factors favoring the expansion of manufacturing. The southern Piedmont is the leading cotton textile manufacturing region in the world, both in the

number of active spindles and in fabric production. Much rayon is also manufactured.

### Appalachian Ridges and Valleys

The Appalachian Mountains are composed of closely folded sedimentary rocks that were once deposited on the floor of an ancient sea. The rocks—mainly sandstone, limestone, and shale —differ greatly in hardness. After millions of years of prolonged erosion, the more resistant rocks now form a series of ridges; the exposures of weaker rocks have been removed to such an extent that they form valleys. As a result, the region is characterized by alternate rows of ridges and valleys that extend northeast to southwest from New York State to Georgia and Alabama. The ridges are discontinuous and may end with the dying out of the fold that caused them. In some instances a river may cut through a ridge and thereby form a water gap. Such gaps, or passes, were important in determining the routes followed by the early trails and the pioneer settlers and later by the canals, highways, and railroads. The valleys are generally fertile, and farming in some of them is very successful. The ridges are used for forest land and have few permanent inhabitants. Forestry, mining, and tourism are the leading activities.

The Blue Ridge, the name applied to the eastern-facing front of the Appalachians, is the longest uplift. The northern end of the Blue Ridge, between the Hudson and Schuylkill Rivers, is low and narrow. South of the Schuylkill, it increases in elevation but remains relatively narrow. At about the Virginia–North Carolina boundary a series of ridges and ranges forms a rough mountain area. Just west of the Blue Ridge are such groups as the Unakas and the Great Smokies. In North Carolina and Tennessee, the Great Smokies and the Blue Ridge attain a width of 70 miles. In this section there are many peaks that exceed 6,000 feet in elevation, Mt. Mitchell, 6,694 feet, being the highest in the eastern part of the United States. These mountain masses form important barriers to the east-west movement of goods and people. Areas of hardwoods as well as forests of pine and fir extend the length of these mountains and support a lumber industry. More important, however, is the resort and tourist industry which is favored by the scenic beauty of the region and its coolness in summer. The Shenandoah and Great Smoky Mountains National Parks and the Cumberland Gap and other national monuments have been established in this area. Only a little subsistence agriculture has been developed in protected valleys.

The Great Valley lies west of the Blue Ridge and is the most important depression in the Appalachian Ridge and Valley area. It includes parts of eight states, is 1,000 miles long, and averages about 20 miles in width. Many rivers —Delaware, Susquehanna, Lehigh, Potomac, Shenandoah, James, Roanoke, New, Holston, Tennessee, and Coosa—occupy portions of the Great Valley. Locally the Valley is known by various names, among them the Shenandoah, Lehigh, and Cumberland. The state of Virginia calls it the Valley of Virginia. Although the Great Valley reaches 2,000 feet in elevation in southern Virginia, the floor is generally flat; the

divides between rivers are so gentle that there are no obstructions of importance. The bedrock is a limestone in which many caves and the Natural Bridge of Virginia have been formed. This valley has served as an important artery for travel and commerce for the last two centuries. Soils in the region are fertile, and diversified farming with dairying and livestock production is dominant. Since the valley slopes are relatively free of harmful frosts, apples and other orchard fruits are produced on a large scale, especially in the Shenandoah Valley. During the War Between the States this route was used by both Northern and Southern armies. Among the cities in the Great Valley are Bethlehem, Allentown, Easton, Reading, Lancaster, and York in Pennsylvania, Winchester and Roanoke in Virginia, and Knoxville— famed for atomic energy and the TVA—and Chattanooga in Tennessee.

Between the Great Valley and the Appalachian Plateaus are the many ridges and interwoven valleys that form the remainder of the

*Figure 2-8 Air view of the Susquehanna Valley in east central Pennsylvania. Strip farming for hay and field crops is used on the slopes to control erosion. A young orchard is in the foreground. The ridges and hills at left are in forests. The well-kept farms and buildings indicate that this is a prosperous farming region. (Courtesy of Soil Conservation Service.)*

*Figure 2-9    Forested ridges and narrow valleys along the Pennsylvania Turnpike. (Courtesy of Pennsylvania Turnpike Commission.)*

region. In certain sections, forest-covered ridges dominate over valleys and may be without permanent population. In other places the valleys, although short and narrow, are floored with fertile soil and support productive farms similar to those in the Great Valley. Some lumbering is done. Stone is quarried for cement and other construction materials. Iron ore is mined near Cornwall in northeast Pennsylvania. Practically all of the anthracite of the nation is mined in northeastern Pennsylvania along the Lackawanna and upper Susquehanna Rivers. The chief cities in the hard-coal fields are Scranton, Wilkes-Barre, Pottsville, and Hazelton. Altoona and Williamsport are two of the cities located in valleys among the ridges.

As the area was being slowly uplifted, major rivers like the Delaware, Susquehanna, and Potomac eroded water gaps through the ridges. Frontiersmen and settlers from the older settlements near the Atlantic followed these water-level routes into northern Pennsylvania, western New York, the area along Lake Erie, and west into the Ohio Valley. Hence, the importance of these gaps in the location of settlements and trade routes can hardly be exaggerated. Major railroads today utilize the gaps, and many cities —Harrisburg and Reading, for example—are located at the junction of routes determined by the water gaps and river routes.

The scenery, cool summers, and occasional hot springs have caused the development of many resort centers among the Appalachian ridges. Asheville, in a fertile basin near the Great Smoky Mountains National Park, is a famous resort city. Other resort centers include Gatlinburg, Tennessee, White Sulphur Springs, West Virginia, the Delaware Water Gap, and several hill resorts in Pennsylvania.

The Tennessee Valley Authority essentially covers the watershed of the Tennessee River. Government agencies, with the approval of Congress, organized and developed the project. The TVA was to serve as a pilot plan for regional development, and to act as a guide for future planning in other regions such as the Missouri and Columbia River valleys. Specifically, it was intended to (1) create a 9-foot channel from Knoxville to the mouth of the Tennessee River at Paducah, (2) provide for flood control and the development of hydroelectric power, (3) develop soil conservation and erosion control, (4) provide fertilizers for the rehabilitation of agricultural lands, and (5) encourage the development of agriculture and manufacturing. The Tennessee River is formed by the confluence of the Holston and French Broad rivers in the Great Valley of east Tennessee. With the construction of several dams across the main channel, the river has become almost a series of connected lakes. Nine dams —including Wilson, Kentucky, Watts Bar, and Chickamauga—have been built across the river proper. Numerous other dams, such as the Norris, Douglas, and Cherokee, have been built on tributaries of the Tennessee. Chemical, aluminum, and other manufacturing plants have located in or near Knoxville and Chattanooga because of the available hydroelectric power. The first atomic energy plant was developed at Oak Ridge. Since 1950 many TVA power installations have been expanded and supplemented by coal generating plants.

## Appalachian Plateaus

In spite of the hilly aspect of the Appalachian Plateau, if one looks over the country from a high viewpoint it is apparent that all the summits are of nearly the same height and that once they were joined to form a flat surface. The bedrock is similar to that in the Ridge and Valley area; however, it was only gently warped during its uplift instead of being closely folded. The hills, then, are the result of erosion of the uplifted plateau by thousands of streams. In general the plateau is so deeply and widely dissected that only remnants of the former surface remain. Westward the plateau slopes down and gradually merges with the Interior Lowlands. Small areas of flat land occur along the river bottoms and, with the gentler slopes of the usually steep-sided valleys, are the principal sites of farmland. More than half the plateau is wooded, and although the best timber has been cut, some logs and mine props are still produced.

The northern Allegheny Plateau includes the Catskill and Pocono Mountains as well as the Finger Lakes district of New York. Along with portions of northwest Pennsylvania and northeast Ohio, this area has been glaciated and is more extensively eroded than farther south. Many lakes are scattered among the forest-covered hills. In the Poconos, Catskills, and Finger Lakes areas a thriving tourist industry has developed. Cool summers, scenic hills, and

*Figure 2-10  A blast furnace. This type of structure is a recurrent landscape feature in the central section of the Allegheny Plateau. (Courtesy of United States Steel Corporation.)*

*Figure 2-11 This 20-ton automatic coal-mining machine takes the place of 4 ordinary machines in cutting, drilling, blasting, and loading and assures a 4-ton flow of coal each minute. (Courtesy of National Coal Association.)*

placid lakes with large cities nearby are all inducements to the vacationer.

Dairy farms from which fresh milk is shipped to city markets or processing plants are common. Much land is in pasture but hay, corn, and small grains are the usual crops. Farming on the steep slopes has frequently resulted in badly eroded fields, land abandonment, and decrease in the local farm population. In Pennsylvania, especially in Indiana County, millions of conifers have been planted on the gullied hills from which, within a few years, they are harvested and sold as Christmas trees.

In western Pennsylvania, northern West Virginia, and eastern Ohio is the world's largest known area of high-grade bituminous coal. It underlies about 43,000 square miles. The availability of this source of power is the most important factor in the location of the manufacturing belt in the United States, especially the manufacture of iron and steel and other heavy goods. In this area the towns are generally of two types, farm market centers with fine old houses and shady streets, and mining towns in many of which the operators built the houses all alike. These latter towns are almost devoid of trees and beauty. Huge piles of waste rock

dominate the landscape. Bituminous coal production is highly mechanized both in the surface, or strip, mines and underground. Cutting, loading, sorting, cleaning, chemical treatment, and blending of the coal is done by machines.

Petroleum and natural gas are two other sources of available power. The first oil well in the United States was drilled in 1859 in northwestern Pennsylvania. The names of Oil City and Titusville were famous in the early days of the oil industry.

The Pittsburgh district leads the world in the manufacture of iron and steel. The abundance of high-grade coking coal, the ease with which iron ores are imported from the Lake Superior region, the early start of the industry, and the huge demand from nearby industries help to account for the regional importance of iron and steel manufacturing. Pittsburgh is located at the junction of three navigable rivers—Ohio, Monongahela, Allegheny—on a usable water route to the interior and Gulf of Mexico. It also has excellent rail and highway connections. Youngstown, Wheeling, and Johnstown are but a few of the many other steel centers. Besides steel, the district manufactures a great variety of products. Many cities of the Allegheny Plateau are noted for specialties. Akron makes tires; Corning, glass; Elmira, typewriters; Binghamton and Endicott, shoes; New Kensington, Pennsylvania, aluminum; East Liverpool, Ohio, pottery; Painesville, Ohio, plastics; and Canton and Massillon, alloy steels and metal products. In West Virginia, the Kanawha Valley is famed for coal and chemicals.

Starting in West Virginia, the Cumberland Plateau extends through southeastern Kentucky and Tennessee into northern Alabama. Much of the plateau in Kentucky is extremely dissected, producing some of the most rugged hill country in the entire Appalachian Highlands. In Tennessee and Alabama the plateau is less dissected than the Allegheny, the valleys being narrower and the divides wider. Coal is the principal mineral resource of the Cumberland Plateau. The mines of eastern Kentucky, western Virginia, and southern West Virginia rank second only to those in Pennsylvania and northern West Virginia. Most of the coal mined in this region is shipped either to the Great Lakes ports or the Hampton Roads area. Petroleum and forests are also important resources. Tillable areas are small but subsistence farming is the chief support of many people. There are no large cities and, except for the mining communities, the towns are few and small. The population is predominantly rural.

The Cumberland Plateau was originally settled by people of English, Scotch, and Irish stock, moving on upstream eddies of the tide of westward migration. They came so far, and went no farther. This seemed good country to most pioneers for the land was well forested. Game and fish abounded and the little coves of flatter land were adequate for early subsistence agriculture. As population increased isolation

and inaccessibility continued, putting more and more pressure on the meager resources. Lacking better land, descendants of the pioneers planted corn, their chief crop, on increasingly steeper slopes. Here, within a few years, erosion ruined the fields and the crops grown on the hill lands became so pitifully small that they provided only the barest living. In the more remote areas houses are poor and, with their furnishings, were built by the people. Even much of the clothing is of home manufacture. People still hunt game to supplement the larder and gather wild herbs to sell for a little cash. The development of coal mining and lumbering provides work for some. With the improvement of roads more visitors will enter the district, but since there are few facilities for their entertainment the tourist business brings little cash.

## INTERIOR HIGHLANDS

The Interior Highlands, composed of the Ouachita (pronounced Washita) Mountains, part of the Arkansas River Valley, and the Ozark Plateau, are located largely in Arkansas and Missouri, with a smaller area in Oklahoma. This region of folded mountains and dome-shaped plateau is completely surrounded by the plains of the Central Lowland and the Coastal Plain. In many respects the region is much like the Ridge and Valley area and the Allegheny Plateaus of the Eastern Highlands.

White people began settling in the Ouachitas and Ozarks soon after the United States acquired the land through the Louisiana Purchase. These early settlers established subsistence farms and grazed livestock which was driven to market. In some remote areas this pattern still persists. The Oklahoma part of the Ozarks, however, was set aside as Indian land for the Cherokees and the Ouachita area in Oklahoma was given to the Choctaws. In many instances, the Indians made more progress in their development than did the whites. The boundary line between Arkansas and Oklahoma has been referred to as a "cultural fault line" since it so definitely marks the division between people of two races, two cultures.

### Ouachita Mountains and Arkansas River Valley

The Ouachita Mountains are formed by a series of steeply folded sandstone ridges that have elevations up to 3,000 feet and extend in a general east-west direction. Because of these ridges, the rainfall of the region is considerably above that of the surrounding plains, many stations recording over 60 inches annually. Forestry and grazing are the principal activities. Coniferous trees, especially pines, grow well on the poorer, sandy soils. A variety of deciduous trees, dominantly oak and hickory, is found in the valleys. The Ouachita National Forest covers about one-fifth of the total area and there are several state-supervised forests in the rest of the region. Both hardwoods and softwoods are cut, sawed, dried, and marketed for flooring, siding, and general construction. Fence posts are also a common product. In many parts of the mountains, cattle graze over the open range, and the fields are fenced to keep the cattle out. The only important source of bauxite, the ore of aluminum, within the United States is in the Ouachitas, the region mining about 98 per cent of the domestic supply. Large open pits near Benton,

Arkansas, have been greatly expanded since 1945.

Hot Springs, at the eastern edge of the Ouachitas, is the largest city in the area. Noted for its hot baths and the Hot Springs National Park, the oldest national park in the nation, it has become an attractive resort.

The Arkansas River, flowing in a general easterly direction, separates the Ouachita Mountains from the Ozark Plateau. The valley floor is flat and the soil rich. Much of the land is in pasture or is used for specialty crops. There are coal mines within the area. The most important function of the valley is serving as a transportation route through the adjacent higher, rougher areas.

## Ozark Plateau

The Ozark Plateau is a dome-shaped uplift with streams radiating from the broadly rolling central portion, deepening and widening their valleys as they approach the perimeter. The southern Ozarks, known as the Boston Mountains, are higher and have a rougher topography than the rest of the area.

Although much of the more rugged area is forest covered, and lumbering is an important industry, agriculture and grazing are of prime importance. In northwestern Arkansas, the broiler industry has been highly developed; many acres are planted in vegetables, and vineyards are common. Wineries and canneries in the nearby communities buy and process the crops. The rocky hills in both Arkansas and Oklahoma produce large quantities of strawberries. The Springfield Plain section in southwestern Missouri is among the important dairy regions of the nation.

Lead, zinc, and limestone are mined or quarried in the Ozarks. The Joplin or Tri-State district of Oklahoma, Kansas, and Missouri mines much lead and is one of the principal zinc-producing areas of the nation. Southeastern Missouri leads in lead production.

Recreation is rapidly becoming the most important industry in many parts of this area. With the construction of large dams for flood control, power, and recreation, artificial lakes such as Lake-o'-the-Cherokees, Fort Gibson, and Tenkiller Ferry in Oklahoma, Norfolk and Bull Shoals in Arkansas, and Lake of the Ozarks in Missouri have been formed. Each lake is larger than many of the large natural lakes in the eastern part of the United States. Several picturesque limestone caves and big springs also add to the tourist attractions.

## THE SOUTH

For many decades the South has been a region of economic maladjustment. The history of its people and their activities has been a turbulent one. Before the War Between the States the economy was based on cotton plantations and slavery, after the war on cotton and tenant farmers or sharecroppers. Various political conditions along with declining soil fertility and poor farming methods made recovery slow, but by 1900 a semblance of agricultural adjustment had occurred. Because of the high cotton prices during and immediately after World War I, however, much eroded and infertile soil was planted in cotton. In the depression years of the 1930s the South, along with the rest of the nation, found its economy again shattered and many of its people in want. In several respects the South, with its dominant one-crop system and tenant farmers, became the economic problem of the nation.

Since 1935 a new South has been in the process of formation. Recognizing the need for diversification of crops, better soil and forest conservation, and the development of industries, the people of the South, with the aid of the Federal government, again began an economic adjustment. No longer is the region just a "Land of Cotton" and small farms. Although cotton is still widely grown, and there are numerous small farms, the tendency now is toward consolidation of holdings; increased attention to livestock, with greater acreages planted to soybeans, peanuts, and hay crops; terracing, contouring, and fertilizing of the soil; and the development of industries to use the natural resources of the region.

## Physical Setting

Except for the southern part of the Piedmont Plateau, the South is a region of plains, occupying most of the Atlantic and all of the Gulf Coastal Plain. In general, the northern boundary coincides with the 200-day growing season; thus the region extends northward up the Mississippi Valley into southern Illinois. Its western boundary, in Texas near the 100th meridian, is associated with the Cap Rock Escarpment, or "the Break of the Plains," where there is a marked change in elevation. Also within this vicinity is the 25-inch annual rainfall line.

Much of the South is a nearly flat lowland which slopes gently toward the ocean. In places low hills, which mark the outcrop of more resistant rocks, rise above the lower lands formed of silt, clay, and limey marl. Florida is a peninsula built mostly of limestone in which many lakes have been formed by solution. The Everglades, a large swamp area, and Lake Okeechobee occupy the southern end of the peninsula from which a festoon of keys extends toward the Gulf of Mexico. The Mississippi is the major river and with its tributaries, broad floodplain, and delta is the dominant feature that divides the South into two nearly equal parts.

Florida and the Gulf Coast enjoy a humid subtropical climate with little or no frost. Inland, there are two or three months during which freezing temperatures occur and many plants become dormant. Rainfall is usually well distributed and generally totals 40 to 50 inches annually. At some Gulf stations, however, the annual rainfall may exceed 80 inches, but inland, to the west and northwest, the total decreases to 25 or 30 inches. The principal weather handicaps are hurricanes that occasionally affect the coasts, winter cold waves that bring freezing temperatures which may injure fruits and vegetables, and occasional droughts.

## Agriculture

Agriculture is the basic occupation in the South. The long growing season and abundant rainfall favor corn, cotton, and many other crops. Only the lower Rio Grande Valley requires regular irrigation. The soils are highly variable. Those in the river bottomlands and deltas, and the zones of marls and silts inland from the coasts are very fertile; in contrast are the poor soils of the pineflats and sandy hills. When drained, muck soils of the Everglades of Florida and along parts of the Gulf Coast are well suited for vegetables and sugar cane. All through the South marked changes are taking place in agriculture, particularly in the use of machinery, marketing methods, and variety of products grown.

*Figure 2-12  Badly eroded corn field and dilapidated house in western South Carolina. The eroded field is to be retired to kudzu. (Courtesy of Soil Conservation Service.)*

For over 150 years, cotton has so constantly been the money crop that the region is often called the Cotton Belt. The crop has an annual value of over 2.5 billion dollars. The best soils planted to cotton are those of alluvial origin along the Mississippi, Yazoo, Arkansas, and other rivers. The very fertile black waxy prairie soils of Texas are also excellent producers of cotton. The southern Piedmont and a zone of sandy loams on the inner coastal plain from Georgia into North Carolina are traditionally of great importance. Since 1900, however, production in these eastern sections has declined because of soil erosion or depletion, infestation by the boll weevil, replacement by other farm products, especially fodder and pasture crops, and competition for labor from industry. Cotton lands are increasingly dependent on the use of fertilizers. Since 1920 the High Plains in western Texas and southwestern Oklahoma have largely replaced the southeastern areas in cotton production. Mechanization in caring for

and picking the crop, together with development of varieties suited to a drier climate, has made possible the expansion of the industry into these western lands. Since cotton must be picked in dry weather, only small amounts are grown along the southern coast where autumn rains may delay or prevent the harvest. Much labor is needed to produce a good cotton crop. After planting, the growing crop must be cultivated and chopped (hoed) for thinning and weeding. Until the 1930s cotton was picked by hand, requiring much cheap labor. Since then cotton-picking machines have been increasingly used, especially in the newer producing areas of the west where farms are larger than in the older districts. After the cotton has been picked; it is taken to cotton gins where the seeds are removed and the fibers are pressed and bound into bales. Cottonseed is a valuable by-product and is used for edible oils, soap, and other items. In addition to the large quantities consumed by mills in the United States, cotton is exported to many textile manufacturing countries, for the South grows more than 40 per cent of the world's cotton. Location of the principal seaports of the South, like Houston and New Orleans which are close to the cotton fields, is advantageous for export.

Citrus fruits are grown along the outer margins of the coastal plains, but central Florida and the lower Rio Grande Valley in Texas are so seldom reached by frosts that they produce most of the South's commercial crop. Oranges, grapefruit, tangerines, and limes are most significant in Florida. Grapefruit is a specialty in Texas. Normally, citrus fruits come on the market in quantity only at certain seasons. To prolong the marketing season and preserve the products, nearly half the crop is processed into canned fruit and juice, frozen concentrates, and

*Figure 2-13 The extensive acreage devoted to cotton culture is suggested in this illustration. The cotton-picking machine is an outstanding example of mechanized agriculture in the Cotton Belt. (Courtesy of Missouri Resources Division.)*

marmalade. About fifty million gallons of orange juice are frozen and processed yearly in Florida. Noncitrus fruits are grown in almost all inland sections of the region. Important commercial crops of peaches are marketed in South Carolina and Georgia. Oklahoma and Texas are among the nation's leaders in pecan production. Large orchards of tung trees, whose seeds supply an oil for varnish, have been developed in northern Florida and southern Alabama.

Sugar, rice, corn, peanuts, and winter vegetables are among other Southern crops. Sugar cane is grown on the lower Mississippi Delta, especially in southern Louisiana, and to some degree in southern Florida. Although there is danger of crop injury from cold, the development of cold-resistant hybrid varieties has lessened this danger and also doubled acreage yields. Southern Louisiana is a land of big plantations. Planting and caring for the crop, harvesting and transporting the cane, and extracting the sugar at the mills and refineries require large capital investment. Southern rice, like wheat, is planted and harvested by machine methods. Level land underlain by impervious clay is surrounded by dikes to retain the water in which rice stands during much of its growing season. Louisiana, Texas, and Arkansas produce over 60 per cent of the domestic rice. More acres are planted in corn than in any other crop, for corn is the common grain crop of the South. As corn bread, hominy, and grits, corn is widely used for food as well as feed for livestock. Wheat is grown as a money crop in northwestern Texas and southwestern Oklahoma. Peanuts grow well on depleted soils. They are used for food, as raw material by chemical industries, and by food processors.

Truck crops are grown by intensively specialized methods in a number of limited areas. Most of the products, such as vegetables and strawberries, move first from the more southerly areas to Northern markets during the early winter. Within a few weeks a more northerly locality will then come into production. Some growers plant two crops annually, one for the early and one for the late market. The drained muck lands of southern Florida and the silts of

the lower Rio Grande Valley are among the principal producing sections. Thousands of carloads of Southern fruits and vegetables are delivered in season to Northern markets by refrigerator cars and trucks.

Livestock is of increasing importance, notably on the depleted soils of the older settled sections of the South. Fodder crops like lespedeza, kudzu, and cowpeas are good stock feeds and grow well on worn-out land which they enrich while they help hold eroding soils in place. Texas has long been a leading state for cattle, but the recent growth in production of cattle, pigs, and poultry east of the Mississippi is quite noteworthy. The cattle industry benefits from the mild temperatures; the even rainfall that facilitates rapid growth of hay and forage crops makes pasturage available most of the year. Because pork products are popular in the South, corn and hog production has risen. The poultry business has expanded, especially in northeastern Georgia; quantities of fowls are now being processed for shipment to Northern markets. Mild temperatures and available feed are favorable, but learning the "know-how" of hatching, feeding, processing, and marketing poultry is even more important. Although natural conditions favor dairying, its development has lagged, partly because many farmers lack experience. Effort is being made to develop breeds of dairy cows that will be unaffected by the long, hot summers. Beef cattle production also is increasing, and crossbreeding of Hereford and Angus with the Brahmas of India is providing good beef cattle that can withstand the heat of the long summers.

## Forests

The South is a natural woodland area. Its long growing season and ample rainfall cause trees to make double the growth of those in northern climates. Pines predominate on the flat plains; hardwoods are found in the river bottoms. In areas of hilly land the two are frequently mixed. Except on natural prairies in Texas and Oklahoma, farmland, when abandoned, is quickly seeded from the nearby woods and becomes covered with a second-growth forest. In thirty to forty years the pines become large enough for saw logs. A chief obstacle to reforestation in the coastal sections is the large number of forest fires, sometimes set by cattle owners who think that burning improves the grass. Few national forests have been established, but large acreages under private ownership are scientifically handled and form the basis for permanent lumber and pulp or paper enterprises. Logging is possible throughout the year and the logs are delivered to the mills by truck and rail. Many mills are located at seaports or so near them that lumber can be easily exported. Mississippi and Louisiana are the leaders, but lumber is marketed from every Southern state. In total output, the South is second only to the Pacific Northwest. Lumber used for construction, naval stores, and wood pulp are the principal products of the Southern forests.

The southern pines are the principal source of naval stores. Resin, the basic element, is a thick, amber-colored liquid which flows from the tree when a gash is cut in the trunk. Since the resin flows into cups which have been attached to the tree, this activity is called "cupping." After many years of cupping the trees are cut for lumber. The chief naval store products are pitch, which is used in caulking wooden ships, tar for waterproofing, and turpentine. Resin is also used as a raw material for the chemical industries. Savannah and Jacksonville lead in the exportation of naval stores.

The pulpwood and kraft (wrapping) paper industry has had a phenomenal development in the South. Many paper mills have been built, especially in Georgia and the Gulf states. Since trees become large enough for pulpwood in ten to fifteen years the paper and pulpwood industry can be established on a permanent basis. Tree farming is now an important activity in many parts of the South.

## Fisheries

Shrimp, sponges, oysters, and crabs provide the principal source of income from the southern coastal fisheries. Inshore waters, especially

along the lagoons of the Mississippi Delta, supply small shrimp and crabs. Large shrimp are secured by trawlers, fishing at night, in the deeper Gulf waters. Corpus Christi and Galveston are important shrimp ports. From these and several other ports, shrimp are shipped fresh or as frozen or canned products. Oysters are taken mainly from the lagoons on the coasts of Louisiana and Florida. The center of the sponge industry is Tarpon Springs, Florida. Sponges are taken largely by divers.

In a few places snapper and other fish are caught for local markets. In the Mississippi and other rivers in the region, both large and small, fishing for catfish, bass, and other fresh-water fish greatly supplements the local food supply and furnishes very desirable recreation.

## Minerals

In total value the South produces over 25 per cent of the nation's minerals. It exceeds all the rest of the nation in the production of petrole-um. Coal, iron ore, sulfur, phosphate, and salt are also produced in large quantities. Building stones and numerous minerals of lesser importance such as asphalt, glass sand, and kaolin are of considerable local importance. One of the most important factors in the industrial development of the South has been this large and varied mineral reserve.

The Mid-Continent oil field, the most important producer of petroleum in the world, is largely in the southern region. Included in this field are the producing areas in Arkansas, northern Louisiana, most of Oklahoma, and much of northern and western Texas. The Gulf Coast field, the second most important in the United States, is entirely within the South along the Gulf Coast of Texas and Louisiana. Texas ranks first among all states in petroleum production, Louisiana third, and Oklahoma fourth. Arkansas and Mississippi are also important producers of petroleum. During the period 1946 to 1955, the average yearly production of petroleum in the United States was 23,868 mil-

*Figure 2-14 A general view of the Esso refinery located in Baton Rouge, Louisiana. This refinery, the largest in the United States, processes 340,000 barrels of crude oil daily. (Courtesy of Esso Standard Oil Company.)*

lion barrels of which 13,615 million barrels were produced in the South.

The exploitation of petroleum makes startling changes in the landscape. Small agricultural hamlets, sleepy cow towns, or somnolent fishing villages may become booming cities almost overnight. Derricks, pumps, storage tanks, oil field camps, and all the other accompaniments of this industry completely change the activities of the communities in which oil is found. New residential and commercial additions, in many instances whole new towns, have been built for and by the influx of workers required to carry on the various phases of the industry. Good transportation is essential. Along the coast, harbors have been improved and sometimes created by dredging, and breakwaters and docks built to service the tankers that transport petroleum and its products to Atlantic Coast ports and abroad. Pipelines, railroad tank cars, and highway tankers distribute oil products inland.

Seemingly insuperable difficulties have been overcome in developing oil fields along the Gulf of Mexico. Much oil lies beneath coastal swamps and even under the ocean floor. Drilling operations proceed on platforms in quagmires or in open waters. Transporting men and materials over swamps and waters requires wholly new types of vehicles and amphibious boats. Some producing wells are 10 miles offshore in the shallow Gulf waters, and the seaward limit of the oil fields has not yet been determined.

Coastal centers famous for oil production include Beaumont and Port Arthur, Texas, and Lake Charles, Louisiana. Texas City, Houston, and New Orleans all have great oil refineries. More than 40 oil refineries are located along the Gulf Coast of Texas and Louisiana, among them four of the five largest in the United States. Two refineries in Port Arthur and one in Beaumont have a daily crude capacity of over 200,000 barrels each. The largest American refinery is in Baton Rouge and has a daily capacity greater than 340,000 barrels. Smaller cities such as Tyler and Kilgore have developed in the East Texas oil fields. Cushing and

Seminole expanded as a result of the exploitation of the Greater Seminole field in Oklahoma. Tulsa is one of the leading oil financial centers of the world.

Natural gas, usually associated with petroleum, is found in enormous quantities. Formerly much of this excellent fuel was wasted because there were no markets nearby. Invention of spiral steel pipe and machines to lay and weld the sections quickly has made possible delivery of gas from the South to Northeastern industrial and seaport cities. Natural gas is considered the ideal fuel for heating and cooking in homes. Near Amarillo some gas is burned to make carbon black, a product used in many chemical industries. Natural gas is used also as a raw material in certain chemical industries and is considered the best fuel for the making of glass.

Five Southern states—Alabama, Arkansas, Georgia, Oklahoma, and Texas—have reserves of bituminous coal. Arkansas and Texas have also deposits of lignite. Excellent bituminous coal, which can be used to make coke, is mined in Alabama near the end of the Appalachian Plateau and is used in the iron and steel industries of that state.

The largest production of sulfur in the world is on the Gulf Coast of Louisiana and Texas. Water heated under pressure to temperatures higher than 300°F is forced into the sulfur deposits. At such temperatures, the sulfur becomes soluble. The liquid is then forced to the surface by compressed air, run into large storage bins, and allowed to cool and solidify. Gulf Coast sulfur is shipped to chemical plants throughout the world. The chief product made from sulfur is sulfuric acid, but the mineral is also used in making drugs, paper, fertilizer, and a variety of other products.

Phosphate, iron ore, and salt are also mined in the Southern states. Phosphate rock, used for fertilizer, is mined in the Tampa area. This part of Florida supplies 80 per cent of the phosphate used in the United States and exports a large amount besides. The chief iron ore mining region is near Birmingham and is close to good coking coal and limestone. These resources are the basis for the largest iron and steel production in the South. Some iron ore is mined in northeast Texas and forms the base for a small but expanding industry near Daingerfield. Large quantities of salt are mined along the Texas–Louisiana coast.

## Manufacturing and Transportation

Since 1935 the number of manufacturing establishments in the South has greatly increased. Factors that favor the industrial development of this region are (1) vast reserves of petroleum, natural gas, and coal that can be used both for power and for chemical raw materials, (2) resources of timber, minerals, and agricultural products available for processing, (3) a large supply of labor, and (4) good transportation by sea and land. Among the handicaps are (1) a shortage of local capital and lack of industrial experience, (2) the competition of Northern mills which have established reputations, (3) the lack of skilled labor, and (4) the greater distance to the large markets.

Although the South is less densely populated than the Northeast, it has an adequate supply of potential industrial workers. Some of these come from the farms where mechanization, soil depletion, and changes in crop systems have reduced the number of laborers needed. In general, living costs less in the South and wages have usually been below those of the North. Lower operating costs have been a primary reason for the shift of textile mills from New England to the southern Piedmont. Many branch plants of Northern-owned corporations have been located in the South to supply the demands of the region for nationally distributed articles. Examples include assembly plants for automobiles, farm machinery, and heavy goods on which important savings in freight charges from the home plants to the South can be made.

The pattern of manufacturing in the region is characterized by wide distribution and great diversity. The Texas Gulf Coast area, particularly in and around Houston, is especially important for chemicals, machinery, oil refining, and shipbuilding. Elsewhere, Birmingham leads the South in steelmaking. Memphis processes agricultural products and lumber. The Dallas–Fort Worth section has a variety of industries including meat packing, wearing apparel, automobile assembly, and airplane manufacture. Tulsa produces oil field equipment, pottery, glass, and airplanes. Oklahoma City is noted for meat packing and airplane assembly. In the vicinity of New Orleans, Mobile, Tampa, and other Southern cities are smaller industrial districts which make practically all types of manufactured goods.

Transportation in the region is aided by the broad lowlands that offer few hindrances, except that of rivers which must be bridged, to the building of railroads and highways. There are many navigable rivers, of which the Mississippi is the major artery for bulky freight. The Black Warrior River in Alabama is used to carry coal. A few canals are noteworthy. Houston, an inland city, has become a great seaport by dredging and improving a shallow river and developing the Houston Ship Canal. A dredged waterway connecting the Mississippi River and Lake Ponchartrain has greatly increased waterfront land available to industrial development in the vicinity of New Orleans. The Intracoastal Waterway is located through much of its route from New Jersey to Miami in waters protected by offshore islands. Thousands of pleasure craft travel on this waterway yearly.

## Cities and Towns

The uniform flat surface of the rural South favors a fairly even distribution of population. Only the swamps and areas with the poorest of sandy soils have few inhabitants. Zones of superior soil like the black waxy prairie in east central Texas and the Yazoo bottomlands of northwestern Mississippi support many prosperous farms. Rural hamlets and villages are numerous throughout the region. Most of them have a consolidated school and a post office which serve the immediate vicinity. A small general store or two, filling stations, and possibly a drug store, garage, and cotton gin comprise the local business establishments. Two or three small churches are found in almost every

village. Many of the people drive to the larger towns or cities to buy most of their needs.

The South is not a region of large cities. This fact stands out particularly when the South is compared with the other regions in the eastern part of the United States. Only a score of cities in the South have populations of 100,000 or more. Three states—North Carolina, South Carolina, and Mississippi—have no cities in this group. The two largest cities are Houston and New Orleans, each having over 600,000 inhabitants. Within the region, Texas has more large cities than any other state; San Antonio, Austin, Dallas, and Fort Worth are either in good agricultural regions or near a good supply of water. Houston and Corpus Christi are Gulf ports.

In many instances some local factor has spurred the development of cities. Birmingham, Tulsa, and Oklahoma City grew big because of local iron ore or petroleum development. Memphis is important for wholesale and retail trade in addition to its manufacturing. New Orleans and Houston, the two chief Southern ports, lead in tonnage of trade and rank among the first 10 ports of the nation in this regard. Smaller Gulf ports include Corpus Christi, Galveston, Texas City, Port Arthur, Mobile, and Tampa. The ports on the Atlantic like Wilmington, Charleston, Savannah, Jacksonville, and Miami have smaller hinterlands than the Gulf ports, thus their ocean-borne trade is less although some, in particular Charleston, have magnificent harbors.

### Recreation

Tourists and vacationists spend hundreds of millions of dollars in travel through the South and while staying at coast resorts from the Carolinas to Texas. Both the Atlantic and Gulf Coasts of Florida are major resort areas. More visitors come in the winter season, but many

*Figure 2-15   Recreation is big business in many parts of the United States. Miami Beach, Florida, is famous for its many large resort hotels. (Courtesy of Miami Beach News Bureau.)*

are encouraged to vacation in the summer by the cheaper rates of the "off season." Streamlined trains, airplanes, buses, private cars, and pleasure boats bring thousands of visitors to Florida daily at the height of the season. Miami Beach stretches for nine miles on an island offshore from Miami. It boasts of almost four hundred hotels with a capacity to care for visitors far in excess of most larger cities. Palm Beach, Fort Lauderdale, and Daytona Beach are a few of the Florida east coast resort towns in the section between Jacksonville and Key West, which is at the end of a noted overseas highway that follows a row of coral islets. Resorts in west Florida center around Tampa Bay, and include the cities of Tampa and St. Petersburg. The central Florida lake district is of increasing popularity with vacationers and retired Northerners. Westward along the Gulf of Mexico are numerous resort areas including Gulfport, Biloxi, and Galveston. The warm sunshine, freedom from frost and snow, sandy beaches for sun and water bathing, and sport fishing are the leading attractions. Many retired elderly people move to Florida.

The South has a pleasing and restful landscape with many places of historical interest as well as some unique natural attractions. The Everglades National Park, at the southern tip of Florida, has virgin swamps and forests famous for birds, alligators, wild animals, and curious plants. The flowers in season are an attraction in themselves. The gardens and old mansions of Charleston, South Carolina, are world renowned, as are the old buildings in St. Augustine and New Orleans.

## CENTRAL LOWLAND

The Central Lowland, the heart of the United States and often called the Middle West, is superlatively endowed by nature. Covering the northwestern portion of the Eastern states, the region extends from the Eastern Highlands to the Great Plains, and from the Canadian border to the Ozarks and the South. The surface is level to moderately rolling, the soil is generally fertile, and the Great Lakes offer advantageous inland transportation. The region has a stimulating continental climate with adequate summer rainfall and a growing season sufficiently long for mid-latitude crops. Minerals found in the region include large deposits of bituminous coal, petroleum and natural gas, iron ore, copper, lead, zinc, and building materials. There is some available water power, many rivers for transportation, and water for industries. The original vegetation cover was varied. Large forests of conifers predominated around the upper Great Lakes; a mixed forest of broad-leaved deciduous species was found in the middle United States; and tall-grass prairies extended from Illinois westward to the Great Plains.

In utilizing these resources man has developed numerous and varied activities. Within the Central Lowland is the world's largest corn-producing area, the Corn Belt. Few parts of the world equal the region for pork, beef, dairy, and poultry products. Large crops of hay, soybeans, wheat, oats, and other grains are harvested. Manufactures rank high, especially the output of steel and machines. Rail transportation is highly developed and the largest freshwater freighters in the world ply the Great Lakes. Within this region is the nation's center of population as well as the center of its agricultural activity.

### Agriculture

Although the Central Lowland ranks high in manufacturing and mining, agriculture is the foundation of the region's development. Since the area is so large, there are diversities in length of growing season, soils, topography, and distance from markets that have brought about differences in agricultural practices, crops, and livestock. The northern half of the region was repeatedly covered by continental glaciers which strongly modified the surface features. Glacial erosion and the damming of drainage by debris dropped by the melting ice resulted in the formation of tens of thousands of lakes, ponds, and swamps. When drained, the beds of

*Figure 2-16   An aerial view of contour strip cropping near Garnavillo, Iowa. In most parts of the Corn Belt farming practices are excellent, thus the region is the best agricultural area in the nation. (Courtesy of Soil Conservation Service.)*

shallow lakes and swamps usually make superior farmland, especially good for the production of corn, sugar beets, celery, and varied other crops. Glacial soils may be stony but they are fertile. The soils have been formed of mixtures of rock waste and humus derived from many sources. The limestone and other soluble materials in these soils have not been leached as much as in unglaciated soil. The best soils south of the limits of glaciation are those of alluvial origin, usually found on the valley floors, and the prairie soils where the topsoil is deep and there is an abundance of humus from plant stems and roots. Those soils which developed under a cover of deciduous trees contain more humus and are more fertile than those formed in areas of pine forests, where the soils are apt to be leached and low in usable plant foods.

The Corn Belt, extending from western Ohio to eastern Nebraska and from central Minnesota to central Missouri, dominates the country's agricultural production. In this area, gla-

ciers generally leveled the topography and improved the soils. Summers are rainy and hot—just what corn needs for best growth—and the region has assured markets since it is close to the center of the nation's population. Corn is grown extensively outside this central area but nowhere else does it so dominate the cultural landscape. Nevertheless, although more land is planted in corn than in any other crop, little corn is marketed as grain. In addition to corn, many other crops such as oats, wheat, barley, and hay are planted, making the area important for its diversified farming. Frequently, such crops as clover and other legumes are plowed under to enrich the soil. Good farm practices and an income from a variety of crops and livestock are basic to Corn Belt farming.

Excellent and extensive sets of farm buildings are characteristic of most farms. Most farmers use tractors for power as well as much other agricultural machinery. Railroads and highways form a close net over the Corn Belt, no farm being over a few miles from a town or shipping point. The eastern part of the Corn Belt was originally covered with a forest of mixed hardwoods; thus an adjunct of most farms is the wood lot. Wood lots add beauty and variety to the scenery, supply fuel and posts, provide a refuge for birds and small game, and furnish some saw logs for sale. Where the prairies once were, the country is still open, but crops have replaced the native grasses. Trees were frequently planted to shelter the houses, and groves around the farmsteads stand out on the level land. Approaching the Great Plains, however, even the farmsteads may be treeless.

Winter wheat, planted in the fall, is the chief crop southwest of the Corn Belt but spring wheat, sown in the spring, is the principal crop to the northwest. These crops predominate in the zone of transition between the Central Lowland and the Great Plains, where the rainfall is not sufficient to produce good corn or where the growing season is too short for its maturing. Kansas and Oklahoma are the principal winter-wheat states and the Dakotas lead in spring-wheat production. The wheat belts continue west into the Great Plains area. Wheat farms are large, becoming greater in size toward the west as the amount of yearly rainfall decreases. Wheat is raised as an annual crop or in rotation with grain sorghums or other suitable crops.

The Wheat Belts are a contrast to the Corn Belt. Here agriculture is extensive and less varied. Farm homes are far apart, the villages are smaller and have fewer functions. Grazing is an important source of income in the Winter-Wheat Belt. The wheat, after being planted in the fall, comes up and may be pastured by feeder stock during the winter. In the spring these animals are sold through various markets to the farmers of the Corn Belt. The wheat then develops and is harvested. Practically all work is done by machines. Groups of combines, with their crews, start working the wheat harvest as the crop begins to ripen first along the southern margin. The crews then move north with the season, many starting the harvest in Oklahoma or Texas and ending in the Prairie provinces of Canada. Many elevators are located along railroad sidings far from hamlets or villages. During the harvest season, activity around these elevators is great. Long strings of box cars are often stationed near them just before harvesting starts. The wheat is moved to the larger centers as rapidly as possible. Enid, Oklahoma, a small city, has the second largest wheat storage capacity in the nation—64.5 million bushels.

*Figure 2-17   These large elevators help make Enid, Oklahoma, one of the principal wheat-storage centers of the nation. Compare the size of these huge buildings with the box cars beside them. Over 40 million bushels of wheat can be stored in this large elevator. (Courtesy of Enid Chamber of Commerce.)*

Minneapolis, to which much of the wheat from the Dakotas is shipped, ranks first with a storage capacity of 97.6 million bushels.

An agricultural transition zone is found between the Corn and Cotton Belts from the Cumberland Plateau to the Mississippi River bottoms. This is a hilly region and includes the Ohio Valley and central and western Kentucky and Tennessee. Some fertile valleys and wide basins like the Bluegrass region of Kentucky and the Nashville Basin occur. Much of the hill land is wooded and the landscape is varied. Frequently, steep slopes have been cleared and planted to corn and tobacco. Heavy rains on the bare, cultivated slopes have caused much erosion and resulted in poverty for the hill farmers. In the fertile river valleys and the Bluegrass and Nashville Basin areas, farming is generally very successful. There is a striking difference between the big mansions, blooded livestock, and well-tilled, productive fields of the fertile areas, and the unpainted shacks, skinny mules, and eroded, weed-infested plots characteristic of much of the hill country. Although corn is widely grown—with poor success on eroded hills and with good results on river bottoms and fertile plains—it is not a dominant crop. Tobacco is the major cash crop. Though total production is large, heavy labor demands and exacting soil requirements restrict the amount of land planted in tobacco to from 4 to 14 acres on the smaller farms. The large and well-managed estates plant much more. Burley tobacco, used in making cigarettes, is preferred in the Kentucky Bluegrass, but in western Kentucky and north central Tennessee dark-fired tobacco, used for snuff and chewing tobacco, is grown. The Kentucky Bluegrass and the Nashville Basin are areas of fertile limestone soils, thus regions of superior pastures. Here purebred cattle and blooded horses are raised.

Northward from the Corn Belt the winters increase in length and severity. The summers are rainy and long enough for excellent hay and forage crops. The growing season is too short for corn to mature, but much corn is produced for use as silage. Pastures are generally good, and most areas of swampy, hilly, and cutover land can be used for grazing. In this region of rather short summers, farmers do better by using land for forage crops and hay rather than grains. Small amounts of rye and barley are usually raised as cash crops since they are hardier than wheat or corn.

Dairying is the primary type of farming. Not only are climatic conditions favorable for forage but the region is close to the markets of Chicago, Detroit, and other large cities. Cooperative creameries and cheese factories, the latter a specialty of Wisconsin, provide an additional market for cream, milk, and milk products that can be stored and distributed throughout the year. Milk-condensing factories are also numerous. The dairy region is one of big, well-built barns that protect the animals during the long, cold winters and also provide storage space for hay and other feeds. This is the area where a young couple, beginning as dairy farmers, is told "build your barn first, and your barn will build your house." Near cities most milk and cream is marketed fresh. Increasing remoteness from market is reflected in more specialization in butter and cheese or condensed and powdered milk. Farmers who separate their milk and sell only the cream use the skimmed milk as feed for poultry and pigs. Calves and some beef animals are regularly marketed, which gives the dairy farmer an additional income from meat products.

Some parts of the region produce such specialty crops as the sugar beets raised in the lowlands of the Saginaw Valley in Michigan and the truck crops grown near urban markets. Potatoes grow fairly well on the relatively poor soils and in the short summers of northern Michigan and Wisconsin. Of special importance is fruit. Many large orchards have been planted along the shores of the larger lakes. These lakes, by their effect on temperatures, help to prevent frost damage in spring and fall. The eastern shore of Lake Michigan, the Door Peninsula of Wisconsin, and the southern shores of Lakes Erie and Ontario are famous for fruits. Practically all kinds of mid-latitude berries and fruits, except citrus, are among those grown. The fruit business is helped by the nearby large urban markets. Although some fruit is sold fresh, much of the crop is processed by freezing, canning, or preserving for marketing throughout the year.

## Minerals

The Central Lowland is well endowed with fuels, iron, and other minerals. The Eastern Interior coal fields of Illinois, southwestern Indiana, and western Kentucky rank next in production after the Appalachian fields. Also some coal is mined in Missouri and Iowa. Although most of the bituminous coal is not as suitable for coking as that from the Appalachian fields, it is an excellent power resource. The iron and steel manufacturing centers are so located that imports from mines in Pennsylvania, West Virginia, and eastern Kentucky are easily accessible.

Petroleum and natural gas, produced locally, have contributed much to the industrial progress of the Central Lowland. The principal producing areas are the northern extension of the Mid-Continent field in Kansas, the southern Illinois and Kentucky field, and the various pools of Indiana, Ohio, and Michigan. Additional supplies are brought in by pipeline from the South. Oil refineries are located in many places, some of the principal ones being in Whiting and East Chicago, Indiana, and Wood River, Illinois.

The iron ore deposits in Minnesota and Michigan are the most important in the United States, supplying over 80 per cent of the nation's output of 100 to 200 million tons per year. The Mesabi Range in Minnesota is the most productive single source in North America, furnishing over 60 per cent of the total output. Most of the mining is from deep open pits. The Cuyuna and Vermilion Ranges, also in Minnesota, the deep mines of the Marquette, Iron Mountain, and Menominee Ranges of Michigan, and the Gogebic Range in both Michigan and Wisconsin are other sources. Enormous deposits of taconite, a low-grade ore, are now being developed in Minnesota. By concentrating this material it will be possible to maintain production long after the high-grade hematite ore has been exhausted. The iron mining district has cold, snowy winters and short summers. Once the area was well forested, but

*Figure 2-18 An open-pit iron mine at Eveleth, Minnesota. The ore is mined by power shovels, then transported by trucks of 30-ton capacity to loading stations from which the ore is raised to the surface by means of a conveyor belt. (Courtesy of United States Steel Corporation.)*

uncontrolled cutting of the trees and forest fires have depleted this resource. The conditions of soil and climate are unfavorable for crops other than hay. Without the mining company taxes that support good schools and public services in well-built cities like Virginia and Hibbing, Minnesota, this area would have few inhabitants, except dairymen and resort operators.

Copper from the Keweenaw Peninsula in northern Michigan was known to the Indians and was developed by white men over a century ago. For many years it was the leading copper producer of the world but as mines became deeper and ores less rich, the costs increased and forced some mines to close. A new mine, however, began operations in 1950.

Rock, clay, sand, and gravel deposits are widely distributed. Limestone for building is quarried in central Indiana, for flux in steel-making in northern Michigan, and for cement in practically all Middle Western states. Clay is used in making brick, tile, and other ceramic products. Brick and tile plants are common because of the amounts of good clay available and the large markets. Glacial deposits of sand and gravel are used in roadmaking, building construction, and railroad maintenance. The tonnage used is enormous and transportation of these raw materials, the finished clay products, and cement is facilitated by level topography and numerous water routes.

## Transportation

The five Great Lakes and their connecting waterways form the busiest inland water route in the world. In addition, these lakes affect the climates and the location of recreation and manufacturing areas, as well as the distribution of population. The long lake freighters equal many ocean carriers in size and carrying capacity. The large lake port cities, long shore lines, and rich hinterlands make this a populous and busy commercial and industrial region.

Traffic on the Great Lakes totals about 200 million tons of freight annually. Four commodities—iron ore, coal, limestone, and grains—make up 90 per cent of the tonnage. The lakes lie between producing and consuming regions;

thus the waterway provides the world's cheapest freight rates per ton-mile for transporting materials in bulk. The major movement is down the lakes, from western Lake Superior to the southern shores of Lake Michigan and Lake Erie, carrying iron ore and grains. Limestone is moved from quarries near the water's edge in the vicinity of Alpena, Michigan, to dockside steel mills. Coal from Lake Erie ports moves up the lakes.

Ice usually closes the lakes to navigation for three to five months of the year; thus ships make as many trips as possible during the open season. To facilitate quick turn-around, the docks, loading and unloading devices, and the ships themselves have been especially designed. Channels have been dredged and four big locks built to form the Soo Canal so as to lift and lower ships between Lakes Superior and Huron. To help the automobile and truck traffic between Canada and the United States, a large bridge has been built over and a tunnel dug under the Detroit River. A gigantic bridge has been erected over the Straits of Mackinac. A few car ferries, built to break through the ice floes, operate across Lake Michigan all winter.

Over 60 million tons of iron ore are moved over the Great Lakes each year. At the upper lake ports of Duluth, Superior, Two Harbors, Marquette, and Escanaba ore trains run along docks, on high trestles, 2,000 and more feet long. The ore is dumped into pockets, from which chutes carry it into the open holds of vessels. Ships of 12,000 to 16,000 tonnage can be loaded in a few hours. At lower lake ports such as Conneaut, Cleveland, Erie, and Buffalo, huge clamshell unloaders bite the ore out of the holds with almost equal speed. Cargoes of coal, limestone, and grain are likewise loaded and unloaded in remarkably short times.

The construction of the St. Lawrence–Great Lakes Seaway will offer an improved opportunity for ocean-going vessels to dock at inland ports. The present Canadian Welland Canal, connecting Lakes Erie and Ontario, is rather narrow and not designed for use by the largest lake freighters. It must be deepened, widened, and straightened for greater usefulness. Small

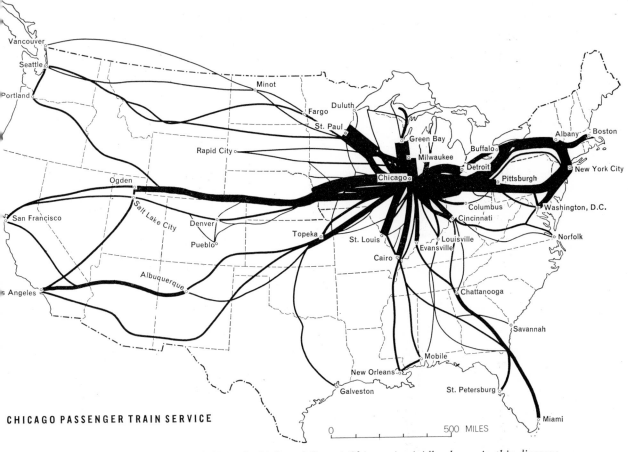

CHICAGO PASSENGER TRAIN SERVICE

*Figure 2-19  The high nodality of Chicago is vividly shown in this diagram. Note especially the heavy passenger traffic movement between Chicago and the East. (Adapted from a map, courtesy of the Chicago Association of Commerce and Industry.)*

craft can reach the Mississippi River from Chicago, via a canal and the Illinois River through Illinois from Lake Michigan.

Inland transportation facilities in the Central Lowland are better than those in any other region of the United States (Figure 2-19). The region is crisscrossed by a railway network that extends into practically every town and city as well as numerous villages and hamlets. Chicago is recognized as the leading railway center of the nation. The location of the city near the southern tip of Lake Michigan, and the level topography of the area, make Chicago the focus of rail lines from west, south, and east. In addition to the Great Lakes waterway, which serves most of the larger cities of the region, the Ohio and Mississippi Rivers and some of their tributaries are important arteries of transportation. Coal, sand and gravel, and other bulk goods, in addition to bargeloads of automobiles and oil, are frequently moved by water. Wide paved highways connect most of the cities, and the towns are connected by all-weather roads. All the larger cities and many of the smaller ones are served by national and international airlines.

## Industries and Cities

Agreeable climatic conditions, navigable waterways, favorable topography, a large supply of mineral fuel, and a variety of raw agricultural products caused and aided the development and expansion of manufacturing. Along the southern shore of Lake Erie, from Buffalo to Toledo, is one of the chief manufacturing regions of the nation. Although a variety of products is made in each city, many cities are also noted for some specialty product. Toledo is famed for glass, Lima for diesel engines, Akron for rubber goods, Lorain for iron and steel pipe, Sandusky for paper products, and Cleveland for steel. The Detroit area, to the west of the Detroit River and Lake St. Clair, is the heart of the world's automobile industries. Huge plants in this vicinity and in Flint, Pontiac, South Bend, and Toledo have turned out more than 6 million cars within a year. A host of Middle Western cities manufacture parts for automobiles, trucks, and aircraft.

Around southern Lake Michigan, from the Door Peninsula on the west to Grand Rapids on the east, is a manufacturing area that processes vast quantities of the agricultural products grown in the Central Lowland. Large meat packing plants are located in the Chicago area. Large quantities of grains are used in the Milwaukee brewing industries. Most towns and cities have creameries and canneries. Hides are processed and made into shoes in Milwaukee, Chicago, and other places. Nationally important manufacturing centers include Gary, steel; Grand Rapids, furniture; Battle Creek, breakfast foods; Green Bay, papermaking; Indianapolis, pharmaceuticals; and Moline, farm implements.

Smaller manufacturing areas have developed around the larger river cities. The Minneapolis–St. Paul section processes the agricultural products of Minnesota and nearby states; Minneapolis specializes in flour milling, St. Paul in meat packing and cheese production. St. Louis, at the confluence of the Missouri and Mississippi Rivers, is important for food processing, meat packing, chemical industries, furs, shoes, and railroad equipment. Louisville and Cincinnati are both important Ohio River ports. Cincinnati has large factories producing soap and machine tools. Louisville is an important distillery center and tobacco market. Kansas City and Omaha are the largest industrial centers on the Missouri River. Each has large stockyards, meat packing plants, and flour mills as well as factories which produce agricultural equipment. Other highly industrialized cities include Fort Wayne, South Bend, Evansville, Racine, and Peoria.

Many cities and towns which are not on waterways also have developed industrially as well as commercially. One such area extends from central Ohio, across Indiana to central Illinois. Dayton, noted for the making of cash registers and refrigerators, is an important rail and distributing center. Columbus, Indianapolis, and Springfield, each the capital of its state, are wholesale and retailing centers for their immediate areas. In each are manufactured some of the agricultural machines used in the Corn Belt. Near the western edge of the Central Lowland are several smaller cities of special local importance. Des Moines is the state capital, a center for manufacturing farm machinery and processing local raw materials. Wichita processes wheat, meat, and oil, all produced in the state. The city is also a leading center for the making of airplanes. Lincoln, Sioux City, Sioux Falls, and Fargo serve as distribution and processing centers of their respective areas.

Chicago, with a population of 5.5 million persons in its metropolitan area, is the largest city in the Central Lowland and the second largest in the United States. The city is frequently referred to as the transportation center of the world since it is the focus of many major highway routes, a railway center where 23 trunk-line railroads and many terminal lines meet, an international airway port, and also an important waterway terminal since it is located on the shore of Lake Michigan and has canal and river connections with the Mississippi River and the Gulf of Mexico. With such adequate transportation, the city has developed as the natural processing place for the Corn Belt and the hay and dairy region. Chicago is a leading meat packing center, a manufacturer of flour and other food items, an important producer of agricultural machinery, and the retailing and wholesale center for the Middle West.

Detroit, the fifth largest city in the nation, has more than 3 million people in its metropolitan area. Located on the west bank of the Detroit River, the city developed because of its strategic position between Lakes Huron and Erie.

Among the first manufactures was carriage making. Partly because of the early start in this type of industry and inventions by its citizens, Detroit became the leader in the automobile industry. Other numerous and varied industries such as saltworks, chemicals, aircraft, drugs, and furniture making have also developed.

Cleveland, the largest city bordering Lake Erie, has a metropolitan population of 1.5 million. The city is near the center of the Lake Erie industrial region, serving as the transshipment point for Mesabi iron ore going to the Pittsburgh and Youngstown areas as well as coal being shipped westward from the Appalachian field. Large steel mills, oil refineries, machine shops, and food processing plants are among its many industries. Like Chicago and Detroit, the principal retail district is near the lake shore.

## Recreation

The vacation and tourist industry brings hundreds of millions of dollars in income to residents of the Great Lakes states and lesser amounts to the people in other parts of the Central Lowland. Excellent beaches, forested surroundings, and fishing are among the attractions. Then, too, highways, railroads, and airways make it possible to reach the resort areas in a few hours, or at the outside in a day's travel, from the big Middle Western cities. Along the shore line of the Great Lakes region are hundreds of resorts. Inland Michigan, Minnesota, and most of Wisconsin have been strongly glaciated with the resulting formation of thousands of lakes—17,000 in Minnesota alone. Thousands of private vacation cabins and many resorts have been built along the lake shores and river banks. In the fall the forests of northern Michigan, Wisconsin, and eastern Minnesota are visited by hunters after deer and other game. The amounts spent on recreation, hunting, and fishing support many communities which, after the decline of the lumber industry, would have been depopulated without this outside income. Many state parks, such as Itaska State Park at the source of the Mississippi River in Minnesota, have been established. Isle Royale National Park, the only national park in the region, is on an island in Lake Superior.

### EXERCISES

*1.* What geographical factors aided the development of the United States east of the 97th meridian? Which factors retarded its development?

*2.* What advantages did the site of New York have over Boston? Philadelphia? Baltimore? Is the geographical advantage as great now as it was in 1776? Why?

*3.* What minerals are essential for the development of the steel industry? Where are these minerals mined? What city leads in steel production? Why has it become the leading steel center?

*4.* What is the Fall Line? Where is it? Why were many early American cities located along this line?

*5.* What is the principal soil type in the South? What changes have been made in land utilization in the South during the past 50 years? Why were these adjustments necessary?

*6.* What is the principal soil type in Iowa and Illinois? What are the chief crops of these states? Why has it not been necessary to make agricultural adjustments similar to those made in the South?

*7.* What are the five largest cities in the eastern part of the United States? What are the geographical advantages and disadvantages of each?

*8.* What are the principal minerals mined in the Mesabi Range, Joplin district, Mid-Continent area, and the Kanawha Valley? What are the chief ways in which these minerals are transported to points of consumption?

*9.* Where is the most important manufacturing area in the United States? What geographical factors have aided the development of this area as a manufacturing region? What are its chief handicaps?

*10.* Why is the recreation industry gaining in importance? Where are the principal recreational areas in the eastern part of the United States? What are the chief attractions in each area?

*11.* What factors helped determine the site of Washington? If the site for a new capital was being selected today what city would you suggest be chosen? Why?

*12.* Why were the pine forests of the upper Great Lakes region logged so rapidly? What are the advantages for paper manufacturing in the Southern states? Maine? Holyoke?

## SELECTED REFERENCES

Black, John D.: *The Regional Economy of New England,* Harvard University Press, Cambridge, 1950.

Fenneman, Nevin M.: *Physiography of Eastern United States,* McGraw-Hill Book Company, Inc., New York, 1938.

Garland, John H. (ed.): *The North American Midwest,* John Wiley & Sons, Inc., New York, 1955.

Hart, John Fraser: "Functions and Occupational Structures of Cities of the American South," *Annals of the Association of American Geographers,* 45:269–286, September, 1955.

Klimm, Lester E.: "The Empty Areas of the Northeastern United States," *Geographical Review,* 44:325–345, July, 1954.

Parkins, Almond E.: *The South,* John Wiley & Sons, Inc., New York, 1938.

Prunty, Merle, Jr.: "Recent Quantitative Changes in the Cotton Regions of the Southeastern States," *Economic Geography,* 27:189–208, July, 1951.

Smith, Villa B.: "Overseas Trade on the Great Lakes–St. Lawrence Seaway," *Journal of Geography,* 54:327–339, October, 1955.

*Soil,* U.S. Department of Agriculture, Yearbook, 1957.

Stern, Peter M.: "New York City," *Focus,* 2(10):1–6, June, 1952.

"Ten Rivers in America's Future," *Report of the President's Water Resources Policy Commission,* vol. II, Washington, 1950.

Weaver, John C.: "Changing Patterns of Cropland in the Middle West," *Economic Geography,* 30:1–47, January, 1954.

———: "Crop Combination Regions in the Middle West," *Geographical Review,* 44:175–200, April, 1954.

Zelinsky, Wilbur: "The Changing South," *Focus,* 2(2):1–6, October, 1951.

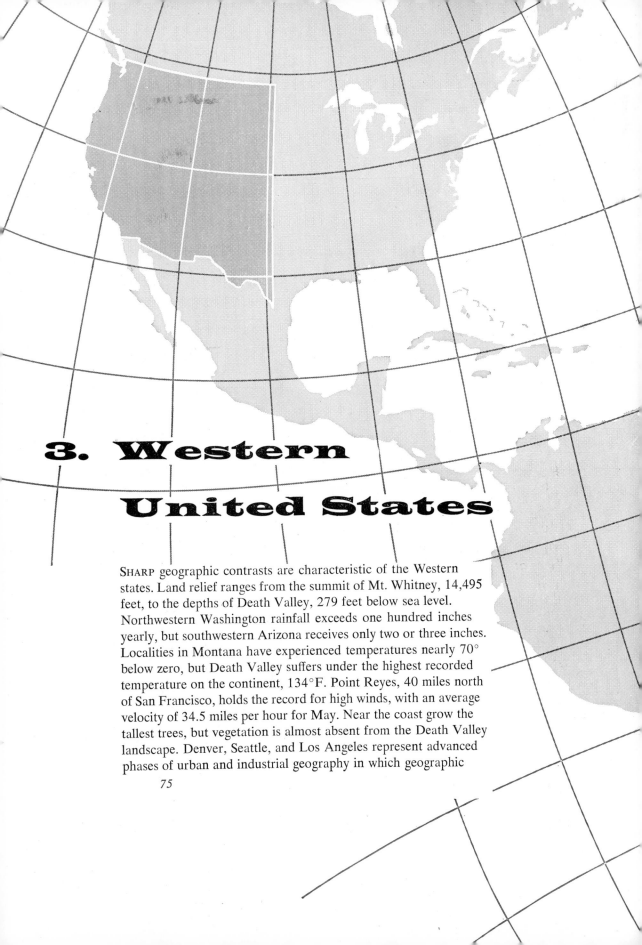

# 3. Western
# United States

SHARP geographic contrasts are characteristic of the Western states. Land relief ranges from the summit of Mt. Whitney, 14,495 feet, to the depths of Death Valley, 279 feet below sea level. Northwestern Washington rainfall exceeds one hundred inches yearly, but southwestern Arizona receives only two or three inches. Localities in Montana have experienced temperatures nearly 70° below zero, but Death Valley suffers under the highest recorded temperature on the continent, 134°F. Point Reyes, 40 miles north of San Francisco, holds the record for high winds, with an average velocity of 34.5 miles per hour for May. Near the coast grow the tallest trees, but vegetation is almost absent from the Death Valley landscape. Denver, Seattle, and Los Angeles represent advanced phases of urban and industrial geography in which geographic

URBAN POPULATION

★ Cities over 1,000,000 population
■ Cities 500,000 to 1,000,000
▲ Cities 200,000 to 500,000
● Cities 100,000 to 200,000
· Cities under 100,000

REGIONS

1-Great Plains
2-Rocky Mountains
3-Intermontane basins and ranges
4-Cascades-Sierra Nevada
5-California valleys and coast ranges

0         300 MILES

*Figure 3-1   In general the cities and towns in the western part of the nation are smaller than those in the eastern part. Note that only one city exceeds a million in population and that there are large areas with only a few small towns.*

relationships are complex; in contrast, a cattle ranch on the open plains of Wyoming is a simple type of economic activity (Figure 3-1). In the West, dense population and intensively farmed irrigated land may adjoin unpeopled and untilled deserts and wilderness.

The Western United States occupies approximately one-half of the nation. Beginning with the 49th parallel at the north, the boundary extends to the Pacific at the Strait of Juan de Fuca, then southward along the sea to Mexico where the irregular border is partly defined by the Rio Grande. Although marked by bluffs at the north and south, the eastern boundary is blurred, with only gentle slopes near its midportion at an altitude of about 1,000 feet. A decrease in precipitation between the 97th and 100th meridians causes marked changes in vegetation, soils, and land use, and these geographic conditions delimit the eastern boundary of the region more effectively than altitude differences.

Figure 3-2 *Physical factors dominate in the determination of regional boundaries. Mountains form many of the definite boundaries.*

PHYSICAL REGIONS OF THE WESTERN UNITED STATES

0          300 MILES

## GREAT PLAINS

Largest of all western provinces is the Great Plains (Figure 3-2). This broad zone extends from the Canadian border southward through Texas to the Rio Grande. The Great Plains consist of east-facing slopes descending from altitudes of 4,000 to 6,000 feet along the Rockies to only 1,000 or 1,500 feet along the eastern borders. The western edge is veneered with alluvial deposits from the mountains. On the basis of winter temperatures, the plains may be divided into northern and southern sections near the South Dakota–Nebraska boundary.

Streams on the northern plains are mainly tributary to the upper Missouri River; those of the southern plains flow into the Mississippi and lower Missouri River or the Gulf of Mexico. Channels of the streams are often shallow with broad, low banks, and some stream gradients are so low that many rivers have braided (multiple) channels. Where the channels are deeply cut, badlands of steep and eroded slopes develop between the nearly level interstream divides and the river floodplains. In western Nebraska sandhills have developed. Southward the high plains of Texas and the Staked Plains (Llano Estacado) are eroded less than most other sections.

The weather of the Great Plains is of the semiarid steppe or continental type, with severely low temperatures in winter during cold waves, though there is a high frequency of sunlit days. Well-defined warming winds called chinooks often sweep eastward down these plains in springtime. When the strong winter wind storms called blizzards occur with their drifting snow, transportation is impeded and grazing becomes difficult for the cattle. Summer days may be hot, but nights are cool. The annual temperature range—the difference between the mean temperatures of the coldest and warmest months—may be as great as 60°F. or more. Rainfall of about 10 to 15 inches a year necessitates irrigation or special dry farming methods of raising crops. The southern plains have moderate to mild winters and warm summers, the January mean at Amarillo being 35°F, the July mean 77°F; here evaporation is so rapid that in some years the meager rainfall is inadequate to support good pastures or dry land crops.

If the precipitation of 10 to 20 inches annually on the plains were dependable, farming would be more profitable, but where ranchers must obtain water from mountain streams or reservoirs if irrigation is to succeed, great expenditure of time and money is required. Nevertheless, many reservoirs have been built in the shallow natural basins and the low-banked river channels, and the water is used to irrigate sugar beets, alfalfa, and other crops. The more

*Figure 3-3 Windbreaks, made by rows of trees, have been developed in many parts of the Great Plains. Windbreaks help prevent soil blowing and also shield the wheat or other crop until it has a good start. Notice the great stretch of level surface. (Courtesy of Soil Conservation Service.)*

elevated surfaces, locally called "benches" in Montana, are devoted to dry farming. In rich areas the farms are smaller and the population correspondingly larger than in the dry-farming regions.

The native grasses, before destruction by overgrazing or cultivation, provide a moderate income, since they are suitable for large-scale pasturage, but so much grassland has been destroyed that each year sees less available for commercial purposes because once destroyed it is difficult and expensive to replace. For this reason, conservation of vegetation and soil in the semiarid Great Plains is of prime importance to a grazing economy—a matter all too often ignored or misunderstood by those who live in the humid realm of the United States.

The Indians who lived on these broad and grassy plains depended principally upon wild animals for their food, shelter, and clothing, the bison, or buffalo, being their most important animal. The meat from these creatures was a staple food that could be dried for future use. Hides formed the Indian tepee, and the hairy robes made warm beds and clothing. Dry droppings, called "buffalo chips," were the common fuel for cooking in this treeless country. Other game and fur-bearing animals supplemented the buffalo. The Plains tribes were nomadic and after the introduction of the horse about 1540, the tribesmen were able to hunt bison from horseback and the animals were used to pull burdens placed on a set of poles called a "travois," having a pair of shafts attached to the horse at one end and dragging the burden on the other.

In the mid-nineteenth century the white man began to displace the Indian and to replace herds of buffalo with herds of cattle. Sheepherding became a secondary activity where native fodder was too sparse for grazing cattle. This extensive grazing economy prevailed until the last quarter of the nineteenth century when, after a series of humid seasons and high prices for wheat, much of the native grass was plowed under and the land was planted to grain. For a time the change to extensive wheat farming paid, but it took only a few years of subnormal precipitation to make this type of agriculture unprofitable. Eventually the plowed land was abandoned and then, after a cycle of humid years, the circumstances were repeated.

Since grain farming brings uncertain profits, and since neither wheat fields nor beef cattle can support many people, throughout most of the Great Plains the population density is less than 18 per square mile, except in the cities, and vast areas cannot support more than two per square mile. Agriculture is extensive and is carried on by the use of large plowing, planting, and harvesting machinery. With the exception of coal and petroleum, mineral deposits are of small importance.

In general, exploitation of mineral resources or the development of agriculture requires large investment in equipment or stock. Shortages of building timber, great distances separating settlements, scarcity of fuel, and deficiency of water combine to provide an environment broad in outline and extensive in scope. Settlements other than ranches are small and widely spaced service centers which bear strong resemblance to each other. They are usually along stream channels where water is obtainable, or along railway lines where they can maintain contacts with distant places.

Living in the Great Plains has not been easy. Those who succeeded in conquering the handicaps of this dry land were forced to develop a generous and cooperative attitude toward less fortunate neighbors. As a result, democratic viewpoints and a willingness to lend aid prevail among the Great Plains dwellers, most of whom have known hardships. Here the landscape is wide and open, without the polluted air of Eastern cities. Though ranches are very large, they can be operated with relatively few laborers and cowhands. In the early history of these plains, laborsaving devices such as barbed wire, the high windmill, and mechanical pumps aided the rancher in changing the landscape from cattle kingdom to wheat field. More recently, the radio, automobile, and electric pump have been important to the farmers. Distinctive features of the Great Plains cultural environment have spread throughout the United States. Modern

*Figure 3-4 Cattle and ranches are common sights in the Great Plains. Roundup time is always an important time in ranch life. (Courtesy of Montana State Planning Board.)*

ranch houses, cowboy music, certain words and phrases in our speech, western motion pictures, western fiction, and picturesque clothing, all are derived from the pattern of the Great Plains cattle ranch of the late nineteenth century.

*Northern Great Plains*

Although grazing has always been a leading industry in this region, under the auspices of the Bureau of Reclamation and other Federal agencies, many irrigation projects have been built, thus allowing a more intensive use of the land. One of the largest is the Fort Peck Dam on the Missouri River in Montana; built to control floods, it also impounds water for irrigation.

Other projects are located in the Yellowstone Valley near Billings, the Milk River plain in northern Montana, near Williston, North Dakota, and north of the Black Hills on the Belle Fourche River. Alfalfa, sugar beets, and grains are important irrigated crops, and the rural population has increased in density on the reclaimed lands. Hard spring wheat of superior quality for flour is the principal cash crop on unirrigated fields. Hydroelectric power is generated in large amounts, notably near Great Falls on the Missouri River; here are electrolytic plants for refining the ores from the mountains. Discovery of petroleum in Wyoming, Montana, and North Dakota is of local economic importance. In general, however, this is a region of ranches, small supply towns, and railway settlements; it is not noted for its cities or manufactures.

Set in the midst of the northern Great Plains, the dome of the Black Hills offers sharp contrast to the surrounding lands; here are forests used for their timber supply. Minerals, especially gold ores, occur at Lead and Deadwood. The rugged mountains—including Mount Rushmore, famous for its giant carved heads of four presidents—the relatively pleasant summer weather, and the forests combine to make this part of South Dakota attractive to tourists. One town, Rapid City, east of the Black Hills, serves as a point of entry and as a service center. In Montana, other mountain outliers rise above the plains, including the Crazy, Little Belt, Big Snowy, Judith, and Bearpaw Mountains.

## Southern Great Plains

Water supplies are precarious in the southern Great Plains. Irrigation projects have reclaimed some land, and locally it is profitable to plant crops of sugar beets, alfalfa, and melons in east-ern Colorado, and cotton in Texas. When rainfall is adequate, winter wheat is raised by dry-farming methods. The grain sorghums are extensively grown for fodder. Traces of the old-time cattle economy remain, but during the last half century there has been a tendency to transform much of the land into farms. Valuable deposits of petroleum and natural gas are worked in New Mexico and Texas near Amarillo; in New Mexico near Carlsbad are productive potash beds.

Like the northern plains, this is not a region that attracts many people, though tourists come in numbers to see the subterranean caverns in the mountains near Carlsbad. Settlements are largely of the ranch service type or are related to transport. The southern extremity of the Great Plains lies in southern Texas and is known locally as the Edwards Plateau. This brush-covered upland is used for grazing by sheep and Angora goats, the latter producing mohair.

By far the largest and most important city of the Great Plains is Denver, which not only commands the plains, but lies so near the South-

*Figure 3-5   Landscape of the Northern Rocky Mountains, Shoshone National Forest, Wyoming. Note the glaciated surfaces, the timber line, and the general ruggedness of the region. (Courtesy of U.S. Forest Service.)*

ern Rockies that it serves both these extensive regions. It is particularly important for wholesale and retail trade. Several main highways and transcontinental railways focus on Denver. It is also district headquarters for many agencies of the Federal government. Tourism is a major industry of this mile-high city. Pueblo is a trading and iron-smelting center. Colorado Springs, the site of the Air Academy, is popular with health seekers and tourists.

## ROCKY MOUNTAINS

North America's backbone—the Rocky Mountains—is a natural feature so impressive to the traveler that it becomes a milestone on any journey across the United States by train, automobile, or air. Here in imposing grandeur from Canada to Mexico is a wilderness of peaks and valleys, separating the streams that flow west to the Pacific from those which flow east to the Atlantic. On these mountains are the beginnings of the Western forests whose tree species differ from those of the woodlands east of the grass-covered Great Plains. Rugged mountains, deep snows, and wide vistas make crossing these mountains a memorable experience.

Indians used the Rockies for hunting, fishing, and berry picking. They usually wintered in protected valleys or basins when the heavy snows made the mountains inhospitable. During the first half of the nineteenth century traders, gold seekers, and farmers struggled over the Santa Fe, Overland, and Oregon Trails to the Promised Land in New Mexico, Utah, California, and Oregon. When gold was discovered in the Rockies, swarms of miners searched every mountain gulch for placers and quartz mines. Of the hundreds of settlements founded by the miners, many remain though more have become ghost towns. Railroads and highways were built to serve the mines, and transcontinental routes to Pacific Coast cities were located through the valleys and passes over the continental divide. Stockmen and farmers made permanent settlements and even dry valleys became prosperous when irrigated. The population is scanty, however, and settlements are in the valleys except for some mining towns.

### Northern Rocky Mountains

The Rocky Mountains are divided roughly into the Northern and Southern Rockies, with the central Wyoming Basin as the point of partition. These mountains reach their greatest width in Montana, Idaho, and Colorado. In the north the trend of the ranges is generally northwest to southeast, but in the south their alignment is about north to south. Some ranges such as the Big Horn and Wind River Mountains in Wyoming are distant from the main system. In the Northern Rockies individual ranges are often separated by long, narrow, depressed valleys called trenches. The longest of these is the Rocky Mountain Trench, extending northwest for over 1,200 miles, from the Bitterroot Valley in Montana into Canada (Figure 4-13). In much of Idaho the mountains resemble deeply eroded plateau uplands rather than elongated ridges. South of Yellowstone Park is the rugged Grand Teton range.

The width and ruggedness of the Northern Rockies have made this part of the United States not easily accessible, and parts remain underdeveloped in spite of timber and mineral resources. Millions of acres lie within national parks or forests and are protected against commercial exploitation. Although most mountains are covered with conifers, much accessible commercial timber has been cut.

Within these mountains lie sources of many streams, including the Columbia, Snake, Missouri, and Yellowstone Rivers. Canyons provide reservoir sites, and hence large amounts of power are being developed, as well as storage for irrigation and flood control. Hungry Horse Dam in northwestern Montana, completed in the early 1950s, is intended to help control the Columbia River flow and amplify present power sources. Other dams and power plants are on the Clark Fork, Snake, and other tributaries to the Columbia.

Minerals obtained from these mountains are

important in the national economy. Mining is well developed in western Montana at Butte, near Helena, the state capital, and in many smaller towns. Here copper, gold, lead, zinc, and silver ores have brought wealth, but, as is usual in most mining centers, the profits seldom remain in the communities. A second mining center is the Coeur d'Alene district in the Idaho panhandle, important for lead, zinc, and silver. The city of Coeur d'Alene itself is concerned with farming, lumbering, and tourists. Farther south in Idaho are many scattered mining communities.

This is a district in which agricultural pursuits are of small importance although in some valleys agriculture is possible. Of greater importance is good grazing, in lower parts of the valleys in winter and on mountain pastures in summer. This practice is widespread throughout the Northern Rockies for both cattle and sheep.

The geography of the Northern Rockies is not conducive to the growth of large urban centers. Communities are of the Western ranch service type with some being important for lumbering and mining. Locally they may serve large areas like those around Missoula, Kalispell, Bozeman, and Livingston.

Mountain scenery justifies three national parks. Yellowstone National Park in northwestern Wyoming is noted for Yellowstone Lake, Yellowstone Falls (Figure 3-6), and the many evidences of vulcanism such as hot springs, mud pots, and geysers. Yellowstone National Park is reached by both highways and railroads, and is sufficiently accessible to attract well over a million visitors each summer. Adjoining on the south is the impressive ridge of the Grand Tetons included in a national park near the Jackson Hole country of Wyoming. Tourism and grazing are the chief industries of this part of western Wyoming. Glacier National Park in northern Montana has jagged peaks, mountain

*Figure 3-6 Canyon and falls of the Yellowstone River in Yellowstone National Park. The falls are 308 feet high. (Courtesy of National Park Service.)*

lakes, mountain glaciers, and sparkling water-falls.

In many sections of the Rockies, rugged landscapes appeal to the tourist who prefers to spend his vacation hunting, fishing, or camping. Some mountain valleys favored by campers are occupied by natural lakes; among the better known are Priest, Pend Oreille, and Coeur d'Alene in Idaho, Flathead in Montana, and Yellowstone and Jackson Lakes in Wyoming. These mountains and valleys have no good east-west passes; indeed there is no crossing without steep grades, swift streams, canyons, and peaks. High altitudes with heavy snows and low winter temperatures make road construction and maintenance difficult. Railways traversing these mountains do so only at great expense for both construction and operation.

## Wyoming Basin

The Wyoming Basin in central and southwestern Wyoming separates the Northern and Southern Rockies. It has geographical conditions similar to those of the Great Plains from which it is nearly isolated by the Big Horn and Laramie Mountains. Rainfall is deficient, and the Basin remains largely a land of open, grass-covered slopes that provide for grazing of cattle and sheep on large ranches although some irrigation is developing along the edges. Small supply towns are strung along transcontinental railways and highways. Coal is mined in the southwest at Rock Springs, and Casper and Rawlins represent the larger settlements. Petroleum is of importance at Salt Creek. This open basin, because it nearly severs the Northern and Southern Rockies, has been an important transport route for rail and highway for more than a century. Travelers on the Oregon Trail made full use of its springs, and the railroads found it the easiest transmontane route at a later date. Today the Wyoming Basin provides a gateway through the Rockies, used by transcontinental railways and highways.

## Southern Rocky Mountains

South of the Wyoming Basin, the long, narrow trenches of the Northern Rockies are replaced by the high-level, basin-like North, Middle, South, and San Luis Parks of Colorado, and the Estancia, Roswell, and Tularosa Basins of New Mexico. In Colorado, the Front Range rises abruptly to more than 14,000 feet at Longs Peak, Pikes Peak, and other summits. Farther west is the Sawatch Range, and then a confused maze of mountains in southwestern Colorado, of which the most prominent are the San Juan Mountains. The Wasatch Range, with its eastern extension in the Uinta Mountains, dominates Utah.

Travel in an east-west direction through the mountains and basins is difficult. Settlement tends to focus about mountain passes, presence of minerals, or cattle ranches where hay and some other crops are raised. Where water supplies can be obtained from nearby mountains, as in the vicinity of Grand Junction, Colorado, intensive agriculture may be practiced, and the population density is correspondingly greater. In the grazing areas population density is low with widely dispersed ranch settlements.

Minerals, including molybdenum, have been exploited, and some towns, like Leadville in western Colorado, depend upon mining. Cripple Creek is a gold mining town near Colorado Springs and Pikes Peak. Except for mineral wealth, the smallness of resources within the mountains prevents great economic expansion; the urban centers related to this area are located in adjoining regions and include Cheyenne, Boulder, Denver, Colorado Springs, Pueblo, and Trinidad, a coal mining town, as well as Las Vegas and Santa Fe. Several of these cities are outstanding tourist centers.

To some extent, the presence of mountain passes has furthered the development of nearby cities. Travelers may avoid difficult routes by taking the broad gap through Wyoming up the North Platte Valley between the Big Horn and Laramie Ranges, and west across the Great Divide Basin and South Pass into the Great Basin and Snake River country. Passes across the Colorado Front Range lie at high altitudes. Raton Pass, 7,834 feet, crosses the Southern Rockies between Trinidad, Colorado, and Raton, New Mexico, and is traversed by main line railway and highway. Some passes are higher than 10,000 feet. Lack of a convenient pass west of Denver was partly overcome by building the Moffat Tunnel through the mountains fifty miles west of that city. The Arkansas River crosses the southern end of the Front Range through the Royal Gorge, a deep, narrow canyon very impressive to tourists. West of Denver, Rocky Mountain National Park contains Longs Peak and has major resort areas nearby. In New Mexico, the Southern Rockies are reduced to low ranges, and the wide basins or valleys become of correspondingly greater importance for grazing; generally they are too dry for much other activity.

New Mexico represented the northern limit of Spanish settlement in the seventeenth century, but Spanish settlers did not entirely supplant the Indian population, with the result that present cultural and racial patterns are mixtures of Indian, Spanish, and American. New Mexico shares with California, Arizona, and Texas a strong Spanish-American influence that is discernible in language and architecture. Santa Fe, the state capital, founded by the Spaniards, is famed as the terminus of the Santa Fe Trail in covered-wagon days and is visited by many tourists. Taos and other Indian pueblo towns in this region also are popular with tourists.

Despite completion of many reclamation projects, including the Elephant Butte Reservoir, farming in southern New Mexico basins is mostly limited by water obtainable from the Rio Grande or its tributaries. There is little prospect of expanding the cultivated land, though in recent years there has been population growth, especially marked in Albuquerque. Nearby is the Los Alamos reservation for testing atomic weapons.

In the western elbow of Texas, the Rocky Mountains are even more broken than in New Mexico. In the Davis Mountains they rise higher than 8,000 feet in a section so dry that agriculture is precarious and extensive cattle ranching is the chief economic activity. For this part of the country, El Paso is the urban and transportation center as well as the gateway to Mexico. The city is important for general trade and for smelting local ores. Below El Paso, the Rio Grande enters a mountainous country so impressive that the Big Bend has been set aside as a national park, although most of the region is used for grazing.

## INTERMONTANE PLATEAUS, BASINS, AND RANGES

Between the Rocky Mountains and the combined Sierra Nevada–Cascades is a large region generally deficient in rainfall. Though it includes all or parts of nine states, it is sparsely populated. The altitude varies from below sea level to over 12,000 feet in several peaks. Relief features are diversified and include many broad plateaus, scores of mountain ranges, and extensive basins and valleys. Most of Nevada, half of Utah, and large expanses in other states have no drainage that reaches the ocean. The climate varies from near-tropical deserts to continental extremes of temperatures. The vegetation is usually of the desert and steppe type although the higher plateaus and mountains support forests of conifers because of the greater rainfall at these altitudes. Much of the region is used for grazing cattle, but some sections toward the north have enough rainfall for wheat cultivation; in others, crops are irrigated. This intermountain region with its wide variations in geography is divided into four parts, the Colorado Plateau, the Southwestern Basin and Range province, the Great Basin, and the Columbia Intermontane province. Much of the region is a barrier to be crossed by rail lines and highways leading to the cities and populated valleys of the Pacific Coast, but locally there are important centers of settlement in the interior.

### Colorado Plateau

The Colorado Plateau is centered around the junction of the four states of Arizona, New Mexico, Colorado, and Utah. It consists of uplifted rock strata that reach 5,000 to 10,000 feet in elevation. The surface has been eroded by streams under arid conditions, with the result that deep canyons, arroyos (gullies), gorges, badlands, and other evidences of extreme erosion have dissected the plateau surface. The Grand Canyon of the Colorado River is the outstanding geographic feature, with subunits bearing separate names like the Kaibab, Kanab, and Paria, which lie north of the river and are separated from each other by its tributaries. South of the river are the Coconino, Kaibito, and others. Though most of the rock is sedimentary, there are some volcanic materials in Arizona where the San Francisco Peaks, a group of extinct volcanoes, rise to a maximum altitude of 12,794 feet.

Though its environment seems repressive to human development, the Colorado Plateau was the setting for the Indian villages called pueblos. Their high cultural level was apparent from the excellence of their stonework, basketry, pottery, and weaving. In a land deficient in rainfall, the Indians carried on irrigation by flood waters, depending upon maize as their staple crop. After the introduction of sheep, cattle, and horses by Spaniards, their food supplies improved. Today the picturesque life of the pueblo villages attracts tourists, and Indian tribal products and customs are on display at the annual celebration in Gallup, New Mexico. The Indian hogans (huts) are an interesting feature. Lands in northeastern Arizona have been set aside for the exclusive use of the Indians but they have only a meager water supply. Although the Indians receive some income from flocks or herds, economic conditions are generally unsatisfactory and poverty is widespread.

Except for one transcontinental railway line across northern Arizona and some good highways few routes traverse the Colorado Plateau. Some towns are located with reference to rail facilities, and from the former mining center of Kingman on the west through Williams, Flagstaff (a popular winter sports resort), Winslow, Holbrook, and Gallup eastward to Albuquerque the settlements are expressions of rail and highways. Perhaps the least settled part of the United States is the rough terrain surrounding the "four corners" where the states of Arizona, Utah, Colorado, and New Mexico meet.

For permanent residents, resources of the Colorado Plateau are limited. Both petroleum and natural gas are produced, and in uranium mining New Mexico leads all states. Commercial timber is available only on the higher lands because of serious moisture deficiency at lower elevations. Grazing is the most important industry throughout the area and is widespread among both white settlers and Indian. Water, or its absence, controls the distribution of settlements. Small farms are found in deep canyons where temperature is warm throughout the year, or on the plateau surface where some farm crops can be grown if there are steady springs, or if underground water supplies can be obtained. Such enterprises, however, are relatively few in number; more common are ranches with herds of cattle or flocks of sheep.

Northwestern Arizona with its Grand Canyon of the Colorado, a national park, enjoys some income from tourists, since the canyon can be reached by rail or highway. Below the canyon the river itself is important since it provides water and power for urban centers of southern California, and irrigation water for the Imperial Valley and Arizona, an accomplishment made possible by several dams. Hoover Dam is downstream from the scenery of the Grand Canyon, and impounds Lake Mead; both are tourist attractions, although neither contributes greatly to the wealth of the Plateau. Besides the Grand Canyon, national parks have been established in southern Utah at Zion and Bryce Canyons, both spectacular examples of erosion in multicolored sedimentary rocks. In addition there are several national monuments such as Cedar Breaks in Utah, and sites of historical and archeological interest in Arizona. In southwestern Colorado the Mesa Verde National Park contains outstanding examples of ancient Indian cliff dwellings.

## Southwestern Basins and Ranges

The southern rim of the Colorado Plateau descends to lower altitudes in a series of cliffs. Southwest of these steep escarpments lies an arid and semiarid land marked by tilted-block ranges resulting from faults. These fault-block mountains alternate with basins or "valleys" covered with debris washed from the mountains. This southwestern Basin and Range province occupies parts of these states and includes the Imperial and Coachella Valleys of California, the Salt River valley of Arizona, and the upper Rio Grande Valley in New Mexico.

For decades southern Arizona was regarded as unfit for habitation by white men and was left to its primitive inhabitants. If water is available, its fertile soils are productive, and therefore, important irrigation projects have been completed in the Salt River Valley, tributary to the Gila River. Here, where ancient prehistoric people irrigated their crops, modern irrigation works have been built to make the valley a prosperous producer of winter-grown vegetables and citrus fruits, as near Tempe, Mesa, and Phoenix. The area is dominated by the city of Phoenix, the state capital, which has also gained greatly from the winter tourist trade, and the establishment of many industries, especially in the field of electronics.

In southeastern Arizona, Tucson, a university town and aircraft-manufacturing center, attracts tourists with its clear, sunny, and almost frostless winter weather, although the summers are excessively hot. Farther south the towns of Bisbee, Ajo, Globe, and Morenci are copper mining towns; the latter is the largest producer in the state. San Manuel, northeast of Tucson, is the newest development with an output of about 100,000 tons of copper per year making it the fourth largest producer in the United States. Nogales is a border town dependent upon income from transportation. In the southwest, Yuma is reached by one transcontinental railway line and highways that serve the transportation needs of southern Arizona and New Mexico. Most residents are bilingual because numbers of Spanish-Americans have taken up permanent residence north of Mexico. They have left an indelible stamp on the culture of this part of the Southwest.

In spite of desert landscapes, relics of former civilizations, and pleasant winters, this is a region of limited economic potential, resembling

*Figure 3-7   Hoover Dam on the Colorado River. (Courtesy of Bureau of Reclamation.)*

the Mexican Plateau across the international boundary. Summer temperatures mount well above 100°F, but low relative humidity keeps the weather endurable. Rainfall is only 3 to 5 inches a year but erratic cloudbursts sometimes occur. No dense population has developed except in irrigated valleys, and small settlements are more characteristic than urban areas. Left to themselves, these drought-ridden lands are too unfavorable in climatic aspect to support many people although residents obtain water from the few perennial streams or underground sources. When sufficient water is available, high summer temperatures provide excellent growing conditions for specialized crops.

The most extreme subtropical desert in the United States is located in the Imperial Valley, a region of interior drainage in southeastern California. This lowland represents the old sea floor which has been cut off from the northern end of the Gulf of California by the Colorado Delta. It is so hot and dry in summer that before 1900 it was regarded as worthless land;

earlier, it was a difficult obstacle to immigrants arriving in California by the southern route. Although desert conditions are still apparent, water is now obtained from the Colorado River, transforming an otherwise barren landscape into a productive hothouse for whose products the rest of the nation pays high out-of-season prices. The prevailing economy is based upon air and rail transportation and refrigeration facilities which transport and preserve perishable commodities to markets outside of California. This has been accomplished at considerable expense and by installations such as the All-American Canal, the principal distributing system for water from the Colorado River. The northern part of the basin (Coachella Valley) specializes in grapefruit and dates. The city of Palm Springs has become a popular winter resort because of its sunshine and mild weather at that season. Between the Coachella and Imperial Valleys lies a salt lake, the Salton Sea, about thirty miles long, formed by an accidental diversion of the Colorado River in 1905.

## Great Basin

The Great Basin is a region of interior drainage between the Wasatch Mountains on the east and the Sierra Nevada on the west. The term "basin" is somewhat misleading because the region is broken by fault-block ranges aligned north-south, and separated by intervening basins filled with debris washed in from higher altitudes. In structure both the Sierra and the Wasatch Mountains are larger counterparts of the fault-block ranges. The Mojave Desert of California is a southern extension of the Great Basin, whose northern section, sometimes called the Basin and Range province, merges with the Columbia Intermontane province.

Since most of the Great Basin is in a rain shadow position, the mountains and basins have insufficient precipitation for agricultural activities other than grazing. Irrigation is practiced where water is available, but the crops are chiefly alfalfa and other fodder and hay used for feeding livestock in winter. Because of the high altitude, weather may be severe. Furthermore, dry, cold winters and strong winds causing dust storms are characteristic. Population is relatively small in the state of Nevada although it doubled between 1940 and 1958 and now exceeds 240,000. This land will support few people. With care, its residents can carry on grazing profitably and, therefore, the typical rural settlement of importance is the ranch service and supply center or, in some places, the mining center, which is often decadent. Examples of the latter, once important for gold and silver, include Virginia City, Goldfield, Bullfrog, and Tonopah, which are so picturesque that they attract tourists.

On the western side of the Basin the largest community is Reno, a university and trading center. Reno has also many gambling places, since gambling is legal in Nevada. In southern Nevada is Las Vegas, famed for its gambling and resorts, but also important for chemical manufactures. Salt Lake City is located on the broad piedmont between Great Salt Lake and the western face of the Wasatch Mountains and serves as a trade, commercial, educational, religious, tourist, and railway center as well as the state capital. Its prosperity is based partly on irrigated grain farms and fruit lands extending northward and southward along the piedmont. To the north is Ogden, a railroad and supply city. A short distance west are the salt flats of the Salt Lake Desert and the saline deposits of Lake Bonneville, ancestor of the present Great Salt Lake. This whole region is deficient in agriculture, but some grazing is carried on and there is mineral wealth of importance, especially the copper ores at Bingham, Utah, and Ely and Yerington, Nevada. Provo, Utah, is near sources of coal and iron and has an iron and steel plant. There are other mines that produce coal, silver, lead, and zinc.

A few places in the Great Basin have water supplies, particularly those along the Humboldt River in northern and western Nevada where the stream disappears in the Humboldt Sink. Among these are communities such as Winnemucca, Elko, and Fallon and a few settlements along transcontinental highway routes. Carson City has the smallest population of any of the nation's state capitals. In general, the economic

*Figure 3-8 Copper mine at Bingham Canyon, Utah. The operating area covers 956 acres, and the mine consists of a series of levels with switchbacks. The over-all distance from the bottom level to the top level on the west side is 2,010 feet. The mining area contains about 168 miles of standard-gauge track, most of which is moved continually to meet operating needs. (Courtesy of Salt Lake Chamber of Commerce.)*

future of this part of the United States seems limited.

To the southwest along the eastern face of the Sierra Nevada, at an altitude of more than 3,500 feet, lies the long trough-like depression known as Owens Valley. Here in a mid-latitude steppe developed a profitable grazing economy and some fruit growing, but in 1909 the demand for water by residents of the city of Los Angeles prompted purchase of water rights from the valley for urban use, forcing the abandonment of Owens Valley agriculture. Prospects for any further development are poor as long as water is carried by aqueduct southward to Los Angeles. Nearby, a large basin of interior drainage contains Searles Lake, actually a marsh, which is an important source of commercial borax, potash, and other salts. In the Mojave Desert in the south, conditions are more favorable for

agriculture, particularly in its western angle, the Antelope Valley, which obtains water by pumping from wells. In the heart of the Mojave, the town of Barstow serves as an important rail junction.

Southeast of Owens Valley lies a similar but much deeper trough, Death Valley, 279 feet below sea level. Of all places in the United States it seems least suited for human occupation, but pleasant winter weather attracts some tourists, and desert scenery is so impressive that the valley has been set aside as a national monument. Summer temperatures are so high that visitors are discouraged. Some years ago deposits of borax in this valley were developed, but cheaper sources are now available and the Death Valley borax works have been abandoned. Other minerals occur but lack of water is a handicap to development.

## Columbia Intermontane Province

The Columbia Intermontane province lies between the Rocky Mountains on the east and north and the Cascade Range on the west, and grades into the Great Basin to the south. The province, which was formerly called the Columbia Plateau, varies in elevation from a few hundred to over 10,000 feet above sea level, and is a region of diverse relief features. It can be divided into the Snake River Plains and the Columbia Basin, which are separated by the Blue Mountains and associated uplifts. The Snake River Plains occupy a broad crescent-shaped basin, floored with lava, from Yellowstone Park on the east across southern Idaho into Oregon. Idaho and eastern Oregon drain into the Snake River, which has cut a deep canyon into the lava flows.

The Columbia Basin occupies parts of eastern Washington and Oregon and western Idaho. Irregularly saucer-shaped, it is enclosed by the Cascades on the west, the Okanogan Highlands on the north and the Rockies on the east. To the south are the Blue Mountains. The Columbia Basin has diverse physical feature, with plains, plateaus, ridges, mountains, and hills. The bedrock is a lava called basalt, covered in places by recent sediments. The Columbia River crosses the region and receives water from the Snake and other streams. Near the northern edge of the basin are the "channeled scablands," formed during the glacial period by floods of melt-water that eroded channels. These were later abandoned, leaving deep, rock-walled, dry gorges in the "scabrock," as the bare lava is called locally. The largest of these, Grand

*Figure 3-9   Contour farming, crop rotation, green manuring, strip cropping, and stubble mulching are practiced simultaneously on this field near Lewiston, Idaho.*

Coulee, extends from the Columbia River to the desert now being reclaimed by the Columbia Basin Project. In eastern Washington near Idaho are the Palouse Hills, which are covered with fine, fertile loess (silt) and receive sufficient precipitation for raising wheat and peas without irrigation.

The Snake River Plains in southern Idaho are the most highly developed part of that state. The climate is continental with low winter and high summer temperatures. Rainfall is often less than 10 inches a year, and irrigation is necessary for most crops. Originally the plains were covered with grass and sagebrush and were used for grazing cattle and sheep. This industry still continues, and many lambs are fattened for market on the irrigated crops of the plains. The Snake River has cut a canyon below the general level, and in this are many sites suitable for dams and reservoirs, several of which have been developed. The soil on the plains is fertile, and is productive where it is irrigated. Crops include alfalfa, wheat, beans, sugar beets, hardy fruits, and the famous Idaho potatoes.

For many years this part of Idaho was thinly populated because of aridity, but since 1900 many reservoirs have changed the situation. Good soils and water attracted settlers, and today prosperous modern cities line the Snake Valley from Idaho Falls through Pocatello and American Falls as far west as Twin Falls. Elsewhere, irrigation prospects are less promising and the surface is generally unsatisfactory for farming, except in lowlands near the Oregon-Idaho boundary where prosperous little cities like Caldwell are found. The capital at Boise, near the foot of the mountains, dominates a lo-

*Figure 3-10    Erosion on land in summer fallow, showing effect of hard rain on bare ground.*

cal fruit and grain district and was once a supply center for gold and silver mines in the mountains.

The Blue Mountains, the Wallowas, and other mountains lie in the path of winds blowing up the Columbia Gorge and receive the rainfall required by the forests that cover them. Logging, mining, and grazing are important industries. The supply cities, Pendleton, La Grande, and Baker, are located in valleys or at the foot of the ranges.

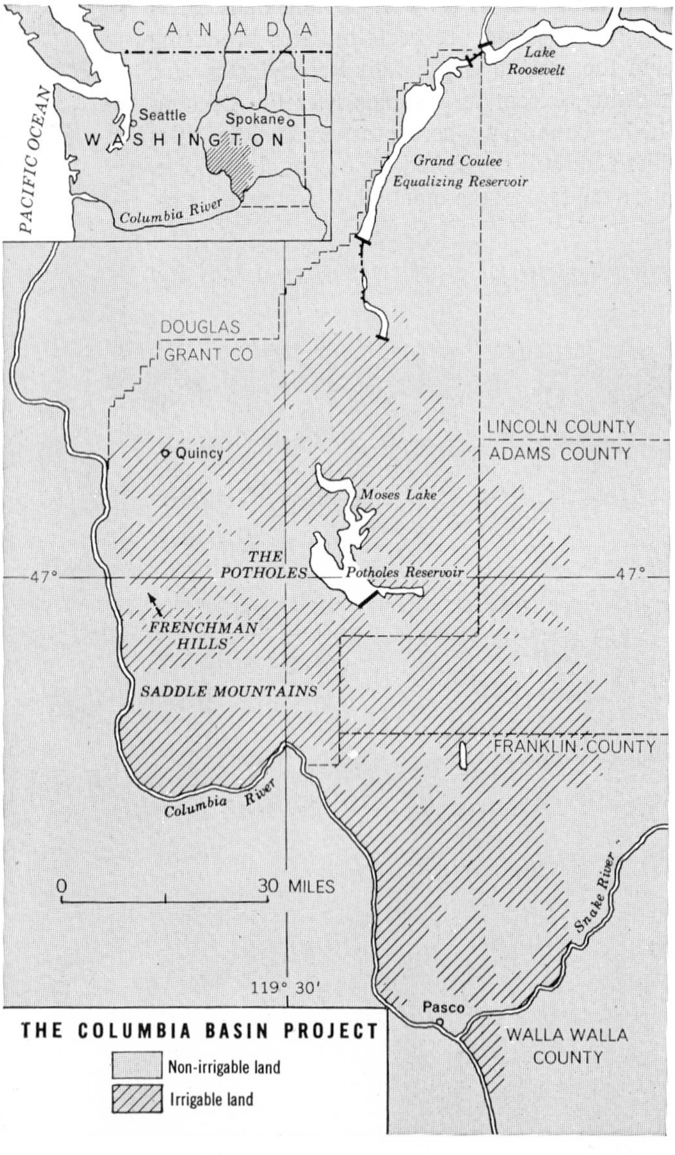

In the nearby Columbia Basin precipitation is greatest in the subhumid higher rim, decreasing to an arid condition on the plains in the lee of the Cascades. Maximum precipitation occurs in winter. The moderate annual temperature range is intermediate between that of the marine west-coast and the continental interior.

From the late 1860s into the 1880s, the Columbia Basin in eastern Washington and parts of Oregon and Idaho was devoted to grazing cattle and sheep on the open range. In the 1880s, wheat replaced livestock on the good Palouse Hills soil and in other areas where rainfall was sufficient. With the coming of the railroads, wheat growing greatly expanded. Today this Inland Empire produces over 100 million bushels of winter and spring wheat annually, as well as dry peas and other crops. In the midst of the Columbia Basin, dry farming was uncertain and irrigation was begun before 1900; thereafter it was known that, with water, the soils and climate in valleys east of the Cascades were well adapted to fruits. The development of the Yakima, Wenatchee, Okanogan, Walla Walla, and other valleys in Washington and the Hood River valley in Oregon followed, using sources of water from the Cascades; the Blue Mountains supply Walla Walla. These valleys furnish a fourth of the nation's commercial apple crop as well as quantities of pears, apricots, cherries, peaches, and other fruits. The Yakima Valley is also noted for alfalfa, sugar beets, potatoes, and other irrigated crops.

The plains in the central part of the Columbia Basin lie too high above the entrenched Columbia River to secure its abundant flow, so this region long remained a thinly populated, poor grazing country. In the 1930s the Federal government began construction of the multiple-purpose Grand Coulee Dam. During the 1940s

THE COLUMBIA BASIN PROJECT

Non-irrigable land

Irrigable land

*Figure 3-11 Water is supplied to the irrigable land from the Grand Coulee Equalizing Reservoir, not from the Columbia River or Lake Roosevelt. Gravity flow carries the water to the irrigated fields.*

*Figure 3-12   Grand Coulee Dam on the Columbia River. (Courtesy of Bureau of Reclamation.)*

this supplied hydroelectric power for atomic energy, aluminum, and other metallurgical plants, and by the 1950s irrigation was begun. A million acres of land in the Columbia Basin will ultimately be reclaimed and devoted to intensive farming. Here some 40,000 farms of 10 to 40 acres raising fruit, alfalfa, sugar beets, beans, melons, potatoes, and other irrigated crops will offer a strong contrast to the large mechanized wheat farms of 1,000 acres or more in the Palouse Hills where there is only enough rainfall for dry farming.

Communities such as Yakima, Walla Walla, and Wenatchee serve local farm needs; Moscow, Idaho, and Pullman, Washington, are educational centers. Pasco is a railroad center and, with Kennewick and Richland, forms the Tri-Cities area near which are the Hanford atomic energy works.

At the north, Spokane dominates this part of the Columbia Basin as well as tributary valleys in the mountains of Washington, Idaho, western Montana, and British Columbia. The city is a creation of the railroad age since passes immediately eastward permit rail lines to cross the Northern Rockies. Westward the city has excellent rail connections with Seattle; it is a rail and air center of major importance. Spokane's industrial complex includes flour milling, meat packing, sawmills, pulp and paper manufacture, and the extraction and fabrication of aluminum.

The Columbia Basin and adjacent areas have enormous potential water power. The dams at Grand Coulee, Chief Joseph, McNary, and Bonneville and one under construction at the Dalles are projects of the Federal government. Others are under construction at Priest Rapids and on the Snake River. There are privately owned hydroelectric plants on the Snake, Spokane, and Clark Fork Rivers. The total rated capacity of hydroelectric power plants in the region is nearly 6 million horsepower and new plants under construction will increase this.

## CASCADE MOUNTAINS AND SIERRA NEVADA

The Cascade Mountains and Sierra Nevada extend from the Canadian border across Washington and Oregon as far as southern California. They function as a geographic unit, despite differences in landscapes, structure, and resources, since they separate two very different regions. West of the ranges lie fertile, well-watered, well-populated lowlands and valleys. East of the dividing crest is the semiarid and desert intermountain region with its sparsely populated

*Figure 3-13 Mt. St. Helens and Spirit Lake, Washington. Once an active volcano, this beautiful peak with its surrounding wilderness area is becoming an increasingly popular center of recreation. (Courtesy of Northern Pacific Railway.)*

basins, plateaus, and ranges. The railways and highways across the Rocky Mountains, the intermountain region, and the Cascade–Sierra Nevada region were built to reach Pacific Coast cities and favored lowlands like the Willamette Valley. Comparatively few people stopped along the route to settle in the mountains or deserts, so only small amounts of freight and few passengers originate there today. The Cascades and Sierras are impressively scenic, with resources of timber, minerals, and water power, but they never will support a large population. Their resources are exploited mainly by those who live near the Coast; and this natural wealth helped the growth of Coast cities and industries.

## Cascade Mountains

The Cascades are built mainly from volcanic materials that form a broad platform above which tower snow-capped volcanic peaks, of which only the southernmost, Lassen, has erupted in this century. The range is from 50 to 100 miles wide and extends from Lassen Peak into British Columbia. Summits exceed 10,000 feet and in Washington they include Mt. Rainier, 14,408 feet, Mt. Adams, Mt. Baker, Mt. St. Helens and Glacier Peak; in

Oregon are Mt. Hood, Mt. Jefferson, the Three Sisters, and Mt. Thielson; and in California, Mt. Shasta and Lassen Peak. Crater Lake in southern Oregon occupies the site of a former volcano as high as Shasta. River and glacial erosion has been very active, and the mountains are characterized by steep canyons, rugged ridges, and glacial lakes. There are many existing glaciers, 28 on Rainier alone. Much of the Cascade Range is included in national forests, insuring conservation of the forest reserves and the maintenance of the tree cover needed to control the flow of streams used for power, irrigation, and the water supply of cities.

The Cascade Mountains are impressive in their elevation and in the grandeur of the tall green forests that clothe their slopes. Above the general summit level of about 6,000 feet rise snow- and ice-covered peaks that seem like white sentinels looking down upon the lowlands. The Cascades are a major barrier, both climatic and economic. They function negatively in the geographic pattern since they pose transportation problems that are overcome only at great cost. The north-south trend of the range places it at right angles to the principal traffic movements; therefore, it becomes imperative to seek passages for highways and rail-roads. Land transport is difficult across these crests, particularly in winter when summits are snowbound. In the Cascade Range the most famous pass is the Columbia River Gorge through which the river crosses the mountains at such low levels that the stream has been canalized. Northward from the gorge are passes of moderate altitude, useful through most of the year. Best known and lowest is Snoqualmie Pass, 3,127 feet, connecting the Puget Sound lowland on the west and the Columbia Basin on the east by highway and rail. Other passes in western Washington include Naches, Stampede, Stevens, and White. There is some east-west traffic across the Cascade Range in Oregon, with one railroad and several highways crossing the mountains.

In these volcanic mountains there are few valuable minerals except in northern Washington where mines produce gold, copper, and zinc. Some coal is mined near Cle Elum. In northwestern Washington are beds of limestone utilized for portland cement. The principal economy depends on the vast timber resources and hydroelectric power supplied by mountain streams and dams on Skagit, Lewis, Snoqualmie, and other rivers. Mountain resources support many people on nearby lowlands; for example, east of the crest in Oregon, Bend and Klamath Falls are devoted to handling lumber, and river valleys tributary to the Columbia are developed for irrigation of choice apples and soft fruits. Mountain uplands along the east-facing Cascades provide summer sheep pasture; in winter, the animals are kept on irrigated lowlands of the Yakima and Kittitas Valleys.

Mt. Hood, Mt. Baker, and other peaks and passes in the Cascade Range attract many visitors by fine scenery and good opportunities for winter sports. There are three national parks; that of Mt. Rainier includes the most extensive ice fields in the United States. The southernmost

park is Lassen, set aside because of its distinctive volcanic features. In southern Oregon, a volcanic crater in Crater Lake National Park apparently was enlarged by a catastrophic eruption and is now occupied by Crater Lake, noted for its depth, nearly 2,000 feet, and deep-blue color. Between Oregon and Washington where the Columbia River crosses the Cascades in its gorge, the landscape is covered with forests and is distinguished by cascading streams plunging over cliffs to join the Columbia. Set in this gorge is Bonneville Dam built by the Federal government for hydroelectric power. It is tied by transmission line to the Grand Coulee and other power dams in the Columbia Basin and on the western side of the mountains. This abundant power has encouraged expansion of industrial output in the Pacific Northwest, especially in the fields of electrochemistry and aluminum refining.

In the vicinity of the 42nd parallel, the Oregon-California boundary, the Cascades and Sierra Nevada merge with an old mountain system or plateau known as the Klamath Mountains. Here a confusion of ranges rises over 7,000 feet and interposes a barrier between the Willamette and Sacramento Valleys of Oregon and California.

### Sierra Nevada

For a distance of 400 miles from Lassen Peak south of the Tehachapi Mountains, the crest of

*Figure 3-14  Bonneville Dam on the Columbia River. (Courtesy of Bureau of Reclamation.)*

the Sierra Nevada rises to summits above 14,-000 feet. In cross section this mountain block has a long westward-facing slope and an eastern face so steep that it gives the impression of a vertical wall. The bedrock, mostly granite, is deeply eroded by streams and glaciers on its western flank. There are many glacial lakes in the high Sierras and other evidences of glacial erosion.

The high mountain barrier of the Sierra Nevada greatly interferes with east-west transportation in northern California since heavy winter snows often make trans-Sierra travel difficult. Although the northern Sierra is not as high as the southern, its ruggedness prevents easy crossing. The Feather River Canyon is used by rail and highway at considerable expense. Near Lake Tahoe are several passes; Donner, 7,189 feet, which is also traversed by rail and road, is the most useful of these, but winter snows are so deep that the pass is kept open only with great effort. South of Lake Tahoe most of the passes are higher than 9,000 feet and are useless except in midsummer. For more than 100 miles, the east-facing escarpment is so steep that no wheeled vehicle can traverse this barrier. In the south, Walker Pass, 5,248 feet, is used for highway travel, but only at the southern end of the Sierra, at Tehachapi Pass, 3,790 feet, can railways find a route through the mountains.

Since the western mountain slope receives the full force of Pacific storms, precipitation is sufficient for extensive forests. For years softwoods have been produced commercially, but cutting of the accessible timber will limit further expansion of this industry. Several groves of big trees, or sequoias, have been set aside in national parks, and much timbered land has been placed on a reserve basis as national forests. Yosemite National Park, famed for its waterfalls and canyon, has more than a million visitors annually. Kings River Canyon and Sequoia are other national parks.

Zoning of temperature and precipitation has caused zoning of vegetation on the western slope of the mountains. In the foothills below 2,000 feet, chaparral mixed with digger pines covers the eroded slopes. From 2,000 to 5,000 feet, with more precipitation, there is a zone of western yellow pine, sugar pine, and the big trees. In the zone from 5,000 to 7,000 feet are several varieties of pine. Up to 9,000 feet are juniper and mountain hemlock, with unforested mountain meadows above that. Commercial timber is obtained chiefly from altitudes below 5,000 feet and is taken by highway or rail to towns for processing and shipment.

The combination of mountain meadow, impressive stands of trees, cool and clear summers, and streams stocked with fish attracts many tourists to these mountains each year. The season generally is limited to summer, though in Yosemite and some other places winter sports draw visitors. Peaks of the Sierra Nevada take the form of sharp-edged pinnacles posing a challenge to experienced mountain climbers, with altitudes so great and approaches so rugged that they are climbed only by the hardy.

Grazing of animals pastured on upper slopes during summer and lower slopes in winter is a further resource. Such migration occurs, particularly in the pasturing of herds of sheep, but sheepherders are few in numbers.

Mining of placer gold has been carried on in the Sierra Nevada foothills for over a century, but the cost of extracting the ores that produced these deposits became so high in the 1940s that most deep quartz mines were closed. Gold discoveries in the foothills encouraged American settlement during 1849–1850, and though few of those who sought the metal became wealthy, they and their descendants settled California's farming lands. Upon the collapse of gold mining many ghost towns were left, and these, combined with pleasant summer weather, a forested landscape, canyons such as Yosemite and Kings River, and other attractions, form the basis for a tourist industry.

In northern California, Shasta Dam impounds waters of the upper Sacramento and provides electricity for northern California cities and farms. Shasta Dam has other functions; it controls the flow of water in the Sacramento so that the valley is less subject to floods, and it regulates river flow in summer to aid navigation and provide water for irrigation when rain is slight. Additional dams on the tributary streams are needed for further flood control, irrigation, and power. The western slope of the Sierra Nevada also provides water for Millerton Lake at Friant Dam and for the power and wa-ter installations on the Tuolumne and Mokelumne Rivers, which serve San Francisco and Oakland respectively. Other reservoirs conserve water on the San Joaquin and provide power for smaller cities and for local irrigation of suitable land.

## CALIFORNIA VALLEYS AND COAST RANGES

The valleys and coastal lowlands of California support nearly as many inhabitants as all the rest of the Western United States. A chief reason for this is the Mediterranean climate so pleasing to visitors and so favorable for growing fruits, vegetables, and all kinds of farm crops. Large areas of fertile soil, water for irrigation, and resources of petroleum and accessible timber further economic growth. In addition, there are terminals for outlets of a vast hinterland and seaports where transcontinental routes meet ocean shipping. Largest production and the most populous areas are in the Central Valley and the Los Angeles lowland. From these, many smaller valleys penetrate the mountains or lie within the Coast Ranges which parallel the Pacific Ocean and hem in the Central Valley on the west.

### Central Valley

The Central Valley of California, often called the Great Valley, is an elongated lowland drained by the Sacramento River from the north and the San Joaquin from the south, except for a small basin of interior drainage at the southern end. It is bordered on the east by the Sierra Nevada and on the west by the California Coast Ranges. At the confluence of the Sacramento and San Joaquin Rivers there is an extensive delta formed where the combined streams flow through Carquinez Strait into San Francisco Bay. Shut off from the moderating effects of the Pacific Ocean, summers in the Central Valley are generally warmer than in the coastal areas. The Sacramento-Stockton region, however, is somewhat tempered by afternoon breezes from San Francisco Bay.

The broad floodplains and alluvial piedmonts of the Central Valley, with their warm summers, mild winters, and meager winter rains, supported only a small population of primitive Indians before 1849. The coming of the Americans brought a brief period of dry farming of small grains, followed by irrigation.

*Figure 3-15   Shasta Dam on the Sacramento River. (Courtesy of Bureau of Reclamation.)*

Today this valley is prime farmland. Peaches, pears, asparagus, celery, potatoes, beans, and sugar beets are grown on the delta lands. Melons, cotton, citrus fruits, and alfalfa as well as wine and table grapes are grown in the San Joaquin section. Even the dry southern end of the Great Valley produces cotton, alfalfa, and potatoes.

The disintegration of the large cattle and grain ranches, characteristic of the early years of the valley, was accelerated after 1875 upon completion of the Southern Pacific Railroad. Small farm service centers were established, and many communities specialized in high-value subtropical crops. In the Sacramento Valley,

for example, Yuba City and Marysville now specialize in canning peaches and Willows grows rice. Sacramento owes its agricultural origins to the miner's needs but its later growth came from its importance as a state capital, and as an urban center it dominates its part of the Great Valley.

Small communities in the delta process fruit and vegetable crops and the port of Stockton, connected with the sea by a channel dredged deep enough for ships, is locally important. Nearby Lodi is noted for wine and table grapes. In the San Joaquin Valley, almost every small community has its own agricultural specialty. Fresno is a center of dried-fruit production, particularly raisins; others towns ship melons, table grapes, and figs. A common thread—dairying—runs through the economic fabric, and this valley has many milk condenseries.

The southern part of the Central Valley is dominated by Bakersfield, important for railroad activities. In the last quarter century the fertility of this area combined with water from the mountains has given impetus to the city's growth. In addition, this section of the valley has been important for petroleum, and Bakersfield is a center for sale of oil well supplies. Most oil production has been north and northwest of Bakersfield in the desert on the western side of the valley. Here are the McKittrick and Coalingo oil fields. Agricultural land near Bakersfield is farmed in wheat and irrigated cotton, and these developments have nearly drained several large shallow lakes lying west and north of the city.

In the valley of California is one of the principal reclamation projects in the United States, the Central Valley Project (Figure 3-16), in which a coordinated program has been set up

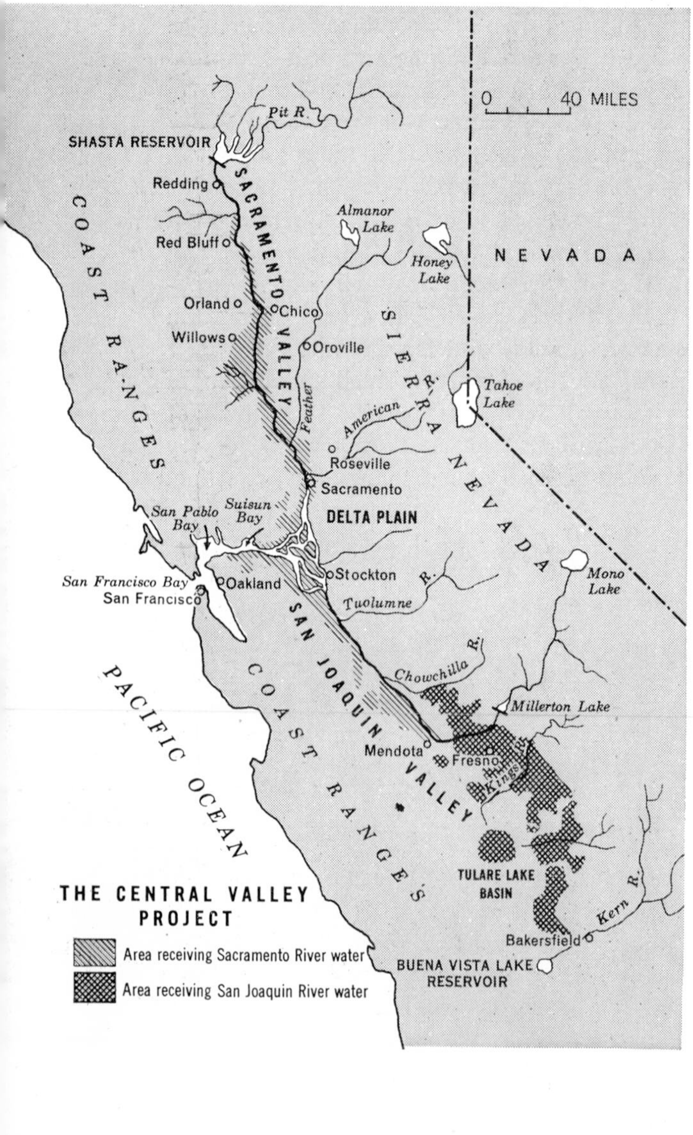

THE CENTRAL VALLEY PROJECT

▨ Area receiving Sacramento River water
▩ Area receiving San Joaquin River water

*Figure 3-16   Note that Sacramento River water is being used in the San Joaquin River valley. Some of the water stored back of the Shasta Dam in northern California is used to irrigate fields in the south central part of the Great Valley of California.*

to assist agriculture. The Sacramento and its tributaries normally flood in spring and early summer when melting snow from the mountains sends overloaded streams to the lowlands, with resulting serious inundations. During a part of the year, the Sacramento Valley has more water than it can use. On the other hand, the San Joaquin and the southern interior basin have inadequate flow; in spring and in summer they may be critically short of water. It was proposed, therefore, that lakes and dams be built in the upper Sacramento to retard stream flow and regulate the Sacramento River. Surplus water is taken across the Sacramento Delta by aqueduct and a pumping system to supply ranches along the lower San Joaquin. Water which would normally supply the lower San Joaquin section was then diverted to the dry basins near Bakersfield where expansion of irrigated land is in progress. This elaborate plan is essentially complete and seems to give satisfactory results. If California continues to produce high-value subtropical crops, projects of this sort are needed so that additional land can be irrigated to feed a growing population.

## Southern California

Many visitors, especially winter tourists, think only of southern California when the state name is mentioned. The area is roughly triangular, extending from Santa Barbara on the west to San Bernardino and Riverside on the east, and south to San Diego and Mexico. Inland the region is rimmed by the San Gabriel and San Bernardino Ranges on the north and the San Jacinto and other ranges on the east. The Los Angeles lowland, heavily floored by sediments washed from the mountains, is divided by low ranges or hills into a number of valleys including the San Fernando, Ventura, Santa Maria, and San Bernar-

*Figure 3-17 Picking oranges in southern California. The pickers use small clippers to cut the orange from its stem. Note the deep and well-cultivated soil in this grove. (Courtesy of Los Angeles County Chamber of Commerce.)*

dino. Southward the mountains crowd nearer the coast, leaving a lowland that is but a few miles wide between Los Angeles and San Diego. Offshore the tops of submerged coast range peaks project above the Pacific as small rugged islands, of which only Santa Catalina Island, a popular resort, is important.

Parallel mountain ridges are transportation obstacles in the southern Coast Ranges, but a few passes connect desert and coast. Of these, Cajon Pass, 3,623 feet and San Gorgonio Pass, 2,559 feet, is each occupied by a railroad and highway. Los Angeles has poor approaches from the north although Tejon Pass traversed by highway connects the southern San Joaquin Valley and Los Angeles. West from the city for 100 miles, the steep faces of the Santa Monica Mountains descend abruptly to the shore. Though a highway has been notched from the sea cliffs, it is not a first-class route and is expensive to maintain. Southward, two routes lead to San Diego along the coast and through interior valleys.

Favored by sunny weather, mild winters with little threat of frost, fertile alluvial soil, and moderate supplies of water for irrigation, the lowlands and valleys of southern California have experienced an extraordinary agricultural development. Small though the area is, compared with other farm regions of the United States, its production of citrus and other fruits, nuts, melons, vegetables, sugar beets, and hay, along with dairy and poultry products, puts Los Angeles County among the nation's leading counties in value of agricultural output.

The Los Angeles lowland is one of the country's leading sources of petroleum. Without coal and remote from large hydroelectric plants, industry in southern California depends primarily on petroleum and natural gas for its development.

In southern California, climate is a fundamental resource. During the last quarter of the nineteenth century out-of-state visitors began to be attracted by the warm, sunny winters, and the great influx of settlers and migrants began. Nearly 5 million people live in the Los Angeles lowland and adjacent valleys and coastal areas.

The coastal lowlands, originally covered by short grass and scrub trees, were the first part of Upper California encountered by the Spaniards in their northward march from Lower California. The mission fathers brought seeds and cuttings with them—citrus fruits, grapes, and the fig and olive. They introduced horses, cows, sheep, and many grains; in these lay the foundation of California's rise as an agricultural state. As soon as the Americans tapped water sources for irrigation, the grazing economy of the Spanish-Mexicans gave way to land subdivision in the late nineteenth century. Smaller tracts were then supplied with water, and the land was brought under cultivation spe-

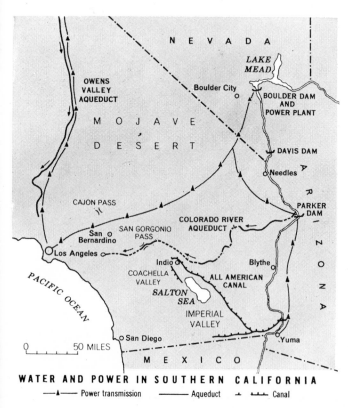

**WATER AND POWER IN SOUTHERN CALIFORNIA**
—▲— Power transmission    ——— Aqueduct    ⊥ ⊥⊥⊥ Canal

*Figure 3-18   The Colorado River is of special importance to southern California. Note that it furnishes water for irrigation in the Imperial Valley and also for municipal use in the Los Angeles area. Electricity is generated at Hoover Dam.*

*Figure 3-19 Air view of the Los Angeles business district showing the freeway that provides a route for rapid movement of cars from the outlying districts into and through the city. (Courtesy of Los Angeles County Chamber of Commerce.)*

cializing in subtropical fruits. Accommodations for winter tourists were expanded rapidly, and many visitors became permanent residents. This phase of life in the southern valleys continued until the 1900s when discovery of new petroleum fields—the first oil well was drilled in 1880 —provided fuel for industry and helped to spur a growth of population which eventually became more urban, establishing a large consumer market. This marked the beginning of California's progress toward an industrial existence.

Los Angeles, which now has over 2 million inhabitants, soon took the lead from surrounding communities, and so urban growth has eclipsed agricultural activity in southern California. Water supply, transportation, and location were poor at Los Angeles, but the city progressed in spite of its geographical environment. Los Angeles went far outside southern California for water, obtaining supplies from Owens Valley and later from the Colorado River by way of the Metropolitan Aqueduct. There was no good natural harbor; the present harbor, 18 miles south of the city, is artificial. There was no good land connection with the rest of Cali-

fornia or the nation until the Southern Pacific Railroad reached Los Angeles in 1875 and the Santa Fe in 1887.

Aggressive advertising has advanced the growth of Los Angeles. Population and wealth have come to southern California out of proportion to available resources. California's pressing needs for cheap farm labor brought a diversity of people into the area, Japanese, Mexicans, Negroes, and Europeans. Now these people provide labor for many southern California industries such as petroleum refining, tire manufacture, fish processing, fruit packing, motion picture production, and the aviation industry. In recent years production has expanded to include plastics, light metal wares, synthetic fabrics and fibers, pottery, automobiles, steel, and a long list of goods for which there is no seeming geographical explanation. It is apparent that though coastal southern California clings to its Spanish-Mexican past, only a trace of this background remains.

Many cities around Los Angeles are agricultural centers though they are affected by industrialization. Older and distant communities like

Ventura, Oxnard, Santa Maria, San Bernardino, and Riverside are pleasant towns whose farmers and ranchers still grow subtropical crops. Towns and cities nearer Los Angeles may carry on some industry as well as serve nearby farms. These include San Fernando, Santa Ana, and Anaheim. Originally some outlying centers were winter resorts, but this aspect of existence has disappeared in the larger communities, particularly in Santa Monica, Redondo Beach, and Long Beach. Beverly Hills, Pasadena, Van Nuys, Westwood, and Inglewood are dormitory towns and may, like Beverly Hills, be surrounded by the city of Los Angeles and yet retain separate municipal identity and function.

Westward from Los Angeles, facing the sea and backed by the Santa Ynez Mountains, the city of Santa Barbara is secluded, for it cannot be reached easily from the land side and has no satisfactory harbor. As one of the earlier mission communities it has never been important for industry or agriculture. Like Pasadena its principal development has been residential, with characteristics of a superior year-round coastal resort.

San Diego has a first-class harbor and naval installations to support it, as well as some industries such as fishing and the manufacture of aircraft. Geographically it is handicapped by insufficient water supply, rugged mountains and desert to the east, and, on the south, an international boundary that prevents access to its normal hinterland.

### California Coast Ranges and Valleys

The Coast Ranges forming the western rim of the Central Valley of California are a land of ridges and basins whose direction is roughly parallel to the coast itself, a condition associated with faulting. The Coast Ranges present a bold face to the Pacific, but the submerged northern ends of some of the troughlike valleys provide access to the anterior and the Central Valley. Thus the submerged block forming San Francisco Bay is a breach in the Coast Ranges leading to the San Joaquin Valley; others include Humboldt, Tomales, and Monterey Bays. The most significant parts of the Coast Ranges are not the mountains themselves but the intervening valleys in which are all of the cities and most of the people. The mountains are sparsely populated.

In the Coast Ranges, California natives were low in the scale of civilization, having inadequate food. Like Indians of the Northwest Coast they relied largely on fish; other food included acorn meal and small animals that could be trapped. Though they lived in villages there was little social organization. With the coming of the Spaniards, Mexicans, and Americans, the human economy of this region shifted to higher levels.

In spite of proximity to the coast, people who live in the Coast Range valleys are not directly concerned with the sea though fishing is important in a few places. Most valleys are occupied by farmers or, as they are known in the west, ranchers. Their farming is dependent on the marine climate, particularly in the production of specialty crops such as artichokes, flower or mustard seeds, lettuce, sugar beets, apples, grapes, and apricots. On some of the mountains there is good grazing land, and here beef cattle are raised on big ranches. Between 35° and 38° north latitude, the central Coast Ranges enjoy more precipitation than in the southern mountains, and their summits receive amounts sufficient to support forest growth. In sheltered valleys, the Coast redwoods are found 100 miles south of San Francisco. Where water is obtainable, most valleys are used for raising specialty crops. Where drought prevails, there are traces of the old-time, large-scale ranch economy. The central Coast Ranges and their valleys all but prevent penetration from the sea, and indeed there is no first-class harbor between Los Angeles and San Francisco.

Largest and longest of the valleys is the Salinas, through which the Salinas River flows for more than 100 miles to reach Monterey Bay. The upper valley has scattered farms, but the lower section is intensively farmed in irrigated sugar beets, lettuce, alfalfa, melons, and near Watsonville, apples. The urban center, Salinas, is derived from earlier ranching activities.

Inland from Salinas is the Santa Clara Valley, growing specialty crops and fruit in its lower northern portion. The crops, however, differ from those in the Salinas region, for the lower Santa Clara is dominated by large groves of prunes, apricots, and peaches. Of some importance are alfalfa and dairying. The urban center is San Jose, like Los Angeles one of the early Spanish pueblos. Lately its industries have grown, but it functions mainly as a processing center for fruits. This valley is faced with a problem of subsurface seepage of salt water coming from San Francisco Bay.

South of the 38th parallel, San Francisco Bay is the most conspicuous geographic feature of the coast. Much of the bay is shallow, but inside the Golden Gate and a little to the south, depths are sufficient for large vessels. The eastern side of the bay has been dredged to allow ocean vessels to reach the port of Oakland. Two peninsulas impinge upon the Golden Gate like a pair of tongs; the southern prong is occupied by San Francisco, confined to its peninsula which is only seven miles wide. The northern (Marin) peninsula is very rugged.

San Francisco failed to develop under Mexican rule. With the discovery of gold in California and the subsequent rush of immigrants, the city became a disembarkation point for settlers entering the state by sea. Thus the character of the city as a center of trade and commerce was established, and though San Francisco now has industries such as coffee roasting, metal processing, and sugar refining, its dominant function is that of a trading and financial center. A century ago, common labor in California was in such demand that many immigrants were non-English, including Latin-Americans, French, Germans, and Chinese. Each of these stocks left its imprint upon the life of the city and their variety has given San Francisco a cosmopolitan tinge not duplicated in any other Coast city. San Francisco's water supply problem led to the building of an aqueduct to bring water from the west-facing, snow-covered slopes of the Sierra Nevada.

On the eastern side of the bay, the separate municipality of Oakland is part of the San Francisco metropolitan area. Here are industries that were unable to find sufficient cheap land in San Francisco, and Oakland is noted for its food processing, milling, and other industries. North of Oakland, specialized satellite cities line the shore to a point beyond Carquinez Strait. Among these cities are Berkeley, a residential and university center, Richmond and Martinez with oil refineries, Crockett with a cane sugar refinery, and Pittsburg, Hercules, and Giant, with chemical plants.

The northern California coast ranges are unlike the central and southern ranges. Since they are more rugged and have less access to the sea, inferior harbors, and few passes, they are more isolated. The mountains lack intervening valleys, and transport is restricted to routes parallel to the coast. Only in the southern section facing San Francisco Bay are there valley floors suitable for agriculture, those of the Santa Rosa, Sonoma, and Napa Rivers. In these lowlands there is water for irrigating alfalfa and vineyards, but the land available for agricultural expansion is limited. Dairying is associated with excellent pasture afforded by the long, narrow, coastal terraces kept moist by cool, damp air. Except in the Salinas, Santa Clara, and a few other smaller valleys, this region is incapable of supporting many people and most towns are small. Some dry or remote valleys are used more for grazing than for crops. In the north, a lowland at the mouth of the Eel River is dominated by the towns of Eureka and Arcata. The economy of these communities is based on lumbering, especially of the Coast redwoods.

## PACIFIC NORTHWEST COASTAL PROVINCE

Between the Cascade Range and the Pacific Ocean and from Canada into the Klamath Mountains of northern California is a humid region with mild winters and cool summers. Here, in a belt about 100 miles wide from west to east, the Douglas fir, western hemlock, cedar, and spruce attain their maximum growth and the region might well be called "Evergreen Land." The marine west-coast climate not only favors tree growth, but makes possible dairying and growing small fruits in the wider valleys.

Most of the people live in the Puget-Willamette Lowland between the Cascade Range and the Coast Ranges adjoinng the Pacific Ocean. The lowland is a troughlike basin whose northern part is submerged to form Puget Sound. The rivers in the north drain into Puget Sound or Grays Harbor on the Pacific, and those in the south flow into the Columbia or the Willamette, its major tributary.

### Coast Ranges of the Pacific Northwest

These mountains lie almost parallel to the Pacific shore and are somewhat lower in altitude than the Coast Ranges of California. Coastal uplift has produced a series of marine terraces like giant steps facing the sea, thus this is a rugged and scenic coast, with few corridors connecting with the interior, and lacking the long, narrow valleys of the California ranges. The principal opening through the Oregon and Washington coast mountains is the wide estuary of the Columbia River, which breaches the mountains at right angles in 46° north latitude.

This and the opening at San Francisco Bay are the only routes by which ocean vessels may navigate west-coast streams to reach Portland or Stockton. Mightiest break through the coastal mountains is the Strait of Juan de Fuca connecting with Puget Sound and leading to protected ocean ports far inland. Elsewhere in Washington a wide gap of the Chehalis River connects Grays Harbor with the Puget Lowland, and a narrower route connects the lowland with Willapa Bay. In Oregon, Coos and Tillamook Bays are connected with the Willamette Valley by fairly satisfactory routes through the Coast Range. A mountain knot, the Olympics, occupies northwest Washington, separated from the Cascades by Puget Sound and from Vancouver Island by Juan de Fuca Strait. The Olympics reach elevations that support glaciers and snow fields, and part of the area is set aside as a national park. The highest peak is Mt. Olympus, 7,954 feet.

In Oregon and Washington, the Coast Ranges generally are lower in altitude and more easily traveled than those of California. Nevertheless, construction of railways and highways in this terrain is so expensive that some sections are isolated. The northern mountains are forest covered, chiefly with coniferous softwoods. This

*Figure 3-20 Mount Olympus in the Olympic National Park, northwestern Washington. The broad snow field near the summit is the White Glacier. (Courtesy of National Park Service.)*

timber is of great economic importance. In the wider valleys specialized farming is carried on. To some extent the deep forests have been exploited for timber, but much untouched forest serves as a scenic resource. Since only the edges of the mountains are reached by highways, tourists attracted by scenery or fishing are fewer than visitors to the Cascade parks. Because of the forests and the expense of clearing, agricultural land is at a premium except in sheltered places on the eastern side of the Olympic Peninsula. South of the Olympic Mountains the landscape is moderately dissected, and there the coast is submerged at Grays Harbor, Willapa Bay, and the Columbia River embayment. Fishing, lumbering, and paper manufacture are found here, but like the mountains to the north, this is a remote region and its population density is low.

The Columbia River estuary, which is traversed only by ferry in its lower course, is so broad and deep that it is a major interruption to any north-south travel between northwestern Oregon and southwestern Washington. Astoria, Oregon, is on the south shore, but in spite of its fur-trade fame and its position on deep water, the city is so far from other activities in Oregon that its growth has been slow. South of Astoria the Oregon coast is rugged but not high, with shallow harbors at Coos Bay and Tillamook. Since some short streams cross the mountains to reach the sea, residents of the Willamette Valley go to the coast if they wish a seaside vacation, and there are many summer resorts in spite of heavy fog. Lumbering is the leading industry, dairying has been profitable, and in southwestern Oregon some minerals have been located, but mining is small in scale.

Flats along the upper Rogue River Valley and the Umpqua have good soil and conditions suitable for deciduous fruits. The Rogue Valley is famous for its pears. Small centers such as Medford and Roseburg supply needs of fruit-growers, farmers, and lumbermen.

The moderate climate of the Pacific Northwest imposes few hardships on those who live there. Winter is the rainy season, and the days are short, with much cloudy weather and high relative humidity. Temperature range is small throughout the year. Summers are pleasant and high temperatures are rare. The landscape remains green all winter, and except in the higher mountains, the snowy ground characteristic of winter in the northeastern United States is lacking near the northwestern coast.

## Puget-Willamette Lowland

Natives of the mountains and valleys of western Oregon and Washington had advanced to a comparatively high point in civilization at the time they were displaced by intrusion of the British and Americans. In a landscape of dense, dark forests, the Indians relied upon tree products for most of their needs. The forest supplied fuel and planks for boats and houses. Berries and other fruits contributed to the food supply. The Indians hunted wild animals for food and skins, but they obtained most of their food by fishing along interior streams and on the coast. Social organization had advanced beyond that of most other American aborigines and in spite of conflicts, the tribes generally lived together in peace and in comfort.

This balance between human activities and food and shelter provided by natural resources of the region was upset by the arrival of frontier fur traders and trappers entering the Northwest from the Canadian plains or through coastal harbors. As the Willamette Valley and the Puget Lowland became better known, Americans interested in agricultural potentialities came to the Pacific Northwest between 1842 and 1848, and began farming the land. It was in this period that numerous settlements began.

Although land and water transport was inadequate and markets were distant, development continued. The gold rush to California in 1850 created an excellent market for lumber in that state. Supplies of fruit, grain, and fish were ample, and fortunately there was little effective Indian opposition to the new settlements.

Wealth was available from forests, but commercial exploitation of timber resources came only with improved transportation after 1900. Since then lumbering has proceeded at such pace that there is concern over exhaustion of this resource. Conservation measures now look toward cropping Northwestern forests on a sustained-yield plan which will make it possible for the Pacific Northwest to continue as a major lumber producer. The forests of the Northwest provide us with paper, shingles, plywood, building material, telephone poles, and other necessities of modern life.

Lowlands of western Oregon and Washington have been famous for a century for certain crops; indeed, the fertility and cheapness of land in the Willamette Valley attracted settlers over the Oregon Trail to the Northwest. Since it was possible to raise many crops with which they had been familiar in the East, there was a trend toward the establishment of Eastern farm practices in the Northwest; hence, parts of this valley resemble Ohio or Illinois, with their barns, farm animals, and houses repeating the mid-nineteenth century rural complex of the American Middle West. In addition to staples such as oats and potatoes, Northwest agriculture developed some specialty crops such as berries, mint, spring flower bulbs, and commercial seeds.

With mild winters, plentiful rain, and a long growing season, agriculture normally is profitable although occasional summer drought makes it desirable to irrigate some land in July and August. Native grasses and introduced forage plants do well and beef cattle and sheep are raised, but there is concentration on dairy products. In some localities the emphasis on dairying is so great that exports of processed milk, cheese, and butter are large. Other industries include poultry and small fruits. Expansion of commercial farming is limited by the extent of valley lands and by the cost of removing stumps from farmland and pasture.

Fishing, especially of salmon and halibut, is a third economy in the Northwest. Demand for this food has been so great that sea and streams have been overfished, and production is less than formerly. Commercial fishing is maintained largely through conservation measures such as restocking streams and restricting on the gear used and the time of year when fish may be

caught. Minor economies include manufacturing, tourism, and mining. Recent exploitation has demonstrated that the Northwest has mineral wealth or is accessible to mining centers. As a result, and with the aid of hydroelectric power, industrial growth has been speeded.

The Willamette Valley, only 125 miles long and about 35 miles wide, is highly productive. It contains three-fourths of Oregon's people in 5 per cent of the state's area. Its grain, wool, lumber, fruit, fish, and other commodities have provided cities with material for manufacturing a variety of goods and so attracting increasing numbers of permanent residents. Urban communities have grown, especially the city of Portland near the confluence of the Willamette and Columbia. To secure outlets for the productiveness of the region, the lower Columbia has been dredged, making Portland a seaport 100 miles distant from the Pacific. Portland, however, is not wholly dependent upon products of western Oregon; the city taps eastern Washington and Oregon by a transportation corridor through the Cascades at the Columbia River Gorge. Portland's location, combined with actual and potential water power, has led to industrialization, population increase, and expansion of markets.

Smaller cities of the Willamette Valley serve both general and specific functions. Salem is a center of the state's political activity, Corvallis, the site of Oregon State College. Eugene, with the University of Oregon and woodworking plants, Oregon City, with pulp and woolen mills, and other communities prosper from broad agricultural and economic bases. Few centers in the Western United States have raw materials, power, and other advantages to the same degree as towns and cities of the Willamette Valley.

Northward from the river at Portland the lowland extends to Puget Sound. Unlike the Willamette, dense forests prevailed here, occupying terrain whose features were determined by heavy glacial outwash and deposition. Disturbed drainage patterns and deposits of stony till hinder farming, even after clearing of timber. Forest clearing has left much land covered

with stumps and intractable for intensive farming except in fertile alluvial valleys. Milk, poultry, vegetables, bulb and seed crops, and small
fruits are among the farm products, but most
of the lowland is unsuited for growing grain
other than oats. Average farm size in one
county is only 5 acres.

The northern Puget Lowland is submerged
by waters of Puget Sound. Long, narrow, deep
channels make up the Sound, whose confused
landscape includes irregular peninsulas and
many small islands. Originally virgin forests

reached the shore, but today the lumber mills
have left only second- and third-growth coniferous and deciduous trees.

Seattle is the dominant city though it must
compete with neighboring Tacoma. Of the two,
Seattle enjoys the superior geographic position
nearer the open sea, enhanced by the Snoqualmie and other passes east of the city. As recently as 1935 Seattle and Tacoma were regional capitals for the Puget Lowland, meeting
needs of local markets, with Seattle maintaining
trade with Alaska and the Orient. That trade

*Figure 3-21   View of Seattle looking west of north with Elliott Bay and the
port facilities in the foreground, the retail core at right center, and Lake
Union in the middle distance. Note the proximity of the heart of the city to
the deep water anchorage. (Photograph by Pacific Aerial Surveys, Inc., used
by courtesy of Department of State.)*

continues, but since 1940 both have become diversified manufacturing cities, processing fish and foods, with timber, flour milling, meat packing, boatbuilding, furniture making, copper smelting, aircraft manufacture, and other industries. Their manufactures are mostly of the lighter type, dependent on supplies of cheap hydroelectric power. These cities received their growth impetus from the establishment of sawmills, then became inactive until mining attracted large numbers of people to Alaska and the Yukon. These ports remain transportation centers, but now Seattle and Tacoma have joined other manufacturing cities of the nation.

## IN PERSPECTIVE

### The United States

During the century that followed Independence the people of the United States busied themselves with expanding the Republic to the Pacific, consolidating political control over its 3 million square miles, and developing its widespread resources. The energy of the people went into clearing and plowing land for farms, founding new cities, logging the great forests, discovering and exploiting minerals, building railroads, starting and expanding manufacturing industries, and conducting the many other enterprises required by the complexities of modern life. The country showed small concern for international relations although the Monroe Doctrine did oppose further foreign colonization in the Americas. Two world wars compelled the United States to discontinue a policy of isolation and to concern itself with foreign problems as well as with those of domestic importance. Without deliberate intention, the country has grown to the status of a world power. It has become a defender of democratic institutions everywhere, a supplier of goods, money, and trained advisers to many peoples that need help. It has tried to maintain peace in a world that is in political turmoil. In a word, the United States has grown from a youthful, agricultural country preoccupied with developing its own resources into a mature, industrial nation that is a pivotal factor in world affairs.

In its growth to economic maturity the United States made mistakes. There was often needless waste in destruction of wildlife, soil erosion, deforestation, and wasteful mineral exploitation, but once the injurious methods were recognized, remedies were devised. A strong tendency has developed for land to be used more efficiently than in the past. The major uses of land in various sections of the country are shown in Figure 3-22.

The highest proportion of cropland is in the Corn Belt and Northern Plains states where nearly one-half of the land is tilled. Here are plains with good to excellent soils, adequate rainfall, and a moderately long growing season. No other part of the country has nearly so much cropland. The South has 20.4 per cent; the Northeast 18.1 per cent; New England and the Mountain states less than 10 per cent; and the Pacific states only 7.6 per cent. Improved farm practices, the substitution of tractors for hay-eating horses, the use of fertilizer, control of pests and diseases, and the development of hybrids or other improved plant species help account for increased production on the farmland of the United States.

Grazing and pasture land is concentrated in the 17 Western states, where 45 to 55 per cent of the land is in this category. Here inadequate rainfall restricts crops mostly to those produced by irrigation or dry farming. East of the Great Plains pastures amount to less than a fifth of the total area. Forests occupy 55.9 per cent of the total land in the Northeast, while in New England the proportion increases to 76.7 per cent. The South, excluding the southern plains, has from 50 to 60 per cent of its land in forests and the Lake states nearly 45 per cent. The three Pacific Coast states have 47.4 per cent of their area in forests or woodland, and the Mountain states 21.5 per cent. The least forest land is in the northern Great Plains where only 2.4 per cent of that region is so classified. These statistics indicate that there is enough forest

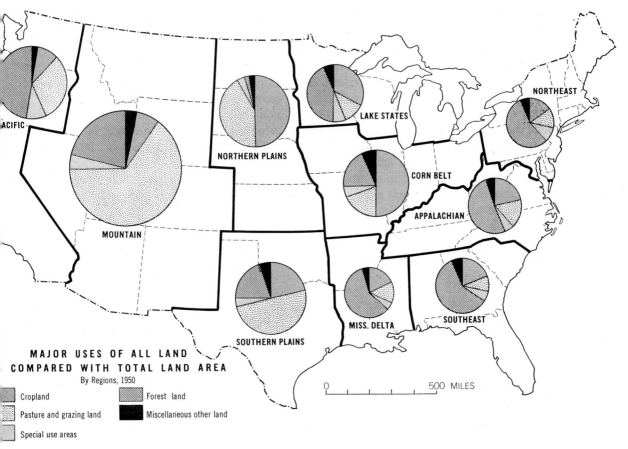

**MAJOR USES OF ALL LAND
COMPARED WITH TOTAL LAND AREA**
By Regions, 1950

Cropland

Pasture and grazing land

Special use areas

Forest land

Miscellaneous other land

0          500 MILES

*Figure 3-22    The difference in land utilization within the various regions de-
pends upon the adjustments made between man and nature. In the Corn Belt
and the Northern Plains about 50 per cent of total area is classified as cropland. In the Mountain states and the drier areas to the west, over 60 per cent
is used for grazing. Note the area in the Eastern states used for industry.*

land in the United States to grow most of its timber requirements if the forests are well managed. Great improvement in forest management has been made since the turn of the century, and waste has been reduced.

Special uses for land include roads, railways, farmsteads, industrial sites, cities, parks, wildlife refuges, airports, and military reservations. In the Middle Atlantic states 13 per cent of the total area is in this classification but in the rest of the country the proportion drops to 3 to 8 per cent. Miscellaneous uses account for 2 to 8 per cent of the total land and include marshes, sand dunes, beaches, and areas of bare rock.

The United States is fortunate in the variety and amount of minerals mined. Although the nation is the largest producer and consumer of bituminous coal and petroleum, at the present rate of usage the reserves of each will continue to meet the needs of the nation for a long period of time. Iron ore is not as easily procured as in the past, but large quantities of some grades are still available. Lead, zinc, copper, and bauxite are mined in various parts of the country. Nonmetallic minerals such as fertilizers, building stones, and sulfur are more than sufficient to meet the national needs.

Since 1900 the United States has become the leading industrial nation of the world. The accessibility of raw materials for manufacturing, the ease with which various types of transportation could be developed, the large supply of fuel and water power avaliable, intelligent labor, and a surplus of capital have been responsible for the rapid growth. Giant industrial centers such as Chicago, Pittsburgh, Cleveland, Detroit, Philadelphia, Baltimore, and St. Louis as well as numerous smaller cities and towns have made the northeastern quarter of the country the leading industrial area. New York, Norfolk, Boston, and other ports have aided this growth by giving easy access to the markets of the world. Smaller industrial areas have developed around some of the larger cities in other parts of the nation, along the Gulf coast of Texas and Louisiana, and about the larger cities near the Pacific. Almost 17 million persons are now employed by manufacturing industries which have an annual payroll approximating $70 million. The value added to the goods manufactured exceeds $116 billion yearly.

Since 1940, the population has increased at a rate of between 1 and 2 million persons each year. To support such a rapidly growing population, land and other resources must be used in an efficient manner. More careful use of natural resources gives further evidence of the nation's maturity.

### EXERCISES

*1.* What are the principal vegetation areas of the western half of the United States? Where is each located? What is the relationship between landforms, climate, and vegetation?

*2.* Where are the areas of greatest population density? Why can these areas support a much denser population than other parts of the Western states?

*3.* How do the economic activities of the Great Plains differ from those of the Central Lowland? What geographic factors largely cause these differences?

*4.* Where is the Imperial Valley? How has man changed his economic activities in this area? Where else in the Western states is man using the land as intensively?

*5.* What is the geographic significance of Mt. Whitney and Death Valley? Where is each located?

*6.* What is the largest city in the Western States? What were its handicaps? How has it overcome some of these? What are the chief manufactured products of the city?

*7.* What is the principal land use in the Columbia province? What is the chief land use of the Colorado Plateau? How do you account for the great differences in land utilization?

*8.* Where are Owens Valley, San Joaquin Valley, Willamette Valley, and Antelope Valley located? Why is each important?

*9.* What minerals are obtained in the Western states? What are the principal uses of each? What different methods of metal mining are necessary?

*10.* What mountains are in eastern California and central Washington and Oregon? How do the mountains affect the amount of rainfall on their eastern and western sides? How does land utilization west of the mountains differ from that east of the mountains?

*11.* What geographical advantages has San Francisco? What handicaps? What are the chief industries of the Bay area?

*12.* Why are Seattle and Portland the largest cities in the Pacific Northwest? What are the advantages and handicaps of each?

*13.* Why are there so few large cities in the territory between the Great Plains and the Sierra-Cascade Mountains? What cities in this area have populations greater than 100,000?

### SELECTED REFERENCES

Atwood, Wallace W.: *The Rocky Mountains,* Vanguard Press Inc., New York, 1945.

Clawson, Marion: *The Western Range Livestock Industry,* McGraw-Hill Book Company, Inc., New York, 1950.

Fenneman, Nevin M.: *Physiography of Western United States,* McGraw-Hill Book Company, Inc., New York, 1931.

Freeman, Otis W., and Howard H. Martin: *The Pacific Northwest,* 2d ed., John Wiley & Sons, Inc., New York, 1954.

Kraenzel, Carl F.: *The Great Plains in Transition,* University of Oklahoma Press, Norman, 1955.

Mather, Eugene: "The Production and Marketing of Wyoming Beef Cattle," *Economic Geography,* 26:81–93, April, 1950.

Meigs, Peveril, 3d: "Outlook for the Arid Realm of the United States," *Focus,* 4(4):1–6, December, 1953.

Meinig, Donald W.: "The Growth of Agricultural Regions in the Far West: 1850–1910," *Journal of Geography,* 54:221–232, May, 1955.

U.S. Bureau of Reclamation: *Central Valley Basin,* Washington, 1949.

————: *The Colorado River,* Washington, 1946.

————: *The Columbia River,* Washington, 1947.

U.S. Department of Agriculture, Yearbook, *Water,* Washington, 1955.

————: *Soils,* Washington, 1957.

Webb, Walter P.: *The Great Plains,* Ginn & Company, Boston, 1931.

Zierer, Clifford M.: *California and the Southwest,* John Wiley & Sons, Inc., New York, 1956.

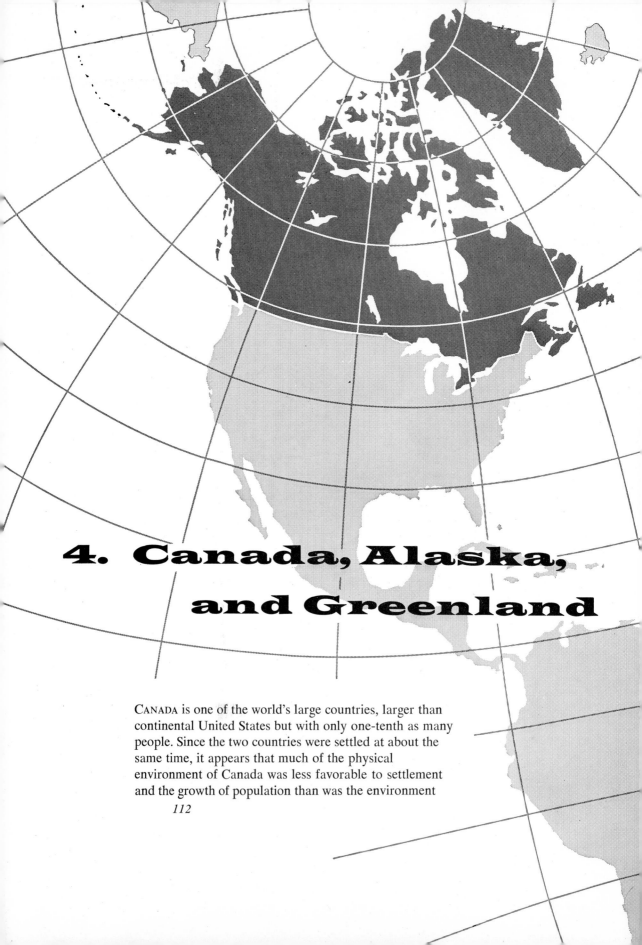

# 4. Canada, Alaska, and Greenland

CANADA is one of the world's large countries, larger than
continental United States but with only one-tenth as many
people. Since the two countries were settled at about the
same time, it appears that much of the physical
environment of Canada was less favorable to settlement
and the growth of population than was the environment

of the United States. With population densities in North America rising, increased pressure is being placed upon the continent's natural resources; hence, more attention is being given to the wealth which has lain untapped and undeveloped in the northern parts of the continent. In order to understand some of the differences and similarities between Canada and the United States, one should be familiar with the physical geography and resources of Canada and understand how these factors have played a part in the history of Canadian settlement and in the present expanding Canadian economy.

Canada is a self-governing, independent nation, with a total land area of 3,845,144 square miles, extending north-south about 2,800 miles (40 degrees of latitude). Canada also claims a sector of the Arctic Ocean extending to the North Pole, where the boundary touches an area claimed by the Soviet Union. Canada's width averages about 3,500 miles, and covers about 88 degrees of longitude, or about one-quarter of the distance around the world.

Canada's population of more than 15 million is spread along the southern sections of the country, with 70 per cent of the people living within 100 miles of the United States border. Central and northern Canada is not attractive to settlers chiefly because the growing season is short and the winters are long and cold. Although Canada and the United States were settled by the same racial stocks, and most of the present residents speak the same language, dress similarly, and carry on the same occupations, Canadian culture has a distinctive flavor.

Politically, Canada is a federal monarchy organized into ten provinces and two territories. Canada has the same sovereign as Britain, and is a member of the British Commonwealth of Nations, but is completely independent in both domestic and foreign relations.

The Canadian provinces fall into natural groupings. In the Atlantic provinces or Maritimes are Nova Scotia, New Brunswick, and Prince Edward Island. To this group, in 1949, was added Canada's tenth province, Newfoundland, which was formerly a self-governing Dominion in its own right. Central, or frequently "Eastern," Canada consists of the populous provinces of Quebec and Ontario. Quebec, Canada's largest province, is twice the size of Texas. Each of the Prairie provinces, Manitoba, Saskatchewan, and Alberta, is almost the size of Texas. In the far west is the mountain province of British Columbia, which covers an area as large as California, Oregon, and Washington together. Northern Canada is sparsely settled. This large area of 1.5 million squares miles remains in territorial status, being governed from the federal capital in Ottawa.

## PHYSICAL SETTING

### Relief Features

Canada has a great variety of landforms. Topographic features range all the way from extensive flat plains, like the Clay Belt south of Hudson Bay, to high, sharp-crested mountains like the Rockies. In a general way, the northern half of North America can be likened to a saucer in shape, with the center of the depression being occupied by shallow Hudson Bay and its adjoining lowlands. The outer parts of the continent tend to be high or rugged, whereas the interior areas are low or rolling (Figure 4-1).

**Appalachian-Acadian Region.** Maritime Canada is part of the Appalachian System which extends southwest-northeast through eastern North America. The mountains of the Appalachian System are represented by a series of arcing ranges, extending northeastward from the Green and White Mountains of New England. These low forested mountains are called the Boundary Ranges in southeastern Quebec where it borders Maine. Northeastward, elevations rise to over 4,000 feet in the flat-topped Shickshock Mountains of Gaspé Peninsula. A continuation of this system is found in western Newfoundland in the South and North Long Ranges, which have elevations of about 2,000 feet.

East of the linear mountains is a lower re-

*Figure 4-1  Many of the physiographic regions of Canada are continuous with those of the United States. Note that the Canadian Shield extends southward from Canada into the area around the Great Lakes.*

gion of hills, uplands, and plains, known as the Acadian section. Central New Brunswick is rough and hilly, but the eastern part, a poorly drained lowland, can be considered as a small-scale equivalent of the Atlantic Coastal Plain east of the Appalachians. This lowland includes all of Prince Edward Island province and the north coast slopes of Nova Scotia. The remainder of Nova Scotia is a rocky upland with elevations of 200 feet near the indented coast line and about 1,000 feet inland. Much of central Newfoundland is a rolling plateau about 1,000 feet high, which slopes to less than 500 feet on the east and northeast. The indented and island-ringed coast line rises so directly from the sea that there is very little lowland on the island.

**St. Lawrence Lowland.** The most important economic unit in Canada is the small St. Lawrence Lowland region. Although having only about one-fiftieth of the country's area, it has more than half the population, and produces almost three-quarters of the total value of Canadian manufactures. The Lowland is a northeastern extension of the Central Lowland region of North America. In Canada, it is broken into two sections by a rocky southern arm of the Canadian Shield which crosses the St. Lawrence River and appears as the Adirondack

Mountains of New York State. The eastern part of the St. Lawrence Lowland, in southern Quebec and especially around Montreal, is extremely flat. The western part of the Lowland —the peninsula between Lakes Huron, Erie, and Ontario—has a rolling surface resulting in part from glaciation.

**Canadian Shield.** The largest physiographic region in Canada is the Canadian Shield. It forms a huge horseshoe of almost two million square miles of ancient (Pre-Cambrian) rock around Hudson Bay. These worn-down hills and uplands have a rough, rocky, knobby character over most of their surface. Relief is seldom over 500 to 1,000 feet. There are many lakes of glacial origin and a few level areas marking the bottoms of former glacial lakes. One of these lowlands is now called the Clay Belt. Although the Canadian Shield is valuable for its mineral wealth, rough topography, thin soils, and poor drainage have limited settlement and transport.

In general the Shield has an upturned edge on the southeast, which gives a long inward slope, and long rivers which drain toward Hudson Bay. The outer edge of the Shield is highest in the upwarped, glaciated peaks of northern Labrador. Much of Quebec and northern Ontario is a rocky upland of about 2,000 feet altitude. Lower land covered by marine and lacustrine deposits along the Nelson River in northern Manitoba divides the Shield into an eastern and a western section. The northwestern part of the Shield has the same rocky hills and innumerable lakes that characterize its eastern section, but most elevations are under 2,000 feet.

**Hudson and James Bay Lowland.** West and south of Hudson Bay is the Hudson and James Bay Lowland. The section between Moose River, Ontario, and Churchill River, Manitoba, is underlain by flat-lying, sedimentary rocks, and therefore has a different landform character than the hard rocks of the Canadian Shield. The lowland is very flat and poorly drained. Streams wander slowly across the boggy surface, after having passed through several rapids across the Shield.

**Interior Plains.** The Interior, or Great, Plains consist of flat-lying sedimentary rocks located between the Canadian Shield and the Cordillera system of mountain ranges. The Plains rise in three levels across the southern part of the Prairie provinces. The Manitoba lowlands are generally under 1,000 feet in altitude, but the plains of southeastern Saskatchewan are about 2,000 feet above sea level. The upland of southwestern Saskatchewan and southern Alberta slopes upward from 2,000 feet to almost 5,000 feet at the base of the Rocky Mountains. In the Northwest Territories the plains narrow to the northward because of the eastward trend of the Shield. Although the plains are the largest area of favorable level topography in Canada, the shortness of the growing season toward the north has limited agricultural settlement.

**Cordilleran Region.** The Canadian Cordilleran region is much narrower than is its counterpart in the United States. The linear ranges and valleys are not so wide and the plateaus are smaller than those to the southward. Areas which are topographically favorable for settlement are also much smaller in the Canadian Cordillera (mountain systems) than in the mountains of the United States. The eastern rampart is the scenic Rocky Mountains which end in the plain along the Liard River of northern British Columbia. The eastern wall continues to the north in the Mackenzie Mountains, which curve westward toward the Brooks Range in northern Alaska. Along the Pacific, the Coast Ranges have some of the most spectacular scenery in Canada since they rise directly from sea level to 7,000 to 9,000 feet above the many twisting fiords which indent the coast. The highest mountains in Canada are found in the St. Elias Range of southwestern Yukon. These ranges continue across southern and central Alaska, being crowned by Mt. McKinley, and terminate in the Aleutian chain. Between the principal mountain systems are minor ranges and several broad plateaus incised by deep river valleys. The largest is the Interior Plateau of British Columbia. Farther north, the Yukon Plateau slopes westward through Alaska to a low plain along the coast of the Bering Sea.

**Arctic Islands.** It is merely for convenience that the Arctic Islands are considered a separate physiographic region; actually, there is very little uniformity of landforms throughout the islands. Topographic features range from the high, alpine, ice-capped peaks of Baffin, Devon and Ellesmere Islands, to the broad, extremely flat, lake-covered lowland of eastern Victoria, southern Prince of Wales, and King William Islands. Many of these northern islands are large. Baffin Island is as large as the province of Manitoba, or four times the size of New York State. Victoria Island is twice the size of Ohio, and Ellesmere Island is equal to Minnesota in area. Only since World War II, after air

photos were taken, have the outlines of the islands been known with any accuracy. The many channels between the islands are filled with solid or moving ice most of the year.

**Greenland.** Greenland is governed as a county of Denmark, with full local autonomy. Structurally, however, it is considered part of the North American continent. The east and west coasts have high mountains which come together at the southern tip of the island. Filling the space between the mountains, and rising above them in a broad dome, is the huge mass of ice which constitutes most of the surface of Greenland and overflows its edges in many places. The elevation of this icecap is about 10,000 feet above sea level in the central and southerly areas. Most Greenlanders live in the ice-free strip of fiorded coast along the southwestern edge.

*Figure 4-2 Glaciers are beautiful rivers of ice as they flow down from the coast mountains inland from Knight Inlet, British Columbia. Westerly winds which rise over the coast mountains drop their snowfall on the western slopes. The packed snow turns to ice and begins to move. (Courtesy of R.C. A.F.)*

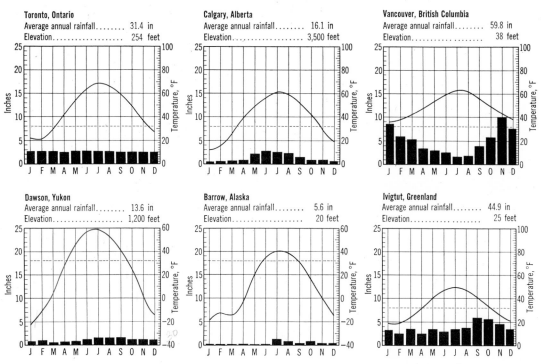

Figure 4-3   Climate graphs of Northern North America.

## Climate

There are many Canadian climates. These climatic regions range from areas of continuous cold to sections which are mild most of the year, from regions of very wet to extremely dry; and from areas of high heat in summer to icecaps where summer never comes (Figure 4-3).

To varying degrees, Canadian climates are influenced by two large bodies of water. The warm waters of the North Pacific bathe Canada's western shores. The air masses which pass over this water body bring mild temperatures to the west coast throughout the winter. The water keeps the summers cool. During winter, these mild, moist air masses drop heavy precipitation on the western slopes of the Cordillera as the air is forced upward to cross them.

The Arctic Ocean lies to the north of Canada. Cold waters from this source move southward and eastward into Hudson Bay and along the coast of Labrador. The cooling influence of the Arctic is thus carried far southward and into the interior of northeastern Canada. In ad-

dition, the Arctic Ocean is a source area for cold air masses along the northern mainland. In winter, these cold masses move southward from the Mackenzie River valley, spreading out over the Prairie provinces and moving into the United States. In summer, the cold air masses have a more easterly movement toward Hudson Strait. Northeastern Canada has an Arctic climate in summer, therefore, and remains cool because of the cold waters around the coast and the dominance of cold air masses above it. This Arctic climate, which covers about one million square miles of the country, is among the causes for the scanty economic development of this 27 per cent of Canada.

Since Canada is a large land mass in middle and northern latitudes, much of the climate is continental. The land mass cools off in winter, and all but the coastal strips are cold for several months. In summer the land heats up and most of southern Canada has many hot days.

The great indentation of Hudson Bay prevents the climate from being more continental. Although the bay contains cold water in sum-

VEGETATION ZONES OF CANADA

- Tundra
- Forest-tundra
- Open woodland
- Boreal forest
- Mixedwood forest
- Cordilleran forests
- Parkland
- Grassland
- Deciduous forest
- Acadian forest

0       500 MILES

GREENLAND

*Figure 4-4   East of the Cordilleran forests the vegetation zones of Canada trend in an east-west direction, as do the climate belts. Note that the zones are wider along the Atlantic shore than in the western part of the nation.*

mer and is frozen over in winter, it moderates the regional climate. For example, the section northwest of Hudson Bay, which is the coldest part of mainland Canada on a monthly average, is 30 degrees warmer than the coldest areas in the great land mass of the Soviet Union, in a comparable position and latitude. During the summer, the extremely cold areas of the Soviet subarctic warm up remarkably, but the Canadian cold regions are apt to remain cooler because of the marine effect. Furthermore, the smaller land area of Canada is not large enough for the occurrence of the extreme annual temperature range characteristic of Siberia in the northern interior of Asia.

## Vegetation

Since vegetation is a good indicator of climate, the map of vegetation zones can be considered suggestive of the climatic regions of Canada (Figure 4-4). Canada's forested area, although the third largest in the world, covers only one-third of her total area, about 1.3 million square miles. Because of unfavorable environmental conditions, about 45 per cent of this area is not considered capable of producing merchantable timber. The remaining 712,000 square miles is classed as productive forest.

Because of the variety of climates and landforms, Canada has several vegetation regions.

A small area of deciduous forest, similar to the northern hardwoods of the United States, is located in southwestern Ontario north of Lake Erie. Since these trees indicated favorable environmental conditions, most of the forest has been cut down and the area is now in agricultural land.

North of the Great Lakes and St. Lawrence River is a transitional forest zone known in Canada as the Great Lakes mixed forest region. It contains both deciduous and coniferous trees. The deciduous trees gradually disappear to the northward and are replaced by the more hardy conifers such as spruce, pine, balsam, and tamarack. This forest region, which is close to the industrial centers of the St. Lawrence Lowland, supplies much of the forest wealth of eastern Canada.

To the northward the Boreal (Northern) Forest region stretches from the coast of Labrador to northern British Columbia, Yukon Territory, and Alaska. It is almost entirely a coniferous forest, although there are stands of deciduous birch and aspen in the southern sections, notably across the central Prairie provinces. Within the region, there are innumerable lakes, swamps, muskegs, and bare rocky hills—all treeless areas which are the remnants of continental glaciation. The combination of rough topography, poor drainage, and harsh climate, which shows in the stunted forests, also indicates why so little of the area is settled and the few trading posts are so far apart.

North of the Boreal Forest about 27 per cent of Canada is in the treeless Arctic. The 50°F July isotherm, which defines the southern limit of the Arctic as a climatic region, coincides closely with the northern limit of tree growth. North of the tree line there is a 50- to 100-mile-wide zone of tundra vegetation, mosses, lichens, grasses, and low bushes. Beyond this, and over much of the Arctic Islands, tundra is confined to the lowlands. Most of the rocky hills and glacial deposits are bare. Another treeless area is the strip of grassland which lies south of the Boreal Forest in the Prairie provinces, but this is the result of low annual precipitation. In this prairie region is grown much of Canada's wheat.

The most arid part, near the Montana border, has considerable land in irrigation.

Owing to the variety of climates and landforms found in British Columbia, the vegetation regions are small and varied, differing in both area and vertical distribution. Many of the mountain ranges, particularly northward in Yukon Territory, rise above the tree line, thus greatly increasing the treeless area.

## Soils

Since agriculture has been confined to the southerly areas, soil types in Canada have not been completely mapped. Many of the soil zones are similar to those in the United States.

The best agricultural lands are the gray-brown forest soils in the St. Lawrence Lowland of Ontario and Quebec. Most of these soils are formed from glacial materials. The remainder of eastern Canada has generally poor, acid, leached soils called podsols. Soil cover is by no means complete in the Canadian Shield, where rocky ridges comprise much of the land, and poor drainage results in many lakes, swamps, and muskegs. The northern part of the region is underlain by permafrost (permanently frozen subsoil), which increases drainage problems and makes the soils cold for root crops. In eastern Canada, there are still a few million acres of arable land unoccupied and available for settlement. Areas of such soil are often isolated, however, and much of the surface is environmentally not favorable for crop production, particularly if agriculture is to be commercial, as Canadians desire, rather than subsistence.

The utilized soils of western Canada are found chiefly in the grassland and park-land vegetation regions. They have developed in areas of sedimentary rock but have been greatly modified by glacial deposition. Some of the soil zones are the same as those found in longitudinal arrangement across the Great Plains of the United States, but in Canada the pattern is concentric. The brown soils are in the center, in the driest parts of southern Alberta and Saskatchewan; around them are the dark-brown soils and farther outward are the black soils, which have more effective precipitation. North of Edmonton and Prince Albert, the gray forest soils are poorer, and clearing for agriculture has been slow. These soils extend northward into the Mackenzie River valley. The gray soils are areas of expanding pioneer settlement. At present, however, it appears more practical to develop marginal lands closer to the markets of southern Canada.

The soils of the Cordillera are quite complex, as might be expected in a mountainous region. The useful ones are limited in area and confined to narrow river valleys. Because of the heavy rainfall, some of the coastal soils, where they are not alluvial floodplain deposits, are strongly leached and are used mostly for dairying and grazing.

## POPULATION DISTRIBUTION

Canada's population of more than 15 million is spread thinly across the southern part of the country. More than half of the people are concentrated in the small area in southern Ontario and Quebec where the original settlements prospered and where history and environment have favored further expansion.

On the east, the island of Newfoundland has a total of only about 370,000 people. Since the fishing industry first drew settlers to the island, 90 per cent of the people live along, or very near, the coast. There is only one large city, the port of St. John's. The rest of the population is scattered around the coast in hundreds of small towns and villages ("outports"). The coast of Labrador, which is part of Newfoundland politically, is sparsely occupied; less than 10,000 people live in an area of 112,000 square miles.

The three Atlantic provinces have a total population of about 1.3 million, which has increased very slowly since the turn of the century. Because of limited economic opportunities on the eastern edge of Canada, population increases have been siphoned off to industrial Ontario or the agricultural West. Nova Scotia, with a rocky interior and good fishing banks offshore, has a coastal pattern of settlement. New Brunswick also has some coastal settlement, but the greatest concentration is along the valley of the St. John River in the western interior. Much of rough, forested northern and central New Brunswick is unoccupied. Tiny Prince Edward Island, Canada's smallest province, is almost fully occupied, as indicated by the virtually static population during the last fifty years.

The province of Quebec has almost 4.5 million people, the majority of them descended from the few thousand original French settlers. Most of the people live in the St. Lawrence Lowland, with smaller populated pockets northeast in the Saguenay Valley, and northward in the Clay Belt. This region has good soils for farming and nearby water power for operating the mills that provide many jobs. The industrious French-speaking people have had large families and have filled southern Quebec and adjoining areas with an energetic population, rural and urban. In the center of the southern Quebec population core, and a hub of transportation, is Montreal, Canada's largest city, which contains almost one-tenth of Canada's population.

With almost 5 million people, Ontario has the largest population of any Canadian province. As in Quebec, the southern tenth of the province has about 85 per cent of the population. The average density in this southern area is about 125 persons per square mile. During the last century, after most of the good soils were occupied, people began concentrating in the cities to process the agricultural, forest, and mineral resources of the region. Soon, southern Ontario became the industrial heart of Canada. Northern Ontario has a few cities which are based on mining, forestry, or transportation, but the over-all pattern of settlement is spotty. Northwestern Ontario, like most of central and northern Quebec, is still virtually untouched by white settlement. Unfavorable environmental conditions of topography, drainage, and climate indicate that these areas will remain empty for a long time to come.

Manitoba's population of about 800,000 is located principally in the narrow belt between Lake Winnipeg and the United States border. About one-third of the provincial population lives in the urban area of Winnipeg, Canada's fourth city. The remainder consists mainly of rural settlers on the fertile black soil to the westward. The northern two-thirds of this Prairie province is in the forested, lake-covered Canadian Shield, and is occupied chiefly by Indians. Although the Shield is being penetrated in Ontario and Quebec, the waves of settlers which entered the Prairie provinces after 1920 have not had time to push far into the western Shield.

Saskatchewan's population of 850,000 remained fairly stable from 1931 to 1951. The rural population, occupying large, mechanized farms, spread across the black and dark-brown soils. Average density of population ranges from 5 to 8 persons per square mile. The northern half of the province, in the stunted forests and lake-covered Shield, is almost unoccupied.

The width of the settled area across the prairies increases from east to west, and has its greatest extent in Alberta. This fast-growing province has more than one million people. The main belt of population concentration is in a south-north zone from Lethbridge through Calgary to Edmonton. The outlying pocket of agricultural settlement in the Peace River area is beyond the present limits of continuous settlement. Settlement has been confined primarily to the good soil zones and park-land forest belts, and is scanty in the areas of poorer natural environment. The discovery of mineral resources, notably petroleum, has supplemented the agricultural economy and has increased the size of the cities and stimulated manufacturing.

British Columbia is Canada's third province in population, but a great deal of its area is not easily habitable. Of the total population of 1.3 million, about half is concentrated in the one large urban area of Greater Vancouver in the southwest. In the surrounding lowland of the lower Fraser River to the east of the city there is an average population density of about 100 persons per square mile. The rest of the population is scattered along the linear valleys between the high mountain ranges of the southern and southeastern interior. The southwestern corner of the province has the best combination of climate, level land, and a variety of natural resources and power. Although population is increasing throughout the southern part of the province, the greatest increases continue to come to the southwestern corner.

TABLE 4-1. NORTHERN NORTH AMERICA

| Country or division | Area, sq miles | Population * |
|---|---|---|
| **Canada** | 3,845,144 | 14,430,000 |
| Alberta | 255,285 | 970,000 |
| British Columbia | 82,997 | 420,000 |
| Manitoba | 246,512 | 798,000 |
| New Brunswick | 27,985 | 526,000 |
| Newfoundland | 154,732 | 374,000 |
| Nova Scotia | 21,068 | 653,000 |
| Ontario | 412,582 | 4,766,000 |
| Prince Edward Island | 2,184 | 103,000 |
| Quebec | 594,860 | 4,174,000 |
| Saskatchewan | 251,700 | 843,000 |
| Northwest Territories | 1,301,903 | 9,096 |
| Yukon Territory | 207,076 | 9,096 |
| **Alaska** | 586,400 | 126,000 |
| **Greenland** | 840,000 | 23,000 |

* Primary data for 1956.

The two northern territories have but a few thousand people. Yukon Territory, a vast region of 207,000 square miles, has only 10,000 people, chiefly found in small settlements along the Yukon River. In the Northwest Territories, most of the 6,000 white inhabitants live along the Mackenzie River or on the shores of Great Slave and Great Bear Lakes. Although Canada is often cited for its northward movement of population, the numbers involved are still small, and most of the country's economic expansion is in the southern sections, or across middle Canada. In northeastern, or Arctic, Canada there are about 8,500 Eskimos; most of them live in the Northwest Territories, but some live on the coast of Arctic Quebec. These migratory people occupy the region with an average density of one Eskimo per 100 square miles. Eskimos do not live on the far northern group of Arctic Islands.

## THE REGIONS

### Atlantic Provinces and Newfoundland

**Relief Features.** The east coast regions of Canada are hilly, and in a subdued way have a wide variety of landforms (Figure 4-5). In northwestern New Brunswick is an upland surrounded by low mountains. This elevated basin opens to the northwest and forms the main pass and transport route into eastern Canada between New Brunswick and the densely settled lowlands of southern Quebec. The central part of New Brunswick is a rough, hilly area, with rounded peaks over 2,000 feet in elevation. These Central Highlands have a great reserve of forest cover, but otherwise are little used and are almost uninhabited. Eastern New Brunswick is a swampy, poorly drained lowland. Settlement is restricted to forestry centers at the

*Figure 4-5  The St. Lawrence Lowland is one of the best developed regions in Canada. Each region has its own cultural and physical characteristics.*

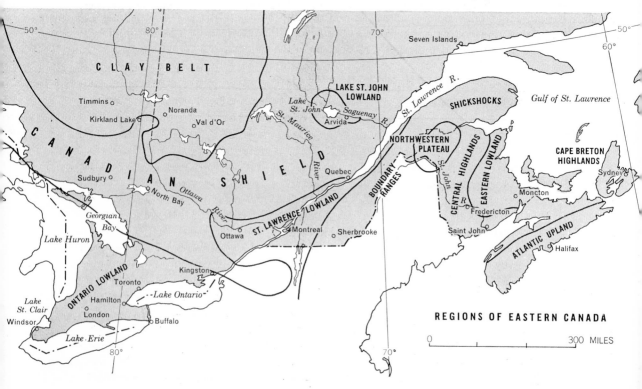

REGIONS OF EASTERN CANADA

0 _____ 300 MILES

river mouths and to small coastal villages, which combine subsistence agriculture with fishing. The Eastern Lowland includes Prince Edward Island and northwestern Nova Scotia, in both of which soils are more favorable than in eastern New Brunswick.

Most of Nova Scotia is a rocky, rough area of old rocks. Relief is not great, but nearly everywhere are rounded hills, steep slopes, and disrupted drainage. Most of the rolling upland rises directly from the sea in an indented coast line noted for its good harbors.

Newfoundland is an elevated plateau which is highest on the western side, where altitudes reach 2,000 feet. Poor drainage makes bogs, swamps, and barrens common. The east and northeast have an irregular coast line which provides sheltered harbors for fishing villages.

**Climate.** Eastern Canada has a marine climate with mild winters and cool summers in its coastal sections, changing to a humid-continental type with more severe winters and warm summers in the interior valleys and northwestern New Brunswick. In the same pattern, southeastern Newfoundland is the least cold part of the island, but the northern peninsula has a winter climate similar to Labrador and the nearby mainland. The frost-free season averages about 120 days in the more favored areas of some valleys. Many of the uplands, however, have a marginal climate for agriculture, with less than 80 days without frost.

On the coastal areas of Nova Scotia and Newfoundland precipitation averages more than 50 inches annually, but it decreases inland. It is evenly distributed throughout the year. A greater percentage falls as snow in the interior areas.

**Resources and Economic Development.** Although there are broad similarities in the physical environment of the four Atlantic provinces, local differences produce distinct variations in the major occupations of the people in each section. All of the region, however, suffers from its geographic position on the eastern edge of Canada. Its local population is too small to be

an adequate market, and it cannot export to the industrial areas of central Canada.

In Newfoundland fishing is the major economic activity. The interior of the island is often barren in places, soils are poor, and the summer climate cool with the result that agriculture is limited to a few of the more favored areas near the coast. Therefore, most of the people have turned to the sea for a living. The catch, mainly cod, generally comes from inshore waters within a few miles of the coast, and is salted or dried in the many small villages which dot the indented shoreline. Filleting and freezing plants are being established at the main settlements to improve the quality of the fish exported. Some fishermen, with larger schooners or new trawlers and better equipment, fish off the south coast of Labrador in summer, or join the fleets of other nations on the Grand Banks, southeast of the island.

Parts of the west coast and the northern interior of Newfoundland have a good cover of coniferous forest which is being used for pulp and paper. Because of its elevation and ample precipitation, there are many good waterpower sites on the island to assist forestry development.

Mining is carried on at only a few places in Newfoundland. On Bell Island, in Conception Bay, high-grade iron ore is dug from mines that extend out under the ocean. Much of the production moves to the coal deposits of Cape Breton Island to become the basis of the steel industry at Sydney, Nova Scotia. Lead and zinc are mined in central Newfoundland. St. Lawrence, near the southern tip of Burin Peninsula, is a major source of fluorspar, used in smelting and especially for aluminum manufacturing.

In Nova Scotia, most of the pockets of good valley land were occupied in the nineteenth century. Agricultural land is used chiefly for hay and pasture as a basis of a livestock and dairy industry. The major agricultural region is the Annapolis-Cornwallis Valley where apples are grown and mixed farming is practiced. The forested uplands of Nova Scotia, looking much like parts of New England, were a source of shipbuilding material in the last century, and still supply lumber for export and some pulpwood.

The sheltered harbors of an indented coast line, and one of the world's good fishing grounds offshore, have long been natural attractions for the fishing industry. As in Newfoundland, most of the Nova Scotia catch comes from inshore waters along the coast, but many schooners and draggers go out into international waters above the Sable Island Banks.

The complex rocks of Nova Scotia have produced a variety of minerals, but present output is small. Coal is obtained from the fields of eastern Cape Breton Island, which dip under the sea. This bituminous coal is of good grade and the reserves are large, but it is far from any major market in Canada, and cannot compete in central Canada with imported American coal. Nova Scotia is Canada's chief source of gypsum; it also produces salt for the fishing industry and barytes for petroleum drilling and paint.

The economic development of New Brunswick is based on the land. The long, fertile valley of the St. John River is a major agricultural region of the Atlantic provinces. Hay and pasture development indicates a mixed farming economy with emphasis in dairying. The upper valley, which adjoins the noted Aroostook potato region of Maine, specializes in potato production, partly for export.

About 80 per cent of New Brunswick remains in forest cover. Forests, used mainly for pulp and paper product, rank as the second source of wealth in the province. Mills are located at the mouths of rivers emptying along the northeast coast, and in the upper St. John River valley.

The herring fishery of the Bay of Fundy is important to parts of southern New Brunswick which have large canneries. There are a few fishing villages along the east coast, but fishing frequently only supplements the part-time subsistence farming of the French-Canadian settlers.

Prince Edward Island is sometimes called the garden province. Not only is it small in size, but it is almost completely cleared and fully used as farmland. The rolling lowland, nowhere over 500 feet, has distinct reddish soils which respond well to fertilizers. The island is noted for its disease-free seed potatoes which are exported, and for its high-quality livestock. Al-

*Figure 4-6   The indented coast of Nova Scotia has only scattered areas of agriculture. The remaining sections of the province are densely forested. The town of Chester, on Mahone Bay, is a summer resort. (Courtesy of R.C.A.F.)*

though agriculture is the major occupation of the people, there are a few fishing villages along the coasts. Charlottetown, the capital, is the only city on the island.

The Atlantic provinces have only a few cities. St. John's, the capital of Newfoundland, has most of the little amount of manufacturing which is done on the island. Cornerbrook, on the west coast of Newfoundland, is a major pulp and paper center, with one of the world's largest mills. Halifax, the capital of Nova Scotia, has a number of manufacturing industries based on imported raw materials. The city is most important as a port, but it is also the administrative and cultural center of the province. The port of St. John, with about 70,000 inhabitants, is the largest city of New Brunswick. Its manufactures are based both on local agricultural and forestry resources and upon imports. Fredericton, the capital, is mainly an administrative and educational center.

## St. Lawrence Lowland of Quebec and Ontario

**Relief Features.** The most important lowland in Canada lies between Lakes Huron, Erie, and Ontario and along the St. Lawrence River (Figure 4-5). Physiographically, southern Ontario and Quebec closely resemble the American states adjacent to the lower Great Lakes. There are also many similarities in the cultural landscape.

The eastern section of the St. Lawrence Lowland, which is mainly in southern Quebec but includes part of eastern Ontario, is much flatter than the western area. The Quebec lowland was once the bottom of an arm of the sea which extended into North America when the land was depressed at the end of the Ice Age.

The Ontario part of the lowland is more rolling with the Niagara Escarpment as its most notable landform feature. This sharp rise of several hundred feet extends across northern New York State, with a steep-facing north slope. The Niagara River flows over the escarpment, forming scenic Niagara Falls, which is slowly eating a gorge southward into the escarpment

wall. West of the Niagara River, the escarpment swings around the end of Lake Ontario, rising above the city of Hamilton, and extends northward to Bruce Peninsula, west of Georgian Bay. The east-facing escarpment has been crowned by several hundred feet of glacial debris north of London, and the resulting rolling upland is the highest part of southwestern Ontario.

**Climate.**   Southwestern Ontario has the highest monthly mean summer temperatures recorded in Canada, 70 to 73°F. Average summer temperatures decrease to the east and north. The flat southwestern corner of Ontario averages 175 frost-free days annually, the second longest period in the country. Sections near the lakes have 150 days, and all of the lowland has at least 125 frost-free days. Since southwestern Ontario has a longer growing season, in part because of its southerly latitude, crops can be grown there that are not found in the rest of the country.

In southwestern Ontario winters are mild, resembling those of eastern New York State. Severe winter cold, below zero degrees, occurs on only a few occasions during the usual winter. Temperatures decrease to the northeastward. Cold spells, when temperatures drop to −20 or −30°F, are possible in most winters. About half the Canadian population lives in winter conditions which are little different from those of Northeastern United States.

Annual precipitation is fairly evenly distributed seasonally. It follows the eastern Canadian pattern of decreasing from east to west. The Quebec lowland receives about 40 inches annually, decreasing to less than 30 inches in the southwest corner.

**Resources and Economic Development.**   Although manufacturing is the basis of population concentration and urban development of the St. Lawrence Lowland, behind it is a well-developed, prosperous agriculture. Much of the region had been settled by about 1850 and most of the good land was occupied and cultivated by 1900. With favorable level to rolling topography, a long frost-free period, and sufficient precipitation, a diversified agriculture developed. As the urban population increased with manufacturing, farming had the further advantage of a large local market.

Quebec lowland farms are good examples of a mixed farming economy with a dairy emphasis. Most of the land is used for hay, pasture, and oats, but most farms grow other grains and potatoes besides. Near the back of the long, narrow farm lies the wood lot, from which maple syrup and sugar are obtained each spring, and pulpwood is harvested. The Quebec habitant loves his land and cares for it well. Generally, his family is large, and the farm supplies much of its food. The main income is derived from the sale of wood products, livestock, and dairy produce. Near the large cities, as in other parts of North America, dairying and truck gardening become the major agricultural occupations.

Southern Ontario has a greater diversity of agricultural production, and tends to have more commercial crops than does Quebec. The southwestern part of the province has a climatic advantage over the rest of the lowland in that crops ripen two to four weeks earlier than in the rest of the region. Corn is a major crop in this southwestern peninsula, and the area is considered to be part of the Corn Belt. As in the American Corn Belt, winter wheat is grown in rotation, and soybeans are rapidly becoming a significant crop. In land use, this region looks quite similar to many parts of Ohio.

The sandy soils of the central north shore of Lake Erie are Canada's chief tobacco belt. It supplies about 90 per cent of the country's tobacco and has a surplus for export. Farms are generally small, having an average of about 30 acres in tobacco. Many of the farmers are Central European immigrants who entered Canada after World War I.

The north side of Niagara Peninsula, lying between Lakes Erie and Ontario, is one of Canada's three major fruit areas. At the base of the Niagara escarpment is a prosperous region where miles of well-kept orchards cover the fertile lowland east of Hamilton. It is Canada's main source of peaches and grapes, and has

about half of the Canadian supply of pears, cherries, and plums. The rest of peninsular Ontario is primarily a dairy region, looking quite similar to many parts of Wisconsin.

Mining is relatively unimportant in the St. Lawrence Lowland. The region is underlain by flat-lying sedimentary rocks, which dip gently to the west. Very large reserves of salt are under southwestern Ontario and eastern Michigan. Some of the earliest petroleum wells in North America came into production near Sarnia, Ontario, and the region still produces a little oil and natural gas. At several places across the lowlands, limestone is quarried for use as building stone or raw material for the chemical and fertilizer industries.

Forestry is relatively minor in southern Ontario, but achieves more importance near the edge of the Canadian Shield and in Quebec. Most of southern Ontario has been cleared for agriculture, but the furniture industry, originally based on local hardwoods, is still located west of Toronto.

The economic development of the St. Lawrence Lowland has been greatly aided by the Great Lakes and St. Lawrence River system which is a transportation artery and a source of electric power. The Great Lakes themselves are used by a large fleet of long lake freighters that carry iron ore and wheat during the nine-month navigation season. The return journey to the Duluth-Superior or Port Arthur–Fort William ports may bring coal or manufactured goods. To Canada, the Great Lakes trade is especially important for bringing wheat from the southern Prairie provinces to the flour mills of southern Ontario and Quebec, or to Ontario lake ports from which the wheat is moved by rail to Montreal for overseas export.

The only breaks in through navigation of the Great Lakes are at the Sault Ste. Marie rapids and at Niagara Falls. Both these hazards are now bypassed by wide canals 30 feet deep. The Great Lakes have been little used by ocean shipping because of the shallowness of the canals, 12 to 14 feet, which Canada built around the several rapids in the St. Lawrence River between Lake Ontario and Montreal.

The St. Lawrence–Great Lakes Seaway project has dams and canals under construction which will enable ocean-going vessels to penetrate to the Great Lakes ports. The project is the greatest single development under construction on the continent. The cost, about 5 billion dollars, is being shared between Canada and the United States, and the project will require many years to complete. It has the dual purpose of improving navigation and producing hydro-electric power. The seaway will provide a channel at least 27 feet deep and open the whole of the Great Lakes to ocean shipping. Vessels up to 20,000 tons will be able to use the channels and canal locks. Cities on the Great Lakes will become ocean ports. The Middle Western section of the United States and much of the most populous part of Canada will be benefited. Installations at the dams will generate over 12 billion kilowatthours of electricity. This power will attract chemical plants and many other industrial establishments. The chief natural handicap will be the blocking of navigation by ice during three or four months each winter.

The Great Lakes–St. Lawrence system is a major source of electric power for parts of the Canadian lowland. The chief developed site in southern Ontario is at Niagara Falls; the main source of energy in southern Quebec is at Beau-

harnois, near Montreal. Each of these power plants produces over a million horsepower. Their power output is comparable to that of Hoover Dam in the United States.

The lowlands of southern Ontario and Quebec produce about three-quarters of the value of manufacturing in Canada, and the largest share of this industry is in Ontario. This region is, therefore, similar to the heavy manufacturing belt which lies south of the Great Lakes in the United States. Manufactures include iron and steel (Hamilton), automobiles (Windsor), clothing (Montreal), shoes (Quebec), petroleum refining and chemicals (Sarnia), rubber goods (Kitchener), cereals and machinery (London), nonferrous smelting and refining (Montreal), electrical goods and agricultural machinery (Toronto), and pulp and paper (Three Rivers). Canadian manufacturing plants resemble those south of the border, and, in fact, many Canadian industries are but the branch plants of large American companies. Much of the increased population and expanding resource production of Canada can be attributed to the energetic industries and busy cities of southern Ontario and southern Quebec.

The St. Lawrence Lowlands have about half of the population of Canada. In the region are 18 of the 34 Canadian cities with more than

*Figure 4-7 Aerial view of the Thousand Islands Bridge (Ivy Lea) spanning the St. Lawrence River, Ontario. (Courtesy of Canadian Government Travel Bureau.)*

*Figure 4-8   Aerial view of Montreal, Quebec. (Courtesy of Canadian Government Travel Bureau.)*

30,000 people. Greater Montreal, with 1.25 million people, has as large a population as the whole province of British Columbia. Greater Toronto, with about 1 million persons, has almost as many people as the three Atlantic provinces. The total population of the next three large cities—Hamilton, Ottawa, and Quebec—is about equal to the total population of any one Prairie province. Most of the cities scattered across the lowlands are located on the Great Lakes or St. Lawrence system, owing to original settlement along this route. Other cities are found on excellent road and rail connections away from the Great Lakes area. The cities are spaced fairly evenly, indicating the relative importance of the surrounding agricultural hinterland upon urban growth.

## Canadian Shield

**Relief Features.** The Canadian Shield has as its base hard, worn-down rocks of Pre-Cambrian geological age, which are some of the oldest known on earth. These roots of mountains are now mainly rocky, knobby hills. The sky line is fairly even, indicating that the region was reduced by erosion to a peneplain and later uplifted to make a plateau. The surface of the upland is locally rough. There are numerous rivers, most of which have rapids, and a myriad of lakes of irregular shape and size.

The Shield extends in a huge semicircle around Hudson Bay (Figure 4-9). The eastern section has been upwarped in northern Labrador, where alpine peaks and ridges rise sharply above a fiorded coast line to heights of 4,000 to 5,000 feet. Elevations decrease to the southward, where the southern rim of the Shield rises steeply 1,000 to 2,000 feet above the Gulf of St. Lawrence and the estuary of the St. Lawrence River.

Eastward in Ontario the Shield's outer edge has altitudes of 1,500 feet. The steep, rocky shores of Lake Superior are indented with many sheltered harbors. Since drainage divides are close to the Great Lakes, the longest rivers of the Shield empty toward the central area which is occupied by shallow, cold Hudson Bay. Knobby rock hills again become characteristic, with altitudes of about 1,500 feet, east of Great Slave and Great Bear Lakes. The slope is eastward to the broad, poorly drained lowland west of Hudson Bay, or northward to a similar, but smaller, lowland along the Arctic coast.

Within the large area of the Shield there are lowlands which are distinct physiographic subregions. Two of these, for example, are the Clay Belt and the Lake St. John Lowland. The former was created during the wane of the last Ice Age when a large glacial lake, Ojibway, which formed in front of the ice, was prevented from draining southward by the northward slope of the Shield. After the disappearance of the lake, a gently undulating plain was left over about 30 million acres. Only part of this area is potentially arable, for the frost-free period is short, soils are poor and sandy, and drainage is inadequate. Nevertheless, these two lowlands contain much of the region's population.

**Climate.** The climate of the Canadian Shield is almost that of Canada, since the Shield covers such a large area. The section northwest of Hudson Bay is the coldest part of mainland Canada, averaging January temperatures of $-25°F$. Only the southeastern part of the Shield, from southern Labrador to Lake Superior has a January average above $0°F$. Although winters are cold, they do not prevent work continuing in the mines and forests. Summer temperatures show a wide range according to latitude. The northern sections of the Shield have a true Arctic climate, with no month averaging above $50°F$. The longest frost-free period, 140 days, is found northeast of Georgian Bay. Most of the southern fringe between Lake Superior and the north shore of the St. Lawrence River has 100 days or more free of frosts.

Precipitation decreases to the west and north from about 40 inches annually in southern Labrador and the north shore of the Gulf of St. Lawrence. Much of the annual precipitation is snow and the hilly areas, just north of the population centers of the Quebec Lowland, have

*Figure 4-9 The Canadian Shield from the eastern boundary of the Mackenzie Valley. This view, taken near Yellowknife, Northwest Territories, shows the stunted forest, low rocky hills, and many small lakes that are characteristic of the Shield. (Courtesy of R.C.A.F.)*

become popular for winter sports and resorts. In the Northwest Territories, the Shield receives only 10 inches of precipitation, since the cold air which passes over the region contains very little moisture, and there are few topographic barriers to help cause rainfall.

**Resources and Economic Development.** Most of the population in the Shield is engaged in the extractive industries, such as mining or forestry. Since exploiting these primary resources does not need a large population, the growth and, therefore, the possibilities of large-scale permanent settlements in the Shield center about agriculture. Well-developed agriculture requires level to rolling topography, good soils, and favorable climate. These requirements are met only in some of the former glacial lake bottoms in the southern part of the Shield. The largest area of potential agricultural land, a small part of which is occupied, lies in the Clay Belt. The exact amount of good agricultural land is not yet known, but it is probably between 5 and 10 million acres.

Settlement moved into the Clay Belt in the early part of this century, following the railway lines which were built across the Shield. Most of the communities grew up as mining or forestry centers, but around these, where the character of the land permitted, agriculture slowly developed. In Quebec settlement has been more compact, in parish villages, with community life and facilities which have encouraged the hardy French-Canadian pioneers to remain in the region.

The Canadian Shield is the storehouse of minerals, which, as it slowly opens, is one of the bases of the optimistic, expanding economy of Canada. Mining is the major occupation of many people, and the reason for most cities and much of the transportation in the Shield. The ancient hard rocks have undergone widespread mineralization. Thousands of centuries of erosion have exposed many deposits formed deep underground. Few minerals of the Shield were exploited until recently, and the developments are still mainly on the outer edges of the region.

In the far eastern section a large deposit of high-grade iron ore came into production in 1954. Extending across the Labrador (Newfoundland)–Quebec boundary, this 100-mile iron zone contains a reserve of at least 500 million tons of ore. The deposit has economic significance since it is being developed at a time when the high-grade Mesabi ores of the United States are seriously depleted. Ore is shipped to Eastern United States ports and to Great Lakes steel centers. To the southward, near the Gulf of St. Lawrence, North America's largest deposit of titanium came into production in 1950. The ore is carried up the St. Lawrence River to the plentiful electrical power obtained at Sorel, Quebec, for processing.

The chief gold mining belt, which is mainly responsible for making Canada a leading world gold producer, is located near the Ontario-Quebec boundary. Among important gold centers are Kirkland Lake, Larder Lake, and Timmins, in Ontario, and Noranda and Val d'Or in Quebec.

North of Georgian Bay, at Sudbury, is the world's chief source of nickel, where several mines account for 70 to 75 per cent of the world's supply of this strategic metal. The region is also Canada's main source of copper, which is a by-product of the nickel ore. In addition, this rich mineral zone produces a large share of the world's output of certain lesser known, but valuable, minerals such as platinum and palladium. Canada's dominance of world nickel production was further increased in 1954 when the new deposits discovered at Lynn Lake, in northwestern Manitoba, began moving to the smelter near Edmonton.

The Lake Superior region has been noted for its iron ore in the United States, but only smaller discoveries were made on the Canadian side until deposits at Algoma and Steep Rock were developed. From these properties millions of tons of iron ore are annually exported to the United States. Modern geophysical methods of prospecting, chiefly from the air, have found several large iron deposits, as well as other minerals. Thus, the Lake Superior region, close to water power and water transport, has a promising future.

The northwestern part of the Shield was but scantily prospected prior to World War II. Basic information on geology and mineralization is still being gathered. The newest mining center is at Uranium City, north of Lake Athabaska, which began producing pitchblende in 1953. This deposit, along with the production of the older mine at Port Radium on Great Bear Lake, places Canada among the leaders in the production of this valuable ore which is the source of radium and uranium.

Much of the southern part of the Shield is densely forested, but northward, where the climate is more severe in summer, the trees become smaller and less numerous. The forest is Canada's chief source of pulpwood logs and supplies much lumber from its southern section. Quebec, with the largest area of Shield forest, produces 50 per cent of Canada's pulp, while Ontario has 30 per cent. Numerous large, modern pulp and paper mills are scattered throughout the southern Shield, usually located on rivers, and served by railways. They are turning the forests into newsprint paper, which often ranks as Canada's most valuable export, going mainly to the United States. It has been estimated that three out of every five newspapers in the world are printed on Canadian newsprint paper.

The pulp and paper mills are generally situated at the mouths of rivers which carry log rafts and furnish the needed water power. Mills are found on the north shore of the St. Lawrence estuary, throughout the Saguenay and Lake St. John Lowland, up the St. Maurice River valley, in the Ottawa River valley, and along the north shore of Lake Superior. Within the Shield proper, only a few of the northward-flowing rivers are utilized. The western part of the Shield, although well-forested on its southern edges, is little exploited as yet since it is farther from the market in Northeastern United States.

The Canadian Shield has the greatest amount of developed and potential water power of any of the physiographic regions of Canada. Its large size and a number of physical advantages account for the Shield's water power resources.

Precipitation is adequate throughout the southern sections. The poorly drained surface of the Shield, with its innumerable, interlocking lakes, forms an excellent reservoir area. The southward-flowing rivers have a notable drop, or fall line, where they spill over the edge of the Shield to the Great Lakes or St. Lawrence Lowland. To these natural advantages must be added the factor of location with regard to the population concentrations of eastern Canada, and markets in the industries of the St. Lawrence Lowland.

More than half the developed water power of Canada is in Quebec, which produces more than 6 million horsepower. The largest single area of developed power in Canada is in the Saguenay Valley, meant primarily to serve the aluminum center of Arvida. Other concentrations of developed power are along the Ber-

*Figure 4-10 Clerk at Hudson's Bay Company post at Arctic Bay, 1,200 miles from North Pole, with Arctic fox skins, both white and blue. (Courtesy of Hudson's Bay Company.)*

simis, St. Maurice, and Ottawa Rivers. Each valley produces about 2 million horsepower from several large dams. The Winnipeg River in Manitoba has a large hydroelectric power plant and another site used by a paper company. The Shield sections in Manitoba and Saskatchewan have many potential power sites, but the demand for power is less since the mining and pulp industries are not fully developed. As Canadian industries and settlement push northward into the Shield one of the big advantages is the potential hydroelectric power which is well dispersed and easily available.

Many parts of the Shield are completely unoccupied and some sections are inhabited by only a few hundred migratory Indians who still follow a hunting and trapping life. Rural population tends to be rather sparse, whereas a high percentage of the settlement is found in urban centers. These towns and cities are all located along the few major transport lines—rail, road, or water. Most of the settlements are supported by the extractive industries of mining and forestry, but there are also towns which are transportation hubs, supply centers, or at water power sites. Since most of the cities are new they have a pleasant, clean appearance. Stores are modern and homes are neat and well built. There is little of the frontier character in Shield cities, although they are the "new north" for eastern Canada.

Most of the large cities are in northern Ontario. They include the mining centers of Sudbury, Timmins, and Kirkland Lake, and the transportation cities of Port Arthur–Fort William, Sault Ste. Marie, and North Bay. The largest group of settlements in the Quebec Shield is in the Saguenay–Lake St. John Lowland. The St. Maurice Valley has the industrial city of Shawinigan Falls located on the fall line at the edge of the Shield.

## Interior Plains

**Relief Features.** Although the Interior Plains are frequently dismissed with the word "flat," there are actually several physiographic features which break the monotony of the flat areas. Of four main subdivisions (Figure 4-11),

the three southern sections increase in elevation from east to west—from 800 feet near Lake Winnipeg to above 4,000 feet in the Rocky Mountain foothills.

The Manitoba Lowland coincides generally with the area covered by ancient glacial Lake Agassiz; in the southern part it is drained by the sluggish meandering Red River. To the northwest, the lowland rises through a series of old gravel terraces and beach lines to an abrupt escarpment which forms the eastern boundary of the Saskatchewan Plain. In general, the rolling character of this plain is the result of the entrenchment, by downward erosion, of the rivers and their tributaries into a cover of glacial deposits.

The Alberta Plateau has level to rolling topography similar to the Saskatchewan Plain but altitudes are higher. There is greater dissection in Alberta, where the rivers have cut 100 to 200 feet into the glacial drift and sedimentary bedrock. Above the plateau rise hills of more resistant rock, such as the Cypress Hills, 4,700 feet. The Alberta Uplands at the foot of the Rockies are more hilly than the plateau. The drainage is to the northeastward, through the Athabaska, Peace, and Hay Rivers, toward the Arctic Ocean.

**Climate.** Summer temperatures show very little variation over the large area of the Interior Plains. The southern prairies typically have many searing hot days followed by cool nights. Average monthly temperatures in winter decrease from southwest to northeast. In general, the winter weather conditions of clear, cold days, and occasional blizzards, are similar to those experienced in the adjoining states of Montana and North Dakota.

The areas having the longest frost-free period, 120 days, are located in the western part of the Red River Plain, and along the South Saskatchewan River in southern Alberta. Most of the Manitoba Lowland, Saskatchewan Plain, and southern Alberta has an average frost-free period of more than 100 days, which is generally sufficient for the maturing of grain.

The Interior Plains receive scant rainfall

which may vary widely from the average. The greatest annual precipitation, 20 inches, is received in southern Manitoba and along the foothills of southwestern Alberta. Precipitation decreases toward the interior to a minimum of about 12 inches along the central part of the South Saskatchewan River. More important than annual precipitation, however, is the seasonal distribution. In Saskatchewan, for example, 80 per cent of the annual amount falls during the six summer months from April to October when it is most useful for agriculture.

**Resources and Economic Development.** Agriculture is the major occupation of the people of the Interior Plains and is closely related to types of soil, climate, and vegetation.

Ranching is the characteristic form of land use across the brown soils of southwestern Saskatchewan and southeastern Alberta. For the Canadian plains, these areas do have a long frost-free period, but the precipitation of about 12 inches is marginal for agriculture. The average ranch covers 10,000 to 15,000 acres, not all of which, however, is productive grassland. Ranching is also carried on in the southern Foothills Belt southwest of Calgary.

Irrigation is one of the means of making this dry region productive. The common method of irrigation is by small dugouts or earthen dams. Both types are used to supplement yields produced by normal dry-farming practices. On the other hand, the large dams and irrigation projects, chiefly located in Alberta, bring water to land which could not produce if it were not for the irrigation works. It has been estimated that about three million acres of land could be irrigated in the southern Prairie provinces, about one million acres of which are now served by irrigation projects. Compared with the present

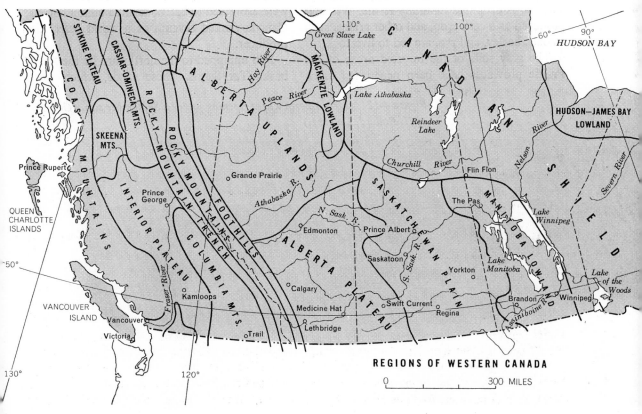

*Figure 4-11   The regions of western Canada are largely the result of physical factors with the mountain influence dominating.*

REGIONS OF WESTERN CANADA

0                    300 MILES

60 million acres under cultivation in the region, it is apparent that irrigation acreage can be but a small percentage of the total farmland.

On the dark-brown soils, wheat uses 70 per cent of the cultivated acreage. Prairie wheat production is essentially a one-crop economy which is made possible by continued and increasing use of chemical fertilizers. Another feature of the wheat belt is the increasing size of farms resulting from mechanization. Amalgamation of farms and the decreased need for hired farm labor cut rural population. Neighbors are far apart in this flat, lonesome region where many farms cover a full section of 640 acres. The great wheat production of the region, 400 to 600 million bushels annually, and the low density of population, mean that the southern prairies are one of the world's important food surplus regions.

The black soil zone is favorable environmentally for mixed farming. Precipitation is more effective, as indicated by the park-land vegetation of tall grasses and groves of trees. The soil is deep and naturally fertile. Wheat is produced as a cash crop, and other grains, such as oats, barley, and rye, are fed to livestock.

The gray soils of the forested areas of the Prairie provinces have been penetrated much more slowly than the grasslands. Poorer soils, time and cost of clearing, and lack of transportation have all been factors in delaying settlement. The pioneer fringe of agriculture trends northwestward across the Interior Plains from Lake Winnipeg to the Peace River area of British Columbia. Land use generally emphasizes grain and pasture production, but legume seed, which has high value for its small bulk, is an important cash crop.

The sedimentary rocks of the Plains yield different types of minerals than the hard rocks of the Shield. Petroleum is the most spectacular of the mineral resources. Although several small fields had been discovered before World War II, the first big fields were found in the Edmonton area in 1947–1948. Their use was furthered by building pipelines eastward to Lake Superior, and then across Michigan to Sarnia, Ontario, to reach the people of southern Ontario; pipelines run westward to Vancouver to supply the Pacific Coast province and adjoining states to the south. In 1955, Canadian petroleum reserves were estimated to be about three billion barrels. Canada ranked seventh as a world petroleum producer.

Still untapped to the northward lie the Athabaska Tar Sands. These sands, which cover

*Figure 4-12    Hard Alberta wheat ripening under a September sun. (Courtesy of H. Pollard, Calgary.)*

about 20,000 square miles along the Athabaska River around Fort McMurray, contain a petroleum reserve estimated at about one hundred billion barrels, about equal to the world's present known reserves of liquid petroleum. Although the petroleum has been separated from the sand experimentally, it has not yet been done economically.

Alberta also has large reserves of natural gas. The chief production comes as a by-product of the Turner Valley oil field, southwest of Calgary, and from the large gas fields of Viking-Kinsella, southeast of Edmonton. There are numerous smaller fields.

The Canadian Interior Plains have coal reserves which rank among the world's largest. Southern Alberta and Saskatchewan have a reserve of 75 billion tons, chiefly bituminous. Production is minor, however, because the coal is too far from the industrial and population centers in the St. Lawrence Lowland. Locally, coal meets strong competition from petroleum and natural gas.

With large reserves of petroleum, natural gas, and coal, it seems likely that industry will move to these power sources, particularly in Alberta. The general character of the plains region is changing from a dominant agricultural economy to one where manufacturing is more significant. Some of this manufacturing may be related to chemical production, for the plains also produce salt, sodium sulfate, gypsum, and limestone, and have large reserves of potash.

At present the Interior Plains are sparsely populated. Large parts of the northern sections are unpopulated. In the south, most of the area averages 5 to 8 persons per square mile. Winnipeg, with one-third of the people of Manitoba, is the largest city of the plains. Its strategic transportation position south of Lake Winnipeg in the center of southern Canada forces all east-west transport lines to funnel through it. Edmonton, which is Canada's fastest growing city, and Calgary are headquarters of the Alberta oil industry, but also have sound agricultural hinterlands. Regina and Saskatoon, the chief cities of Saskatchewan, are smaller, and are mainly supply service centers.

## Cordillera of British Columbia and Yukon

**Relief Features.** The Cordilleran mountain system in British Columbia is compressed into a width of about 600 miles of spectacular rugged grandeur (Figure 4-13). The alignment pattern of the mountain ranges and plateaus is similar to that of the United States section of the Cordillera, but the width of the system in Canada is not as great.

The Rocky Mountains rise abruptly above the plains to form the eastern range of the Cordillera. They are a nearly continuous wall of sharp peaks and ridges broken only by a few passes. Some of the most spectacular mountain scenery in North America is found in Banff and Jasper National Parks. Several peaks rise to altitudes of over 10,000 feet, and the highest peak is Mt. Robson, 12,972 feet. The Rocky Mountains decrease in altitude northward and terminate in the broad plain of the Liard River in northeastern British Columbia. Another mountain system, the Mackenzie Mountains—not in the same line, but offset to the northeast—arcs along the Yukon–Northwest Territories boundary, and swings across north central Yukon as the Ogilvie Mountains. Another arc of this eastern system of mountains rises above the Mackenzie River delta and extends westward along the Arctic coast as the Brooks Range of Alaska.

The western boundary of the Rocky Mountains is the Rocky Mountain Trench, one of this continent's outstanding topographic features. The Trench is a linear valley, some 1,200 miles in length, extending from south of Flathead Lake, Montana, to the southern Yukon. This generally flat-bottomed valley, 2,000 to 3,000 feet above sea level, varies in width from 2 to 10 miles. It is an important, strategic through route running southeast-northwest through the mountain masses of the Cordillera. West of the Trench lie two high mountain systems, which are distinct from the Rockies. In the south is the Columbia Mountain system and to the north, the Cassiar-Omineca Mountains which form the western wall of the Trench, and extend into Yukon Territory. The Interior

Plateau of British Columbia is comparable in position to the Colorado and Columbia Plateaus of the United States. Narrow in the south, it broadens to the northward and is deeply entrenched, particularly in the south, by the Fraser and other rivers.

The Coast Mountains rise in row after row of jagged peaks above the ocean in southwestern British Columbia. Since several of the peaks are above 9,000 feet (Mt. Waddington, 13,-260 feet), and tower above an indented, fiorded coast, the relief is much greater than in the eastern ranges such as the Rockies. The Coast Mountains are less of a wall to the northward where they are broken by the Skeena, Nass, and Stikine Rivers.

Off the west coast of British Columbia is a partly submerged mountain range, of which Vancouver Island and the Queen Charlotte Islands are the main masses. This mountain system continues northward in the many rugged islands off the Panhandle of Alaska. A high wall of mountains appears in northwestern British Columbia and southwestern Yukon in the St. Elias Mountains, having the highest peaks in Canada. These spectacular, ice-capped mountains, which discharge glaciers out to the Alaskan coast, have several peaks above 15,000 feet. The highest peak in Canada, crowning this range, is Mt. Logan, 19,850 feet.

**Climate.** Since the Cordillera of British Columbia and Yukon has a north-south extent of about 1,400 miles, it shows a wide variety of climates. These range from the mildest Canadian weather in winter, in southwestern British

*Figure 4-13 The Rocky Mountain Trench is a 1,200-mile-long trough in the Cordillera. In the picture the Trench is occupied by the Fraser River flowing northward. The wall of the Rocky Mountains rises on the right (east) and the Caribou Mountains of the Columbia System on the left. (Courtesy of British Columbia Government.)*

Columbia, to the cold Arctic Coast of northern Yukon Territory. The area has the wettest station in Canada, on western Vancouver Island where an average annual precipitation of 250 inches is recorded, and the driest station in southern Canada only 250 miles eastward in the Interior Plateau.

Winters are mild on the coast, averaging about 35°F in January, but temperatures decrease rapidly inland and northward to a January mean of −20°F in central Yukon. The marine influence keeps summers cool in the coastal strip, but the southern interior valleys can become quite hot. Although summers are slightly cooler to the northward there are not the wide differences that exist in winter.

Annual precipitation is heavy on the exposed west coast, which is struck by storms from the Aleutians during the winter. Most stations average 100 inches or more, each having a definite winter maximum. A dry summer is characteristic of the southern coastal sections. Because of the protective rain shadow effect of the Coast Mountains the interior areas are dry. From 10 to 20 inches are the usual amounts recorded, with effectiveness (lower evaporation) increasing to the northward.

**Resources and Economic Development.** Forestry is the most valuable industry of the Cordilleran region. The mild, wet climate of the coast section has endowed the area with some of the world's largest trees. The lumbering economy which characterizes Washington and Oregon extends northward into British Columbia. The forests of Douglas fir, western cedar, and hemlock are rapidly being cut to make this region one of the world's major sources of export lumber. Most of the industry is concentrated on Vancouver Island and the southwestern coast, with the large mills being located around the mouth of the Fraser River and at good harbors on the island.

Mining is characteristic of most mountainous areas, and the Canadian Cordillera has been fortunate in having its share of mineralization. At Kimberley, in southeastern British Columbia, is one of the world's largest lead-zinc-silver mines, which in some years has produced as much as 10 per cent of the world's lead. The concentrates from this big mine are transported by rail to the smelter and refinery at Trail, on the Columbia River, which is near the hydroelectric power of the Kootenay River. There are several other mines in this Kootenay region producing a variety of base metals. Copper and coal are mined in southwestern British Columbia.

The famous Klondike gold rush of 1898 was the reason for the establishment of Yukon Territory in the Canadian Northwest. Goldseekers moved northward along the Inside Passage steamer route to Skagway, Alaska, and crossed the Coast Mountains to the headwaters of the Yukon River. They then floated downstream to the rich alluvial gravels of the Dawson region and the tributaries of the Klondike River. Within a decade, however, most of the easily accessible gold had been found and the boom was over. Gold production is now supplemented by rich silver-lead deposits near Mayo, which have proved valuable enough to be connected by an all-season road with the railhead at Whitehorse, Yukon.

Fishing is an important occupation along the coast, and the reason for many small settlements. As in the Panhandle of Alaska, salmon fishing is the most valuable part of the industry. Starting in midsummer in Alaska, and by late summer in southern British Columbia, the salmon begin arriving off the river mouths to migrate upstream to spawning grounds. The Nass, Skeena, and particularly the Fraser, which has the largest drainage basin, are the chief salmon rivers. Canneries are distributed along the coast to be near the fishing grounds, with the largest canneries being located near the mouth of the Fraser River.

Halibut fishing ranks second in importance to salmon and centers on Prince Rupert. Halibut are caught in the deep waters around the Queen Charlotte Islands. Fishing for herring during the winter allows year-round use of many vessels which are operated during the summer salmon runs. Herring are processed into oil and fertilizer.

Water power is abundant. As a mountainous province, with heavy rainfall on the coast, it is not surprising that British Columbia has a water power potential as large as that of the state of Washington. The main disadvantages are that the rainfall is seasonal, and many of the coastal rivers are short. Most of the developed power of the province is found near the southwestern

*Figure 4-14   Looking north over Vancouver, British Columbia. The agricultural lands of the Fraser River delta are in the foreground. The city is in the center and the sheltered harbor is in the upper right. (Courtesy of British Columbia Government.)*

corner where most of the people and industries are, but potential power sites are well scattered. Near the central west coast, the headwaters of the Nechako River, a tributary of the Fraser, were dammed and diverted through the Coast Mountains by tunnel to produce hydroelectric power for a large aluminum smelter built at tidewater at Kitimat. Similar diversions of the Yukon River headwaters to the heads of coastal fiords are possible in northwestern British Columbia and Panhandle Alaska.

Agriculture is confined to the narrow valleys, less than 1 per cent of the province being in cultivation. Half of the cultivated land is in the southwest, across the Fraser River delta and along the east coast of Vancouver Island. In the southern interior of the province, the Okanagan Valley uses irrigation to produce more than half of Canada's apples, many of which are exported. This narrow valley also competes with the Niagara Peninsula of Ontario as Canada's chief source of cherries, peaches, and pears. The largest areas of level to rolling land and potential arable land are across the railway belt of central British Columbia, from Prince George to Prince Rupert, and in the well-established grain farms of the Peace River area east of the Rockies.

Agriculture has been carried on in the valleys of Yukon Territory since the gold rush days at the turn of the century. It declined in importance with the decrease in population when the rush was over. Most agriculture now consists of gardening in each of the small settlements, where vegetables, hardy grains, and grasses grow quite well.

British Columbia has ranked as Canada's fastest growing province for two decades, and in this characteristic is similar to the Western states of the United States. Most of the population has concentrated in the southwestern corner which has a mild climate, some good agricultural land, forest resources, fisheries, and excellent ports. Half the province's 1.3 million people are in the Greater Vancouver area, which includes New Westminster on the Fraser River. The capital and second city of the province is Victoria on southern Vancouver Island.

Interior cities are smaller and usually perform some particular local service.

Although the Yukon Territory had 30,000 people at the turn of the century, the population had fallen to about five thousand in 1940. About one-third of the present population of approximately ten thousand is located in the crossroads town of Whitehorse, on the Alaska Highway and at the head of rail from Skagway, Alaska. The historic mining center of Dawson is almost a ghost town with fewer than one thousand persons.

## Northwest Territories

**Relief Features.** The Northwest Territories cover one-third of Canada, hence one would expect to find a variety of landforms. The Territories comprise three administrative districts. Mackenzie District, on the west, is essentially the broad Mackenzie River lowland, but also includes the northwestern part of the Canadian Shield. The Mackenzie Lowland is a flat, poorly drained plain of glacial deposition, into which the wide Mackenzie River has cut a valley about 100 to 200 feet in depth.

Keewatin District lies west and northwest of Hudson Bay. A poorly drained, lake-dotted lowland, with a mixture of water-laid and glacial deposits, extends inland, mantling or subduing the rocky hills of the Canadian Shield.

Franklin District includes all the Arctic Islands outside of Hudson Bay, and also Melville and Boothia Peninsulas on the mainland. There is no uniformity of landforms in the Arctic Islands. The eastern islands have a long mountain range which is the highest in eastern North America. The upwarped, eroded edge of eastern Baffin Island rises to altitudes of 7,000 to 8,000 feet, with similar altitudes reported in northern Ellesmere Island. Small icecaps crown many of these high areas. To the westward, the islands slope to broad, barren plateaus, which in many places rise directly from the sea. The central part of the southern group of islands is a flat, lake-covered lowland, rising a few hundred feet in sloping ancient beach lines above shallow straits and seas. The western and northwestern islands are rolling and hilly, but altitudes seldom exceed 2,000 feet.

**Climate.**   Although all of the Northwest Territories are cold in winter, there are wide differences in summer conditions. The Mackenzie River valley is in the subarctic climatic zone, and therefore has a climate unlike the rest of the Territories which are in the Arctic zone. Winters are cold throughout both regions. On a monthly average, the coldest sections are northwest of Hudson Bay on the mainland and in the far northern islands facing the Arctic Ocean. The greatest extremes of cold are recorded in the subarctic Mackenzie Valley; −60 to −70°F occur during many winters. The Arctic Islands, which are moderated by the water around them, have not recorded temperatures below −63°F.

A marked distinction in climate occurs in summer when the subarctic Mackenzie Valley warms up. July monthly averages of 60°F are equal to those experienced much farther south in the Clay Belt of Ontario and Quebec. Daytime temperatures frequently rise into the 80s. The Arctic region to the northeast, however, never warms up, and July averages remain under 50°F. The latter area is kept cool by the cold waters around the shores and the dominance of cold air masses overhead. Because of their interior and northerly position, precipitation is low throughout the Territories. Ice conditions greatly influence accessibility. In the north ice forms along the shores of the Canadian mainland and Arctic Islands in early September and by about early November around Hudson Bay. The region is then closed to sea transport, and planes cannot land on the lakes until the ice thickens. In Hudson Bay harbors, the ice begins to break up in late June; melting proceeds northward until early August, when the northern islands have open water. Air photos indicate that the ice around the north-

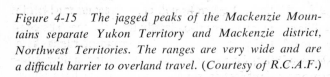

*Figure 4-15   The jagged peaks of the Mackenzie Mountains separate Yukon Territory and Mackenzie district, Northwest Territories. The ranges are very wide and are a difficult barrier to overland travel. (Courtesy of R.C.A.F.)*

western islands never breaks up from year to year.

**Resources and Economic Development.** Most of the developed resources of the Northwest Territories are in Mackenzie District. Mining produces the most valuable output and is based upon three minerals, pitchblende, gold, and petroleum. Pitchblende, a source of uranium and radium, is obtained from the outer edge of the Canadian Shield on the eastern side of Great Bear Lake, where Port Radium is the place from which the valuable ores are shipped by air. Gold is also mined from the western edge of the Shield at Yellowknife on the northeastern arm of Great Slave Lake. These mines must be rich to withstand the high cost of transporting supplies. Petroleum is the only mineral of significance produced from the lowland region. Many of the wells are capped and present production supplies only the local market of the Mackenzie Valley. Nickel is being mined at Rankin Inlet.

Other resources of the Territories are less significant in the Canadian economy, but may play a greater role in future development. A plant to manufacture wood products has been established at Fort Smith, midway between Lake Athabaska and Great Slave Lake. There are agricultural lands of limited quality in many parts of the Mackenzie River valley. They frequently need drainage and are troubled by permafrost near the surface. At present, the land is not being settled since better land is still available farther south.

Commercial fishing started in Great Slave Lake in 1946 and a large, but controlled, harvest of lake trout and whitefish is taken each year. Fish are caught in both summer and winter (through holes in the ice) and shipped in refrigerated transport to southern Canadian cities and the United States.

*Figure 4-16    An Eskimo summer camp consists of tents on the rocky beach at Cape Dorset, Baffin Island. The canvas tents are obtained from the trader. Each holds one family. (Courtesy of J. L. Robinson.)*

In the last century, the historic fur trade was the main industry of the Mackenzie Valley and the chief reason for most of the small post settlements. About one-tenth of Canada's fur catch still comes from the area, and trapping is the major activity of the few thousand Indians of the Valley.

The Arctic region includes northeastern Mackenzie District, most of Keewatin District, and all of the Arctic Islands. Since the region is treeless, all lumber for houses is imported. There is no agriculture. Glaciation scoured the ridges, and soils found in lowlands are not yet mature. Mineral resources are the hope for the future.

## ALASKA

The territory of Alaska was purchased by the United States from Russia in 1867. Essentially an isolated peninsula, situated at the northwest

The region has a great deal of bare rock exposed at the surface. Furthermore, nearly all of the Arctic mainland, and most of Baffin Island, is underlain by the same old rocks which are mineralized in many places in the southern parts of the Shield. Although mineralization has been reported from several locations in Arctic Canada, none has yet proved large enough, or rich enough, to withstand the high cost of development.

White fox furs have been the principal export of the Arctic region. The Arctic or white fox, one of the few fur-bearers living north of the tree line, is trapped by the Eskimos and traded for the guns, tools, equipment, and food of our civilization. The Eskimos also sell handicraft products to nearby trading posts.

All but a few hundred of the 6,000 white inhabitants of the Northwest Territories live in the Mackenzie River valley. The largest settlement, the gold mining center of Yellowknife, has about 3,000 persons. To have the needed water transport, all the other small settlements are located on the river or the two large lakes.

The native inhabitants of the Territories are Indians and Eskimos. The tree line, which separates the Arctic from the subarctic climate, is also a cultural line separating Indians and Eskimos. The Eskimos, who number about 8,500, live north of the tree line, across the mainland of Arctic Canada and along the coasts of the southern group of Arctic Islands (Figure 4-1).

There are wide differences in the level of culture and acceptance of white civilization among the Eskimos. All too frequently their character has been generalized on the basis of a few groups which are better known. Some, such as those near the delta mouth of the Mackenzie River, are modern, well-equipped trappers, and a few of them herd reindeer. Others, such as those in the interior near Boothia Peninsula, still live by hunting caribou and seals as their forefathers used to do.

corner of North America, Alaska sprawls over 586,400 square miles, nearly one-fifth of the area of the forty-eight American states. The

Aleutian Islands extend toward the Kamchatka Peninsula of Siberia, nearly 1,000 miles west of easternmost Asia, and the coastal panhandle reaches to within 400 miles of Washington state. The territory is crossed by the Arctic Circle, and interior Alaska has a severe continental climate, unlike the milder marine climate of the south coast.

## Physical Setting

**Relief Features.** The landforms of Alaska range all the way from flat, marshy plains to the highest mountain peak in North America. At the northwestern end of the Cordilleran region, the landform patterns are generally a continuation of ranges, valleys, and plateaus of the Cordillera of British Columbia and Yukon.

The St. Elias Mountains rise to altitudes of 10,000 to 15,000 feet in southeastern Alaska, where Yukon Territory, British Columbia, and Alaska all come together. The St. Elias Range breaks into a complex of mountains to the northwest, such as the Chugach and Wrangell Mountains, and then separates into two definite chains. The southerly spur is the Kenai Mountains which form the backbone of the peninsula of the same name, and reappear as the rugged parts of Kodiak Island.

The main mountain chain arcs northward as the Alaska Range, which averages 8,000 to 10,000 feet in elevation, but is crowned by North America's highest peak, Mt. McKinley, 20,300 feet. The Alaska Range has several mountain chains within it and, in places, is

Figure 4-17   *The rough topography of Alaska and the Yukon Territory tends to make many elongated regions of relatively small areas. Such topography is a definite hindrance to the development of transportation.*

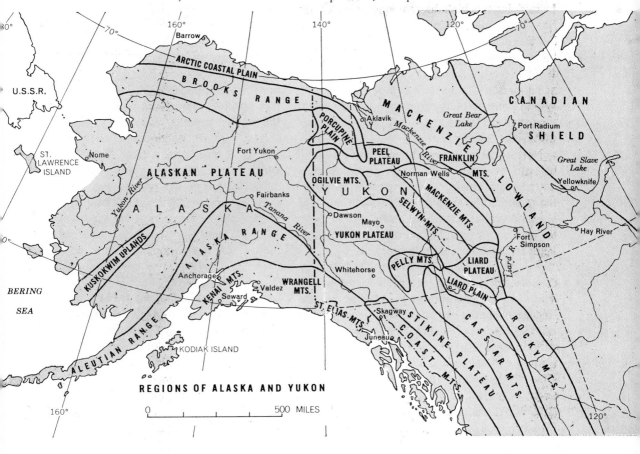

about 150 miles wide. The mountain system swings southwestward through the Alaska peninsula and merges with the sharp, volcanic peaks of the Aleutian Range. Many peaks of this latter range are above 10,000 feet, but elevations decrease across the Aleutian Islands, where peaks are generally between 4,000 and 5,000 feet. Some of the mountains of this long island arc are still active volcanoes.

The central part of Alaska is a region of broad plateaus and plains, quite different in appearance from the mountainous southern section. The land slopes to the west from altitudes of about 2,000 feet at the Yukon border to broad swampy lowlands at the delta of the Yukon River on the Bering Sea coast. Across the rolling region the Yukon River and its main southern tributary, the Tanana, have cut broad valleys, flowing generally across flat-bottomed valley floors.

The northern wall of Interior Alaska is formed by the high barren mountains of the Brooks Range. It broadens to about 200 miles in width across north central Alaska. The mountains are quite rugged, with some peaks above 10,000 feet, but the ranges are broken by a few valley passes. The western end of the mountain system consists of lower ranges (2,000 feet), the rounded Delong and Baird Mountains near the Arctic Ocean coast.

North of the Brooks Range a broad foothill belt slopes down to a tundra-covered, lake-dotted coastal plain. Several rivers wind across the plain and have entrenched slightly into the glacial deposits. Permafrost underlies the Arctic lowland and is one of the reasons for the many lakes and swamps across the surface.

**Climate.** Alaska is a land of diverse climates. The many misconceptions of Alaskan climate frequently are the outcome of not being specific as to which part of Alaska is being discussed.

South central Alaska and the Panhandle have a marine climate quite different from the interior. Temperatures are moderated by the relatively warm water which lies offshore in the Gulf of Alaska. Summers are generally cool, with July average mean temperatures of about

55°F. Winters are surprisingly mild for the northern latitude. January average mean monthly temperatures are about 30°F, which is only about 10 degrees cooler than Seattle. Precipitation is very heavy on this south coastal area. Storms from the Aleutians come in upon the mountainous coast throughout the year, but drop the greatest quantities of rain and snow from September to December. Most settlements, unless they are sheltered behind island mountains, average about 100 inches annually. Some stations have recorded as much as 150 inches of precipitation. Rainfall generally decreases to the westward along the southern coast, with about 60 inches being a common average.

Central Alaska has a continental climate characterized by cold winters and relatively warm summers. Average January temperatures are slightly above zero near the Bering Sea coast, but are −10 to −15°F in the east central interior. Extreme temperatures of −60 to −70°F may be experienced at some time during most winters. Summers are cool near the Bering Sea coast, 50 to 55°F for the July averages, but may become warm inland. Extremes rising into the 80s are common. Because of interior position, annual precipitation is only 10 to 20 inches, with a maximum of rainfall coming in the summer months.

The northern Arctic coast and most of the Brooks Range have a true Arctic climate in which summer monthly averages remain below 50°F. Although the winters are longer than those of interior Alaska, extreme temperatures are not as low, because of the modifying influence of the waters of the Arctic Ocean which though cold are warmer than the land.

*Resources and Economic Development*

Most of the people of Alaska live in the south central and southeastern sections of the country. Fishing is one of the major occupations. Trading for fur seals and sea otter skins was one of the chief reasons why Russian ships visited the Alaskan coast more than 150 years ago, resulting in several Russian settlements and many Russian place names. The Pribilof Islands remain one of the world's major sources of fur seals, thanks to the present wise management and controlled harvesting of the herds.

The salmon industry began to expand at the turn of the century, particularly with improvements in the canning industry. It is now Alaska's major source of income and is the chief reason for many south coast settlements. Declining catches after 1950 indicate that the fishery may be overexploited. Salmon are netted and trapped as they approach the coastal rivers in summer. There is usually a large migration of seasonal workers into southeastern Alaska, especially to work in the canneries located at such places as Ketchikan, Wrangell, and Petersburg. Although the salmon catch makes up about 80 to 90 per cent of the value of the fishing industry, there are also catches of halibut, herring, cod, smelt, and king crab.

Placer gold was the attraction that made Alaska famous at the turn of this century. The gold rushes to Nome and Fairbanks occurred at about the same time as that to the fabulous Klondike in the Yukon Territory. Gold continues to be the basis of the mining industry, with the major share coming from the large lode mine at Juneau, and from the alluvial gravels near Fairbanks. Mining declined in Alaska during World War II and has not yet regained its prewar status. Alaska has produced several strategic metals such as tin, tungsten, platinum, antimony, and mercury, but the deposits have not proved large enough, or of sufficiently high grade, to withstand the high production costs. Most of the mines have operated near the coast where accessibility has made costs lower. In the interior, the coal of the Nenana region, along the railway, is used, as is coal of the Matanuska Valley. A petroleum reserve has been established around Point Barrow for the United States Navy. As yet, however, no large fields have been discovered.

Alaska's forest industry has not developed to a large scale. The largest trees and heavy stands are in the south central and southeast coastal areas. There are several small lumber mills on the coast, and a pulp and paper mill operates at Ketchikan. Central Alaska is part of the Boreal Forest region, which covers Yukon Territory and much of north central Canada. Trees are smaller than on the coast and the forest cover is interspersed with a great many swamps, muskegs, and small lakes.

Agriculture may be the future means of expanding the permanent population of Alaska. To be sure the coastal regions, which have growing seasons of 140 or more days and ample precipitation, unfortunately have cool summers and very little level land. Crops can, and do, grow well in Alaska, but the agricultural regions have always suffered from such economic problems as high costs of production and lack of a large local market. Subsistence agriculture for local needs is quite possible in several sections of Alaska, but commercial agriculture similar to that familiar to most American settlers faces more difficulties.

With only about 15,000 acres in cropland in all of Alaska, agriculture is still a minor activity. This acreage is, however, but a small part of the potential arable land. The chief agricultural regions are in the Matanuska Valley and on Kenai Peninsula. The Matanuska Valley, settled in the middle 1930s, is now Alaska's chief agricultural region. It has a market inland along the Alaska railway, and in the nearby coastal cities, such as Anchorage. Agriculture is also practiced, on a smaller scale, in the Fairbanks area of the interior.

## Population

Alaska's population almost doubled in the decade 1940–1950, increasing from 73,000 to about 130,000. The increased population has been almost entirely due to the movement of whites from the United States. The military population is not included in this estimate. Native population has remained fairly stable, totaling about 34,000 in 1950—16,000 Eskimos, 12,000 Indians, 6,000 Aleuts.

About two-thirds of Alaska's white population is found in the many urban centers around the Gulf of Alaska coast. Since agricultural land is quite limited in extent, most people are urban dwellers, concerned chiefly with fishing, transportation, defense, local manufacturing, and business. Anchorage is the largest city in Alaska and is growing rapidly. About one-third of the white population of Alaska was in the Cook Inlet region in 1950. In the Panhandle section the two largest cities are Juneau, the capital, and Ketchikan, each with about 6,000 inhabitants.

About 30,000 whites were living in the central parts of Alaska in 1950, about two-thirds of them in the Fairbanks district. The city of Fairbanks is the important transportation hub in the interior and also has some local gold dredging and agricultural development.

Three groups of native peoples occupy fairly distinct regions of Alaska. The Eskimos are found on the west coast, around the mouths of the Kuskokwim and Yukon Rivers, and the northwestern coast to about Point Barrow. Most Eskimos live in small villages along the coast, although there has been a tendency recently to concentrate in greater numbers in a few towns such as Nome, Kotzebue, and Barrow. Their way of life is changing rapidly but is still based chiefly on wildlife resources such as fur-bearing animals, caribou, fish, seals, and in some places, reindeer.

The Aleuts are the hardy native inhabitants of the barren, foggy Aleutian Islands. They are chiefly fishermen or sea hunters, but have been declining in numbers. The Alaskan Indians are found mainly in southeastern Alaska, although some live in the interior region. The coastal Indians are primarily fishermen who live in many small villages among the Panhandle islands, or along the irregular shores.

## GREENLAND

### Physical Setting

**Relief Features.** The Danish county of Greenland is the largest of the Arctic Islands off the mainland of North America. Its area of 840,000 square miles is equal to all the Northeastern and Great Lakes states from New England to Nebraska; Greenland is as large as Mexico. Greenland is only 12 miles from Ellesmere Island, the northeastern Canadian island, and is inhabited by the same Eskimo stocks that migrated across northern Canada. On these bases it may be considered part of the North American Arctic.

Greenland is a high, mountainous island, about 85 per cent of which is covered by a thick icecap which extends to below sea level in some areas. High mountains rise abruptly from the sea along the fiorded west and east coasts, reaching altitudes of 6,000 feet on the west and 10,000 feet on the east. Behind the mountains, and frequently spilling through and around them in beautiful, twisting glaciers, lies the Greenland icecap. It resembles a flattened dome which arches above the sharp, rugged coastal mountains to altitudes of about 10,000 feet. The thickness of the ice has not been fully determined, but recent expeditions equipped with sounding devices report thicknesses in places of about 10,000 feet. This suggests that Greenland is actually an ice-filled basin.

The largest areas of low to rolling land are located in Pearyland in northern Greenland. This lake-covered lowland is ice-free, since precipitation is apparently not sufficient to result in an accumulation of snow. The other major ice-free section is the one where most Greenlanders and Danes live, on the southwest and west central coast.

**Climate.** Because of the northerly latitude and the cooling effect of the large mass of ice, Greenland has a Polar climate. In addition, the coasts of east and north Greenland are bathed by cold, ice-covered water discharging from the Arctic Ocean. In contrast, however, the southwestern coast has warmer water offshore, derived from the North Atlantic Drift (Gulf Stream), which moderates the climate. Most harbors of the southwest remain ice-free throughout the winter. In summer the small valleys become warm enough for vegetables to grow in the open. More than twenty thousand sheep and a few goats are grazed. With these more favorable climatic conditions it is not surprising that most of the population lives on the southwestern coast.

## Resources and Economic Development

The modern Greenlander has changed greatly from the early Eskimo inhabitants who used to depend upon seals, white whales, walrus, and narwhals for food. Many Greenlanders are now commercial fishermen, and the mainstay of their economy is the codfish. The kayak is rapidly disappearing and is being replaced by the motorboat and/or fishing cutter. Fishing is carried on by the Greenlanders fairly close to shore because of their small boats.

A thousand years ago Norse settlers attempted agriculture in the valleys of southwestern Greenland. In recent years agriculture has revived and, in the Julianehaab district, several Greenlanders are now farmers. Sheep now outnumber people. The country has surplus meat and wool for export. Vegetables and grasses grow well, and there are a few head of cattle and many chickens. However, much food must still be imported into the Greenland settlements.

Although mineralization has been reported from several places, only two products, cryolite and lead, have proven valuable enough for export. The government-controlled cryolite mine at Ivigtut, in the southwest, has been the world's major source of this very strategic mineral, which is used in the production of aluminum. Lead is mined in east Greenland just north of Scoresby Sound. Greenland also produces coal for local needs from Disko Island.

## Population

The large area of Greenland has only 20,000 inhabitants. Most of the inhabitants are of Eskimo origin, but now call themselves Greenlanders, and have a strong mixture of Danish blood. Many people live in small villages, usually near the open southwest coast where sealing and fishing is dominant. Occasionally,

*Figure 4-18   The old settlement of Narssaq, Greenland. The winter water duct for the slaughterhouse is shown near the foot of the mountain. (Courtesy of Danish Information Office.)*

groups live at the heads of the fiords. The larger towns are growing in importance as commercial centers, and include Egedesminde, Godthaab, and Julianehaab.

Two smaller settlements of more primitive peoples are located outside of the main concentration on the west coast. To the northwest, around Thule and New Thule, to its north, live Eskimo hunters who resemble some of the Eskimos of the Canadian Arctic. They are cut off from the rest of settled Greenland by the icecap which occupies the whole coastal area along Melville Bay. East Greenland has had a few Eskimo inhabitants from time to time, but the area is poorly endowed with game and icebound most of the year. Recent resettlement of the Angmagssalik region, south of the central area, and at Scoresbysund has been successful; eastern Greenland now has about 1,500 persons. The north and northeast coasts of Greenland are unoccupied.

## IN PERSPECTIVE

### Northern North America

North America, north of the United States, is a vast extent of land in general only sparsely populated. Its area is over 1.3 times that of the continent of Europe but the region has only about 4 per cent of the population of Europe although the two land masses are in approximately the same latitudes. The physical structure of northern North America influences climatic conditions in such a way that, under present conditions, most economic development has been discouraged.

Canada is a nation of great potential. Vast plains areas, when used more intensively, will produce much larger grain and pasture crops. Range lands that are now scarcely used will, in the future, become sources of large meat supplies. In general the mineral wealth of Canada is undeveloped; much of the area has not been explored in detail. One of the world's largest forest areas extends across the northern part of the provinces and the southern part of the territories. Undeveloped power sites offer great future possibilities for producing hydroelectric power. In spite of its northern location and climatic handicaps, Canada is potentially one of the world's great industrial as well as agricultural nations.

Because of topography and climatic handicaps, Alaska does not have the potential of Canada. Although mining and fishing activities are important and some valley areas have been partly developed agriculturally, Alaska is of primary importance as a defense outpost for North America. With the development of polar flying and with future improvement in world relations, Alaskan airfields will become important connecting links for the world's air transportation systems.

Greenland, the world's largest island, is largely ice-covered. Its small native population has been protected and governed wisely by Denmark. Under present conditions the future development of the island can only continue the present trend.

All parts of northern North America have been fortunate in their political development. No forts exist along their common boundaries. Canada, Denmark, and the United States work together in harmony and for the mutual benefit of all.

## EXERCISES

*1.* What is the approximate area of Canada? How does Canada compare in size with the United States and the U.S.S.R.? How do the provinces of Canada compare in size with the states of the United States?

*2.* What is the population of Canada? How does the population of Canada compare with the population of the United States? In which part of Canada do most of the people live? Why are the other parts of Canada sparsely populated?

3. What are the chief agricultural regions of Canada? In what ways are they similar to the agricultural regions of the United States? What are the chief limits to agricultural land use in Canada?

4. In what ways are the physical regions of the United States and Canada alike? How do they differ? Which regions extend from one country to the other?

5. Where are the tundra and taiga located with respect to each other? How do the two differ in respect to climate, vegetation, population density, and land utilization?

6. What geographic factors influenced the development of the fishing industry along the coast of Newfoundland? In what ways does the eastern fishing industry differ from that along the western coast?

7. Where is the chief Canadian manufacturing area located? What is its relationship to the manufacturing area of the United States? Why are the principal products of the two areas similar?

8. What is the status of Canadian territory north of 60° north latitude? What is the political relationship of this area to the rest of Canada? Why

do more people live in the Yukon than in the Northwest Territories?

9. What are the four largest cities in Canada? Which are ports? What locational advantages and handicaps does each city have? What are the most important activities in each?

10. How does the area of Alaska compare with the area of Texas? How does the population of the two places compare? In which part of Alaska do most people live?

11. What are the most important economic activities of Alaska? What geographical factors aid or hinder these activities? Why will the population of Alaska never be very large?

12. What is the largest North American island? To what nation does it belong? What are the principal geographical handicaps of the island? What does it produce for world trade?

13. How have minerals affected the development of Canada? Alaska?

14. What products are made from the forests of Canada? Where are the mills located with respect to water? Why?

## SELECTED REFERENCES

Canadian Department of Mines and Technical Surveys, Geographical Branch: *Bibliography of Periodical Literature on Canadian Geography, 1940–50*, Ottawa, 1952.

Canadian Department of Trade and Commerce, Bureau of Statistics: *The Canada Yearbook*, Ottawa, 1956.

————: *Canada Handbook*, Ottawa, 1956.

Collins, H. B. (ed.): *Science in Alaska*, Arctic Institute of North America, Washington, 1952.

Currie, A. W.: *Economic Geography of Canada*, The Macmillan Co. of Canada, Ltd., Toronto, 1947.

Eiteman, Wilford J., and Alice B. Smuts: "Alaska a Land of Opportunity—Limited," *Economic Geography*, 27:33–42, January, 1951.

Lloyd, Trevor: "Progress in West Greenland," *Journal of Geography*, 49:319–329, November, 1950.

Putnam, D. F. (ed.): *Canadian Regions*, J. M. Dent & Sons (Canada), Ltd., Toronto, 1952.

Robinson, J. Lewis: *The Geography of Canada*, Longmans, Green & Co., Toronto, 1950.

Royal Danish Ministry for Foreign Affairs: *Greenland*, Copenhagen, 1952.

Stern, Peter M.: "Alaska," *Focus*, 4(1):1–6, September, 1953.

Taylor, Griffith: *Canada—A Study of Cool Continental Environments*, Methuen & Co., Ltd., Toronto, 1950.

U.S. Department of the Interior, Office of Territories: *Mid-century Alaska*, Washington, 1951.

# 5. Middle America

THE location of Middle America has favored close
relationships between that area and the United States.
The United States buys a large majority of the
region's products and supplies the greatest part of
its imports. Middle American countries are important
exporters of sugar, tobacco, minerals, bananas,
and other tropical fruits, and in turn they buy
textiles, petroleum products, automobiles,
machinery, and a host of other goods. The region is
increasingly attractive to tourists. On islands and
mainland, visitors find interesting scenery, sun and
warmth during winter months, and the opportunity
of becoming acquainted with varied cultures and
ways of life very different from those of the United
States. In some countries, modern hotels and
amusement places have been built to attract a
wealthy clientele. Economical accommodations are
also available, especially outside the major resort
areas. Mexico, Cuba, Haiti, Jamaica, Puerto Rico,
and the Bahamas are among the countries that
derive a substantial income from tourists and
other visitors.

The peoples of Middle America include American

150

Indians, of both pure and mixed blood, Spanish, English, French, Dutch, and other Europeans. In particular mainland localities and on many Caribbean islands, Negroes and mulattoes predominate. Over 220,000 people from India live in Trinidad.

In the seventeenth and eighteenth centuries European powers fought great naval battles in the Caribbean region. Caribbean waters were crossed by the galleons carrying treasure to Spain, and the buccaneers who lurked in the region had Port Royal, Jamaica, and certain of the Bahama Islands among their home ports. During the colonial period, New Englanders traded with the Caribbean islands, exchanging dried fish and other products for sugar, molasses, and rum. In the days before artificial refrigeration, ice cut on the lakes of wintry New England was eagerly welcomed by the tropical sugar planters.

During the nineteenth century men from the United States had many and varied connections with Middle America. The Gold Rush to California took some gold hunters over the Panama and Nicaragua routes. American soldiers of fortune helped in, and caused, insurrections in Cuba, Mexico, and Central America. More significant was economic penetration of the area by miners, sugar planters, banana growers, and other enterprising persons. After 1898, as a result of the Spanish-American War, Cuba became independent and Spain ceded Puerto Rico to the United States. In the early years of this century the digging of the Panama Canal and the purchase of the Virgin Islands from Denmark were events of special importance to this country.

Middle America has a land area approximately one-third that of the United States. It is comprised of Mexico, the Central American countries, and the islands of the West Indies. Included are ten independent nations, and colonies or possessions of Great Britain, France, Netherlands, and the United States. Environmental, racial, and cultural contrasts are tremendous, both within and among these major political divisions, yet elements of similarity are sufficient to give a geographic unity to the area as a whole.

## PHYSICAL SETTING

### Relief Features

The dominant surface feature of Middle America is the highland backbone and its associated volcanoes. Bordering coastal lowlands are usually narrow. A major exception, however, is the low, featureless plain of the Yucatan Peninsula which is related geologically to flat areas underlain by limestone in Cuba, Florida, and the Bahamas. Inland from this peninsula, the northwest-southeast trending structures of the Mexican highlands bend eastward through southern Mexico, Guatemala, Honduras, and northern Nicaragua, to dip under the Caribbean and reappear in the Greater Antilles. A second range extends to the southeast through Central America and into northwestern Colombia, where it is separated from the Andean system by the lowlands of the Atrato River.

Three interoceanic passes breach the highlands. One crosses the 130-mile wide Mexican Isthmus of Tehuantepec at a maximum elevation of 800 feet. A second is part of a structural depression through Nicaragua diagonally from Greytown to the Gulf of Fonseca. It follows the Rio San Juan to Lake Nicaragua, which has an elevation of a little over 100 feet above the Pacific only 17 miles away. The third route is followed by the Panama Canal. All three breaches, as well as the Atrato lowlands of Colombia, have been crossing-places since colonial times, but the Panama route has been the most important. There is also a possible route through Honduras. Enlarging and deepening the present Panama Canal to sea level also is being considered.

Mexico north of Tehuantepec is essentially a plateau, bordered on the west by the wide and rugged Sierra Madre Occidental, with peaks over 12,000 feet high, and on the east by the lower, more easily traversed Sierra Madre Oriental. The plateau surface is broken by mesas,

mountain ranges, and alluvium-filled basins. It is highest, 5,000 to 9,000 feet, in the south, where it terminates along the 19th parallel in an area of volcanic mountains and ash-filled basins. In this area lofty volcanic cones such as Orizaba, 18,700 feet, Popocatepetl, 17,887 feet, and Iztaccihuatl, 17,342 feet, rise above the general level. South of the volcanic rim are the Balsas Valley and the Sierra Madre del Sur. These can respectively be related structurally to the synclinorium (huge downfold) of the Gulf of California and to rugged Baja California to the north, and to the Central Valley of Chiapas and the Sierra Madre de Chiapas to the east.

Between the lowlands of Tehuantepec and those of Nicaragua, highland elevations are greatest on the Pacific side. There, volcanic debris and lava largely obscure the underlying structures and form a plateau-like highland with ash-filled basins nestling among volcanic cones. With the exception of British Honduras and Costa Rica, each country has mountain peaks approximating 6,000 feet or higher. In Costa Rica, the Meseta Central, an ash-filled basin, is 3,000 to 4,000 feet above sea level.

In the Greater Antilles one line of highlands may be traced from mountainous Puerto Rico westward, through the Cordillera Central of the Dominican Republic, the northern peninsula of Haiti, the Sierra Maestra of southeastern Cuba, and the Cayman Islands, to southern British Honduras. Another group extends through the southern peninsula of Haiti, the Blue Mountains of Jamaica, and the Swan and Bay Islands to the mainland. The highest elevation in the West Indies, 10,417 feet, is in the Dominican Republic.

The Lesser Antilles can be divided into high and low islands. The high islands are mountainous, being the tops of volcanic peaks which in some cases are still actively building or emerging from the sea. Fringing deposits of coral

*Figure 5-1 Mexico has many colorful towns and small cities. Halfway between Mexico City and Acapulco is the town of Taxco, famous for its silver industry.*

limestone often form reefs and raised terraces. The low islands are relatively level and generally are of coral formation covering submerged mountain peaks.

## Climate

There are five main types of climate, each with characteristic associated vegetation and human activity (Figure 5-2). South from near the Tropic of Cancer, the trade winds blow from an easterly direction and temperatures at sea level are hot all year. In this area rainfall differences on windward and leeward slopes, together with the decrease of temperature with increased elevation and exposure to the sea, provide the principal basis for climatic differences. The climate on the east and northeast sides of the high islands and the mainland is classed as rainy

tropical; that on the west and southwest sides, wet-and-dry tropical; elevations above 2,500 feet are of the tropical highland type. North of the Tropic of Cancer, in northern Mexico, the degree of rainfall deficiency becomes the basis of classification. The climate is largely tropical steppe or tropical desert.

One of the principal weather problems confronting Middle America is the hurricane. It is an annual hazard from late August to November. Usually the area most affected is the northern half of the West Indies. Occasionally, however, these storms strike along the east coast of Mexico.

**Rainy Tropical.** The rainy tropical lands are hot, humid, and rainy all year. Rain is usually heaviest from May to November when precipi-

*Figure 5-2   Note the influence of the trade winds and the topography upon the climatic types. In general the rainy tropical climates are on the northern and eastern sides of the land masses, but the deserts and steppes are in the northwestern and interior part of the area.*

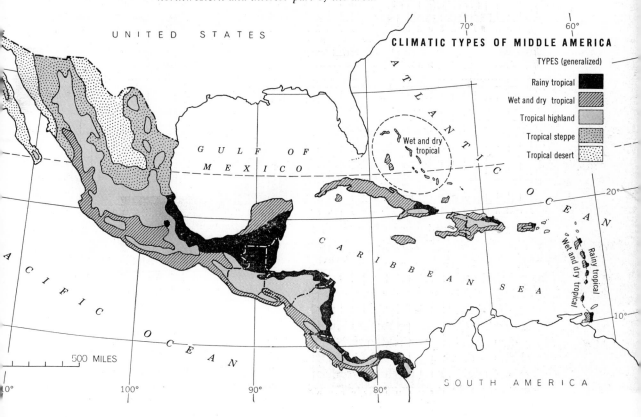

CLIMATIC TYPES OF MIDDLE AMERICA

TYPES (generalized)

Rainy tropical
Wet and dry tropical
Tropical highland
Tropical steppe
Tropical desert

tation normally brought by the trade winds is supplemented by convectional showers accompanying the northward shift of the doldrums. Such places are regions of selva (broadleaf-evergreen rain forest) generally sparsely populated by subsistence farmers and gatherers of forest products, but locally more densely occupied because of banana and cacao plantations.

**Wet-and-Dry Tropical.**   Areas having a distinct dry season during the winter months, when the rain shadow effect of the highlands athwart

the trade winds is greatest, are classed as wet-and-dry tropical climates. Summer rain is convectional in origin. Where precipitation is heavier, the vegetation is semideciduous or scrub forest; savanna grassland prevails where precipitation is lighter. Along the Pacific coast there are patches of rain forest as far north as Guatemala. In such places, the summer rainfall is heavy enough to compensate for the dry season. Areas with wet-and-dry tropical climate are somewhat more favorable for human occupation than the wet equatorial and, there-

*Figure 5-3   Climate graphs for Middle America.*

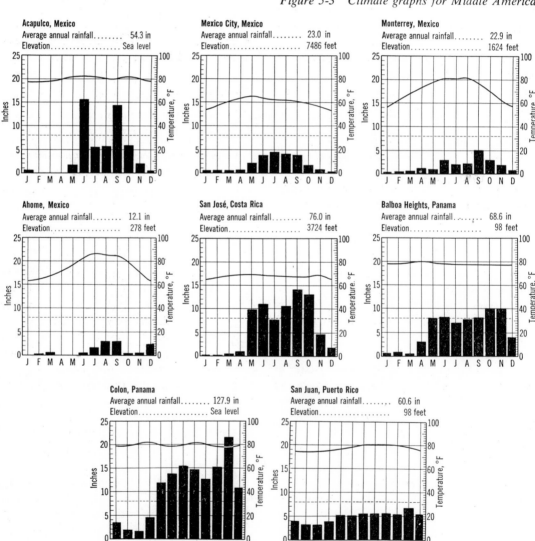

fore, are generally more densely peopled. Cattle grazing and raising sugar cane are important activities.

**Tropical Highland.**   Climates in the highlands vary greatly within short distances because of differences in elevation, orientation of slope to the sun, and rain-bringing winds. Summer rain and winter drought are characteristic, although slopes on the east side have the year-round precipitation of the adjacent rainy tropical lowlands. Vegetation, as a consequence, is also varied. Rain forests clothe the wetter, east-facing exposures, whereas the seasonally dry western parts have a scrub forest or grassland cover. Mixed forests, pine forests, or evergreen-oak forests occupy higher lands.

In highlands, several altitudinal temperature zones are commonly recognized. The lowest, called *tierra caliente,* lying below 2,500 feet elevation, commonly has either rainy tropical or wet-and-dry tropical climate. Above this zone and up to 6,000 or 7,000 feet is *tierra templada,* with average annual temperatures of 60 to 75°F. This is the coffee zone. In Mexico and Central America, except in Nicaragua and Panama, it is the zone of greatest population concentration. Higher still is *tierra fría,* extending to the tree line at a height between 11,000 and 13,000 feet. Mexico City lies in the lower part of this temperature zone. Only Mexico, Guatemala, and western Panama have areas of any size in *tierra fría.* Alpine pastures, above the tree line, are largely limited to Mexico. This country is also the only one having peaks extending above the snow line, located at an elevation of approximately 15,000 feet.

**Tropical Steppe and Desert.**   Northwestern Mexico is desert or steppe land. Near the California border there is a little precipitation from winter storms; this is the only exception to the characteristic summer maximum of rainfall in Middle America. The desert in the lower, northern part of interior Mexico is explained by the dry prevailing winds and mountains to the east and west. Higher surrounding lands with steppe climate, especially to the south, commonly receive more rain, or the rain is more efficient because of lower temperatures. The sparsely populated desert and steppe areas are used mostly for grazing, with irrigation farming, especially of cotton or other cash crops, being locally significant.

## POPULATION

In Mexico and Central America the racial and cultural mixtures are Indian-Spanish, but in the West Indies they are Negro-European. In both areas, colored or mixed races predominate. In many sections, Occidental culture is but a veneer over an Indian or Negro base. Commonly, only the small upper class, normally white or near-white, lives in an essentially European manner. However, native life and culture are being modified by increasing contact with the people of the United States.

In the mainland countries, mestizo people are most numerous, except in Guatemala, where two-thirds are pure Indian, and in Costa Rica, where almost one-half are white. Nowhere else do Caucasians make up more than one-tenth the population. Negroes are most common in Panama and in the Caribbean lowlands of Costa Rica, Nicaragua, and Honduras. Most of these migrated to the area during the present century to aid in construction of the Panama Canal and to work on banana plantations.

In the West Indian islands, however, there are few mestizos and almost no Indians. Negroes and mulattoes are dominant, except in Puerto Rico where possibly two-thirds of the people can be classified as white. One-third of the Cubans also fall into this category, but in the other islands the percentage of white people is much lower. In some it is less than 1 per cent.

To the Spaniards, the Indians represented wealth, sometimes in the form of gold and silver which the Indians had accumulated, but always in the form of labor to be exploited and incidentally Christianized. The valley of Mexico and the highland basins of Guatemala were most densely occupied and were the centers of the highest cultural development before the Spanish arrived. Indians there were well-disciplined, sedentary farmers accustomed to hard labor. Although many perished, most managed to survive under their new Spanish masters, hence Negro slaves were not needed. Thus, the more densely inhabited areas of pre-Columbian times are the most heavily peopled today. Also, the greater was the proportion of Indians to incoming Spanish, the more Indian is the present population.

In the West Indies, however, the Indians, though fairly numerous, were unaccustomed to hard, steady labor. Rounded up and enslaved to work the plantations and mines of the larger islands—gold was found in Hispaniola within a month after establishment of the first Spanish settlement—these half-wild beings quickly died or were killed when they rebelled against their masters. They succumbed also to newly introduced European diseases. Almost at once, importation of African slaves was necessary. Cuba, Hispaniola, and Puerto Rico became outfitting points through which passed the manpower and culture of Spain to the farthest ends of the empire. Thus is explained the near absence of Indian blood, the larger proportions of white blood, and the presence of Spanish institutions and language. The Republic of Haiti is an exception. Its language today is French, and the race and culture largely Negro, because it became French in 1697 and all whites were slaughtered or driven out by revolting slaves in 1790–1791.

The smaller islands were never effectively occupied by the Spaniards. During the seventeenth and eighteenth centuries they became pawns of war because they were held in high

*Figure 5-4  Most of the people of Middle America live in the highland valleys or on the plateaus. Note the great density of population in Puerto Rico, the western half of Cuba, and around Mexico City.*

esteem as sugar colonies. Many Negro slaves but only a few white overseers were needed to grow sugar cane. Consequently, the population became almost entirely black and the official language, law, and religion that of the respective mother country.

Population density in the Caribbean ranges from 1,319 per square mile in Barbados, the Western Hemisphere's most densely settled rural area, to expanses with practically no inhabitants (Figure 5-4). Population is commonly in clusters separated by sparsely settled lands. In each cluster is an urban core, the focus of economic and social activities. The rural people commonly dwell in villages rather than in dispersed farmsteads. Each mainland country, except El Salvador, has large areas which are thinly occupied. Political boundaries usually fall through such lands and bear little relation to natural divisions.

## ECONOMIC DEVELOPMENT

### Agriculture

Although mining has long been locally important, forest products are gathered, and in some places industrialization has begun, agriculture remains the principal means of livelihood in all Middle America. Much of the land is still in large holdings, either the great feudal type haciendas inherited from the Spanish, or the newer, foreign-owned commercial plantations. Be they landless workers for day wages or tenants on large holdings, small farmers working their own land, squatters with no legal claims to the plots they till, or dwellers on the communal farms of Mexico, most people have a low level of living. Poverty, poor health, and malnutrition are ever-present problems. The great majority exist mainly by subsistence farming. Although some farmers by skill and irrigation have improved their living conditions, many live almost as did their Indian or Negro ancestors.

Agricultural methods are usually primitive and crop yields low. The best land is in the hands of the large landholders who use it for cash crops. The small farmers, and production of food for home consumption, are relegated to areas of poorer soil and steeper slopes. Caribbean America is an old land, yet the frontier attitude of wasteful exploitation of resources, both natural and human, still persists. Fortunately an awakening is taking place.

### Transportation

Land transportation associated with each population cluster is oriented toward the sea. Only the capitals of Mexico, Guatemala, and El Salvador are connected by rail, but all the capitals, except Tegucigalpa, have railroads to the sea. All also have highways to the Pacific, but except from Mexico City and Panama City roads to the Atlantic are few. The Pan-American Highway is not yet completed across the Mexico-Guatemala, Costa Rica–Nicaragua, Costa Rica–Panama, and Panama-Colombia boundaries. External contact has thus been largely by water, although the recent high development of air transport facilities has made this much less true. Exports are mostly raw materials; imports, manufactured goods.

## MEXICO

Mexico shows as great a diversity of physical environment, race, and culture as one might expect to find in several different countries (Figure 5-5). The 26 million people are probably 30 per cent Indian and over 60 per cent mestizo. The official language, law, and religion are of Spanish origin, yet some 2.5 million Mexicans speak one of the more than 50 Indian tongues in use and perhaps half of these people can speak no Spanish.

Although minerals normally supply two-thirds of the exports and industrialization is increasing, Mexico's problem of how to raise the standard of living remains essentially agrarian. Sixty-five per cent of the gainfully employed are in agriculture, which is largely subsistence in character. Village life is the rule. Fewer than 10 per cent of the population dwell on isolated farmsteads; less than 25 per cent in cities of over 10,000 people.

Actually the natural endowment for agriculture is rather poor. More than half the area is too dry to cultivate; additional amounts are too rough, or are excessively hot, wet, and possess only poor soils. Only about 8 per cent of Mexico's surface is cultivated—a little over one acre per capita (Table 5-1). Moreover, because of soil erosion and misuse, primitive tillage methods, poor seed, drought, and frost damage, yields per acre are commonly low.

Crops of a wide variety are grown, but maize, cotton, sugar cane, and wheat together account for half the total by value; maize alone for 25 per cent. Maize, with beans, chile, and occasionally meat for supplements, is the people's staple diet along with pulque, a native drink, which is consumed in some parts of the country. Unfortunately, the lands naturally capable of producing the heaviest yields of maize do not coincide with the centers of denser popula-

*Figure 5-5   Mexico, like the United States, is divided into a series of political units called states. Each state has its capital. Mexico City, the national capital, is not in any state, but is in a federal district.*

## TABLE 5-1. LAND UTILIZATION IN MEXICO

| Division | Land area, in thousands of hectares | Per cent | | | | |
|---|---|---|---|---|---|---|
| | | Crops | Pasture | Forest | Other productive noncultivated | All other |
| North Pacific | 41,245 | 2.8 | 19.3 | 7.3 | 0.4 | 70.2 |
| North | 80,032 | 4.5 | 47.9 | 23.4 | 5.1 | 19.1 |
| Central | 27,606 | 19.7 | 23.3 | 14.4 | 1.1 | 41.5 |
| Gulf Coast | 23,753 | 10.8 | 10.0 | 27.9 | 17.4 | 33.9 |
| South Pacific | 23,829 | 9.1 | 13.0 | 26.7 | 0.9 | 50.3 |
| Nation | 196,465 | 7.6 | 29.6 | 19.7 | 4.5 | 38.6 |

SOURCE: Nathan L. Whettin, *Rural Mexico,* University of Chicago Press, Chicago, 1948, Table IA, p. 576.

tion. Although over half of the cultivated land is in this grain, Mexico has difficulty producing enough of it for a proper diet.

As late as 1930, 78 per cent of all agricultural land was controlled by 2 per cent of the owners. Today, however, large estates are mostly a thing of the past. The government has expropriated such holdings, and from them created *ejidos* in accordance with laws growing out of the revolution which began in 1910. *Ejidos* are agrarian communities which hold the land in common, although the cropland may be worked either by individuals or on a cooperative basis.

Since the land is now distributed on an equable basis, further progress must be in increasing crop yields and the acreage tilled. About 1 acre of cropland in 8 is now irrigated, and further ambitious governmental reclamation and conservation projects are under way.

An estimated three-fifths or more of the potentially arable land is already in use. The problem is the more difficult since an exceptionally high birth rate increases population by about 500,000 annually.

Like most Latin-American countries, Mexico has a central core of dense settlement, with scattered smaller populous districts and sparsely occupied outlying areas. For comparative purposes the political units of Mexico may be grouped into five divisions: Central Mexico, the Gulf Coast, the North, the North Pacific, and the South Pacific. Facts concerning land area, land use, and population in these divisions are shown in Tables 5-1 and 5-2.

### Regions

**Central.** This region is the heart of the nation. Although the area occupies only one-seventh of the country, about half the popula-

## TABLE 5-2. POPULATION AND AREA OF DIVISIONS

| Division | Estimated population, in hundred thousands | National population, per cent | Approximate area, sq miles | National area, per cent | Population per sq mile |
|---|---|---|---|---|---|
| Central | 13.9 | 47.5 | 106,586 | 14 | 130.0 |
| Gulf Coast | 3.5 | 12.0 | 91,713 | 12 | 38.0 |
| North | 6.1 | 21.0 | 309,002 | 41 | 20.0 |
| North Pacific | 1.75 | 6.5 | 159,247 | 21 | 11.0 |
| South Pacific | 3.6 | 13.0 | 92,003 | 12 | 39.0 |

tion live in it. It is also the region of greatest industrial development. In addition there are important mineral resources and three of the four top-ranking cities, including Mexico, D.F., the largest, are located on the Central Plateau.

At least two advanced civilizations flourished in Central Mexico before the Spanish conquest. The influence of one, that of the Toltecs, was greatest between A.D. 600 and 1200. The ruins of their capital, Teotihuacan, 28 miles northeast of Mexico City, together with the great pyramids of the Sun and the Moon, built by a pre-Aztec people, are a prime tourist attrac-

tion. The Toltecs absorbed many Mayan cultural traits which they passed on to the Aztecs who arrived later. The Aztecs belonged to the same linguistic group and probably originated in the same section of the arid north. They established their capital, Tenochtitlán, on the present site of Mexico City, about 1325, and ruled over a large surrounding area. Conquest of the Aztecs in 1521 by Cortes and 600 Spaniards is one of history's great military feats.

Central Mexico includes the mountains and basins at the higher and more humid southern end of the Mexican Plateau, volcanic cones

*Figure 5-6   The regions of Mexico are based on both physical and cultural factors. The intensity of land utilization varies greatly from region to region.*

*Figure 5-7 Aerial view of the principal business district of Mexico City. Note the wide boulevards and many modern buildings.*

which rise majestically above the general level, and the deep-cut valleys along the plateau's southern margin. The population is concentrated in the basins where the land is level, the soils usually fertile, and the temperatures cool and healthful. In general, winters are mild with occasional frosts and infrequent snow, and summers are relatively cool. There is usually enough rain, 20 to 40 inches annually, to support agriculture, although irrigation is often practiced. Recognizing that temperatures vary with altitude and rainfall with exposure, the climate of Mexico City, 7,486 feet above sea level, can be considered fairly typical of that of Central Mexico.

Although it is Mexico's leading agricultural area, only one-fifth of the area of Central Mexico is cultivated. More land is in pasture. More still is nonproductive, too dry, or on eroded slopes long since deforested to supply firewood and charcoal. Maize and beans are the leading crops. Considerable wheat is produced and also sugar cane in lower, warmer places like Morelos. Drier areas near the larger population centers are commonly devoted to the maguey plant. From its juice is fermented pulque, the national drink of the poorer classes. Much fruit, vegetables, and flowers are supplied the Mexico City market from the famous so-called floating gardens of Lake Xochimilco nearby. There is also a notable development of dairying tributary to Mexico City. However, most milk and much meat consumed in rural areas is from goats.

Mexico City is not only the national capital and the focus of the economic, social and cultural life of the nation, but the fourth largest city in Latin America, with over 2 million inhabitants. Included within its rectangular pattern are numerous parks and plazas, attractive suburbs, and buildings ranging from colonial age structures to ultramodern, multistoried apartments and office buildings. The location on the drained bed of part of Lake Texcoco has created a problem for the city. Under the weight of streets and buildings, surface levels have subsided, in places as much as 16 feet, as ground water was pumped from the wells driv-

Figure 5-8 Canal in the floating gardens of Xochimilco near Mexico City. Flowers, fruits, and vegetables are raised for market. The gardens are also a tourist attraction. (Courtesy of Pan American World Airways.)

Figure 5-9 Mexican charros taking part in a rodeo in Amecameca near Mexico City.

en into the soft subsoil to provide the city's water supply. Consequently, the level of the storm sewers in relation to the Gran Canal del Desaque, completed in 1900 to drain the basin north through a tunnel in the mountains to the Río Pánuco, is such that during the rainy season considerable areas are commonly flooded.

Mexico City is the nation's leading manufacturing center. Typically, Mexican manufacturing is light industry, producing consumer goods from domestic raw materials. The bulk of the industrial activity in the capital is concerned with textiles, clothing, food products, beverages, furniture, tobacco goods, shoes, paper, chemicals, ceramic wares, and lighter metal products. Handicraft industries, practiced in the home or in small shops, are common here as elsewhere in the nation.

The capital is also the focus for Mexico's excellent network of air transportation, its 15,000 miles of railroad, and its 13,000 miles of highway. Consequently, the capital is the major center for tourism, the Republic's largest single source of dollar income. Many tourists travel to Mexico City over the Pan-American Highway, which was opened from Laredo, Texas, in 1936, and has since been completed to the Guatemalan border. The total length of the highway in Mexico is 1,745 miles.

Other cities of particular note in Central Mexico are Guadalajara, second largest city of the republic, and an important transportation and commercial center; Puebla, the fourth largest city and the leading cotton textile manufacturing center; Pachuca, the world's most important silver mining community; and Cuernavaca, a tourist paradise. Taxco, a small colonial town, long famed for silversmithing, is just outside the division.

**Gulf Coast.**   The Gulf Coast region has a level surface and a hot, rainy climate. Much of the land is covered with rain forests. In the state of Veracruz, however, the coastal lowlands, which are often swampy and have considerable areas of savanna, are backed by the forested eastern slopes of the Sierra Madre Oriental which lie in the *tierra templada*. Still higher towers snow-capped Orizaba, one of North America's highest peaks. Precipitation is especially heavy and causes a dense forest cover in the lowlands of the Isthmus of Tehuantepec, the state of Tabasco, and the southern part of Campeche. Less rain, a distinct dry season, and rapid drainage into the underlying limestone account for the scrub forest vegetation in the northwestern part of the Yucatan Peninsula.

Although the Gulf Coast region ranks high in output of agricultural products, it still contains many of the undeveloped agricultural resources of the nation. Much of the coffee of Mexico, the world's fifth largest producer, is from this zone. Banana exports, largely from the Gulf Coast area, exceeded 14 million stems in 1937, but have now dropped to less than 2 million stems annually. Maize yields are higher and more dependable than elsewhere in the nation, and the grasslands, though tropical, support many cattle. From the forests of the Isthmus of Tehuantepec, and those extending south into the Yucatan Peninsula, is gathered much of the world's chicle. About half the world's henequen, as sisal is locally called, is grown in Yucatan. The annual yield of over 100,000 tons of fiber is largely exported to the United States for the manufacture of binder twine and cordage. Cotton is also grown in this region. Within the Gulf Coast region is located the largest reclamation and power project ever undertaken in Mexico, a two hundred million dollar endeavor on the Río Papaloapan.

The principal oil fields of Mexico are located in the Gulf Coast area. Since the first commercial oil discovery was made west of Tampico in 1901, the total production of petroleum within the country has been greater than that in any other nation except the United States, Venezuela, or possibly the Soviet Union. Peak output was reached in 1921 when over 193 million barrels were exported. Fields are largely in three Gulf Coast areas, contiguous to Tampico, south of Tuxpan, and inland from Puerto México. Present annual production of about 60 million barrels is in approximate net balance with yearly national consumption. The petroleum industry is a government monopoly. There are now 14 oil refineries in the country. Tampico is the important petroleum producing and refining center as well as one of the principal ports.

Population is largely centered in small communities. Rural population is densest on the temperate slopes of the Sierra Madre Oriental, focusing on such towns as Jalapa and Orizaba, both centers of cotton manufacturing. Veracruz is a major port on the Gulf of Mexico. It is the principal shipping, trading, and processing center in a fertile reclaimed agricultural area. Puerto México is the Gulf side terminal of a railroad, never very important economically, which was built across the Isthmus of Tehuantepec in 1907. Merida is the commercial and manufacturing center for the henequen area of the Yucatan Peninsula.

The Yucatan area is famous for its Maya ruins. The "New Empire" of the Mayas flourished in this area between A.D. 800 and 1400. When the Spanish arrived, however, the cities were in ruins and their populations dispersed. The Maya culture, in some ways higher than that of the contemporary European civilization, was a mother culture which contributed much, through the Toltec, to Aztec civilization.

**The North.** In this thinly populated semiarid to arid region, winters are cool and summers warm to hot. The surface is largely plateau, but also included is much of the Sierra Madre Occidental, the northern part of the Sierra Madre Oriental, and a segment of the Gulf Coast plain.

Basin floors are lowest and level land most extensive nearer the Rio Grande. Large areas have interior drainage. Steppe grass or desert shrub prevails. Higher mountains, however, may be wooded. The Sierra Madre Occidental has valuable pine forests.

The major land use is grazing. Because of lack of moisture the carrying capacity of pastures is low. Crops almost always must be irrigated. The principal commercial crop is cotton. Nearly one-third the nation's annual yield of over 850,000 bales is produced on *ejidos* in the Laguna district around Torreon, the second largest city of the north. The north as a whole is also the leading wheat-producing section of the republic.

The chief wealth of the region is its mineral resources. Chihuahua, Zacatecas, and Durango are three of the nation's five leading mining states. Mexico is the leading producer of silver and is commonly second in antimony and molybdenum, fourth in lead and mercury, and sixth in gold and petroleum production. Lead, zinc, silver, copper, and gold together total some 85 per cent of the annual value of minerals produced, exclusive of petroleum.

A good-grade bituminous coal, mined at Sabinas in Coahuila, and iron ore, from Durango, are brought together in Monterrey, making this city the only iron and steel center of consequence in Middle America. Monterrey is second only to Mexico City as an industrial city and is the nation's third largest urban community. The border towns of Ciudad Juárez,

*Figure 5-10 Goat herd on road to Chichen-Itza. This part of the limestone plain of Yucatan is checkered with stone-wall enclosed fields of henequen, brush pasture, and idle brushlands containing temporary clearings which produce maize and other subsistence crops. (Courtesy of Paul C. Morrison.)*

*Figure 5-11 Along the Mexico City–Nogales highway west of Guadalajara in Jalisco. Note the dry, eroded, brush-covered slopes used only for pasture, if used at all, and the patches of maize on alluvial flats. (Courtesy of Mexican Embassy, Washington.)*

Piedras Negras, and Nuevo Laredo are much visited by tourists from the United States. Each is a port of entry connected by railroad and highway with the Mexican capital far to the south.

**North Pacific.** Since it is too dry, too rough, or too isolated for development, even for a grazing industry, over two-thirds of the North Pacific area is nonproductive. Population density is lower than in any of the other divisions. Set-tlement is focused where water is available for irrigation, in scattered mining camps, and in the border towns of Tijuana, Mexicali, and Nogales.

Sugar cane and wheat are crops of general consequence. The state of Nayarit is Mexico's primary tobacco-growing area, and the Yaqui Valley in southern Sonora is its leading center of rice cultivation. Long-staple cotton is the main cash crop of the Mexican Imperial Valley oasis, one of the places where the United

States and Mexico are in dispute over water rights. The region's isolation from Central Mexico was partly remedied in 1948 by the completion of a railroad southeast from Mexicali to a junction with the Nogales to Mexico City line. This improvement will help make possible a fuller development of the Colorado Delta area. Copper mines, especially at La Cananea in Sonora and Santa Rosalia in Baja California, are foremost in output of this metal in the republic. Tuna caught off the North Pacific coast account for much of the value of the nation's fisheries products.

**South Pacific.** Separated from Central Mexico by the deep Balsas Valley, the South Pacific area is largely a highland region composed of narrow, flat-topped divides and steep-sided valleys. A strip of coastal plain, the Tehuantepec lowlands, and a flat-floored valley in central Chiapas provide the most extensive areas of level land. Since most of the surface is well watered there are valuable forests. In places where rainfall is light, however, as in interior Oaxaca, irrigation must be practiced.

Isolation is the dominant fact in the life of the region. This causes even mining to be relatively unimportant, although mineralization is believed to be great. Set apart from the main currents of Mexican life, most inhabitants lead a primitive subsistence existence. Yet with improved transportation, considerable areas, now unused, may become productive.

The region has no large cities; Oaxaca is the principal center. Manzanillo, in the northwest, is Mexico's chief Pacific port because of its railroad connection with Central Mexico. Acapulco, today an internationally renowned resort and in colonial times the principal Pacific port, has a much better harbor, but few ships now call there because its connection with Mex-

ico City is by a motor road only. Exports of the South Pacific—coffee, bananas, and forest products—leave mostly through the Atlantic port of Puerto México.

### Progress in Mexico

Both the Mexican government and private interests are making strong efforts to improve the economy of the country. Big, new luxury hotels help attract tourists to Mexico City and other centers, and tourism is an important source of income. Great improvements have been made in education from village schools to the National University of Mexico, famed for its ultramodern buildings. The government is assisting agriculture by reclamation, land subdivision, and instruction in improved farming methods. More than 7 million acres of arid land have been irrigated. Large land holdings have been subdivided for the benefit of small farmers. Government agencies also help farmers in the selection of seeds, the breeding of livestock, and the marketing of crops. Manufacturing has expanded, especially in such light industries as cotton, rayon and woolen textiles, and tobacco processing. Although iron and steel are produced at Monterrey where coal and ore from local sources are used, this supplies only part of the national needs and so could well be increased. Most of the principal Mexican cities have made rapid material gains with the development of industry and trade, and with improvements in transportation, education, and construction. As a close neighbor to the United States it is natural for Mexico to have more trade with this country than any other. Gradually even the people of rural villages are learning about developments in the outside world. Throughout Mexico the people are in process of changing from a primitive way of life to that which is a part of the modern world.

## CENTRAL AMERICA

Six independent countries and a British colony, British Honduras, are included in Central America (Figure 5-12). All of the countries are relatively small, especially when compared with

the other countries of the Western Hemisphere. Nicaragua, the largest, is slightly smaller than Michigan, and El Salvador, the smallest, is only a little larger than Maryland. Guatemala has

**POLITICAL DIVISIONS OF CENTRAL AMERICA AND THE WEST INDIES**

0 _____ 400 MILES

★ Capital of country

*Figure 5-12  Central America and the West Indies include nine independent countries, in addition to territories controlled by European and other American nations.*

the greatest total population, but El Salvador has the highest population density.

## Guatemala

Guatemala is the most Indian of the Caribbean nations, for more than half its people are pure Indian and most of the rest are more Indian than white. It is also the most populous Central American country and the one with the largest external trade. Yet, over 75 per cent of the area is forest or brushland and less than 10 per cent is cropped.

The northern third of Guatemala, in Petén, is a jungle-covered southward extension of the limestone plain of Yucatan. Artifacts and stone ruins indicate a once dense Maya population,

but today only a few primitive Indians live in the area. Chicle and other forest products are exported.

The middle third of the country is a moderately populated region of steep-sided ridges and deep valleys with east-west trends. The valleys widen into rainy, alluvial plains along the Gulf of Honduras. Most thickly peopled is the Cobán area, which has an elevation of 2,000 to 5,000 feet and produces coffee. Population is also fairly dense in the lower Motagua valley, site of older banana plantations and more recently of plantings of abacá. Both neighborhoods have notable Maya ruins. Puerto Barrios is the main port and a terminus of the interocean railroad which extends to the Pacific port

## TABLE 5-3.  CENTRAL AMERICA

| Country | Area, sq miles | Population, in thousands | Population per sq mile | Chief exports |
|---|---|---|---|---|
| Guatemala | 42,042 | 3,200 | 76 | Coffee, bananas, chicle, abacá |
| El Salvador | 8,259 | 2,158 | 261 | Coffee, gold, silver, sugar, balsam |
| Honduras | 43,227 | 1,608 | 37 | Bananas, silver, gold, lumber, coffee |
| Nicaragua | 57,145 | 1,224 | 21 | Coffee, gold, bananas, sesame seed |
| Costa Rica | 19,690 | 951 | 48 | Coffee, bananas, cacao, abacá |
| Panama | 28,576 | 837 * | 30 | Bananas, cacao, abacá, coconuts |
| British Honduras | 8,867 | 78 | 9 | Mahogany, pine, chicle, grape-fruit juice |

\* Excludes Canal Zone.
SOURCE: *The Statesman's Year Book,* Macmillan & Co., Ltd., London, 1956.

of San José. The railway also connects with lines extending to Mexico and El Salvador.

Today, most Guatemalans live, just as when the Spanish arrived, in the fertile, volcano-studded, highland part of the southern third of the nation. These subtropical and temperate elevations of 2,000 to 8,000 feet have 35 to 50 inches of precipitation annually, with a rainy season from April to November. Where uncleared, oak and pine forests thrive. Most of the coffee, which comprises about 70 per cent of the nation's exports, is produced here, especially between the Mexican border and Guatemala City, Central America's largest urban center. Much more land, however, is in subsistence crops. Mountain scenery, Indians following their traditional way of life, colorful markets, beautiful Lake Atitlán, and the ruins of Antigua, the colonial capital destroyed by an earthquake in 1773, are attractions to the tourists who arrive by both air and sea.

A sparsely tenanted, hot, malarial coastal plain, 20 to 30 miles wide, borders the Pacific. In this part of the nation, cattle ranches occupy tracts of savanna grass; much of the nation's sugar cane is grown, and banana plantations have recently become more extensive than those on the Caribbean. Nearly three-fourths of the 7 million stems of bananas cut annually are raised along the Pacific coast, mostly under irrigation.

### El Salvador

Almost no part of El Salvador is unoccupied. It is the smallest and most densely populated Central American nation. Population is greatest in the highlands, which run lengthwise through the country and have a general elevation of 1,500 to 4,000 feet. Only the loftiest of the volcanic peaks extend into *tierra fría*. San Salvador, the capital, at an elevation of 2,240 feet, enjoys comfortable average monthly temperatures that range from 71 to 76°F. The annual precipitation averages 68 inches, with a dry season from January to May.

Although gold and silver together form the nation's second most valuable export, both mining and manufacturing are limited. Sixty per cent of the surface is cultivated. The rest is largely in pasture. Coffee, mainly produced on small and medium-sized farms, dominates the economic life of the nation. Grown in the highlands, it normally comprises over 80 per cent of the exports. However, maize, a food crop, occupies more land. Sugar cane, grown on the narrow coastal lowland, is a second agricultural export, while the world's supply of balsam of Peru, a pharmaceutical gum, is gathered from wild trees along the coast between Acajutla and La Libertad. A railroad runs the length of the country and joins with the Guatemalan system.

## Honduras

Bananas make up some two-thirds of the yearly exports by value of Honduras. The country was formerly the world's largest shipper of this crop. Production has recently been about 13 million stems annually. Reduction from past peak yields of almost twice this number is attributable to damage by sigatoka disease. Most of the plantations are owned by large fruit companies, use Negro labor, and are located on the hot, rain-drenched Caribbean coastal plain. Puerto Cortés, Tela, and Le Ceiba are banana ports. The only railroads in Honduras are those built in connection with the banana industry.

Most of Honduras is mountainous and forested. Forests near the Caribbean are tropical and still contain treasures of mahogany, lignum vitae, and Spanish cedar. Pine and oak forests, with considerable park land, of value for expanding the cattle industry, cover higher surfaces. Because of a paucity of rich soils (recent volcanic action is lacking), a pronounced dry season, and poor roads, agriculture in the highlands is mainly limited to subsistence crops. The Copán area is known for the ruins of an ancient Maya capital. Most Hondurans live in the western half of the country. Large areas in

*Figure 5-13   A donkey carrying abacá stalks from a field in Guatemala. Abacá, or Manila hemp, promises to remain an important plantation crop in Central America where it got its start during World War II when the Philippine industry, which was supplying most of the world's needs, was disrupted by Japanese occupation. (Courtesy of United Fruit Company.)*

the east are not fully explored and are inhabited only by a few primitive Indians. In the mountains there are mines producing gold, silver, and lead. Tegucigalpa, the capital and principal commercial and industrial center of the country, is located in a high mountain valley.

## Nicaragua

Nicaragua is the most sparsely populated, and has the least foreign trade, of any Central American country. Not over 5 per cent of its surface is cultivated and but little more is grazed. Except for a few mining camps, and small seaside settlements among the flat, swampy Caribbean shore, the rough, forested, inaccessible eastern half of the country has few people. Banana production, focused on Puerto Cabezas, is of small consequence.

The country is unusual in that many of its people live in the *tierra caliente*. Population is densest in the lake region, especially between Managua and Granada. Settlement is also fairly dense in highlands to the northeast of the lakes, as in the coffee area of Matagalpa. Most coffee, however, is produced southwest of Managua, the capital. Cattle, raised in grasslands, especially those east of Lake Nicaragua, enter foreign trade, both as live animals and hides. The presence of a possible interoceanic canal route has already been mentioned. A treaty made in 1916 gives the United States exclusive rights to construct and control such a canal.

## Costa Rica

This nation has the largest white population, and is the most democratic and most literate of the Central American republics; more than the others it is a land of small proprietary farms. Yet, nearly two-thirds of the surface is forested

and sparsely populated, if populated at all. Coffee accounts for about 50 per cent and bananas for 30 per cent of the annual exports.

Population is concentrated in the fertile and temperate Meseta Central. Most of the people are white or near-white. In this area is located the attractive capital, San José, and three other of the nation's largest cities. The Meseta Central is the chief producer of Costa Rica's fine-flavored coffee. Large amounts of maize, sugar cane, beans, potatoes, fruit, and vegetables are grown for local consumption. There are also substantial grazing and dairy industries.

In the Caribbean lowlands, settlement is of consequence only along the main line and branches of the Puerto Limón–San José railroad. The world's first large-scale commercial production of bananas was established in these lowlands. Peak exports, in 1913, totaled over 11 million stems. Today, because of Panama

*Figure 5-14 Irrigation tower, or riser, operating on a Pacific Coast banana plantation. The riser nozzle slowly revolves, its discharge covering 3.5 acres with the equivalent of 2 inches of rainfall in a six-hour period. This operation takes place once a week during the dry season. (Courtesy of United Fruit Company.)*

disease, the plantations are all abandoned and the limited export of bananas from the east coast comes from small temporary plantings. The United Fruit Company recently announced plans, however, to reestablish large plantations by reclaiming disease-infested land through flooding it for a year or more, then draining and replanting. Meanwhile, much of Costa Rica's 40,000 acres of cacao has been established in the Caribbean lowlands. Plantings of some 10,-000 acres in abacá during World War II have recently been enlarged. In addition, Negroes, who constitute most of the lowland population, grow considerable food for domestic use.

The banana plantations are now along the Pacific Coast where they have been in operation since 1938. Annual exports of some 15 million stems place Costa Rica second only to Ecuador in world shipments. Golfito and Quepos are the leading banana ports. The plantations must be irrigated during the dry season. They are sprayed to prevent sigatoka damage. It is significant, however, that over 12,000 acres of bananas in the Quepos division have already been abandoned because of Panama disease, and have been replaced by African oil palm, cacao, pasture, and trial plantings of mahogany and teak. Workers on the plantations are largely from Guanacaste. This northwestern province is a scrub forest and grassland area of cattle ranches and cereal production, with a moderately dense mestizo population.

## Panama and the Canal Zone

First traversed by Balboa, who discovered the Pacific in 1513, Panama has since been most significant as an interoceanic pass route. Over the "Old Gold Road" was portaged much of colonial South America's wealth. United States interest in the crossing expanded during the California gold rush of 1849. In 1855 American capital completed the transisthmian railroad, but interest then waned. A French attempt to dig a canal in 1880–1889 failed because of yellow fever and mismanagement. When the Spanish-American War broke out, in 1898, and it took the battleship Oregon two months to travel the 13,000 miles from the Pa-

cific to the Atlantic, need for a canal became evident to the United States.

In 1903, when Panama revolted against Colombian rule, the United States quickly recognized the new nation. By the treaty then concluded, the United States gained the right to build, operate, and defend the canal, and to have jurisdiction in perpetuity over the 10-mile-wide Canal Zone. The Zone has a land area of 362 square miles and a population, including those in the ports of Balboa and Cristóbal, of approximately 50,000. The Panama Canal was completed in 1914. It is 50 miles long and has three sets of lift locks on each side of the summit elevation of 85 feet in Gatun Lake. On the Atlantic side three locks are at Gatun; on the Pacific side one is at Pedro Miguel and two at Miraflores. Its value to the United States as a wartime facility is, of course, inestimable. In addition it has greatly aided the expansion of American intercoastal commerce and trade between the east coast of the United States and the west coast of South America and eastern Asia. Bulky raw materials comprise the Pacific to Atlantic cargo; manufactured goods, most of that moving in the opposite direction.

The Republic of Panama itself is divided into two parts by the Canal Zone. To the east, much of the rough, rainy, malarial, selva-covered land, with maximum elevations of about 4,000 feet, is almost unoccupied except for the San Blas Indians along the Caribbean littoral. To the west, on the Caribbean side of the mountain backbone, precipitation is very heavy and the rain forest is thinly peopled. On the Pacific side, where rainfall is less and more seasonal, there is considerable savanna vegetation. In this area lives most of Panama's population outside of the 22 per cent who reside in Panama City and Colón. The completed Panamanian section of the Pan-American Highway loosely ties this population together. The transisthmian highway between Colón and Panama City was constructed during World War II.

Over two-thirds of Panama remains in forests, the source of cabinet woods and other tree products. Cattle, yielding hides for export, graze much of the remaining surface. Only about 5 per cent is cultivated. Rice is the leading subsistence crop. Bananas, of which 7 to 8 million stems are shipped annually, are mostly produced on the Pacific side near Costa Rica and move out through Puerto Armuelles. The old banana area in the Bocas del Toro region on the Caribbean is now significant for its plantations of cacao, abacá, and coconuts.

## British Honduras

The Crown Colony of British Honduras is the least important part of Central America. The coastal area is a low, flat tropical land having many swamps and vast jungles. In land to the south, elevations increase and form a series of low ridges. In the interior are some areas of savanna. The economy of the country is dependent upon its forests. Mahogany, cedar, chicle, and rosewood are the principal exports. Alligator skins are also exported. Cotton goods, petroleum, and hardware are the chief imports. Most of the foreign trade is carried on with the United States. Racially the people are mainly a mixture of Negro and Indian. Only about 4 per cent are European. Belize is the capital and chief city.

## WEST INDIES

Geographically the West Indies comprise three island groups, the Bahamas, the Greater Antilles, and the Lesser Antilles. Included are the independent countries of Cuba, Haiti, and the Dominican Republic, and various islands associated politically with the United States, Great Britain, France, and the Netherlands.

## Cuba

Nearly 90 per cent of Cuba's exports are sugar and other sugar cane derivatives. Cuba is the world's largest sugar exporter. The industry employs about one-third of the nation's workers and uses more than half its cultivated land. Even slight variations in the quantity or price of sugar marketed are quickly reflected in the nation's well-being. Production reached an all-time high of 7.9 million tons in 1952, but much more than this amount could be produced.

The island is nearly as large as the rest of the West Indies combined. Only a quarter is hilly or mountainous. Soils, derived from the limestone underlying half or more of the surface, are particularly productive of cane. The frost-free climate, with a dry season to raise sugar content, the easily cleared palm-savanna vegetation, the numerous excellent harbors, and nearness to the principal market, the United States, where Cuban sugar receives preferential tariff and quota treatment, are other advantages. The industry is controlled by large companies.

The famous cigar tobaccos, on the other hand, are mostly grown on small farms in central and western Cuba. About half of each crop is exported. Bananas from Oriente, grapefruit from the Isle of Pines, and pineapples and avocados from the Havana area are also shipped abroad. The stress on cash crops is so great that insufficient food is grown for home consumption. Cuba mines some copper and is the second largest Latin-American producer of manganese, but the once sizable output of iron ore is now negligible. Over half the country's people live in cities. Havana has 800,000 residents. Tourists from the United States annually spend large sums on the island.

## Haiti

The French-speaking Negro nation of Haiti occupies the western third of Hispaniola. Approximately 75 per cent of the surface is mountainous. The Cul-de-Sac plain extending east from the capital, Port Au Prince, is so dry that irrigation is necessary. About 90 per cent of the Haitians are rural dwellers who work thousands of small subsistence farms by primitive hoe and machete methods. Evidence of the old French plantations has been largely obliterated. Population pressure—the density is nearly 300 per square mile—has pushed agriculture into the mountains where often only shifting cultivation is possible. This results in deforestation, serious soil erosion, and impoverishment. Cof-

TABLE 5-4.   WEST INDIES

| Political division | Area, sq miles | Population, in thousands | Population per sq mile |
|---|---|---|---|
| Cuba | 44,218 | 5,814 | 132 |
| Haiti | 10,714 | 3,112 | 291 |
| Dominican Republic | 19,333 | 2,347 | 121 |
| Puerto Rico | 3,423 | 2,210 | 646 |
| Virgin Islands (U.S.) | 135 | 26.7 | 20 |
| Bahama Islands | 4,404 | 87 | 19 |
| Barbados | 166 | 219 | 1,319 |
| Jamaica | 4,411 | 1,503 | 340 |
| Leeward Islands | 423 | 120 | 283 |
| Trinidad and Tobago | 1,980 | 678 | 342 |
| Windward Islands | 810 | 283 | 398 |
| Netherlands Antilles | 381 | 176 | 462 |
| Guadeloupe | 583 | 229 | 392 |
| Martinique | 380 | 239 | 629 |

fee is the leading cash crop, some of it growing semiwild.

## Dominican Republic

Differences of language, culture, race, and a lower population density separate the Dominican Republic, which occupies the eastern two-thirds of Hispaniola, from Haiti. Language and culture are Spanish. About 10 per cent of the 2⅓ million people are Caucasian, 20 per cent Negro, and the rest mulatto. Population density is 121 per square mile.

The sparsely peopled Cordillera Central splits the country from east to west. A northern lowland, the Cibao, except for its drier western end, is a heavily inhabited and productive region of small farms. There is a second concentration of population on the southern coastal plain. Territory to the west of the capital, Ciudad Trujillo, is semiarid and must be irrigated. This is a center of sugar production by a few large landholders and associated tenants and small farmers. Sugar constitutes over 50 per cent of the nation's exports. Cacao, coffee, leaf tobacco, beef, and live cattle are also exported.

## United States Dependencies

**Puerto Rico.** Self-government in the Commonwealth of Puerto Rico, taken over from Spain in 1898, is now practically complete. The island's biggest problem is too many people and too little land. Population density is 646 per square mile, and the current rate of increase may be the world's highest. Although 75 per cent of the area is mountainous and irrigation is necessary along most of the south coast, nearly half the surface is tilled. This is less than one-half acre per capita and opportunities for extending cultivation are small. Much food must be imported, especially since one-third of the cropped land produces sugar which makes up 50 per cent of the exports.

Vigorous efforts are being made to improve the level of living. The Land Law of 1941, providing for enforcement of a 500-acre limitation on land ownership, has resulted in the division of large holdings into thousands of smaller properties. Efforts begun in 1947 to attract new industry have already been highly successful. A Tax Holiday Act gives new industry blanket tax exemption until 1959. Other attractions to industry are financial assistance, cheap hydroelectric power, plentiful and cheap labor, a sizable local market, and good access to foreign markets. San Juan is the leading manufacturing center, the capital, and the largest city. The needlework industry, which imports its raw materials, presently employs more workers in home and factory than does any other industry, and its

*Figure 5-15   Paper, glass, and cement mills located on the northern coastal lowlands near the San Juan metropolitan area. In the background are limestone haystack-hills, one with a quarry, and in the distance the central highlands. (Courtesy of Puerto Rico Economic Development Administration.)*

products are second only to sugar among exports. Tobacco, rum, fruits, and molasses are also important exports.

**The Virgin Islands.**   These islands include St. Thomas, St. Croix, and St. John, along with some 50 islets and rocks that are mostly uninhabited. They were purchased from Denmark in 1917 to obtain the site for a naval base at Charlotte Amalie on St. Thomas, and to prevent Germany's gaining title to them. Both the population and the economic importance of the islands have declined although small amounts of sugar and rum are produced and there is some tourist trade.

*British West Indies*

Six groups of West Indian islands—the Bahamas, Barbados, Jamaica and Dependencies, the Leeward Islands that include the British Virgin Islands, Trinidad and Tobago, and most of the Windward Islands—are controlled by Great Britain. Except for the Bahamas and the British Virgins, these islands will be established in 1958 as a new nation, the British Caribbean Federation with its capital at Port of Spain, Trinidad. The population of the new federation is almost three million, and it will have the

status of a dominion in the British Commonwealth of Nations. Members of the federation are: Jamaica, Trinidad and Tobago, the Windward Islands (Grenada, St. Vincent, St. Lucia, St. Kitts, Montserrat), and Barbados. The United States has become more concerned with the islands because of the agreement of September 2, 1940, with Great Britain; that agreement gave the United States the right to establish defense bases on the Bahamas, Jamaica, St. Lucia, Antigua, and Trinidad. Only Trinidad and Jamaica have much importance to the world at large.

**Trinidad.**   Trinidad is a junction point for international air and steamship lines and an entrepôt for a large surrounding area. Its cosmopolitan population is about one-third East Indian, descendants of indentured laborers brought in to work sugar plantations after Negro slaves were freed in 1838. Only 5 per cent of the people are white. Trinidad's production of more than 20 million barrels of petroleum makes the island the most important British colony in the Caribbean. Oil and oil products constitute roughly 75 per cent of its annual exports. The principal fields are in the southwestern peninsula. The famous lake of natural asphalt, located in the northeast part of this peninsula, now produces only a small part of the world's supply.

Three parallel west-east ranges of low mountains or hills cross Trinidad in the north, center, and south, with the highest point, 3,085 feet, being in the north. Between these is undulating lowland. About 40 per cent of the surface is cleared of the original rain forest. Most of the people reside on the drier, west side of the island where wage workers on large estates produce most of the leading crop, sugar cane. Cacao, the colony's second crop, is produced in the east, where rainfall of 100 inches is twice that in the sugar area. Because of attacks of witches'-broom disease, however, cacao production has declined greatly from the time when Trinidad was one of the world's main sources of the commodity. Port of Spain, with its deep harbor, is the business and administrative center of the island.

**Jamaica.** Jamaica is largely an upraised, highly eroded plateau of coral limestone rock with the Blue Mountains of hard resistant rock rising to a top height of 7,402 feet in the east. Only 15 per cent of the surface of 4,450 square miles is level and only 12 per cent is tilled. Coastal plains are widest on the drier south side of the island; rainfall is heaviest, 150 to 200 inches, on the northeastern Blue Mountain slopes. Less than 1 per cent of the people are white. Kingston is the capital. In addition to income from agriculture, Jamaican balances are increased by money sent home by laborers who have gone abroad and that spent by tourists at Montego Bay, Kingston, and other resorts.

*Figure 5-16  Spraying cacao trees against witches'-broom disease. (Courtesy of United Fruit Company.)*

Sugar, so important in early days, is again the most valuable crop. Jamaica was once the world's largest producer of bananas, shipping over 24 million stems one year, but because of plant diseases exports have declined to around 2 million stems annually. Crops of Blue Mountain coffee and of coconuts have also declined. Three aluminum companies, two from the United States and one Canadian, control extensive bauxite deposits. Large-scale shipments begun in 1953 have made Jamaica a leading source of this raw material.

**Barbados and Other British Islands.**   On only 166 square miles, Barbados has 228,000 people, a population density of 1,319 persons per square mile. The staple product is sugar, with molasses and rum as by-products. There is some commercial fishing. The chief city is Bridgetown. Antigua is the largest of the Leeward Islands which include St. Kitts, Nevis, and the British Virgins. The Windward Islands consist of Grenada, St. Vincent, the Grenadines, St. Lucia, and Dominica. Cacao, nutmegs, mace, bananas, arrowroot starch, lime juice, vanilla, coconut products, and cotton are exported. Some rum is manufactured. The Bahamas off southern Florida are chiefly known for their resorts and fishing. Nassau is the principal port.

## Netherlands West Indies

The six islands owned by the Netherlands are divided into two groups, 500 miles apart, and are governed from Willemstad (Wellemstadon) on Curaçao. The northern group is small islets of no consequence. The southern group is important only because of the great oil refineries on Aruba and Curaçao. One refinery on Aruba, established in 1929, has a capacity of 395,000

barrels daily and, excepting the one at Abadan, Iran, is the largest in the world. Refineries on Curaçao were established in 1917 and can refine 275,000 barrels of crude oil daily. The petroleum for refining comes mainly from Venezuela, with some imports from Colombia. Aruba has 70 square miles of area and 53,500 people; Curaçao, 210 square miles and 102,000 people.

## French West Indies

The French West Indies include Guadeloupe, its five dependencies, and Martinique.

**Guadeloupe.**   This island has 583 square miles of area and 240,000 inhabitants. Its two parts are separated by a mangrove swamp. The high, rugged, western part reaches a maximum elevation of 4,867 feet and oddly enough is known as Basse Terre (lowland). The smaller eastern part has a surface less than 400 feet high and is called Grande Terre (great land). Sugar and rum produced on plantations of Grande Terre, and bananas, coffee, and vanilla grown on smaller farms on Basse Terre are the leading cash crops.

**Martinique.**   Martinique is a mountainous island, culminating in the north in Mt. Pelée, 4,428 feet high. This volcanic peak erupted May 8, 1902, destroying the island's principal town, St. Pierre, and 40,000 people. Fort de France is now the largest city. Precipitation varies from over 200 inches on the windward exposures with year-round rain, to as little as 41 inches on the southwest coast where there is a January-to-April dry period. About one-third the island is cultivated. Rum, sugar, and bananas are exported.

### IN PERSPECTIVE

## Middle America

Middle America is of great importance to the United States because of its location. Furthermore, its resources are used to supplement those of our country. Mexico, the largest and

most populous nation in the region, is a leader in inter-American relations, and is also a major field for trade and investment by the people of the United States. The country widens to its maximum width along its northern border where it adjoins the United States. Except for cotton, most of the products of Mexico are marketed in the United States.

Central America and the West Indies are so easy to reach by sea and air routes that the majority of their trade is also with the United States, and they are increasingly popular with tourists. Except in the highlands, most parts of Middle America have tropical climates. The agricultural products of these tropical regions are in demand in the United States, which imports coffee, cane sugar, sisal, bananas, cigar tobacco, fruit juices, cacao, and spices from the area. Mahogany and chicle are among the natural forest products exported.

The United States has made large investments in Middle America, particularly in banana and sugar plantations and in the mining industry. Airlines, railroads, public utilities, and resort hotels are other fields for investment.

Besides Mexico, Middle America is divided into a large number of independent countries and dependencies, and at times in the past the governments of some of these have left much to be desired. Today, however, all the countries of Middle America are making strong efforts to improve living conditions and opportunities for their people. In many places, mills and factories have been started which give jobs to many who previously never worked in industry. Experimental work is being done on many phases of agriculture such as pest control, seed selection, use of fertilizers, irrigation, and mechanization. Such experiments will result in improvement in crop yields and incomes for many people.

Although revolutions do occur sometimes and dictators are not unknown, most elections now are by ballots, not bullets. Middle America is making striking progress in political stability, education, industrialization, construction of highways, improvement of agriculture, and altered attitudes toward others. These and other changes now in the making will cause lasting readjustments in ways of life for most people throughout the region, especially if health and living standards continue to improve.

## EXERCISES

*1.* What countries, territories, and islands are included in Middle America?

*2.* In which part of Mexico do most of the people live? What geographical factors make this area desirable?

*3.* Define the terms *tierra caliente, tierra templada, tierra fría*. Where is each located? What are the principal economic activities in each?

*4.* What racial groups make up the population of Middle America? Where is each group dominant? Which group has made the least cultural advancement? Why?

*5.* What are the regions of Mexico? What are the chief economic activities in each? Why is there such a variety of agricultural production?

*6.* Why are the countries of Central America frequently classed as backward countries? Why is the term "banana republics" frequently applied to the area?

*7.* What non-American nations have colonies in Middle America? What are the chief colonies of each? Why are these colonies important to the mother nations?

*8.* Which West Indian islands are territories of the United States? How were these territories acquired? Why were they acquired? What are the principal problems presented by each?

*9.* Where is the Panama Canal located? Why is it important? Where are possible routes for other canals?

*10.* What are the chief exports of the Greater Antilles? Which nations buy most of these exports? Which islands are the chief producers? What is the relationship between landforms and production?

*11.* What are the chief minerals mined in Mexico? How does mineral production in Mexico compare with that in other Middle American countries?

*12.* What are the principal attractions that cause many American tourists to visit Middle American countries? Which cities are the chief resorts?

*13.* Why have so many people from Puerto Rico migrated to New York?

## SELECTED REFERENCES

Carlson, Fred A.: *Geography of Latin America,* 3d ed., Prentice-Hall, Inc., Englewood Cliffs, N.J., 1952.

Crist, Raymond E.: "Cultural Dichotomy in the Island of Hispaniola," *Economic Geography,* 28:105–121, April, 1952.

————: "Western Cuba: Cultural Traverses in Time and Space," *Scientific Monthly,* 74:91–99, February, 1952.

Dambaugh, Luella N.: "Jamaica: An Island in Transition," *Journal of Geography,* 52:45–57, February, 1953.

Davies, Howell (ed.): *The South American Handbook, 1952,* Trade and Travel Publications Limited, London, 1952.

Garrison, Dorotha J.: "Reclamation Project of the Papaloopan River Basin in Mexico," *Economic Geography,* 26:59–64, January, 1950.

Hansen, Millard, and Henry Wells (eds.): "Puerto Rico: A Study in Democratic Development," *Annals of the American Academy of Political and Social Sciences,* 285:1–166, January, 1953.

James, Preston E.: *Latin America,* The Odyssey Press, Inc., New York, 1950.

Jones, Clarence F.: *Symposium on the Geography of Puerto Rico,* University of Puerto Rico Press, Rio Piedras, 1955.

Jones, Clarence F., and Paul C. Morrison: "Evolution of the Banana Industry of Costa Rica," *Economic Geography,* 28:1–19, January, 1952.

Pearson, Ross: "The Jamaica Bauxite Industry," *Journal of Geography,* 56:377–385, November, 1957.

Pico, Rafael: *The Geographic Regions of Puerto Rico,* University of Puerto Rico Press, Rio Piedras, 1950.

Platt, Robert S.: *Latin America, Countrysides and United Regions,* McGraw-Hill Book Company, Inc., New York, 1942.

Stern, Peter M., John P. Angelli, and David Lowenthal: "British Caribbean Federation," *Focus,* 7(1):1–6, September, 1956.

Wilson, Curtis M.: "El Salvador: A Geographical Reconnaissance," *Journal of Geography,* 48:177–196, May, 1949.

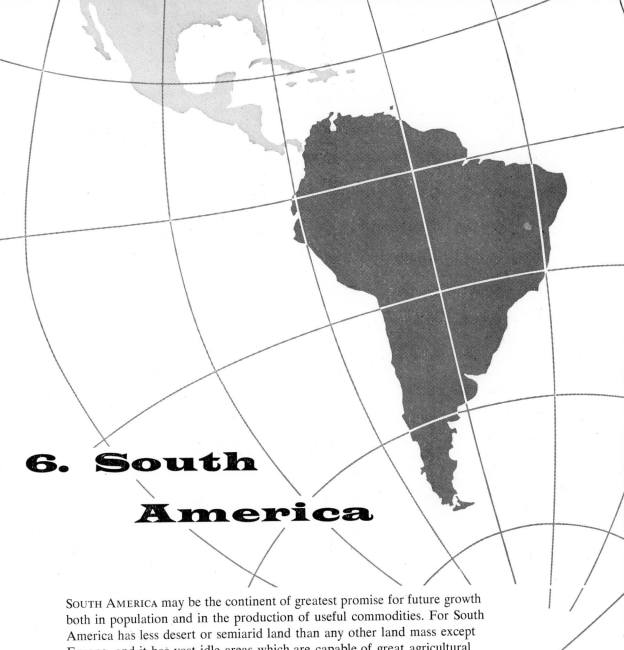

# 6. South America

SOUTH AMERICA may be the continent of greatest promise for future growth both in population and in the production of useful commodities. For South America has less desert or semiarid land than any other land mass except Europe, and it has vast idle areas which are capable of great agricultural development.

Nevertheless, one hesitates in making predictions of future greatness for South America. Since its earliest settlement by Europeans, rapid development seemed likely, yet its expansion has not kept pace with that of its neighbor continent to the north. European settlement in South America began at least a century before Europeans came to live in what is now the United States; yet that nation now is the home of nearly 1.5 times as many people as live in all South America. Gold and rumors of gold and other precious commodities, fact and fancy alike, have given powerful stimulus to the notion that great wealth could be won easily in South America.

*179*

POLITICAL MAP OF SOUTH AMERICA

★ Capital of country

0        500 MILES

**TABLE 6-1. SOUTH AMERICA**

| Country | Area, sq miles | Estimated population, 1955 | Capital |
|---|---|---|---|
| Argentina | 1,804,359 | 19,110,000 | Buenos Aires |
| Bolivia | 424,162 | 3,162,000 | La Paz |
| Brazil | 3,288,042 | 58,456,000 | Rio de Janeiro |
| Chile | 286,396 | 5,931,000 | Santiago |
| Colombia | 439,520 | 12,657,000 | Bogotá |
| Ecuador | 106,000 | 3,619,000 | Quito |
| Paraguay | 157,039 | 1,565,000 | Asunción |
| Peru | 482,285 | 8,714,000 | Lima |
| Uruguay | 72,172 | 2,550,000 | Montevideo |
| Venezuela | 352,143 | 5,774,000 | Caracas |
| British Guiana | 83,000 | 465,000 | Georgetown |
| French Guiana | 35,000 | 28,000 | Cayenne |
| Surinam (Dutch Guiana) | 55,144 | 219,000 | Paramaribo |
| Falkland Islands | 4,618 | 2,200 | Stanley |

SOURCE: *The Statesman's Year Book.*

Much of the actual gold obtained, however, was swift seizure of accumulations which the Indians had made after long periods of painstaking search and careful panning.

An evaluation of South America's prospects for future expansion would recognize the continued possibility of greater production of metals, sugar, and cotton, the woods of both tropical and temperate zone forests, coffee, cacao, bananas, and other products. The evaluation should, however, be directed particularly to the huge areas that, at present, are either unused or are producing below their capacity. A large part of these lands is in climates favorable to a high degree of human health, energy, and efficiency. Other large areas lie in less suitable climates, yet they are habitable and potentially productive (Figure 6-1).

## PHYSICAL SETTING

South America extends from 55° south latitude to 12° north latitude. This span of 67° is 2° greater than that of North America (Figure 6-2). South America lies astride the equator, having its greatest width within the tropics. The continent is mostly a land of warmth and high sun. Nearly 76 per cent is tropical, whereas barely 10 per cent of North America is similarly located. None of South America is in the frigid zone, though a small part of the southern end is close enough to the South Pole to be cold most of the time.

South America, like North America, is roughly triangular with a narrow apex at the south. The two would superimpose nicely, South America covering North America except for California, Florida, and Alaska (Figure 6-3). These bulges account for the larger

*Figure 6-1 Politically, South America is divided between ten independent countries and the three Guianas, each of which is controlled by a European nation.*

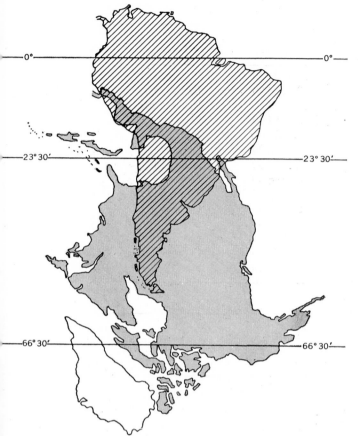

*Figure 6-2  South America and North America similarly placed in latitude. The 23½° line of latitude represents the Tropic of Capricorn for South America, the Tropic of Cancer for North America; the 66½° line of latitude the Antarctic Circle for South America, the Arctic Circle for North America.*

North American area—7,435,000 to 6,860,000 square miles. Three continents are larger than South America; Canada and the United States together are nearly as large.

## Relief Features

The South American pattern of relief somewhat resembles that of North America (Figure 6-4). The western part has a large system of plateaus and mountains, wherein is located most of the highland of the continent; in the east are other highlands which are less continuous and lower, and between these two major uplands is a large plain. In detail, however, the patterns of the two continents differ considerably. The western highland of South America is narrower, higher, and has fewer passes. The eastern highlands are generally plateau-like. The central plain is less extensive than that of North America and is broadest in the Amazon Valley.

**Mountains.** The Andean system extends the full length of the Pacific and along a part of the Caribbean coast, a total length of more than 5,000 miles. In the north there are three distinct ridges, but near the Colombia-Ecuador border they join and continue to the southern end of the continent as a unit. From Colombia southward to about 30° south latitude, there is a complex of plateaus, many of them higher than the top of the highest mountain in the United States. Standing above the plateaus are lofty ranges, the highest in the Western Hemisphere. In these mountains are at least 21 peaks more than 20,000 feet high; in North America, there is only one. Nearly everywhere along the western side, the Andean highland rises abruptly from the Pacific Ocean. The northern half of the Andean Cordillera has considerable land smooth enough for agriculture, and at the time of Columbus most of the people of the continent were living there. This northern Cordillera, being in low latitude, has temperatures which man prefers to those on the plains near sea level.

**Plateaus.** The central and largest of the eastern uplands is the Plateau of Brazil. At its greatest width, it is more than twice as broad as any part of the Andes. In it are a few short mountain ranges. The upland is generally highest near the Atlantic Ocean, and one peak near Rio de Janeiro exceeds 9,000 feet. Mostly, however, the Plateau of Brazil consists of hilly land not too rough for cultivation although little land is tilled in the far interior. Many streams have their sources along the higher eastern side within less than fifty miles of the Atlantic but flow westward, reaching the ocean by circuitous routes of hundreds of miles. In several places, sheets of lava rock and flattish layers of sandstone, both resistant to weathering even in the hot, wet tropics, stand as tablelands with steep escarpments at their borders. This east central part of the plateau contains one of the more productive agricultural areas of the continent, the coffee lands of São Paulo. Within the plateau are rich deposits of minerals, among which is one of the largest deposits of iron ore in the world as well as important sources of gold, manganese, and diamonds. The Guiana Highland also is a plateau of rounded hills, broad tablelands, and a few short mountain ranges. One small river in the area pitches over the edge of a high mesa to form Angel Falls, a drop of 3,212 feet, perhaps the highest waterfall in the world. The Guiana Plateau also is rich in minerals, iron ore, gold, diamonds, and bauxite. Toward the southern end of the continent is Patagonia, a flat, rocky tableland, used mainly for sheep grazing.

**Plains.** The central plains of South America because of their tropical location are of relatively less importance in the economy of the people than the plains of North America or Europe that are situated in the temperate climates. Most northerly is the Llanos between the Andes and the Orinoco River. This flat, grassy plain drains so poorly that in the rainy season the land is inundated for miles. The largest of the plains is the Selva of the Amazon basin. Like the Llanos, it is flat and, for the most part, poorly drained. A low tableland separates the Amazon lowland from the Gran Chaco of Argentina and Paraguay, the next plains area to the south. Like the others, the Gran Chaco is a plain of relatively low productivity and is sparsely inhabited. The Pampa of Argentina and Uruguay extends southward from the Chaco without a change in landforms. Unlike the other South American plains, the Pampa is very productive and supports several million people. With its combination of soils, probably as rich as any in the world, and a climate in which people may live and work with very nearly the maximum of health and energy, the Pampa has become a leader in the economic development of the continent.

*Figure 6-3   South America superposed on North America to show similarity in size and shape.*

### Climate and Vegetation

South America is dominantly a tropical continent; sometime during the year, 75 per cent of its area receives perpendicular rays of the sun. Climatic conditions range from the hot, humid, almost changeless conditions of the wet equatorial to the constantly varying types of climates found in mountain areas (Figure 6-6). Important factors influencing the climates of the continent are the directions of the prevailing winds, the length and heights of the Andes, and the location of the continent.

In its broader part, largely north of 30° south latitude, the rainy tropical and wet-and-dry savanna climates occupy most of the area. In the narrower southern part of South America the mid-latitude climatic types of Mediterranean, marine west-coast, humid subtropical, and steppes predominate. Mountain climate extends the length of the continent.

**Tropical.**   The seasonless rainy tropical climate includes the equatorial lowlands, from

*Figure 6-4   Mountains dominate the landforms of western South America, plains and plateaus the broad areas to the east. The coastal plain of western South America is very narrow, in many places being less than 5 miles wide.*

approximately 5° north latitude to 5° south latitude. The average temperature is about 80°F, and throughout the year there is no appreciable difference. There is no dry season. Rainfall, which is great enough in every month to keep the vegetation always in growth, is heaviest near the base of the northern Andes, both on the eastern and the western sides. Under the stimulus of high temperatures and adequate rainfall at all seasons, the native vegetation has a luxuriance that is not attained in other climates. Where the plant growth has not been disturbed, the ground is covered with tall trees whose branches, commonly intertwined with vines, spread a dense canopy that shades the ground so completely that underbrush and other low growth is nearly eliminated. Forests of this

kind are called *selva*. Along the streams or other openings and on steeply sloping land the dense growth, otherwise concentrated at the treetops, spreads toward the ground. This is the equatorial jungle, the rain forest that travelers usually see.

The wet-and-dry tropical savanna climate adjoins the wet equatorial on both north and south. This climate differs from the wet equatorial in that there is a dry season sufficiently long to retard forest development. Normally it is shortest near the equatorial wet climate, at least three months with less than three inches each of rainfall, and longest on the poleward side where there are normally six months with too little rain for growth of common crops. Temperatures average about 80°F for the warmest and 60°F for the coolest month in all parts except where elevation is responsible for temperatures somewhat lower. The tree growth is much less luxuriant than in the equatorial wet climate. Grass, which can better endure the drought, is tall, lush, and green during the rainy season, but dry and brown in the dry season. Throughout the climatic region, patches of forest and patches of grass intermingle.

The trade winds, which blow along much of the northern coasts of the continent, notably affect the climate, particularly the rainfall. Along the southern part of the Atlantic coast of Brazil, the constant southeast trade winds bring moisture from the ocean and release it as the air rises to cross the highlands near the coast. These winds persist throughout the year; thus the climate and vegetation are those of the rainy tropical climate. A similar condition prevails along the northeastern coast in Brazil, the Guianas, and eastern Venezuela where the northeast trades bring moisture at the time of year when the equatorial calms lie to the south of the equator. This coastal strip, constantly wet, is covered by the selva. Along the Pacific, however, between the equator and about 30° south latitude, the trade winds generally blow offshore. The air, warming as it descends the western side of the Andes, increases its capacity for water. Furthermore, because of the Peru or Humboldt Current, the ocean water nearby is especially cold for the latitude. Both of these factors are unfavorable to rain, and one of the world's driest deserts is developed as a result.

**Temperate.** Along the western margin of the continent, in 30° to 38° south latitude, lies an area with Mediterranean climate similar to that of California in the like northern latitudes. Temperatures vary from 68°F, for the warmest months, to 48°F, for the coldest. The rainfall averages some 12 to 20 inches annually, and nearly all comes during winter. This region lies under the influence of the southern cyclonic wind belt in the winter. The rains come during this season partly because of the cyclones and partly from the cooling of air passing up mountainsides. In summer the region lies in the horse latitudes, the belt of high pressure. The native vegetation, adjusted to rainfall at the season when temperatures are the least favorable for growth, consists mostly of grass and thorny brush. The brush is similar to the maqui of the European Mediterranean and the chaparral of California. Most of the plants are broad-leaved and evergreen and include some drought-resistant trees.

The marine west-coast climate, poleward from the Mediterranean climate, as in North America, is characterized by very heavy rainfall, usually above 80 inches annually, with pronounced winter maximum. The strong westerly winds are chilled as they move up the mountains and heavy rainfall results. The temperatures are cool in midsummer; the winters are frequently disagreeably cold. Because of the moist climate tree growth is tremendous; the largest trees are almost as tall as the redwoods of California.

The humid subtropical climatic area is along the east coast, approximately 25° to 40° south latitude. It differs from the climate of that type in the United States in that summers are cooler,

*Figure 6-5   Angel Falls, located in the Guiana Highlands of Venezuela, the world's highest, 3,212 feet. (Courtesy of Hamilton Wright.)*

CLIMATES OF SOUTH AMERICA

- Rainy tropical
- Wet and dry tropical savanna
- Tropical steppe
- Tropical desert
- Humid subtropical
- Mediterranean
- Mid-latitude desert
- Mid-latitude steppe
- West coast marine
- Mountain, high plateau

0       500 MILES

more nearly comparable to those of the Corn Belt. The winters are like those of the Cotton Belt. Few, if any, climates offer a better combination of conditions favorable both to large crop growth and to human health, energy, and efficiency.

The steppes occupy the land southward from the humid subtropical area. The region is in the same wind belt as southern Chile, but on the leeward side of the Andes; thus aridity is a strong factor in making the land unproductive. There are no forests; instead grasslands, steppe-like in character and of low pasturage value, stretch from the humid subtropical area to the cold, windy, dry southern extremity of the continent.

**Mountain.** Climates of mountains are characterized by temperatures lower than those of nearby plains, and in most instances, by greater rainfall. The average annual temperature at Quito, 9,350 feet, is 54.6°F. At Iquitos, to the eastward on the Amazon, and 9,000 feet lower, the average is 22° higher, 76.6°F; and at Guayaquil, on the Pacific, the average is 78°F. Other comparisons of stations at nearly

the same latitudes also show cooling with increased altitude. The average for the warmest month at Cerro de Pasco, Peru, is about the same as that for November at Washington, D.C.; at Quito, which is near the equator, all months average between 54 and 55°F. These are temperatures of March in central Illinois. Temperatures of the mountains and high plateaus are too low for human comfort.

The mountain rainfall pattern is influenced not by variation with altitude, but by wind direction. On the windward side, rainfall is heavy; on the leeward, it is light. Iquitos, in the lowlands near the eastern edge of the Andes, receives 103 inches per year, and Manaus (Manáos), also on the Amazon but many miles farther eastward, receives 70 inches. Mollendo, on the western, or leeward, slope but farther south, receives less than one inch. In the southern Andes, however, the rain falls mostly on the western side of the mountains since the prevailing winds are the westerlies. Many coastal stations in southern Chile receive more than 100 inches of rain annually, whereas to the east of the Andes in Argentina there is a semidesert area.

## POPULATION DISTRIBUTION

The population of South America, although more than a hundred million, is only about two-thirds that of North America. Indians dominate in the uplands, for there are more Indians in South America than in North America. Only the lowland countries of Brazil, Argentina, and Uruguay have more people of European descent than persons of Indian and mixed blood. Large numbers of Negroes live in the humid tropical lowlands, chiefly along the coasts.

In South America, as in Middle America, the

cluster pattern of population prevails (Figure 6-7). For the most part, each cluster occupies an area of land which, because of favorable climate, landforms, and relative location, is above average for habitation. It is separated from the next nearby cluster by unused land, either undeveloped or unsuitable for agriculture. In some areas, notably in Brazil, each cluster is centered around a core of early settlement and most are expanding outward toward the others. Eventually they will join, since the land between is

*Figure 6-6   Much of South America is in the tropical climates. Southern South America, where the continent narrows, has the greatest variety of climates. The most highly developed area, from Rio de Janeiro to Buenos Aires, is the transition belt between the tropical and continental climates.*

DISTRIBUTION OF POPULATION IN SOUTH AMERICA

Each dot represents approximately 10,000 persons

0                 500 MILES

habitable. In several instances, as in Argentina, Peru, Ecuador, Paraguay, Chile, and Venezuela, a single cluster constitutes the nucleus of a political unit.

## Native Peoples

Early European explorers found South America inhabited by people who had attained a high degree of political and social organization. They had a well-developed agriculture and a culture which functioned better for them than the European civilization which displaced but never replaced it. Although the native population of South America at the time of Columbus can only be conjectured, the estimate of 10 to 15 million in 1492 is larger than the present population of pure-blood Indians.

The Andean Highland supported by far the largest pre-Columbian population. Extending from near southern Colombia to central Chile was the great Incan empire. The efficiency of the old economy is attested by the fact that, under the government of the Incas, the number of Indians was at least twice the total population of the countries now occupying the lands. There is good evidence that those Indians were better fed, better governed, and happier than their present-day descendants.

North of the Incan domain in the Andean Highland, now in Colombia, dwelt the Chibchas. Their civilization was less well developed than that of the Incas, though they practiced agriculture extensively. In what is now Chile, just south of the Incan land, dwelt the Araucanians. The dense forests of southern Chile and their own aggressiveness helped the Araucanians succeed in resisting the expansion of their northern neighbor.

In various other parts of South America dwelt several groups who had very little to do with each other or with the highland people.

They fished in the rivers and gathered some food from the forests; some of them raised root crops of which manioc was most common. In the grasslands of Argentina lived nomadic hunters who obtained most of their food from the guanaco, a wild animal about the size of a deer. In the north were Caribs and Arawaks, primitive farmers, forest gatherers, fishermen, and hunters. Of the South American natives, only the Incas used metals, mostly gold and silver.

## Settlement by Europeans

Early European settlement was carried on mostly by the Spanish and Portuguese, immigration being restricted to citizens of the mother·countries. The kings distributed land in large blocks to court favorites and business leaders. Their allotments were too large for the owners to work individually, or even with laborers brought from their European homeland. From the outset, estates were chosen where there was a considerable native population to provide labor for mines and farms. Since most of the natives lived in regions apportioned to the Spanish, settlement by Spaniards went forward more rapidly. The Portuguese found no deposits of gold and gems, at first. Hence, they began settlement along the eastern coast where they established plantations for growing sugar cane. Since very few Indians lived there, Negro slaves were imported from Africa to work on the plantations.

The Spanish settlements, then, were at first confined to the highlands, for there were the Indians, the labor supply. Later, stimulated by the success of the Portuguese in eastern Brazil, the Spanish planted sugar in the lowlands of Colombia and Venezuela and, as did the Portuguese, used Negro slaves. The lowlands of Argentina, now the best farmland, were long undeveloped.

*Figure 6-7   The areas of dense population are largely clusters about the cities. In the tropical areas the parts having the greatest population are the mountain valleys.*

## Distribution of Races

The present racial composition of the people reflects governmental policies, geographic handicaps, and opportunities for European settlement. The Andean Highlands, south of Colombia, have remained populated chiefly by the aboriginal Indians. Europeans are the leaders in government, business, and religion, but in numbers they are decidedly in the minority. The coastlands to the west are inhabited chiefly by Spaniards. Only along the Caribbean and the Pacific Coast of southern Chile are there many Indians living near the ocean. A considerable proportion of the population of coastal Colombia is Negro; Negroes are even more numerous in coastal Brazil between Rio de Janeiro and the mouth of the Amazon, the regions where early production of sugar was important. The highlands of Colombia and Venezuela have a climate favorable to Europeans, and to these countries many Europeans, including non-Spaniards, have migrated.

Argentina, Uruguay, and Brazil south of Rio de Janeiro have been settled almost entirely by Europeans. The climate here is favorable to them, their animals, and many of their crops. Settlement was slow, however. In the present century, fairly large communities of Germans and Italians have been established. This is the part of South America which is expanding most rapidly and where population density will probably become the greatest.

Yet, with a start of a hundred years on the United States, and with a native population many times greater, population growth has not kept pace in South America. For this we can cite several reasons. Natural increase of the natives was hindered by exploitation, in places to the point of extermination. Fewer Negroes were brought into South America than into North America, for sugar did not attain in South America the economic importance of cotton, rice, and indigo in the Southern states. Governmental policy restricted immigrants to Spanish and Portuguese. Later, because of climatic and physical conditions, South America did not attract Europeans as did North America. Only recently has any part of South America become a melting pot.

No part of the continent should be considered densely settled in the sense that the population has reached the saturation point, unless it be the high, rocky, cold Andean plateaus and mountains. Perhaps they also could be made more productive since there is some runoff water which could be used for irrigation, and since fewer people live there now than were supported during the time of the Incas.

## THE CARIBBEAN COUNTRIES

The independent countries of Venezuela and Colombia and the three dependencies, commonly referred to as the Guianas, are called the Caribbean countries of South America. Except for a small part of southeastern Colombia, the entire area is north of the equator. Venezuela is the only independent South American country that has no territory in the Southern Hemisphere. All these countries have vast territories that are sparsely settled and largely undeveloped. Each has highlands and lowlands in a topographical pattern that greatly influences the activities of the people. In Colombia and Venezuela, however, the highlands offset, to some extent, the climatic disadvantages of the low-latitude tropics. The Caribbean countries are well situated for world trade because their northward-facing coast is near, and pointed toward, the principal world trade lanes, those leading to the United States and northwestern Europe. The Caribbean countries are all areas of great potential.

### Venezuela

Venezuela is a country of contrasts. There are high mountains and low, swampy lands. Each year there is a season of rains and a season of drought. For four centuries, the population remained static. Although there were many Indians when the earliest Spaniards arrived, the population in 1800 was probably not more than a million. During the next hundred years it doubled. Since 1900, however, the population has increased to about 5 million persons. Formerly poor and burdened by debts, Venezuela now has a sound economy and excellent credit. There is essentially no foreign debt. Royalties from petroleum production are the primary reason for this prosperous condition. Gold and diamonds have been produced for centuries, but petroleum is the chief source of the country's new wealth. The northern highland area is well settled and farms are productive, but the rest of the country has little agriculture. Only 1 per cent of the country is under cultivation.

**Regions.** There are four rather distinct regions in Venezuela. A strip of highlands in the northern part of the country supports most of the people. In this region are some high mountain ranges and a small but fertile central plateau. Here is the area of greatest population density and the best agricultural development. The higher part of the upland, the Cordillera

*Figure 6-8  Aerial view of Caracas, Venezuela. Note that the city is located in a level area which is surrounded by mountains. (Courtesy of Hamilton Wright.)*

Oriental, which is the easternmost range of the Andes, branches near the Venezuelan border to form a Y within which is enclosed the second region, the Maracaibo Lowland. South of the highland lies the Orinoco Plain, a region large in size but sparsely peopled. The fourth region is the Guiana Highland, which contains about half of the area of Venezuela but is practically uninhabited.

The Northern Highland embraces about 12 per cent of the area of Venezuela, yet in it live about 70 per cent of the people. In this region are found most of the agriculture and all cities of the country, except for a few sea and river ports. The Central Upland or intermontane basin, that portion of the Northern Highland roughly between Caracas on the east and Valencia on the west, is the most important in population, political influence, and agriculture. Here was the greatest concentration of Indians,

and here the Spanish grew commercial crops by the plantation system. Sugar was first and it continues to be important, though principally for use in Venezuela. Coffee was introduced shortly before 1800 and is now the leading agricultural export, nearly all of it being shipped to the United States. Cacao, a native crop, is grown, and cacao beans are exported. The value is about half that of coffee. Cacao is grown at the lower elevations chiefly in areas protected against strong winds. The other commercial crops, cotton, tobacco, and sisal, are used within the country. Corn occupies more land than does any other crop and is the principal human food as well as feed for livestock. Other food crops are beans, manioc, rice, and potatoes.

Mostly the surface of the upland is rolling to rough, though it is steep along the margins. There are considerable areas of smooth land, notably near Valencia and Caracas where in-

*Figure 6-9   The Lake Maracaibo area of Venezuela is one of the principal oil-producing regions of the world. (Courtesy of Hamilton Wright.)*

tensive agriculture is practiced. The elevation is sufficient to alleviate the extreme heat of the Caribbean coast, yet not sufficient to eliminate growth of sugar. Valencia is 1,500 and Caracas is 3,100 feet above sea level.

The Central Upland is separated from the Caribbean Sea by a narrow range of mountains which rises abruptly from the sea to a height of 8,900 feet. Caracas, the capital of Venezuela, is in an elevated east-west valley which is only eight airline miles from the coast, but a railroad and a modern highway that connect the capital with its seaport, La Guaira, are much longer because they must climb steep slopes that descend over 3,000 feet to the shore.

West of the Central Upland are many small population clusters. Most of the people live in the *tierra templada* at elevations roughly between 3,000 and 6,000 feet. Cattle do well here. Corn occupies the largest acreage, but coffee is the money crop, the Sierra Nevada de Merida being the chief coffee region of Venezuela. A few people live in the *tierra fría,* above 6,000 feet, where corn is grown up to elevations of 7,500 and wheat and potatoes to heights of 10,000 feet. There are pastures in the high mountain meadows. Some valleys are in the *tierra caliente,* below 3,000 feet, low enough for cacao. There is some mineral production in the mountains. The highlands to the east of the Central Plateau are lower, less populous, and produce chiefly subsistence crops and cacao.

The Maracaibo Basin, the smallest region of Venezuela, has contributed most to the economy of the nation. Along the eastern side of Lake Maracaibo are the Bolivar Coastal oil fields with a daily production of a million barrels. Here are over 4,400 producing wells, more than half of them in the shallow waters of Lake Maracaibo. One drilled in 1922 yielded an estimated 100,000 barrels of oil per day. For over 20 years Venezuela exported more oil than any other country, and only the United States produces more. Since the discovery well was completed in 1917, Venezuela has produced nearly 10 billion barrels of petroleum, of which two-thirds were from the Bolivar Coastal fields. Petroleum and its derivatives provide about 95 per cent in value of Venezuela's exports. Oil has changed Venezuela from a poor country to one with a stable economy, no foreign debt, and high credit rating.

Aside from production of oil the Maracaibo Basin is of little importance. The port city of Maracaibo, now having a population of 250,-000, had only 15,000 people before the discovery of oil. Only a few farmers, Indian fishermen, and some workers at the port then lived in the basin. Agriculture has not greatly increased, for the steamy climate is unfavorable to human beings in the land where crop growth could be great.

The other two regions of Venezuela, the Orinoco Lowland and the Guiana Highland, give promise of future importance, but at present they are sparsely populated and make little contribution to the commerce of the country. The average density of population in the lowland, the Llanos, is less than 4 people per square mile. This large plain is a remarkably flat grassland with patches of forest here and there. Although the region is similar in landforms and climate to some densely populated parts of the world, it has not yet been brought into effective use. Mostly it consists of low-grade grazing land. There is a wet season when grass grows luxuriantly but it cannot be grazed effectively since the land is so flat it floods widely, necessitating removal of cattle to uplands. In the dry season, the grass soon becomes dry and brown, having little nutritive value. Insect pests are troublesome at all seasons. The cattle seldom become fat enough in the pastures to furnish a good marketable grade of beef. Some are shipped to the Central Highlands for fattening. Generally they are pastured until they are six or seven years old and then their hides are marketed.

In the Orinoco Lowland, as in the Maracaibo Basin, recent oil production is changing the economic situation. The principal field lies some fifty miles north of the Orinoco River and extends westward from the delta of that stream for over three hundred miles. Although production is less than half that of Maracaibo, nevertheless the Orinoco fields have yielded

CARIBBEAN LOWLAND
OF COLOMBIA

MARACAIBO LOWLAND

*Cauca R.*

*Magdalena River*

THE LLANOS OF THE ORINOCO BASIN

*Orinoco River*

THE GUIANA LOW PLATEAU

GUAYAQUIL
LOWLAND

*Rio Negro*

*Amazon River*

A M A Z O N I A

*Rio Madeira*

*Rio Tapajoz*

DRY
NORTHEAST
BRAZIL

THE ANDEAN HIGHLAND

*Rio Xingu*

INTERIOR PLATEAU AND PLAINS

HUMID
NORTHEAST
BRAZIL

*PLATEAU OF
MATO GROSSO*

*Rio São Francisco*

*PERUVIAN-CHILEAN DESERT*

G R A N   C H A C O

*Rio Paraguay*

*Rio Paraná*

SOUTHEAST CENTRAL
BRAZIL

SUBTROPICAL DRY LANDS

MESOPOTAMIAN REGION

*Rio Uruguay*

SOUTHERN
BRAZIL

CENTRAL
CHILE

*Rio Colorado*

P A M P A S

P A T A G O N I A

*Rio
Negro*

GEOGRAPHIC REGIONS OF SOUTH AMERICA

SOUTHERN
CHILE

0          500  MILES

more than 1.5 billion barrels since production began in 1924.

The Guiana Highland is even less populous than the Orinoco Lowland, averaging less than 1 person per square mile. It is the largest of the regions and has the fewest people. Like the Orinoco Lowland, it has great possibilities of increased utility for producing crops and grazing cattle, yet there is scarcely any agriculture and grazing is not important. The region has considerable possibilities for mining although production is rather localized. One mine is said to have produced 30 million dollars' worth of gold between 1870 and 1890. Gold and diamonds are now produced from placers to the value of more than a million dollars a year each. The diamonds are mostly industrial stones.

Iron is the most important metal mined. Very large deposits of high-grade hematite with an iron content of 50 to 70 per cent have been found. One deposit at Cerro Bolivar is estimated at 500 million tons; another at El Pao is estimated to contain over a billion tons of ore. This is 35 miles south of the Orinoco River port of San Felix. The river has been dredged and jettied to accommodate ocean vessels. Mining is done in open cuts, and the ore transported to the river ports from which it is shipped in ore carriers to such tidewater steel plants in the Eastern United States as those near Baltimore and Philadelphia. Exports total 8 to 10 million tons annually. A steel mill with a capacity of 140,000 tons is planned for Venezuela, which now has only one small plant operating on scrap iron. Although coal occurs it is of low grade and little is suitable for the coke which is needed to develop a large local steel industry.

Along the northern coast of Venezuela are several islands. Most of them are unimportant, fishing and pearling being the chief activities.

The two Dutch island colonies of Aruba and Curaçao are important in the economy of Venezuela and also of Colombia and other Caribbean countries. On Aruba and Curaçao are two petroleum refineries which are among the largest in the world. The gasoline and other refinery products are sold mostly in Europe.

**Foreign Trade.** The per capita foreign trade of Venezuela is the greatest of any of the Latin-American countries; its total trade is exceeded only by that of Brazil and Argentina. Petroleum and derivatives account for 97 per cent of the total exports, in value more than a billion dollars annually. From oil sales, Venezuela obtains the money to buy goods in foreign lands. About two-thirds of Venezuelan imports originate in the United States. From us they buy automobiles and trucks, machinery and other metal products, textiles, chemicals, medicines, and many other items. Milk products to the value of 21 million dollars are imported annually, which seems odd since in Venezuela there are more cattle than people. Demand from the oil fields and Caracas accounts for large imports of foodstuffs which help keep the cost of living very high. This expense could be reduced by growing more food locally.

## Colombia

The population of Colombia is approximately twelve million, somewhat less than that of the metropolitan New York area. The country has an area of about 440,000 square miles or nearly as large as the United States south of the Ohio and east of the Mississippi. Population is strikingly concentrated on densely settled patches of land, each separated from the next one by a considerable expanse almost without people. In most instances each cluster constitutes a political unit, or state, with a boundary zone of empty land rather than a boundary line, al-

*Figure 6-10 The bases for the geographic regions of South America are topography, climate, and land utilization. In the southern part of the continent the regions are smaller and the variety of human activity greater.*

though official boundary lines are recognized. Vast Colombian areas southeast of the Andes in the Guiana tableland, the Orinoco Plain, and the Amazon Plain have a population of only 1 person to 4 square miles of territory. Yet, despite the physical environment which has produced a separation of population groups, Colombia has a remarkably high degree of intellectual development.

**Regions.** Colombia has three major physical divisions, the mountains with enclosed basins in the west, the coastal lowlands narrow along the Pacific and wider along the Caribbean, and the low tablelands and plains in the eastern part of the country.

The western mountains and basins cover about a third of Colombia and contain the large majority of the people. Near the Pacific is a low coastal range, the Serannia Baudo which extends southward from Panama about halfway to Ecuador. In the south near the Ecuador boundary, the Andes branch into three great ranges, the Cordillera Occidental, the Cordillera Central, and the Cordillera Oriental. Between the Baudo and the Occidental is a narrow plain in which the Atrato River flows northward and the San Juan flows southward. Both the Baudo and the plain are sparsely populated, for these

mountains are the rainiest of all South America and are densely covered with selva. The plain is swampy and also heavily forested. Lying between the Oriental and the Central Cordillera is the Cauca River valley. Nearly a third of the people of Colombia live along this river, partly on floodplains and partly on terraces well above in a striking alignment of large population clusters, Medellin at the north; Cali, Popayan, and several others in the central part; and, at the south, Pasto. Between the Cordillera Central and the Cordillera Oriental lies the chief river of the country, the Magdalena. Although people live all along it, their total number is not great because little land is level enough for crops. Within the Cordillera Oriental are several high basins containing densely populated clusters of settlement. These have nearly half the people of Colombia. In one is the capital and largest city, Bogotá. Aside from the valleys and basins in the Andes, there is only one other populous region, the low and relatively small Magdalena Plain in the north. The plains and low tablelands east of the Andes are essentially uninhabited.

**Agriculture.**    As in all other South American countries, agriculture supports most of the people. There are many kinds of crops since the

climatic variations are considerable. Colombia does not extend through many degrees of latitude, yet the great differences of elevation between low valleys and high basins provide great variations in temperature. Temperatures along the Caribbean are uncomfortably warm, about as high as in the Maracaibo Basin (85°F, in July). But at Bogotá, elevation 8,700 feet, the average temperature is 58°F, which is hardly high enough for comfort. Much land is too elevated and thus too cool for crops, though high mountain meadows provide grazing. Some towering mountains reach the level of perpetual snow. In Colombia, the three vertical crop zones—*tierra caliente, tierra templada,* and *tierra fría*—are all represented. The upper limit of farming is approximately 10,500 feet.

In the *tierra caliente,* sugar cane is the leading commercial crop. The principal area of production is along the Cauca River, on its floodplains and low terraces to elevations of about 2,000 feet. Much is grown also in the Magdalena Plain in the north. The total production is large, amounting to about 800,000 tons annually or 150 pounds per person, but scarcely any sugar is exported; most is consumed at home in the form of pancla, an unrefined sugar. Bananas are important in the hot lands. Generally they are grown near the Caribbean ports, for ex-

ample, Santa Marta, from which they are exported to the markets of the United States. Cacao is grown in several hot, wet lowlands where nearby mountains give shelter from the wind. Cotton is grown both in the *tierra caliente* and in the lower part of the *tierra templada.* Cotton and sugar respond best to tropical climates having both wet and dry seasons, the climate of most the lowlands. Bananas and cacao require rain throughout the year, a condition that prevails chiefly along the Pacific Coast. Rice is the most important food crop of the Magdalena Plain.

The *tierra templada* includes most of the populous regions of interior Colombia. In this zone is grown the chief commercial crop, coffee. Colombia ranks second among the countries of the world in coffee production and export. It is grown in or near all of the interior areas of dense settlement, particularly near Medellin, Bogotá, Popayan, and Pasto. Production is about 375,000 tons annually, practically all of which is shipped to the United States. Colombian coffee is superior to most other coffee in grade and brings premium prices on the market. Tobacco, cotton, and beans are grown in the lower sections of the *tierra templada.* Potatoes, wheat, and barley are products of the higher parts. Corn is grown throughout the zone

*Figure 6-11   Llanos of eastern Colombia. (Courtesy of Standard Oil Company of New Jersey.)*

and to some extent also in the warmer lands below. Its acreage is larger than that of any other crop, though the value is lower than that of either coffee or sugar.

In the *tierra fría* corn is grown on the lower slopes up to about 8,800, wheat up to nearly 10,000, and barley and potatoes to 10,500 feet. At elevations too high for crops, the paramos, cattle are grazed in the mountain meadows.

The vast Eastern Lowlands are sometimes considered as a region of future greatness in agriculture and human settlement but, as yet, there is practically no agriculture, not even grazing. Wild tropical savanna grasslands with scattered trees cover most of it.

**Minerals.**   Petroleum is foremost in value of the mineral products. There are two principal oil fields; the smaller is an extension into Colombia of the Maracaibo Basin at the Venezuela border. The other is on the Magdalena River some 300 miles from its mouth. Although production is only about 6 per cent as large as that of Venezuela, Colombia ranks second in South America. In a recent year, three-fourths of the petroleum produced was exported. It is likely that oil production will increase since the rock structures appear favorable, but meager transportation facilities have retarded development.

Although less in value than oil, the precious metals and gems of Colombia have long been famous. The annual value of gold production exceeds 15 million dollars. It is mined from placer deposits widely scattered within the highlands. Platinum is obtained between the coast ranges and the Cordillera Oriental at the headwaters of the Atrato River. Important quantities of emeralds are found not far from Bogotá. About a million tons of coal are mined annually.

**Transportation.**   Colombia is seriously handicapped by difficulties in transportation. The settled areas are separated from each other by exceedingly rough terrain. To travel from Barranquilla, the chief port, to Bogotá, the capital, by surface routes requires a week or more. The traveler would spend at least six days on a boat going up the Magdalena as far

as La Dorada, longer should it be the dry season. He could then go by rail to Bogotá, 185 miles, in one more day. It is easily understood why plane travel is of special importance in a country like Colombia, for by plane the trip is made in two or three hours. As yet, motor roads are insufficient although they are being built. Among these is a road from Buenaventura on the Pacific to the Cauca and Magdalena Valleys and one from Bogotá into southern Venezuela and to an Orinoco River port. Western Colombia is on the route of the Pan-American Highway. Much work has been done on the road although it is not finished.

**Foreign Trade.**   The foreign trade of Colombia is principally with the United States, some 65 per cent of the Colombian import and 80 per cent of the export trade being with that country. Coffee is by far the most important export product, having an annual value of about 400 million dollars. Petroleum is second in value, followed in order by gold, bananas, and hides. The imports are similar to those of Venezuela.

Colombia shows a high degree of prosperity, stability, and progress. The economy is sound. The balance of imports and exports reflects a stable financial position, and a considerable industry helps maintain a degree of self-sufficiency. Tourists enjoy Colombia. The scenery is magnificent, and in settled regions the accommodations are adequate. Further expansion in road building will result in an increase in tourism.

## The Guianas

The Guianas—British, Surinam (Dutch), and French—are the only South American mainland countries which have not become independent of foreign control. Despite three hundred and fifty years under European domination, they remain essentially undeveloped and sparsely populated. Of the 712,000 people, about 465,000 live in British Guiana, 219,000 in Surinam, and 28,000 in the French colony.

The inhabited portion of the Guianas is the narrow coastal plain, originally too swampy for dense forest growth but capable of being drained and cultivated. A few miles inland is the Guiana Highland which attains a maximum altitude of 9,096 feet. Most of this upland is covered by dense selva forest similar to that of the Amazon lowland. The climate is of the rainy tropical type, here as elsewhere hot, rainy, and monotonous.

The earliest settlement was made by the Dutch about a century after the discovery of America. Both Spanish and Portuguese had already visited the Guianas, but the dense forest, the swampiness, and the high humidity discouraged settlement. The Dutch, however, and later the British, successfully drained the swamps and began raising sugar cane. Here, Negro slavery was a failure since escape into the nearby forest was not difficult. The labor problem was solved by bringing in workers from India and the Dutch East Indies. Even now several thousand "Bush Negroes," descendants of those early escapees, carry on subsistence farming in the selva.

British Guiana and Surinam are similar in most respects. The population density is about 4 persons per square mile. The leading crop of each is sugar cane, grown chiefly for export to the mother country. Rice, the favorite food of Asiatics from southeast Asia, is second in acreage and is the most important food crop. Other crops include cacao, coconuts, oranges, manioc, and various subsistence foods. The two colonies differ in only minor respects. There are scarcely any Europeans or native Indians in either colony. Georgetown and Paramaribo are the capitals and principal cities of their respective countries.

Surinam and British Guiana rank first and second among all the countries of the world in the production of bauxite, the ore of aluminum, and together produce nearly half of the world output. All of the ore is exported. The United States received 96 per cent of the Surinam production, Canada 90 per cent of the British Guiana ore. Other minerals include gold and diamonds.

French Guiana is of very little importance. It has a population density of only 1.5 persons per square mile. Cultivation occupies one unit of area in 3,000. The capital city, Cayenne, contains about 12,000 people. Foreign trade is insignificant.

## THE CENTRAL ANDEAN COUNTRIES

In the Central Andes, on gentle slopes at high elevations, Indians have dwelt for thousands of years. It was on the high, cool plateaus of the Central Andes that the Spanish first became established in South America, selecting this region because of its mineral wealth and the considerable supply of native labor. Despite more than four centuries of occupation, the Spanish methods of development of the land and other resources were only partially successful. The modern prosperity of Colombia and Venezuela has not been attained by most Indians living on the high plateaus of the Central Andes.

### Ecuador

Ecuador, named for the equator that bisects it, is the smallest of the Andean countries and has a population of about 3.5 million. The people are unevenly distributed although the patchiness of settlement is less pronounced than that in Colombia.

Extending north-south across the country, in the Andean highlands, is a series of basins and plateaus in which about two-thirds of the country's people live. Most of the inhabitants are Indians, for the basins have not produced enough commercial items to make them attractive to outsiders, even for destructive exploitation. Within the upland valleys, the people use the land for producing subsistence crops. Corn is grown in the lower areas and wheat, potatoes, and barley at higher elevations. Cattle, sheep, and goats pasture on the slopes, cattle being the most important. Llamas, the traditional animals of South American highlands, are few. Within one of these basins is Quito, the capital and second largest city of Ecuador. The Pan-American Highway extends along a line of basin

*Figure 6-12   Quito, the capital of Ecuador, is situated in a high mountain basin almost on the equator. (Courtesy of Pan American–Grace Airways.)*

settlements across the country. Here, also, is most of the railway mileage of the country.

These basins, although much lower than the nearby mountains, are actually very high. Most of the other basins are somewhat lower than Quito, which has an elevation of 9,350 feet. The elevation is responsible for the fact that places at the equator have a climate too cool for human comfort. At Quito, the average temperature of the warmest month is 58°F, which is comparable with the July temperature in the Yukon Valley, Alaska. The average temperature of the coolest month is 56.6°F. The highest ever recorded in Quito is 79°F. Few, if any, places have more nearly uniform monthly averages. Quito is 22° cooler than Iquitos which is in the Amazon plain only about 500 miles to the eastward. Towering above the plateaus and

basins are several volcanic cones exceeding 19,000 or 20,000 feet in height. Examples are Cotopaxi and Chimborazo, both of which are snow-capped the year round.

Most of the people of Ecuador who are not living in the dense patches of settlement in the high-level basins live in a low plain inland from the Gulf of Guayaquil. Here is the largest city, Guayaquil, the chief seaport, and center of most commerce and other business. In and near this plain originate the chief export products of Ecuador, bananas, coffee, and cacao, which have a total value of about 90 million dollars. Other products include straw hats and rice. There is a small oil field on the dry and wind-swept Cape Santa Elena west of Guayaquil. From the northern coastal valleys come tagua nuts, used for buttons, and toquilla straw, used in the making of Panama hats. Both are products of shrubs which grow in scantily forested coastland areas.

A small portion of eastern Ecuador lies within the low Amazon plain. Scarcely anyone other than a few native Indians lives there.

Minerals are less important in Ecuador than in other Andean countries. However, besides petroleum, some gold, silver, salt, and copper are mined.

Burdened by political instability and absentee land ownership, and lacking large exports, Ecuador has not succeeded in establishing a sound national economy. There is still disagreement with Peru and Colombia about the location of parts of the eastern international boundary.

*Peru*

Pre-Columbian civilization reached its highest level in the Incan empire which centered at Cuzco in the highlands of southern Peru. The natives achieved remarkably well-oriented social and political organization. Under the Incas, these Indians developed an effective agriculture and constructed buildings, roads, walls of stone, and irrigation systems that still function where intact. Their economy made much better use of the land than the civilization that was thrust upon them by the Spanish. The economy of the natives was submerged, but not destroyed, during the colonial period and has now partially revived under the impetus of Peruvian nationalism.

**Population Distribution.** The population pattern follows that of Ecuador in several respects. Nearly two-thirds of the people live in the highlands of the middle region. Most of the rest, a third, live on the low coastal plain. The largest city, Lima, is near the Pacific. Few people other than Indians, pure blood or mixed, live on the low eastern plain. In the low coastal region, the people occupy narrow strips of land along streams flowing from the highlands. In the highlands, instead of concentration of population on small, densely populated patches of land as in Ecuador, there is a wider spread of

*Figure 6-13 Peruvian Indians dressed in their traditional garb. Note how barren these mountains near Cuzco are. (Courtesy of Pan American– Grace Airways.)*

habitations. The Amazon lowland in the east, although sparsely populated, contains a third of a million people.

**Regions.** Three Peruvian regions are recognized, the coastal lowland in the west, the high plateaus and still higher mountains in the central area, and the low plain in the east.

The coastal region is essentially rainless. Irrigation is practiced along some 50 streams, all of them having their sources in the mountains. The careful, efficient, productive irrigation practiced by the Incas was upset by the Spanish, who put most of the Indians to work at mining. Recently, efforts have been made to reconstruct the irrigation works, in part for growing subsistence crops but more for commercial production. With the aid of irrigation, a considerable amount of sugar and cotton is grown in this coastal desert area. These two are the leading agricultural commodities exported from Peru. The offshore waters abound with fish. The cold rising water along the coast has an especially rich microscopic life on which the fish feed, and the fish provide food for millions of pelicans, gannets, and cormorants. The excrement and other refuse from these birds undergo a slow chemical change in the cool, almost rainless climate to form a fertilizer called guano. This product has long been utilized. In the past much guano was exported, but now most is used on the west-coast farms. At the northern end of the coastal region, in the Talara area, is a fairly important oil field. Petroleum and its products are third in value among Peruvian exports.

Lima, together with Callao, the port city eight miles away, is the commercial, economic, social, political, and cultural focus of the country. The two cities are connected by a broad highway along which many new commercial and industrial establishments are being built. Lima, because it is centrally located near the coast, with satisfactory although not easy access to the interior by airlines, a fairly large river to provide irrigation locally, and a good harbor, has become the second largest city of western South America.

The mountainous interior is moderately populated, with about 20 persons per square mile. There are four principal concentrations, each with more than a half-million people. Arequipa and Cuzco, the ancient capital of the Incan empire, are the largest cities in the mountainous interior. Most of the people live in agricultural villages within the four principal concentrations. Subsistence agriculture prevails. The distinctive rural animal is the llama, but even in Peru it is much less common than sheep or cattle. The llama is an important source of meat and it is also used as a beast of burden.

The mines of the highlands produce several kinds of metals. Copper is easily first in value although important amounts of lead, gold, silver, and zinc are mined. Peru leads all countries of the world in the mining of vanadium, a metal used in certain alloy steels.

Peru extends eastward beyond the mountains into the Amazon Basin, a low expanse of tropical rain forest. The people live mostly along the Amazon and its larger tributaries. A little rubber, some quinine, Brazil nuts, and timber are produced, but subsistence rather than commercial activities prevail. In this seemingly inhospitable environment is a city of 75,000 people, Iquitos, located at the head of river boat navigation on the Amazon River, some 2,000 miles from the Atlantic Ocean.

## Bolivia

The pattern of land occupation and use is not greatly different in Bolivia from that in Peru. The population is more than 3 million and the area little over 400,000 square miles, giving an average population density of only 7 persons per square mile. The people, at least two-thirds of them wholly or partly of Indian blood, live at high altitudes in densely populated basins or valleys, each separated from the next by land of low utility. In some respects, the landforms are similar to those of Peru, but there are noteworthy differences. Bolivia does not adjoin the Pacific; hence, it has no coastal lowland. The mountain ranges are somewhat better defined, there being three of them, the Cordilleras Oriental, Central, and Occidental. The Oriental and Central are not far apart, but the Occidental is set off from the others by a high plain, the Altiplano, some 500 miles long and 60 miles wide.

There is also climatic similarity to Peru. The highlands are of such elevation as to be always too cool for human comfort and the growth of hot-weather crops. The air is so thin that lowland people experience shortness of breath after only slight exertion. The dissimilarity between Bolivian and Peruvian climate is in two respects —part of the Altiplano is so dry that desert vegetation prevails, and the eastern lowland has a wet-and-dry tropical climate which, for the most part, supports savanna vegetation.

A favored section of Bolivia is the humid, semitropical Yungas region. It is located on the eastern slopes of the plateau overlooking the Amazon lowland. Here, between the elevations of about 2,000 to 6,000 feet, it is possible to raise a variety of tropical and semitropical products, including sugar and coffee. The chief export is coca leaves which contain a narcotic and are commonly chewed by the highland Indians.

The principal concentration of population in the highlands is on the plain near Lake Titicaca where, including the city of La Paz, about a million people reside. Generally the people are subsistence farmers and graziers. They live much as did their ancestors before the arrival of the Spanish, and pay little attention to the po-litical affairs of the country. The boundary line between Peru and Bolivia is largely ignored. Lake Titicaca, at 12,506 feet above sea level, is used as a highway of commerce, and is the highest navigated body of water in the world. La Paz is the business and commercial center of Bolivia and also the actual capital of the country, even though Sucre is officially designated. Second in size is the population concentration which contains the city of Cochabamba, only 150 miles but 2 days by rail from La Paz. This basin is lower, 8,500 feet, than the Titicaca Basin, less chilly, and suitable for more diversi-fied agriculture.

Some of the settlements in other basins, nota-bly Potosí, Corocoro, and Oruro, are based chiefly on mining. Tin is the most important mineral product. Other metals mined include lead, antimony, silver, copper, zinc, tungsten, and gold. Potosí, which once led the world in the mining of silver, is one of the oldest and richest mining cities in the Western Hemi-sphere.

*Figure 6-14   La Paz, Bolivia, is in a valley at 12,500 feet on the Altiplano. (Courtesy of Pan American–Grace Air-ways.)*

Bolivia's production of metals, especially tin, has brought great wealth to a few individuals. (At present the mines have been taken over by the government.) Most of the people, however, are not affected by this wealth. They live as their ancestors lived five hundred years ago, cultivating their fields of potatoes and grain and herding their few cattle, sheep, goats, and llamas by day, and at night huddling in their dirt-floored, windowless huts to escape the chill wind. They are acclimated to the high altitudes and so are able to work and run and dance in the cold, thin air. Yet they stick to their high Altiplano, although the warm Chaco plains in the east would afford them comfort, more crops, better grass for their cattle, and wood and oil instead of dung for the kitchen stoves. Perhaps the new railroad between Santa Cruz and the eastern boundary at Puerto Suarez, where it links with Rio de Janeiro, is the beginning of a march eastward. Petroleum has been discovered in eastern Bolivia and pipelines connect the Camire oil field with Cochabamba and Sucre.

## THE SOUTHERN ANDES—CHILE

Chile extends southward from Peru and Bolivia for approximately 2,600 miles, a distance as long as from Lake of the Woods to Panama, or from southernmost Alaska to Mexico City. South of Bolivia the Andes narrow, first to a series of parallel ridges and then to one tremendous range, a continuation of the Sierra Occidental. A large majority of the 6 million people in Chile live in a long valley, some 50 miles inland from the ocean, which lies between a low coastal range and the mighty Andes. Most of the rest live in the seaport cities.

### Regions

Four geographic regions are recognized in Chile. One of them is the Andes Mountains, which stretches the whole length of the nation; the other three are distinguished from each other by three types of land use adjusted to three contrasting climates, tropical desert, Mediterranean, and marine west-coast.

**Tropical Desert.** The Atacama is a desolate forbidding desert, extending from the northern boundary southward as far as Coquimbo. It may well be the driest desert in the world. At Iquique not a drop of rain fell in a fourteen-year period. In the valley inland from the low coastal mountains there are places where no rain whatever has fallen since the beginning of European settlement. The extreme dryness of the region is responsible in large part for its chief product, sodium nitrate. This soluble salt impregnates the soil near the surface. Iodine is an important by-product of the nitrate industry. From this desert area also come large amounts of borax and salt. Because of climatic conditions all food for the workers must be shipped in; even all the water must be piped from the mountains.

The other important product of this desert is iron ore, mined from a deposit of high-grade hematite at Cruz Grande near Coquimbo. The location near the sea facilitates export. Most of the iron ore is exported to the United States through the Panama Canal.

**Mediterranean.** For human comfort, the climate of central Chile is the equal of any in the world. Here the Spanish found conditions like much of their homeland. Midsummer (January) temperatures are usually about 65°F, and the winter months mostly average above 50°F. As in other regions of Mediterranean climate, rainfall is confined to the cooler half of the year. However, many mountain streams provide ample water for irrigation when it is needed during the summer season. There is a shrub vegetation similar to that of southern California. In this part of Chile live about two-thirds of the people, and in it nearly all the farming and manufacturing activities are located. Approximately half of the people are tenant farmers living on large haciendas (estates). About 3.1 million acres are in crops, with wheat occupying over half the cultivated land. South of the area with true Mediterranean climate, corn and potatoes are important crops. Pastures occupy much of the land, and the livestock industry is carried on extensively. The usual Mediterranean crops are of little significance. Olives are not grown; the summers are not hot enough. Oranges and lemons are unimportant; the home market for them is small, and oranges can be grown in all the other Latin-American countries. Grapes are produced largely for wine. Table grapes grow well, and some efforts are being made to send them into the United States market during our spring and summer.

Land ownership is so highly concentrated into large haciendas that progress in agriculture has been stifled. The proportion of peons in poverty, compared to the few landed aristocrats, is too great for full development of the land, even though it is favored by climate as are few other places in the world.

Santiago, with 1.5 million people, and its seaport, Valparaiso, are the two largest cities in Chile. Santiago, the capital, is located on a broad plain at the foot of the snow-crested Andes about 50 miles from the Pacific. It is the fourth largest city in South America. The principal distributing and trading center of the central valley, the city also dominates the indus-

trial, commercial, and cultural life of the country. Valparaiso is the most important port on the west coast of South America. In addition to being a trading and manufacturing center, it is the terminus of the trans-Andean route to Buenos Aires, and a leading fishing center. The city is built around the curves of the bay and extends into the steep hills which surround it.

**Marine West-coast.**   The rest of coastal Chile, that which lies south of the Rio Bío-Bío at 38° south latitude, has a marine west-coast climate. There is no dry season, although the summers are much less rainy than the winters. The total rainfall during an average year is very great, exceeding 100 inches at Valdivia and even more in other places. Forests cover nearly all of the land. Only in the area between Puerto Montt and Concepción has the land been cleared for agriculture, have railways or roads been constructed, and settlements established.

Between Chiloe Island and the Rio Bío-Bío about a million people live, with farming the chief means of support. Cattle are grazed on the lush pastures of the region, and food crops of wheat and potatoes give satisfactory yields. Most of the lumbering of Chile is done here. Until recently Chile imported considerable lumber; now exports exceed imports. Even so,

*Figure 6-15   Many wheat fields in the Andes are sectioned off by stone walls. (Courtesy of Hamilton Wright.)*

slight use is made of the vast forest, and paper and pulp are still imported.

In far southern Chile, partly at the extremity of the continent and partly on the island of Tierra del Fuego, there are somewhat more than 50,000 people engaged chiefly in raising sheep. This land, on both sides of the Strait of Magellan, is bleak, wind-swept, chilly, and forbidding. There is some grass. In the cool climate, which is dry, though foggy, sheep thrive and produce fleeces of superior size and quality. There are more than 2.5 million sheep here, over a third of the Chilean total. Punta Arenas on the strait is the southernmost city in the world. Between the small settlement, along the Strait of Magellan, and the larger one, between Rio Bío-Bío and Chiloe Island, are a thousand miles of mountainous, deeply fiorded, rain-soaked coastland. It is inhabited only by a few primitive natives, who live along the coast subsisting on the abundant fish resources.

**Mountain.** Along the crest of the Andes, and along the boundary between Chile and Argentina, are many mighty peaks, greatest of which is Aconcagua, nearly 23,000 feet, the highest mountain in the world outside Asia. The mountains are extremely rugged and scenic beyond description and are beginning to be visited by tourists. These mountains have an importance far beyond the implications of their small population, for in them are great deposits of copper and other minerals. Usually Chile ranks second to the United States in copper production. Copper plays the same part in Chilean trade that oil does in Venezuela and tin in Bolivia. In a recent year, copper provided nearly one-half of the value of the country's exports. There are three principal mining localities—all on the western slopes of the Andes, and all developed by United States capital—Chuquicamata, Potrerillos, and El Teniente. Chuquicamata, in most recent years, has been the largest producer of copper in any single mining locality in the world. Hundreds of millions of dollars have been invested by an American company in this property. All food and everything else needed has to be imported; even water is brought from

a distance. Power is generated on the coast from imported fuel oil. A railroad, power lines, homes for employees, reduction works, and quantities of machinery had to be provided before mining could begin. The mountains also contain quantities of sulfur, production totaling about 50,000 tons annually, but high elevations, some up to 20,000 feet, and difficult transportation keep costs above those in Louisiana or Texas. Sulfur is found in the craters of at least sixty volcanoes, all near the Argentine border.

### Foreign Trade

Chile has encouraged development of its mineral resources and other foreign investments; this policy has helped establish trade relationships with the rest of the world on a firm base. With the opening of the Panama Canal, the distance to East Coast markets of the United States was greatly decreased, since Valparaiso and other Chilean ports are almost directly south of New York, Baltimore, and Philadelphia. The time required to reach European ports also became less after the long voyage through the Strait of Magellan could be avoided. Narrow-gauge railways haul the products of the dry north land to Antofagasta, Iquique, and other ports, where they are transferred to ships bound for the United States, England, and other countries. In turn, Chile imports large quantities of manufactured goods from these same countries. Coastal cities in northern Chile like Arica, Iquique, and Antofagasta serve as transit ports for tin concentrates and other exports of Bolivia.

The national boundaries of Chile are well defined, treaties with the neighboring countries of Peru, Bolivia, and Argentina having been concluded. Chile gained much of her nitrate area as a result of the War of the Pacific, 1879–1884, with Peru and Bolivia, when the territories of Tacna and Arica were added. Tacna was returned to Peru, by treaty, in 1929. A large statue, the Christ of the Andes, was erected in the Uspallata Pass to symbolize the lasting peace between these two nations and the arbitration of their boundary dispute.

## SOUTHEASTERN SOUTH AMERICA

The southeastern plain of South America was settled later than most other parts of the continent. It was far distant from the Spanish center of influence at Lima and from the Portuguese settlements of extreme eastern Brazil. There was only a small Indian population; thus, there was no readily available native labor supply. The Pampa contained no gold and the climate was not hot enough for sugar cane production. Yet the plain has become, almost entirely within the last hundred years, the leader in agriculture, manufacturing, commerce, railway mileage, communications, education, and city growth.

Included in southeastern South America are the countries of Argentina, Uruguay, and Paraguay. The first contains most of the people, the largest area, and the greatest wealth.

### Argentina

Although the last of the South American nations to be settled, Argentina has advanced rapidly in commerce, industry, education, and other phases of modern culture since the middle of the last century. Yet her rich land and other resources are used considerably below capacity. Progress should continue and even accelerate for a long time. In Argentina, as in other countries of South America, capital from the United States has helped build supply houses for agricultural equipment as well as manufacturing and processing plants.

Argentina may be divided into six geographic regions—Humid Pampa, Mesopotamia, Gran Chaco, Northwest Oases and Dry Lands, Patagonia, and Andes. Of these the Humid Pampa is by far the most important. In this region are most of the people, most of the industry, and most of the agriculture.

**Humid Pampa.** The Pampa of east central Argentina covers about 250,000 square miles in which natural factors strongly favor agriculture. The land is nearly level, its surface broken only by a few isolated ranges. The soils are fine in texture, mellow, deep, well-drained,

*Figure 6-16   Cattle of the Pampa, Argentina. (Courtesy of Pan American–Grace Airways.)*

black, and very fertile. The subtropical climate is hardly excelled for agriculture. It is warm enough for high-yield crops, yet not too warm for the maximum of human efficiency. The midsummer temperature is the same as that of northern Iowa; the midwinter equals that of central Louisiana. Rainfall at Buenos Aires is the same in amount and similar in distribution to the rainfall at Cincinnati.

Within this favored region, most of the land is in pasture; scarcely any part has less than half in grass. Cattle and sheep are about the same in number, with cattle being foremost in value of farm products. Purebred cattle and sheep are raised on many of the *estancias* (big ranches). There is an important number of hogs in the northeast, especially near Rosario and Buenos Aires. The exports of meat and other animal products are most important in the economy of Argentina since their value is approximately half of the total of all commodities exported. Approximately one-third of all meat in international trade comes from Argentina.

Three important cash grain crops, wheat, corn, and flaxseed, are produced in large volume besides oats, barley, and rye. Many acres of alfalfa are planted for livestock feed. Corn and flaxseed are important crops in the northern part of the Pampa. In the western and southern sections of the region, alfalfa replaces flaxseed and is produced in large quantities along with corn. To the west of these crop areas, where the rainfall is insufficient for good yields, is the great wheat crescent of Argentina where hundreds of thousands of acres are devoted to the production of this crop. About half the corn and a third of the wheat are exported. Usually Argentina ranks third among the nations of the world in wheat export. The corn is a hard flint variety with small grains, a type that is much in demand in Europe, especially for poultry feed. Flaxseed also is exported, formerly in the seed, but since World War II as linseed oil. Most farmers use modern planting and harvesting machines. Much of the agricultural production is on the large estates.

The most extensive railway network in South America has been developed on the Pampa. Since the broad, flat plains are not crossed by numerous rivers and ridges, they offer an almost ideal place for the development of trackage. The chief handicap has been the lack of ballast for track beds. This material, as well as the fuel used, must either be hauled for long distances within Argentina or imported. From Buenos Aires, and Bahia Blanca in lesser degree, the railway net spreads over the plains in fan shape; thus, the coastal cities are easily reached from all parts of the Pampa. Over these rails most of the wheat, corn, flaxseed, wool, hides, cattle, and sheep are moved to the industrial centers along the Rio de la Plata and the Paraná for processing and export. Even alfalfa is shipped by rail. Many of the *estancias* have built their own narrow-gauge rail systems.

Approximately five-sevenths of the people of Argentina live on the Humid Pampa. It is a distinctly cosmopolitan European population, with very few Indians or Negroes. Within this region are the chief cities of Argentina. With over 3 million inhabitants, Buenos Aires is the largest city south of the equator. It is the national capital, and handles most of the exports, imports, and other business of the country. Within it, too, most of the manufacturing is done. The city is an old one, having been first founded in 1536. A few years later it was abandoned but was refounded in 1580. Buenos Aires is an attractive modern city, having many handsome buildings, large parks, and fine streets. The Avenida de Mayo, the principal street, is a wide, tree-lined avenue leading from the President's home to the buildings of the National Congress. Large churches, public libraries, and excellent school buildings are located within the city. A modern subway system aids the city's transportation lines. Rosario is a transoceanic port, a railroad hub, and an industrial and commercial center. Santa Fé is an inland port and distribution center; La Plata is especially important as a meat packing center. Córdoba, at the foot of the Pampean Range near the Humid Pampa, is noted as a communication, cultural, and commercial center.

**Mesopotamian Region.**   That part of Argentina between the Uruguay and Paraná Rivers is called the Argentine Mesopotamia. In general, it is an area of high rainfall, mild winters, and hot summers. Most of the region is a lowland with a rolling topography. Many of the valley bottoms are swampy, tree-covered areas; the higher land is grassy and suitable for pasture.

Much of the economy of the region is based on the raising of cattle and sheep. The cattle, mostly of lower grade stock than that of the Pampa, are more valuable for hides than for meat. The corn and flax belt of the Pampa extends into Mesopotamia. The region produces more linseed than the other areas of the country. In the northern part of the region there are some areas of Paraná pine forests. Yerba maté is also produced.

On the international boundary with Brazil is Iquassu Falls, higher and broader than Niagara Falls. At present, only a few tourists visit the falls. They present, however, a great potential source of hydroelectric power when an increased population demands it.

**Gran Chaco.**   Northwestern Argentina is an extensive lowland plain commonly referred to as El Gran Chaco, the great forest. It is an area of tropical to temperate climate in which scrub forests and grasslands form a savanna country. In this area and to the eastward grows the important quebracho tree. The wood is very hard —the name of the tree means axbreaker—and is especially resistant to decay. The logs have great value as fence posts, telephone poles, and railroad ties. The most valuable product, however, is the tannin which is obtained from the wood. Mills for processing the product are generally located in the forest areas and are usually permanent.

The region is grazed by many cattle, but they are not high-grade animals like those of the Pampa. Recently cotton has become important, about 600,000 bales being produced annually. Population in the Gran Chaco is scant, averaging only about 1 person per square mile. There are no cities or towns of importance and transportation is poorly developed.

**Northwest Oases and Dry Lands.**   Nearly a fourth of the people of Argentina live between the Humid Pampa and the Cordillera. Argentinians commonly call this region the dry Pampa. Within the dry lands of the northwest, the population is concentrated in three clusters, in all of which the economy is based on irrigation agriculture. The one farthest north, Jujuy and Salta, formerly was important as a supplier of meat and horses for the mines of Bolivia and Chile. Now, however, sugar cane and fruits are grown. The cluster next southward, Tucuman, is even more important for sugar cane, producing more than half of the national output. Besides cane, citrus fruits are grown. These subtropical crops are confined to a strip, about 40 miles wide, along the foot of the mountains. The climate south of Tucuman is too cool for sugar cane production. In this southern section, grapes for wine form the chief money crop, and alfalfa is the crop of largest acreage. Here Mendoza is the main population center. Near all three of these clusters, the grazing of cattle is important.

**Patagonia.**   Stretching southward from the Pampa, approximately from the Rio Colorado, is a thinly populated plateau called Patagonia. It is not especially high but is cold in winter and dry and windy at all times. Much of this bleak, wind-swept region is too dry for any use except poor pasture. Small sections in some of the valleys do give relatively good pasture. Nearly all the few people living in Patagonia are engaged in sheep raising. In this region, approximately half the Argentine wool is produced, making the country second only to Australia.

A few irrigation projects, like the one on the Rio Negro, are being developed and give promise of becoming important centers for fruit production. Most of the 23 million barrels of petroleum produced annually in Argentina are obtained from the Comodoro Rivadavia field. Transportation in Patagonia is poor. Only a few miles of highways have been developed, there is but a short railroad mileage, and only a few rivers are navigable. Cities and towns are small and usually far apart. Isolation is the great influence upon the social conditions of the sheepherders and their families.

**Andes.** The Andes, the crest of which forms the international boundary with Chile, are scenically beautiful but of little economic importance. A national park, Nahuel Huapi, is located in the south central Andes amid snow fields and mountain lakes. It is an attractive resort area for both winter and summer tourists. Along the eastern slopes of the mountains is a narrow belt of timber. The mountains are also used for grazing, especially of goats.

## Uruguay

Uruguay is a small nation about the size of Oklahoma. This factor certainly helps explain the uniformity in land use that prevails over the entire country. Almost all land is privately owned and used. There are no waste spaces separating population clusters as in most other parts of the continent. Throughout the country, farming and grazing are of foremost importance. Political stability is characteristic.

The economic interest of the people is centered mostly in raising farm animals. Approximately three-fourths of the exports, by value, are animal products of which wool makes up slightly more than half. The ratio of people to sheep is 1 to 8 and to cattle, 1 to 4. In the United States, where there are more people than these animals, the ratios are 5 to 1 and 2 to 1. A typical Uruguayan landscape includes a large number of fat Hereford cattle and a still larger number of sheep grazing in an expanse of natural grassland that extends to the horizon. Small frame houses form the usual homes of the cattlemen. Because no shelter or stored feed is required there are only a few outbuildings. Barbed-wire fences divide the pastures,

and because little land is tilled, the fences and buildings are about the only additions to the natural landscape. Uruguay is a part of the Humid Pampa, because in every part tall grasses are a conspicuous feature of the rural scene.

Crop production is important, especially in the south. Flaxseed, wheat, and linseed oil, as well as wool, meat, and other animal products are exported. Corn is an important crop throughout Uruguay, though less than wheat in acreage, yield, and export.

Like the Humid Pampa of Argentina, Uruguay is an example of climate favorable to both human energy and high crop yields. At Montevideo, capital, seaport, and chief meat-processing center, the midsummer (January) temperature is that of Detroit and the midwinter (July) that of Vicksburg. The population is increasing rapidly at a percentage rate only a little less than that of the United States. Thus, the time must come when the large pasture lands will be put into crops to provide food for additional people. Uruguay is twice as large as Indiana, but has only about half as many people. Yet, since the climate is more pleasant and the natural environment more favorable for food crops in Uruguay, eventually it should have the denser rural population.

## Paraguay

Paraguay, like Bolivia, is an inland nation. Although the country is industrially undeveloped, and its commerce is less than that of any other South American nation, its natural endowments are good. In general, the weather is mild and rainy and the soil fertile. Most of the western part of the country is a flat plain of the savanna type; the eastern part has a more hilly or rolling surface. There are not many trees and most of them are short and gnarly.

The population is the smallest of any of the independent nations of South America. Many of the people of Paraguay are either mestizos or fullblood Indians. The Guarani language is spoken as frequently as Spanish. Asunción is the capital and principal city of the country.

The nation is divided into two parts by the Paraguay River. Most of the people live in the eastern area on the large ranches. Many of the cattle are of mixed breed, descendants of long-horns, once imported from the plains of Texas, and zebu (Brahma) cattle brought in from India. The fact that there are nearly three times as many cattle as people suggests the chief economy. Cotton, tobacco, and oranges are the principal agricultural products. Tobacco is grown primarily for home consumption. Meat and hides are the chief agricultural exports; however, cotton is also an important item in foreign trade. Yerba maté, the national drink, is brewed from the powdered leaves of the yerba maté tree which grows in many parts of the eastern area. Timber and quebracho extract, used for tanning leather, are important exports.

West of the river is a part of the Gran Chaco. It is a vast, little-known plain with many possibilities for development. Yet scarcely anyone lives in the area. As in the Argentina section, the main product is quebracho. The tree is plentiful and for years has served as one of the chief sources of income. There are possibilities of oil development and the drilling of exploratory wells is in process.

## UNITED STATES OF BRAZIL

Most of South America except Brazil was settled by the Spanish and Spanish is the official language except in Brazil and the Guianas. The treaty of Tordesillas, in 1494, assigned Spain the western part of South America and Portugal the eastern. At that early date very little was known about the size or extent of the continent and the dividing line, roughly 50° west longitude, was too far east for an even division. Later boundary manipulation has very nearly equalized the respective areas. Although there are nine Spanish-speaking countries and only one Portuguese, Brazil contains approximately half the area and half the people of the continent.

The densest concentration of population, and the economic center of the country, is in the subtropical central eastern region in and near Rio de Janeiro and the adjacent states of São Paulo and Minas Geraes. In this region are the chief cities, the national capital, and most of the industry and commercial farming. This region, Southeast Central Brazil, constitutes the core of the country. Northeast Brazil was the first settled region, and from the earliest settlement, the leading sugar producing area of South America. Southern Brazil lies to the south of the core region and is the only part that does not have a tropical climate. Inland to the north and northwest of Southeast Central Brazil is the Interior region, an upland area that is sparsely settled despite some rich mining deposits and a favorable climate. The fifth region is the Amazon Basin, a vast land, most of which is covered by luxuriant forests that are largely unused, and all of which is sparsely populated.

### Southeast Central Brazil

The core of Brazil, the area having the largest concentration of population in South America, is in Southeast Central Brazil. From the Atlantic shore the region extends inland about 250 miles to include the Federal District, the state of Minas Geraes, the city and state of Rio de Janeiro, and the richest and most populous Brazilian state, São Paulo.

Here most of the coffee of Brazil is grown, and coffee is of tremendous importance since it accounts for over half, sometimes over two-thirds, of the value of all Brazilian exports. Coffee helps forge a strong link with the United States, for it is the principal commodity which the United States imports from Brazil, and in most recent years, imports from Brazil have exceeded those from any other country except Canada. In most years Brazil produces slightly more than half of the coffee in the world. Of the 2,500 million pounds imported by the United States in a recent year, 1,355 million were from Brazil.

A coffee grove resembles a cherry orchard. The trees are similar to cherry trees in height and spacing; the fruits look somewhat alike,

*Figure 6-17 Large coffee plantation near São Paulo, Brazil. (Courtesy of Brazilian Government Trade Bureau.)*

and there is similarity in methods of picking. The resemblance ends at the picking, however, for the coffee seeds are dried, sacked, and shipped in bags to the seaports.

Coffee fazendas (plantations) extend in long, finger-like projections outward from São Paulo city, each veined by a major railroad. In these lands is the famous *terra roxa,* a prairie soil, rich in humus and one of the best soils for coffee. Growing of this crop is confined largely to a low plateau, mostly between 2,000 and 3,000 feet, where elevation keeps the air temperate and the tropical location precludes frosts. Since the 1920s coffee growing has been extended southward into Paraná and westward into newly developed parts of São Paulo where unexhausted soils are available.

Each city of this region functions in its own way. Rio de Janeiro, with about 2.5 million people, is the leading port and a business center for the areas immediately tributary, but most of all it is a city of all Brazil, the national capital and the place where most Brazilians desire to live. São Paulo, with over 2 million inhabitants, is the business and manufacturing center for the state of the same name, a response to convenient rural markets and to prosperity derived chiefly from coffee. Santos, the port for São Paulo, is the world's greatest coffee port. It is at the base of a steep escarpment,

the edge of the plateau, 35 air miles away from São Paulo, but 2,680 feet lower.

In the state of Minas Geraes, the exploitation of several rich mineral deposits has long been important. Gold has been mined continuously at Morro Velho near Bello Horizonte for more than a century. The mine is now more than 8,000 feet deep, one of the deepest shafts in the world, and is the source of almost all the gold mined in Brazil. Diamonds have been mined in Brazil equally long. The mines of Minas Geraes produce most of the diamonds obtained outside of Africa. High-grade gems have been found, but lately all but a small percentage are industrial stones worth only a few dollars per carat. This region produces most of the world's commercial quartz crystals, which are used in radar work.

The most abundant mineral, however, is iron ore. A deposit, not far from the gold mines, has an enormous tonnage of ore. If the amount reported, 13 billion tons, is correct, this is the largest known deposit of iron ore in the world. It is high-grade hematite without impurities in harmful amounts. Only about a million tons are mined annually, however, for Brazilian markets are not large and the interior location hampers export. The mines are some 350 miles from the shipping port, Vitória, and high costs of the overland haul make the ore expensive at the port. To stimulate home use of this iron ore a steel mill has been constructed at Volta Redonda, 60 miles northwest of Rio de Janeiro. Manganese also is mined near Bello Horizonte, very nearly all for export to the United States.

### Northeast Brazil

Brazil was first settled along the tropical coast southwestward from Recife, the easternmost point of the continent. In this area, sugar cane was first grown in the Americas, and from the outset, sugar has been first in importance along this narrow coastal region. Since there were few Indians, Negro slaves were brought in to work in the cane fields. In times of active export and high prices, plantations have expanded and population has increased. During times of low prices, the sugar fields are neglected and many of the people migrate inland where they have directed their efforts toward new crops, especially cotton and cacao.

More cacao is produced in the central part of this region than anywhere else in the Western Hemisphere. Here is grown practically all of the cacao of Brazil, about three-fourths of the South American crop and 18 per cent of the total world supply. Only the African Gold Coast produces more.

Demand for these crops has waxed and waned. With changes in income, prosperity has fluctuated and new crops have been tried. In general, however, northeast Brazil is a region of poverty and low standards of living. Although the population has steadily increased, the area is not yet densely peopled even after four and a half centuries of settlement. The region has never been an easy one to utilize. The uniformly rainy climate is not the best for sugar, the soils are only moderately fertile, and the humid heat is unfavorable, even to Negroes. At present, the cacao growers seem to fare best. An expanding Brazilian market for sugar

*Figure 6-18   Copacabana Beach, Rio de Janeiro, Brazil. (Courtesy of Brazilian Government Trade Bureau.)*

could, however, bring about a revival in the growing of cane.

During World War II, Natal, on Cape São Roque, became important in air transportation. The Atlantic is narrowest, less than 2,000 miles, between Natal and Dakar in Africa.

The interior of the northeast is dry. In the state of Ceara, between 250 and 400 miles inland from the coast, is a region where severe droughts occasionally cause calamitous results. The equatorial rains do not reach inland to the region. Normal rainfall is only 25 inches annually. Here the selva vegetation of the coast gives way to native growth of grass, thornbushes, and cacti. In rainy years, herds of cattle do well and crops flourish; in the years of rainfall deficiency, crops wither and the animals, lean because the pastures are scant, do not alone provide enough food. Yet in spite of disastrous droughts and occasional floods, the population has remained moderately dense, more than 40 persons per square mile. Although irrigation has been practiced for centuries, until recently it has drawn upon sources of water that have failed in the very dry years. When there is water, the crops, cotton, rice, beans, maize, and alfalfa, give fairly high yields. The Brazilian government, with the construc-

tion of several large storage dams, has helped to counteract the effects of deficient rainfall by storing surplus water from the occasional floods.

### Southern Brazil

The region south of the Brazilian core is the only part of the nation in which frosts occur. The climate of the Pampa extends into southern Brazil and has been a factor in attracting many non-Portuguese Europeans. Settlement has not been rapid, but has increased steadily to the present. Although the people have been prosperous, democratic, and vigorous, success in settlement has stemmed from the fact that European immigrants, many of whom were German, have been allowed the privilege of obtaining land in family-sized farms. This is one of the few parts of South America where a poor, but capable and ambitious, farmer can secure complete ownership of a farm. Some immigrant farmers at first planted the crops of their north European homeland. Soon, however, they added corn for their livestock. In a few places, an economy has been built around rice or cotton. Hogs are important, and in a small way a hog-corn farm economy is developing. As yet, pastures occupy most of the

*Figure 6-19  The Brazilian National Steel Company plant at Volta Redonda. (Courtesy of Brazilian Information Bureau.)*

land, and cattle and sheep provide most of the income. The people are clustered into three separate groups, each the core of a separate state. There are no mountains or stretches of unused land to separate them. Thus, in time, settlement should be continuous. The Paraná pine furnishes softwood lumber, a rarity in South America. As in many other places in the continent, there is so much land with so few people that intensive cropping lies in the future. In spite of danger from frost, the growing of coffee has become established in northern Paraná state. Porto Alegre, Rio Grande do Sul, is the largest seaport in South Brazil.

## Interior Plateau and Plains

The interior uplands form a vast region north and northwest of Southeast Central Brazil. The region occupies somewhat more than one-third of the area of the nation, but in it are only about 8 per cent of the people. Much of the region is not inhabited at all, or by only small tribes of native Indians. Most of it is a low plateau with a surface of rather gently rolling land or cliff-bordered tablelands. In the west are extensive plains. On the uplands the climate is tropical, but rarely hot; in the higher eastern part the temperature, throughout the year, is about the same as that of northern Indiana in July. Temperatures increase with lower elevations to the northwest, eventually to merge into the rainy tropical climate of the Amazon lowland. The rainfall, 30 to 50 inches yearly, is hardly enough to adversely affect the soils through excessive leaching or to promote dense forest growth.

Even after two and a half centuries of settlement, the land is still in an early pioneer stage of development. Over nearly all the region, cattle provide most of the income. From the earliest time of settlement, sale of their hides has been important, but their meat is too tough for world markets. The introduction of zebu cattle from India should improve the quality and marketability of the beef animals, since the India cattle are resistant to ticks, long the bane of cattle in tropical America.

## Amazonia

The lowland of the Amazon Basin is frequently called the "Green Desert." This large region stretching across northern Brazil is a region of anomalies. It includes about one-third of the area of Brazil; yet it contains barely 5 per cent of the people. It is half as large as the United States; yet it has fewer people than Detroit. The surface is generally flat and the rainfall is abundant; yet there is almost no agriculture. Forests grow with a luxuriance seldom exceeded elsewhere; yet very little lumber is produced. The Amazon is the largest river in the world, but in Brazil it yields no power. For a century and more travelers have extolled the great opportunities for producing food and commodities for commerce; yet the region remains virtually unexploited. Perhaps, some day, its productivity for human use will be more fully utilized, since the region of vast forests and few people extends beyond Brazil into Venezuela, Colombia, Peru, and Bolivia.

Of foremost significance is the forest, and it is with the forest that man must contend. Here is the largest expanse in the world of selva, the equatorial rain forest. Generally the trees are tall, comparable in height to virgin pines of Michigan or Louisiana. The branches of adjacent trees intermingle, myriad lianes (vines) grow in and out among them high above the ground. The tangle of leafy branches and lianes casts a dense shade on the ground, so dense that bushes and other low growth are often absent and one may walk through the forest with little interference other than from the trunks of trees, streams, and puddles of water. Of the hundreds of species of trees, the rubber tree is about the only one that has been much used. This region is the original home of the *Hevea brasiliensis,* the tree from which most natural rubber is obtained. Probably there are more trees capable of supplying rubber in the Amazon Basin than in all the rest of the world; yet, even so, Brazil is not a major producer of rubber.

The climate is monotonous, constantly warm, humid, and rainy. Actually, higher temperatures have been recorded in southern Canada, but in the Amazon Basin there is no relief from the constant warmth and humidity. The annual rainfall averages between 70 and 100 inches; there is no dry season. Daylight and darkness are balanced; the sunshine period is approximately twelve hours every day of the year. As a result of equality of sun angle and sunshine period, temperatures fluctuate very little from one month to the next. At Manaus, on the Amazon near the confluence with the Rio Negro, the average temperature for the warmest month, October, is 83°F, while for the least warm month, April, it is 80°F.

Not many land animals live in the selva, and most of these live partly in the trees. Birds and monkeys provide food for several species of large cats and snakes which also live mostly in the trees. Insects and spiders, here in great numbers, attain gigantic size. All are troublesome and some are dangerous.

Settlements are scattered along the Amazon and its tributaries. Only the rivers are highways. The people at the settlements collect the products of the forest, gums, nuts, and woods. Two cities are the chief entrepôts for trade. Belém (Para), a seaport, is located on the delta of the Amazon. Manaus, although far up the Amazon, is reached by ocean-going vessels because of the great depth of the river. Before 1915, Brazil supplied most of the world's rubber. Since then, however, rubber collecting has been important only during World Wars I and II. There have been attempts to establish rubber plantations but soil erosion, labor shortages, and pests have caused difficulty. As a result, large acreages have been abandoned. The total production in the basin is about 5,000 tons annually. Malaya produces more than a hundred times that amount.

The forests are capable of yielding much lumber, but here also are difficulties. Laborers are few. Many woods are too heavy to float. The valuable species grow intermingled with

useless ones and are tied to them by the many vines. Felling the trees is difficult. The woods are largely unknown to builders in temperate lands. Lumber production must wait. From the forests are obtained several kinds of nuts. Best known, because of their sale during Christmas season, are the three-sided Brazil nuts.

The rivers abound in fish. They are readily available to the people in the river settlements and are an important local source of food.

## IN PERSPECTIVE

### South America, a Land of Promise Long Delayed

More than any other continent, South America offers opportunities for settlement by surplus populations of Europe. For three hundred years, Europeans have migrated to the United States and Canada. Recent restrictions in Anglo-America, however, have reduced immigration there. Europeans can no longer look to that area for a new homeland as they have done in the past. Africa contains much unused land in regions with climate favorable to Europeans, but white people avoid Africa largely because of the competition with the native Negro population. Australia has a much smaller area available for farming than the others.

In South America there are vast areas of empty land where a "White Man's" climate prevails. Southern Brazil and nearby Uruguay are especially favorable in this respect. In them could be grown food for many millions of additional people. Immigrants may obtain land there in family-size farms, to use as they please, and to hand along to their descendants. There they may raise the crops and animals with which they were familiar in Europe.

The Pampa is populated far below capacity

*Figure 6-20   Cattle on a ranch in the state of Rio Grande do Sul, Brazil. (Courtesy of Brazilian Government Trade Bureau.)*

and the Gran Chaco of Argentina, Paraguay, and Bolivia is not too hot for Europeans. There are parts of Colombia also, where people could live prosperously. Chile, especially south of Santiago, is a good land but sparsely peopled. There northwestern Europeans would find a climate like that of their homeland. They could live and farm much as they do in Europe. The interior uplands of Brazil could provide homes for scores of millions of people. The Guiana Plateau also has possibilities. Last to be settled may be the Amazon Lowland. No one can say whether or not Europeans can live there in large numbers and retain their vigor and efficiency. Nor can anyone assert that they can not.

South America is indeed a continent of the future.

## EXERCISES

*1.* In what ways does the South American pattern of relief resemble that of North America? In what ways do the two continents differ?

*2.* What are the latitude limits of South America? What are the climatic regions of the continent? What is the relationship between climatic conditions and latitude? What other geographic factors also influence the climate?

*3.* What is the largest South American country? How does it compare in area with Canada and the United States? How does it compare climatically? Upon which South American countries does it *not* border?

*4.* Where do we find the greatest population density in South America? In which climatic regions are these areas? What are their principal economic activities?

*5.* What and where is the Pampa, Llanos, Selvas, Chaco, Atacama, Patagonia? What are the principal products of each?

*6.* Which political divisions of South America are not independent? What countries control them? Why are they of little economic importance?

*7.* What geographical advantages does Argentina have? Why is agriculture so highly developed? Why is the Pampa the most densely populated part? In what ways are Argentina and the United States competitors for the world's markets?

*8.* What are the principal minerals mined in South America? Why are most of them exported? Which mineral, essential to manufacturing, is almost entirely absent?

*9.* What is the largest river in South America? Why is the region through which it flows poorly developed? How could this region be made more productive?

*10.* What influence have the Andes had upon the countries through which they pass? Why do more people live in the mountains than at their base? Into what divisions have the Andes separated Peru, Ecuador, and Colombia?

*11.* Why does South America offer opportunities for settlement by surplus populations of Europe? Where have groups of Europeans and Asiatics already settled in South America?

*12.* Which European languages are officially used in South America? Why?

*13.* In what businesses and industries has United States money been invested in South America? How does such investment benefit both the United States and South America?

## SELECTED REFERENCES

Carlson, Fred A.: *Geography of Latin America,* 3d ed., Prentice-Hall, Inc., Englewood Cliffs, N.J., 1952.

Griess, Phyllis R.: "The Bolivian Tin Industry," *Economic Geography,* 27:238–250, July, 1951.

Hitchcock, Charles B.: "Resources of the Tropics: II—South America," *Focus* 3(8):1–6, April, 1953.

————: "The Sierra De Perija, Venezuela," *Geographical Review,* 44:1–28, January, 1954.

James, Preston E.: *Latin America,* The Odyssey Press, Inc., New York, 1950.

————: "Patterns of Land Use in Northeast Brazil," *Annals of the Association of American Geographers,* 43:98–126, June, 1953.

Jones, Clarence F.: *South America,* Henry Holt and Company, Inc., New York, 1930.

Platt, Robert S.: "Brazilian Capitals and Frontiers: Part I," *Journal of Geography,* 53:369–375, December, 1954.

————: "Brazilian Capitals and Frontiers: Part II," *Journal of Geography,* 54:5–17, January, 1955.

Price, Archibald G.: *White Settlement in the Tropics,* The American Geographical Society, New York, 1939.

Wagley, Charles: *Amazon Town: A Study of Man in the Tropics,* The Macmillan Company, New York, 1953.

# Part II. Eastern

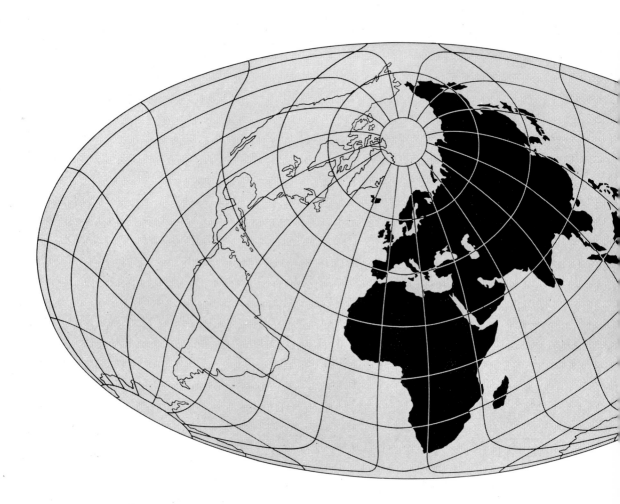

# Hemisphere

The land masses of the Eastern Hemisphere extend from well north of the Arctic Circle to south of the equator halfway to the South Pole. In the "world island," so referred to by some geographers, there are three adjoining continents —Asia, Europe, and Africa. The continent of Australia has been isolated from the others for millions of years. Numerous islands, however, have served as a partial bridge between Australia and Asia. All Eurasia and more than half of Africa are situated north of the equator; Australia is entirely to the south. From the standpoint of physical geography, Europe and Asia form one continent, Eurasia, with Europe essentially a large western peninsula of Asia. Eurasia's separation into two continents is justified on racial, cultural, and historical grounds.

Antarctica is divided between the Eastern and Western Hemispheres but for descriptive convenience is discussed with the former. So far as is known, it consists of a high plateau with some mountains, all nearly hidden by ice.

## PHYSICAL SETTING

### Climate

The great land masses of the Eastern Hemisphere have areas of every type of climate known except the polar icecap. Location chiefly determines the types of climate present in the separate continents. Africa, bisected by the equator and extending only about 35 degrees to the north or south, has climates ranging from the rainy tropical to the Mediterranean type. Europe, situated in middle latitudes to the west of the largest continent, has climates characteristic of the intermediate zone between the tropics and the Arctic. Only a small area near the Caspian Sea is arid, though a larger part toward the north is tundra and subpolar continental. As a whole, Europe is the most favored of all continents climatically. Asia has every climatic type present in the Old World continents except marine west-coast, Europe monopolizing all of this type in the northern half of the Eastern Hemisphere. Australia has the same range of climatic types as the southern half of Africa, but unfortunately much of the continent is a trade-wind desert. Tasmania and New Zealand are in the marine west-coast climate.

## Relief Features

Major relief features in the Eastern Hemisphere are varied and include lowlands or plains, plateaus, old, worn-down mountains, and young, rugged mountains. In general, the shore lines of Eurasia are very irregular when compared to those of Africa and Australia.

The lowlands of Eurasia are very important because on them live more than half the world's population. Many of the plains are underlain by seams of coal and have become the site of great manufacturing centers. Petroleum also occurs in some of the lowlands, for example those near the Persian Gulf are believed to contain the world's largest oil reserves. The largest lowland extends across Eurasia (see map in atlas). Only a few low mountains and plateaus rise above the surface of this vast plain, and except in the Pacific borderlands these are not difficult for man to cross. A large population lives on this plain especially from Western Europe to central Siberia. Because of the severe climate in its most northerly part near the Arctic Ocean and widespread aridity in the southern part in Asia, the population in those areas is small. In Southern and Eastern Europe and in Asia, the plains are smaller than in the north

and are usually separated by mountains or other highlands. Some, like Hungary and Szechwan (Ssu-ch'uan), China, are of a basin character; many are river lowlands like the Po, Ganges, and Yangtze Valleys. Coastal plains are common, although generally rather narrow, and include those of Portugal, Israel, Malabar in western India, and the quite small ones in Japan. Often, these various sorts of lowlands in southern Eurasia are small; nevertheless they have the highest population density of the entire region and contain most of the large cities.

In Africa, the coastal fringe along the Mediterranean Sea and the irrigated Nile Valley are well populated, as are parts of the Sudan region. In contrast, the large but hot and humid Congo Basin, much of the Guinea coast, and the tropical lowlands of East Africa have attracted comparatively few people. In tropical Africa, the highlands usually have more inhabitants than the adjacent lowlands, largely because of the cooler climate.

Although Australia has extensive plains, those in the central and western parts of the continent are so arid that the population is small; much of the desert is uninhabited. The humid lowlands on the east, southeast, and southwest portions contain most of the country's population but are too small in area to support great numbers of people.

Old mountains, with rounded summits, are characteristic of northern Ireland, Scotland, Scandinavia, southern Germany, much of east central China, parts of Siberia, and some areas in southeastern Australia and Tasmania. In many of the old mountain areas, the gentler slopes are tilled and thus support a fairly dense population. The steeper land, used for grazing and forestry, has few inhabitants. Frequently, mining is an important industry.

Young, rugged mountains, such as the Atlas in Africa, the Pyrenees, Alps, Apennines, Balkans, Carpathians, and Pindus in Europe, and the Lebanon and Taurus in Asia, nearly surround the Mediterranean Sea. Other groups of young mountains, curving eastward from the Black Sea area, include the Caucasus, Elburz, Karakorum, Kunlun, Nan Shan, and Himalayas. The upfolded ranges continue southeast through Burma, Thailand, and the Malay Peninsula into the volcano-studded islands of the East Indies. Off Eastern Asia, southward from the Kamchatka Peninsula, are the mountainous islands of Japan, Formosa, and the Philippines. Much of New Zealand also has rugged, mountainous topography.

Plateaus are numerous in Eurasia, with Tibet surpassing all others. This type of highland is especially common in the southern part of the continent and forms the main mass of several peninsulas. Among the plateaus are those of Iberia, Turkey, Arabia, Iran, Afghanistan, Deccan (India), and Yünnan in southwest China. Most of Africa south of the Sahara consists of plateaus with Ethiopia rising high above the rest.

## PEOPLE OF THE OLD WORLD

Representatives of all the major races of mankind reside in the Eastern Hemisphere. Probably the original home of man was somewhere in Asia. The Caucasian peoples are classified into several groups, among which are the Indians of Hindustan and Pakistan, the Semites of North Africa and Southwest Asia, the Nordics of Northwest Europe, the Alpine type in Central Europe, and the Slavs to the east and southeast. The primitive Ainus of Japan are also included with the white race. The so-called Mongolians are found in China, Japan, and Central Asia. The Malays are natives of Burma, the Malay Peninsula, Indonesia, the Philippines, and other island groups. Negroes and Negroid peoples live in Africa south of the Sahara, in New Guinea, in isolated portions of Southeast Asia, and in islands as far east as Fiji. Originally they were the inhabitants of Australia. Polynesians are a mixed race living on Pacific islands from New Zealand to Hawaii. The Malagasy of Madagascar are related to the Polynesians. The Hamites of the Sudan and Ethiopia are another example of mixed ancestry. Through intermarriage, racial characteristics are fused. Thus it is difficult to describe a typical Englishman, German, Frenchman, Korean, or any of a great number of others.

## GEOGRAPHIC RELATIONSHIPS

*Europe*

Europe has the most irregular coast line of any continent. It consists of several large peninsulas—Balkan, Italian, Iberian (Spain and Portugal), Brittany, Jutland (Denmark), Scandinavia—and many smaller ones. Great Britain, Ireland, Sicily, Sardinia, and numerous other islands adjoin the mainland. Iceland and Spitsbergen are distant outliers. Between the peninsulas, major islands, and the mainland are many straits and seas. Some seas, like the Mediterranean, Tyrrhenian, Adriatic, Aegean, and Black as well as the North and Baltic, are nearly landlocked.

There are three great physical relief regions in Europe: (1) the Northwestern Highlands in Scandinavia and Scotland, (2) the Central Lowlands in northern France, Netherlands, northern Germany, and adjacent areas, and (3) the Southern Uplands of mountains, plateaus, basins, and peninsulas in Spain, Switzerland, Italy, and the Balkan countries. The variety of surface forms and areas within the major regions gives rise to a large number of environments, each with its typical industries or occupations. The most extensive lowland plain on earth extends, with few interruptions, from the North Sea across northern Eurasia to eastern Siberia. Densely populated in Europe, the plain supports few people in northern Siberia.

The bulk of Europe's population is crowded onto its plains. The largest of these is the North European Plain which extends from northwest France across the Low Countries, northern Germany, and Poland into the U.S.S.R. Most of the European part of the Soviet Union is included in this plain. In Central and Southern Europe many small plains, valleys, and basins are interspersed between the hills and mountains. Such are common in England, southern Germany, France, Italy, and in the southeast from the Carpathians to Greece. The plains have easy routes for railways and highways, generally favorable conditions for agriculture, and convenient sites for cities. Many have navigable rivers. The Alps, Pyrenees, and Scandinavian mountains are formidable barriers, but, in general, the mountain systems are relatively easy to cross compared with ranges like the Andes or Himalayas.

As a result of the deep penetration of the continent by marginal seas, ocean transport has easy access to all Western Europe. Ocean ports are within a few hundred miles of nearly all parts of the Continent. In addition, navigable rivers and canals bring cheap water transport to localities far inland. No other continent equals Europe in accessibility. Although the Mediterranean shore is girt by mountains, breaks in the barrier allow access to the hinterland. Among these breaks are the Gap of Carcassonne to Bordeaux, the Rhone Valley, the Brenner and other passes from the Adriatic, the route from Salonika up the Vardar Valley, and the Dardanelles. The longest railroad tunnels in the world, the Simplon, 12.5 miles, and the St. Gotthard, 9.25 miles, pierce the Alps and connect the Po Valley with the Rhineland and northern lowlands. Shores of the North and Baltic Seas, however, are usually low and often swampy. Some of these lowlands have been reclaimed for agricultural use by the building of dikes.

Europe has many natural resources. For energy there is coal, petroleum, and water power. There are extensive forests and considerable grazing areas. Iron ore and bauxite are abundant, and there is an ample supply of many other important minerals. In addition to resource supplies of local origin, heavy consumption by both population and industry necessitates large imports of many materials and goods.

The value of Europe's imports greatly exceeds that of its exports. The difference is made up by money spent by tourists and foreign residents, and such invisible exports as interest on investments abroad, money sent home by emigrants, profits on insurance and ships carrying goods for other nations, commissions on sales, services, and management outside the Continent, and income earned abroad by writers, artists, musicians, lecturers, and other workers. In general, Europeans go abroad to work, visitors pay for living and travel on the Continent. After World War II, the United States gave or lent European countries large quantities of goods and much money.

## Asia

The largest of the continents, Asia, has over half the world's population. Large, fertile lowlands with abundant water from rainfall or irrigation, and continuous or long growing seasons make possible two to four crops a year. Most Asiatics consume little meat, and many are vegetarians. In China, where animal food is used, the sources are mainly swine and poultry. Both gain much in weight compared to their food supply, which in part consists of materials that would otherwise be wasted. Furthermore, custom encourages a high birth rate, and standards of living are usually far below those of the United States and Canada.

Although Asia thus supports more than a billion people, the continent has vast deserts, high, frigid plateaus, the greatest mountains on earth, and frozen tundras. All these have few, if any, inhabitants. The enormous size of Asia and the highland barriers handicap transportation. In the midst of the continent, an area larger than the United States is without railroads. Deserts dominate from Arabia through Iran and Tibet into Turkestan and Mongolia. From the Caspian Sea, the lowlands to the east are also desert. Except for concentrated areas reclaimed by irrigation, the land is left to roving nomadic herders. The entire northern coast of Siberia is open to navigation for only a few weeks each year, and small use can be made of the Lena, Ob, and Yenisei Rivers because they are tributary to the Arctic. Smaller plains are common, especially those associated with rivers. Examples include the Sung-hua and Liao Ho plains of Manchuria, Yellow Plain of the Hwang Ho, and Yangtze in China, the Ganges and Indus lowlands, and Mesopotamia. Coastal lowlands also occur but are often narrow.

Plateaus are such numerous and important features in Asia that it might as well be called a continent of plateaus. The greatest are those in the interior which are centered in Tibet, with smaller plateaus in Mongolia, Gobi, Turkestan, western China, Afghanistan, and Iran. Peninsular plateaus in Turkey, Arabia, and the Deccan of India are noteworthy.

Double sets of mighty mountain ranges cross Southern Asia from Turkey to China. The ranges spreading out from the Pamirs, called "roof of the world," in western Tibet are the Hindu Kush to the southwest, the Karakorum and Himalayas on the south and southeast, the Altyn Tagh and Kunlun (Klun-lun) to the east, and the Altai and Tien Shan on the north.

Like Europe, Asia has several protruding peninsulas, and to the east and southeast the ocean is filled with islands large and small. The chief peninsulas are Anatolia (Turkey), Arabia, India, Malay, Shantung (in China), Korea, and Kamchatka. On the south, the Red Sea and Persian Gulf are connected with the Indian Ocean. To the east are the Yellow Sea and the Sea of Japan guarded by the Japanese islands, and farther north the Sea of Okhotsk and Bering Sea. To the southeast, the Philippines and Indonesia are a mixture of islands and seas. The inland Caspian Sea is the largest lake in the world.

The natural vegetation, soils, and land utilization are closely related to the climatic regions. Vast softwood forests cover much of Siberia. Teak and other hardwoods come from the tropical monsoon regions. A great variety of native plants occurs, many of which have been domesticated. Asia is the original home of more cultivated crops and domestic livestock than any other continent.

Besides resources based on agriculture and grazing, Asia has minerals, fisheries, and water power. In minerals, it is rich in petroleum, possibly having more than any other continent. There is much coal in China, and considerable in India, Japan, Vietnam, and Siberia. Many metals are produced. Fisheries are most impor-

tant off the northeast coasts, but are valuable both in the cold Arctic and warm Indian Oceans. The greatest development of water power has been in Japan, where industrialization is most advanced. There are large rivers that descend thousands of feet from their mountain sources to the plains. Among these are the Yangtze, Indus, and Brahmaputra. In the future, great dams will develop the power that will be needed when China, Hindustan, and Pakistan become important manufacturing regions.

## Africa

On the basis of the culture and history of its peoples, this continent can be divided into the Mediterranean lands that are closely related to Europe and Asia, and Central and Southern Africa. The Sahara is the natural zone of separation. Most of the two-thirds of Africa south of the Sahara is a plateau that usually breaks steeply toward the oceans. This causes rapids and falls in the lower courses of rivers, making them unnavigable. The upper Nile flows through the swampy Sudd, where papyrus and other water vegetation choked the channels and prevented water travel. Penetration to the interior was so difficult that until after the middle of the nineteenth century much of Africa was so unknown it was a blank on the map and frequently called the "Dark Continent." When industrialization comes to Africa, the Congo, Niger, and other large, swift rivers will become great sources of power. The continent exceeds North America in its potential water power. Plateau lands in Africa are preferred places for living, especially by Europeans, because of their relative coolness compared to the lowlands.

As yet, most African resources are little developed, but the old rocks have important deposits of minerals. Iron, copper, gold, uranium, diamonds, and many others are mined. Coal is mined in the Union of South Africa. There is, however, little petroleum. Products of the tropical forests, wool and hides from the grasslands, cotton, rubber, cacao, and vegetable oils from the plantations are among the developed resources.

The smooth coast line of the continent is indented by few harbors. The Gulf of Guinea, off the west central coast, is broad and open to the Atlantic Ocean. North of Africa is the Mediterranean Sea and northeast the Red Sea—each enclosed by land except for a narrow strait. Madagascar, in the Indian Ocean, is the only large island, being the third largest in the world.

## Australia

Australia, the smallest of the continents, can be divided into three physical divisions, the Eastern Highlands, the East Central Lowlands which extend north-south across the continent, and Western Australia. Because of the highlands along the eastern edge of the continent, and the continental location within the trade-wind belt, most of the western and central parts are desert. Within much of this arid area the drainage systems are poorly defined, or uncoordinated, and have no outlets to the sea.

The area just east of the Eastern Highlands is the area of greatest population and highest population density. West of the mountains, population decreases rapidly with decreasing rainfall. Near the coast are the largest cities, commercial and industrial centers, and the most productive farms. The large sheep stations are either in southeastern Australia, between the farm lands and the deserts, or in the southwestern part of Western Australia and southwest Queensland. North of the Tropic of Capricorn in the northern and northeastern part of Queensland and the northern part of the Northern Territory, cattle predominate and are numerous near the east, southeast, and southwest coasts.

Broad, curving indentations mark the coast —the Great Australian Bight on the south and the Gulf of Carpentaria on the north. Harbors are few and the coast line is generally smooth Tasmania is the only important island.

# 7. Northwestern and Central Europe

EUROPE is of major significance in the world scene despite the loss of prestige and power caused largely by two world wars, and the upsurgence of backward nationalities which has resulted in their breaking away from European control. Excluding the U.S.S.R., Europe contains 16.5 per cent of the people on only 3.5 per cent of the world land area. The past and present influence of this small geographical area has been of immeasurable importance in world development. The relative significance of many individual countries of Europe has declined but not the potentialities of the Continent as a whole. Its location, the diversity and number of its people, its resources, advanced culture, contributions to science and technology, and tremendous agricultural and industrial productiveness make this second smallest continent of prime concern to every world inhabitant.

227

## IMPORTANCE OF NORTHWESTERN AND CENTRAL EUROPE

Marked political fragmentation is a dominant characteristic of Northwestern and Central Europe. It indicates the deep desire of diverse peoples to have their own sovereignty. The political units range in size from France with 212,737 square miles to tiny Liechtenstein with only 62 squares miles (Table 7-1).

Western Europe is the seat of modern Western civilization and the industrial economy. From each country, people and ideas have penetrated into far corners of the earth. The Industrial Revolution germinated here, grew rapidly, and spread to other parts of the world. Large industrial cities replaced rural areas and

### TABLE 7-1. POPULATION AND AREA OF NORTHWESTERN CENTRAL EUROPEAN COUNTRIES

| Country | Population, in thousands | | Area, sq miles |
|---|---|---|---|
| | Date | Number | |
| **United Kingdom** | 1951 | 50,369 | 94,278 |
| England | 1951 | 41,148 | 53,012 |
| *Channel Islands* | 1951 | 103 | 75 |
| *Isle of Man* | 1951 | 55 | 221 |
| Northern Ireland | 1951 | 1,370 | 5,238 |
| Scotland | 1951 | 5,096 | 30,405 |
| Wales | 1951 | 2,597 | 5,328 |
| **Republic of Ireland (Eire)** | 1951 | 2,961 | 26,952 |
| **Norway** | 1950 | 3,279 | 124,587 |
| Spitsbergen (Svalbard) and Jan Mayen Land | 1950 | 4 | 24,239 |
| **Sweden** | 1952 | 7,151 | 173,347 |
| **Denmark (excl. Faeroe Is.)** | 1950 | 4,281 | 16,576 |
| Faeroe Islands | 1950 | 32 | 540 |
| **Finland** | 1952 | 4,118 | 130,159 |
| **Iceland** | 1952 | 149 | 39,758 |
| **Belgium** | 1952 | 8,756 * | 11,783 |
| **Luxembourg** | 1950 | 299 | 999 |
| **Netherlands** | 1952 | 10,436 | 12,868 |
| **France** * | 1953 | 42,742 † | 212,737 |
| **Germany** † | 1946 | 65,151 | 137,026 |
| Berlin | 1950 | 3,336 | |
| East Germany | 1953 | 17,070 ‡ | 42,392 |
| West Germany | 1950 | 47,696 | 96,634 |
| Saar | 1952 | 971 | 991 |
| **Austria** | 1951 | 6,934 | 32,369 |
| **Switzerland** | 1950 | 4,715 | 15,944 |
| **Liechtenstein** | 1950 | 14 | 62 |
| Total | .... | 330,833 | 1,288,520 |

* Provisional.
† Excluding territories ceded by Italy in 1947 amounting to 708 sq km.
‡ Including displaced persons in camps.
SOURCE: U.S. Population and Vital Statistics Report, *Statistical Papers, ser. A*, vol. 4, no.2, April, 1952, and *The Statesman's Year Book*, 1954.

today dominate much of West Central Europe, with the German Ruhr and the English Midlands as outstanding examples.

Europe's proportion of the world's industrial production decreased from 68 per cent in 1870 to 25 per cent in 1948. Prewar European industrial output was one-third greater than that of the United States; by 1948, it was more than one-fourth less. Rapid industrial growth elsewhere in the world rather than any actual decrease in the Continent itself accounts for the lower relative importance of Europe.

The densely populated industrial core of England, Benelux (Belgium, Netherlands, Luxembourg), France, and Germany is surrounded by areas where agriculture, forestry, fishing, and mining supplant manufacturing in importance. Additional food and raw material are imported to supplement that locally produced. Position and ease of transportation facilitate vital commercial relations with neighboring countries and the rest of the world. The spending by many tourists helps pay for the imports needed by Europe.

## LOCATION AND SHAPE

Northwestern and Central Europe, as here defined, includes 1,055,215 square miles or 57 per cent of Europe (excluding the U.S.S.R.). The fifteen countries would cover about one-third of the United States. From northern Norway to southern France measures 2,125 miles or the distance from Chicago to Los Angeles. Small countries have the advantage of unity, compactness, and ease of exchange of goods and ideas but usually lack sufficient local resources and agricultural land to support a large population.

The strategic buffer zone location between the two world powers, the United States and U.S.S.R., is useful in peace but not in war. The central location in the land hemisphere facilitates world trade especially as Western Europe faces three major water bodies, Arctic Ocean, Atlantic Ocean, and Mediterranean Sea.

No other comparable world area has such disrupted coast lines and irregularly shaped countries. The North Sea, Baltic Sea, English Channel, and Bay of Biscay cause separations and indentations. The peninsulas of Scandinavia, Jutland, Brittany, as well as several smaller ones, add to the irregularity as do the numerous islands, ranging in size from Great Britain and Iceland to tiny skerries along the Norwegian coast. Norway and Scotland exhibit highly fiorded coasts.

## PHYSICAL SETTING

### Relief Features

Western Europe has a very complex physical structure. East of the Carpathian Mountains and the Vistula River is the stable Russian platform. West of this platform, repeated elevation and depression of the land with folding and erosion has left mountains, plateaus, hills, and plains in close proximity.

**Highlands.** The highlands found in Scandinavia, northern Scotland, and Ireland are composed of very old, hard rocks that have been repeatedly uplifted and eroded. Moreover, huge ice sheets during the Glacial Period sculptured, scoured, and smoothed the topography. The fiorded coast line of Norway, with some fiords reaching 120 miles inland, and the rounded highlands of northern Scotland demonstrate the great erosive power of the ice. Most of Norway is a high glaciated plateau averaging between 4,000 and 5,000 feet. The Scandinavian highlands drop sharply to the west but gradually to the Baltic. These highlands include northern Finland and an isolated area in southern Sweden. Soils are generally infertile. Valleys and adjoining lowlands possess limited arable land. Timber and water power are abundant, especially in Scandinavia.

Mountains and plateaus in West Central Europe, although geologically younger than the Scandinavian highlands, have been eroded for so long that their relief is one of rounded maturity. Such remnants extend from the southern uplands of Ireland to the highlands of central Germany and include southwest England, Brittany, Central Plateau of France, the Ardennes, and Vosges. These uplands consist of hard, resistant rock with considerable relief and poor soil. Adjacent basins and lowlands contain more recent deposits of agricultural value. The metallic ores and coal measures which are associated with the highlands form the basis of major industrial regions. Agriculture is limited but grazing and forestry are significant.

The Alpine system, a complex combination of young folded mountains with associated forelands and intermontane basins and plains, dominates Switzerland, Austria, and the eastern borderlands of France. The Alps average 12,000 feet, with higher sharp peaks, such as Mt. Blanc, 15,781 feet. Valleys are narrow, steep, and rocky. The south slope of the Alps is abrupt but the north slope is gradual. The Alps, because of their east-west orientation, are not a major climatic barrier to the marine westerly winds. Despite the high altitudes, numerous passes and tunnels allow remarkably easy north-south communication between the Mediterranean Basin and Northwestern and Central Europe.

The Pyrenees Mountains extend between the Bay of Biscay and the Mediterranean Sea. Like the Alps, they are young folded mountains and form a considerable barrier between France and Spain.

**Lowlands.** Fortunately, Northwestern and Central Europe contains considerable lowland. The great European Plain extends from southeastern England, through western and northern France, Belgium, Netherlands, Denmark, north Germany, Poland, and on into the Soviet Union. It is narrow in the west and widens in the east. Generally, it is level; rolling to hilly topography occurs, but elevations rarely rise over 500 feet above sea level. Much of the existing relief is a result of continental glaciation, and ridges of glacial debris (moraines) border the Baltic in

north Germany and Denmark. Outcrops of slightly folded beds of shale, chalk, and limestone, called "downs" or "scarp and vale," give relief to southern England and northern France. Sand, gravel, and silt of glacial origin cover most of the remaining lowland area; in central Germany there are fertile wind-deposited soils called "loess."

Lowlands border also the Baltic Sea and the Gulf of Bothnia in Sweden and Finland. Generally, southern Sweden and southern Finland are less than 500 feet above sea level, with numerous lakes, swamps, and glacial ridges. The Baltic lowlands are underlain by very old crystalline rocks except for the fertile sedimentary plains of Skåne in the extreme southern tip of Sweden. Soils are usually thin with only limited deposits of fertile marine clay.

**Rivers.** The Alps and associated mountains are the source for the major rivers of Central Europe. Large north-flowing rivers, such as the Oder draining into the Baltic, and the Elbe and Rhine draining into the North Sea, are rapid and of value for water power near their sources, but become broad and sluggish in crossing the great European Plain. France has three major west- or northwest-flowing rivers in the Seine, Loire, and Garonne; the Rhone empties into the Mediterranean. A system of interconnecting canals and rivers gives Western Europe the best inland water transportation network in the world. The British Isles have numerous short rivers, the longest being the Thames and Shannon. Scandinavian rivers draining to the Atlantic are short and rapid; those entering the Baltic are longer, with slower flow. Finland and the Netherlands are handicapped by considerable poorly drained land.

*Climate*

Reliability, the keynote of the climate of Northwestern and Central Europe, fosters agricultural development and other human activities. Temperatures are far more moderate than those of similar latitudes in North America or interior Eurasia (Figure 7-1). Only the rigorous climates of the higher mountains and exposed

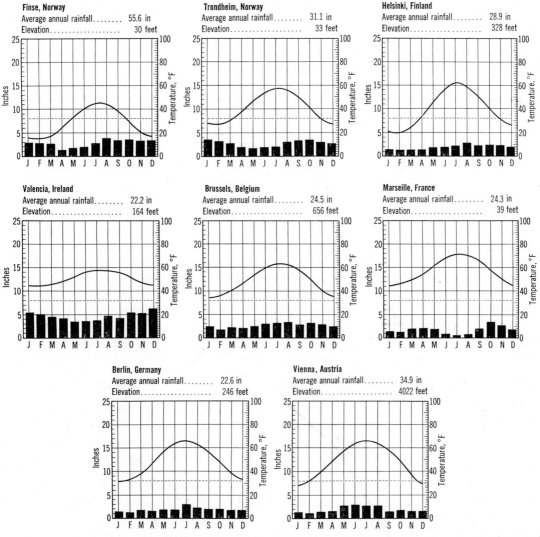

*Figure 7-1   Climate graphs of selected stations of Northwestern and Central Europe.*

areas with heavy rainfall are unsuitable to crops. Barley and rye are grown beyond 70° north latitude in Norway, farther north than on any other continent.

Mild winters, cool to warm summers, small temperature ranges for the latitude, and well-distributed precipitation typify the climate. Position on the western side of a large land mass, prevailing westerly winds off the warm North Atlantic flowing inland without land barriers, and the prevalence of cyclonic influences are largely responsible for these conditions.

The movement of storms from west to east results in frequent weather changes of temperature, wind, and precipitation. The cyclonic influence is especially strong in the winter.

**Marine West-coast.** The British Isles, the western fringes of continental Europe, and southern Iceland are dominated by marine influences. Mild winters, cool summers, evenly distributed precipitation, and damp, cloudy conditions are characteristic. In January, the 32°F isotherm runs north-south along the Norwegian coast and then trends northwest-southeast. The adjoining water moderates the summer temperatures; the long days are warm but rarely hot. The annual temperature range averages between 15 and 30°F. The frost-free period is 180 days or more except in the highlands.

Slightly greater amounts of precipitation normally are received in the winter half-year; spring months are generally the driest. Annual precipitation varies from less than 25 inches in the plains of southeastern England to nearly 200 inches on the exposed peaks of Ben Nevis in Scotland and Snowden in Wales.

**Transitional Climate of Central Europe.**   The climate of Central Europe is transitional between marine Western and continental Eastern Europe. The annual temperature range increases and precipitation decreases eastward with greater distance from the sea. Northeast winds from Siberia bring low winter temperatures and snow for four or five months in eastern Germany, eastern Norway, Sweden, Austria, and Switzerland. Though the North and Baltic Seas do not freeze, the tributary rivers and harbors are icebound. The average is 32 days at Lubeck and 61 days at Stettin. Precipitation decreases eastward from marine Europe, and averages 22 to 26 inches annually with a spring and summer maximum.

**Humid Continental.**   Finland, northern Sweden, and parts of Norway have a humid continental climate with short, warm summers and long, severe winters. This area is partially blocked from the moderating oceanic winds by the Scandinavian highlands. Finland is affected

in winter by cold northeast winds from Siberia. Coniferous forests grow well, but the short growing season limits agriculture to hardy crops.

**Mediterranean.**   Southern France experiences the climate typical of the lands bordering the Mediterranean Sea, having hot, dry summers and mild, rainy winters. In summer, a zone of high atmospheric pressure extends over the Mediterranean Sea resulting in stable conditions. In winter, a southward migration of the paths followed by cyclonic storms brings rains to the area. Winter is the natural growing season as the summers are too dry.

**Tundra and High Altitude.**   The Alps, Scandinavian Highlands, and other highland areas of Northwestern and Central Europe exhibit great climatic zonation and extremes typical of mountainous areas. The Alps form a divide between the climates of Mediterranean and Central Europe.

*Natural Vegetation and Soils*

Natural vegetation and soils in Europe are related closely to the varied relief and climatic conditions. Man's intensive utilization of the land has greatly disrupted the original natural patterns of Western Europe, especially that of vegetation. Rapid soil changes, because of glaciation or type of parent rock, result in much less uniform belts of soil than in Eastern Europe. Nevertheless, the distribution of certain broad associations of native vegetation and soils can be identified. The major characteristics are outlined in Table 7-2.

## DIVERSITY OF CULTURES AND LANGUAGES

The thirteen political units (besides Luxembourg and Liechtenstein) indicate the tremendous diversity of peoples, languages, and cultures of this area. Each country, no matter how small, has developed a national identity and traditions peculiar to its individual culture. In most cases, the country has its own language, within which several dialects may have evolved

because of separation by water bodies or land barriers. Switzerland has four, and Belgium and Finland each have two language and ethnic groups.

Various races of people are found in Northwestern and Central Europe, but language and cultural rather than racial differences form the basis for nationalistic desires and territorial

## TABLE 7-2. PRINCIPAL VEGETATION AND SOIL CHARACTERISTICS

| Vegetation | Soil |
|---|---|
| **Tundra.** Moss, lichens, and low bushes. Dwarf birch, larch, spruce, and sphagnum-peat bogs on southern fringe | **Tundra.** Subsoil permanently frozen, acid, lacks humus. Surface swampy and waterlogged in summer. Little or no agriculture |
| **Taiga.** Cedar, larch, pine, fir, and spruce, common coniferous species. Some deciduous aspen, birch, and alder | **Podsol.** Ashen gray color, highly leached, acid, low in humus. Limited agriculture |
| **Mixed coniferous and deciduous.** Transitional between coniferous and deciduous in north. Oak, beech, hickory association in south. Largely cleared for agriculture | **Podsolic and brown.** Transitional. Gray to brown in color. Brown soils less leached, higher in humus, less acid, with better structure than podsolic. Productive if heavily fertilized and carefully managed |
| **Mediterranean.** Drought-resistant types such as olive, cork oak, cypress, and scrubby evergreen. Deciduous at higher elevations. Shrub and bush growth common | **Mixed.** Varies, depending upon parent material and amount of rainfall and leaching. Alluvial, high-iron-content (red), and volcanic soils common. Lowland soils productive, especially where irrigated |
| **Mountain and moor.** Vertical zonations with Alpine grasslands in the Alps, Pyrenees, and Norway. Moor (heather) found in highlands of British Isles | **Highland.** Thin, rocky, and infertile. Dark-brown soils in Alpine grasslands. Grazing and forestry developed |

problems. Germanic, Celtic, and Romanic languages predominate, with the Asiatic-derived Finnish and Lapp languages found in the north. This diversity of languages, dialects, customs, and traditions is a major barrier to the much-talked-of unification of Western Europe.

The European area was once divided into a few great empires, French, German, Austro-Hungarian, and Russian. During the nineteenth and twentieth centuries, a great nationalistic movement spread across Europe fed by the democratic ideas of equality, fraternity, and liberty generated during the French Revolution. Many nations achieved independence as the great empires were divided, and some nations attempted and failed to dominate Europe by aggressive warfare.

Economic difficulties brought on by two world wars, difficulties in trade, and the loss of colonies by Western European powers have resulted in the consideration of economic unions. Belgium, Netherlands, and Luxembourg have an economic (customs) agreement called the "Benelux Union." Effective February 10, 1953, the Schuman Plan for pooling steel and coal in six Western European nations is another attempt to offset the raw material and market disadvantages of small nations by unification and cooperation. Various organizations with political and collective security implications also have been formed, such as the Council of Europe and NATO (Table 7-3). The success of these attempts is an important step toward unification of Western Europe. Any federal movement faces the tremendous obstacles of strong nationalistic and self-sufficiency movements.

## POPULATION DISTRIBUTION AND PRESENT STAGE OF ECONOMIC DEVELOPMENT

A belt of extremely dense population extends from central and southern England across the English Channel to include northern France, the Low Countries, the Rhine Valley, and the

TABLE 7-3. MEMBERSHIP OF EUROPEAN ORGANIZATIONS

| | OEEC † | Council of Europe | European Coal and Steel Community ‡ | NATO § | Benelux Customs Union |
|---|---|---|---|---|---|
| Austria * | x | | | | |
| Belgium * | x | x | x | x | x |
| Denmark * | x | x | | x | |
| Eire * | x | x | | | |
| France * | x | x | x | x | |
| Germany (West) * | x | x | x | x | |
| Greece | x | x | | x | |
| Iceland * | x | x | | x | |
| Italy | x | x | x | x | |
| Luxembourg * | x | x | x | x | x |
| Netherlands * | x | x | x | x | x |
| Norway * | x | x | | x | |
| Portugal | x | | | x | |
| Sweden * | x | x | | | |
| Switzerland * | x | | | | |
| Turkey | x | x | | x | |
| United Kingdom * | x | x | | x | |

x Members or proposed members.
* Political units in Northwestern and Central Europe.
† Organization for European Economic Cooperation.
‡ Also known as the Schuman Plan.
§ North Atlantic Treaty Organization.

contact zone between the highlands and lowlands in Germany (Figure 7-2). This is one of the most intensely urbanized and industrialized regions in the world. Great Britain has more than 70 per cent of its population living in cities of over 10,000. Both Belgium and Netherlands have a population density of 2,150 persons per square mile of arable land. The Scottish Lowlands, South Wales, eastern Denmark, the southern tip of Sweden, the Swiss Plateau, the Danube Valley of Austria, and the Rhone Valley of France are also densely populated areas.

Surrounding the industrial and commercial cities are thickly peopled and intensively developed agricultural areas. Such handicaps as infertile, sandy, and swampy soil have been overcome by heavy fertilization and scientific farming practices. Pasture, hay, cereal grains, and root crops predominate. Almost all agricultural produce is marketed locally.

Most of the area is characterized by deficiencies of agricultural production and surpluses of industrial products. This, and the need for considerable imports of industrial raw materials, makes Northwestern Europe foremost in world trade. Commercial development is aided by excellent ports, large merchant marines, and good inland transportation facilities.

*Figure 7-2   Note the great density of population in the central part of the region and the low density in the northern highland areas. Belgium and the Netherlands are two of the most densely populated nations in the world.*

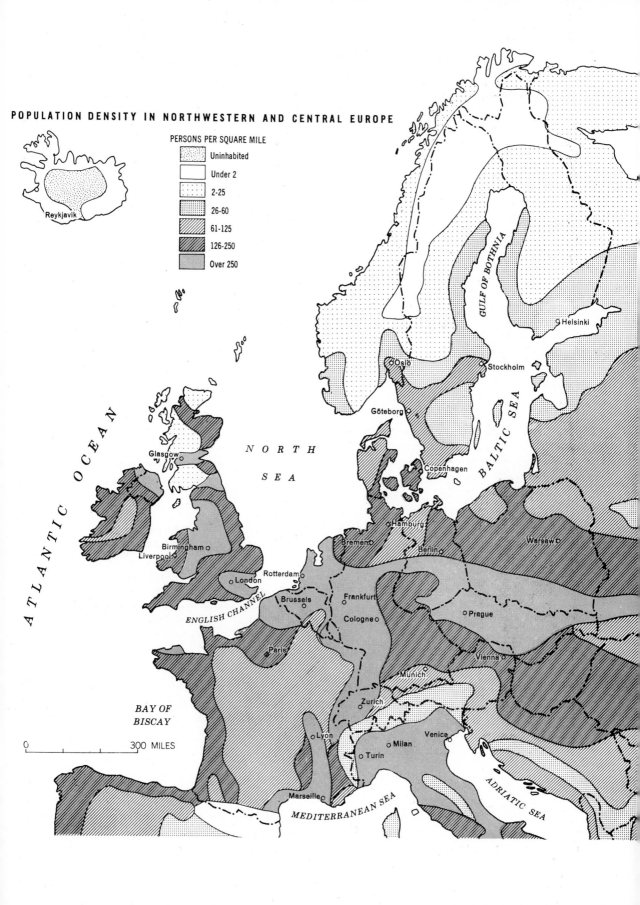

# POPULATION DENSITY IN NORTHWESTERN AND CENTRAL EUROPE

PERSONS PER SQUARE MILE

- Uninhabited
- Under 2
- 2-25
- 26-60
- 61-125
- 126-250
- Over 250

Reykjavik

GULF OF BOTHNIA

Helsinki

Oslo

Stockholm

Göteborg

BALTIC SEA

Glasgow

N O R T H

S E A

Copenhagen

A T L A N T I C   O C E A N

Hamburg

Bremen

Berlin

Warsaw

Birmingham

Liverpool

Rotterdam

London

Brussels

Frankfurt

Prague

ENGLISH CHANNEL

Cologne

Paris

Vienna

Munich

BAY OF
BISCAY

Zurich

Lyon

Venica

Milan

Turin

0      300 MILES

Marseille

MEDITERRANEAN SEA

ADRIATIC SEA

Access to minerals, especially coal and iron, favors industry. Although Great Britain, Belgium, and Germany have large coal supplies each imports some coal as well as nearly all of the petroleum consumed. Low-quality iron ore is available in France and Great Britain. Sweden is an abundant producer of high-quality iron ore. France has a large output of bauxite for aluminum production, and France and Germany have potash. Pyrites, copper, silver, lead, and zinc are found but in insufficient quantities.

Water power is significant in Scandinavia and mountainous Central Europe.

Many peripheral areas of Northwestern and Central Europe are sparsely populated but significant for certain raw materials. They are generally regions of poor soils, rough topography, and severe climate. Forest resources and minerals, notably iron ore in Sweden, are vital to Europe. Much of the agriculture is subsistence, but grazing and dairying are locally highly developed.

## SCANDINAVIAN COUNTRIES AND FINLAND

The northern countries, loosely referred to as Scandinavia, are of increasingly strategic importance in Europe. The five countries of Norway, Sweden, Denmark, Finland, and Iceland have a great deal in common; yet each shows individuality (Figure 7-3). As a result of past association, cultures and traditions are similar. Except for the Finns and Lapps, racial and language similarities exist. The majority of the people stem from the characteristically blond Nordic stock. All of the countries are socialist democracies, although monarchs still reign in Denmark, Norway, and Sweden. The Lutheran religion is strongly predominant. Illiteracy is practically nonexistent.

Physical similarities also are numerous. With the exception of Denmark and the southernmost tip of Sweden, old, resistant rocks are characteristic, and the entire area has been glaciated. Iceland and Norway still possess permanent glaciers. Soils, with a few exceptions, are generally infertile. Coast lines are long and indented; thus, fishing and commercial development loom high in importance. The Atlantic slopes are rugged, abrupt, and fiorded; the Baltic slopes are gradual, with southern Sweden, southern Finland, and all of Denmark being

relatively flat. Population is concentrated in the seaward peripheries of the countries.

The severe climate expected in these high latitudes is offset by the prevailing westerly winds off the warm North Atlantic. This oceanic influence is strongest during the winter as evidenced by the 32°F isotherm paralleling the entire Norwegian coast, which is ice-free the year around. Annual temperature ranges increase eastward (Table 7-4). Summer days are long but rather cool. Precipitation varies from over 60 inches in western Norway to 25 in Finland, and less than 20 in the extreme north.

### TABLE 7-4
### ANNUAL TEMPERATURE RANGE

| Station | Jan. av., deg F | July av., deg F | Annual temperature range, deg F |
|---------|-----------------|-----------------|----------------------------------|
| Bergen | 34 | 58 | 24 |
| Oslo | 24 | 63 | 39 |
| Helsinki | 21 | 62 | 42 |

Agricultural and maritime interests have been foremost in the respective economies, but recently there has been considerable industrial

*Figure 7-3 Scandinavia is an area of peninsulas, indented coast lines, and islands. Note the narrow coastal regions and the dominance of mountains on the Scandinavian Peninsula.*

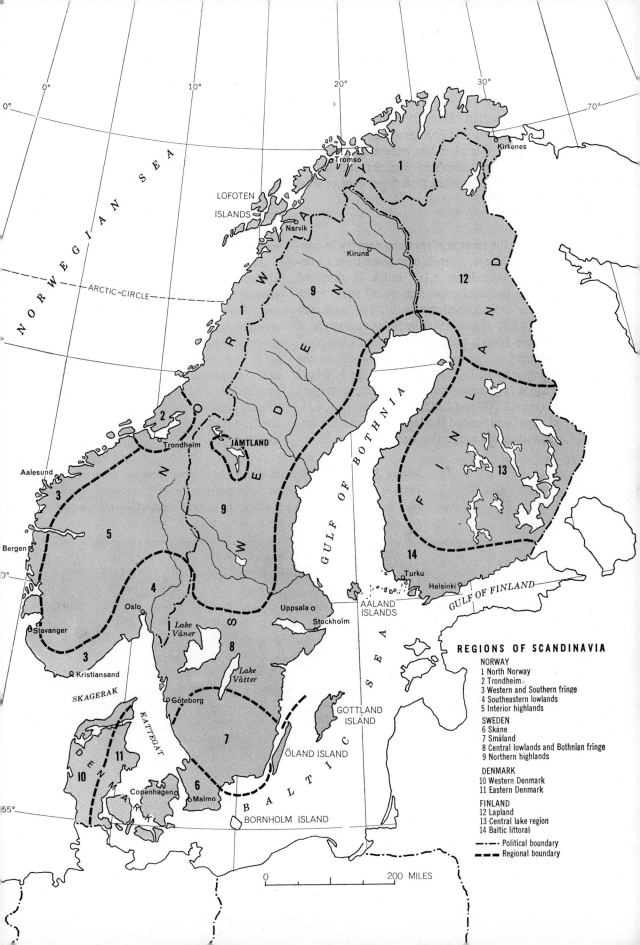

NORWEGIAN SEA

LOFOTEN
ISLANDS

ARCTIC-CIRCLE

N O R W E G I A N   S E A

Tromso

Kirkenes

Narvik

Kiruna

1

12

N
O
R
W
A
Y

9

F
I
N
L
A
N
D

Aalesund

Trondheim

JÄMTLAND

S
W
E
D
E
N

GULF OF BOTHNIA

13

3

N

9

Bergen

5

14

Turku

Helsinki

GULF OF FINLAND

4

Oslo

AALAND
ISLANDS

B
A
L
T
I
C

S
E
A

Stavanger

Lake
Väner

Uppsala

Stockholm

3

Kristiansand

8

Lake
Vätter

SKAGERAK

Göteborg

GOTTLAND
ISLAND

KATTEGAT

7

ÖLAND ISLAND

11

D
E
N
M
A
R
K

10

Copenhagen

6

Malmo

BORNHOLM ISLAND

55°

**REGIONS OF SCANDINAVIA**

NORWAY
1 North Norway
2 Trondheim
3 Western and Southern fringe
4 Southeastern lowlands
5 Interior highlands

SWEDEN
6 Skåne
7 Småland
8 Central lowlands and Bothnian fringe
9 Northern highlands

DENMARK
10 Western Denmark
11 Eastern Denmark

FINLAND
12 Lapland
13 Central lake region
14 Baltic littoral

—·—·— Political boundary
━ ━ ━ Regional boundary

0        200 MILES

development. All countries lack coal, and most of the iron ore produced in Sweden and Norway is exported. Local raw materials supply forest products and food-processing industries. Water power is abundant except in Denmark. The combined merchant marines and fishing fleets account for more than 5 per cent of total world trade.

### Norway

Norway, the most northwestern country in continental Europe, extends over more than 13 degrees of latitude or 1,100 miles. If stretched out, the indented coast line would reach more than halfway around the world. The total area of 124,587 square miles includes thousands of offshore islands and skerries (rocky islets).

Rocky and rugged highlands dominate the topography of Norway. Much of the highland surface is plateau-like in character, averaging between 2,000 and 5,000 feet in elevation. Glaciation has rounded the landforms and cut numerous fiords along the west coast, some extending over 100 miles inland. The 3 per cent of arable area is located primarily along the coast and in the flatter southeast.

Forests cover one-fourth of Norway's land area. They occur at elevations below 3,300 feet in the south and 1,000 feet in the north. The best forests are on the eastern slopes of the highlands. About two-thirds of the commercial forest are coniferous Norway spruce and fir, and one-third deciduous, with birch dominant.

Norway's lack of coal is partially offset by abundant hydroelectric power. Abundant precipitation, melting glaciers, negligible freezing, and high stream gradients give Norway more available water power than any other European country. Pyrites (source of sulfur and sulfuric acid) and iron ore, the principal minerals, normally represent two-thirds of the value of ore production. Molybdenum and silver also are mined. Coal is produced on Spitsbergen (Svalbard), a large group of Arctic islands belonging to Norway.

*Figure 7-4   A typical rural district in eastern Norway. Hay, an important crop, is dried by placing it on wires which keep it off the moist ground. Valuable forests cover the slopes above the cleared land. (Courtesy of Norwegian Official Photo.)*

**Economic Development.** Agriculture, despite the handicaps of relief, climate, and poor soil, engages about one-third of the working population. Dairying and livestock production predominate. Farming often is combined with fishing in the coastal districts and with forestry in the interior. Small farms, 90 per cent owner-operated, and limited mechanization, are characteristic. Hay, pasture, cereal grains, and root crops are grown.

The recently intensified industrial activity, largely based on abundance of cheap water power, now employs 25 per cent of the labor force and contributes over 50 per cent of the national production. Processing fish, forest, and food products and manufacturing electrochemical and electrometallurgical goods are leading industries. A large state iron and steel works, constructed at Mo-i-Rana to supply most of Norway's needs, was completed in 1955.

Many Norwegians look to the sea for their livelihood. From the waters adjacent to Norway and certain foreign waters are landed over 1.5 million metric tons of fish per year. Norway ranks first in Europe and third in the world as a fishing nation. Fish and fish products normally account for 25 per cent of the total value of exports. Herring are caught predominantly south of Trondheimfiord and cod to the north, especially in the Lofoten area. The whaling fleet, operating largely in Antarctic waters, accounts for one-half the annual world catch.

Norway's merchant marine ranks third in the world, behind the United States and Great Britain. About 85 per cent of the merchant fleet is engaged in trade between foreign ports. Though nearly half of the tonnage was lost during World War II, the fleet has been rebuilt to a level higher than prewar.

**Regions.** North Norway, the area north of the 65th parallel, is largely a thinly populated, narrow, barren, mountainous plateau region with a dissected coast line. Cod fishing is of commercial importance in the Lofoten Island waters; cod are dried and salted, and some are sent southward for further processing. Small-scale enterprises often combined with farming predominate. Since the 1940s, several freezing and fish-packing establishments have been erected as part of a plan to increase economic opportunities in the resource-poor north. Narvik is an important railhead shipping iron ore from north Sweden. Tromsö is a center of the coastal whaling and Arctic sealing industry. Iron ore is mined near Kirkenes within a few miles of the U.S.S.R. boundary.

The Trondheim depression, surrounding Trondheimfiord, is a fertile dairying area with hay, oats, barley, and potatoes as the principal crops. Well-forested slopes form the basis of a paper, pulp, and lumber industry. Trondheim is the major commercial and fishing center of the area.

The Western and Southern Fringes area, south of the Trondheim depression, is a fiorded, precipitous, island-dotted coast region with fishing and farming preeminent. The population is concentrated on the coastal islands, the fringes of the mainland, along the fiord borders, and in interior valleys. Farming often is combined with fishing to supplement income. The heavy precipitation, cool temperatures, and rough topography favor hardy fodder crops and dairying. The flat southwest coast is famous for its dairy cattle.

Ålesund is the leading fishing port and herring capital, Kristiansund, the klipfish (dried, salted cod) center, Stavanger a fish-canning center, and Bergen the major port of western Norway. Industry is growing based on available water power. Kristiansand is an industrial center and port on the south coast.

The Southeastern Lowlands dominate Norway. Nearly 50 per cent of Norway's 3.3 million people live in Oslo and seven surrounding counties. A larger proportion of rolling but relatively arable land exists here than elsewhere. As usual, dairying predominates. Excellent forests are found on the slopes, and many farmers work in the forests during the long, cold winters. Sawmills and paper and pulp mills are common. Oslo, the capital and largest city, is the industrial, transportation, commercial, and cultural center of all Norway. It has shipbuilding and a variety of manufactures. Electrochemical and electrometallurgical industries, located in smaller cities, utilize large amounts of hydroelectric power. Sandefiord, Tönsberg, and Larvik are bases for the Norwegian Antarctic whaling fleet.

The interior highlands are sparsely populated. Some forestry is found on the lower slopes, and cattle are summer pastured on the grasslands of the upland plateaus. Communications have been constructed with difficulty. Railroads from Bergen and Trondheim cross the highlands and terminate in Oslo.

**Trade and Problems.**   Norway is normally an exporter of raw materials and an importer of finished goods. Over 80 per cent of the exports consist of three main types of commodities, processed timber products, fishing and whaling products, and ores and metals. Imports are dominated by foodstuffs, coal, petroleum products, textile raw materials, iron and steel, and machinery. Increased earnings from the rebuilt merchant marine, ECA (Economic Cooperation Administration) aid, and self-imposed austerity have done much to offset a trade deficit. Western European countries and the United States dominate Norway's trade. Both economically and politically Norway is oriented toward the West.

**Spitsbergen (Svalbard).**   Norway gained control of the strategic Arctic archipelago of Spitsbergen in 1920. Two-thirds of the 24,095 square miles are permanently covered with ice and snow. A branch of the warm North Atlantic Drift keeps the west coast ice-free for a short summer period. Coal is the most valuable resource; during some years over 700,000 tons have been exported. The inhabitants, mostly coal miners, number a few thousand and about half of them are Russian. Jan Mayen Island and parts of Antarctica also belong to Norway.

*Sweden*

Sweden, the largest and most populous of the Scandinavian countries, is slightly larger than California and ten times the size of Denmark. The population of the country is more than 7 million. Nearly 90 per cent of the people live in the southern half of Sweden, which has a humid continental climate more favorable for crops than the subpolar climate of the northern section.

Sweden occupies a central position in the Baltic area. With landlocked northern and western boundaries, its historic orientation has been toward the east although present trade and economic interests are westward. Politically, Sweden stands aloof as a neutral in Northern Europe. This neutrality, begun in 1814, has been maintained through two world wars and the postwar period. Geographical position has been at least partially responsible.

The surface slopes gradually from the mountainous heights along the Norwegian border to the Baltic Sea. Many large rivers follow this gradient, flowing northwest to southeast. These rivers are vital for hydroelectric power development and transportation of logs to coastal saw mills. Sedimentary rocks occur in the southern peninsula of Skåne, but old crystalline rock prevails elsewhere. Soils are generally thin and infertile except for Skåne and certain marine clay soils in the central lowlands.

Only 9 per cent of the total land area is arable, 55 per cent is forested, 3 per cent is permanent pasture, and 33 per cent is wasteland or uncultivated. Inland lakes and rivers cover about 9 per cent of the total area. Agriculture is aided by a climate moderated by Atlantic and Baltic influences despite the northerly latitude. Glacial scouring was less severe than in Finland or Norway.

**Economic Development.**   The principal natural resources of Sweden are forests, iron ore, water power, and soil. Over 40 per cent of the postwar exports are forest products. Pine, spruce, and birch are the main commercial species. About 50 per cent of the forests are state-owned and an efficient conservation program is in effect.

Excluding the Soviet Union, Sweden mines one-fourth of the iron ore of Europe. The Lapland ores average over 60 per cent metallic content but are high in phosphorus; almost all are exported either via Narvik, Norway, or Luleå, Sweden. The central Swedish (Bergslagen) ore is lower in metallic content but contains less sulfur and phosphorus. Some is exported, some utilized in Sweden's high-quality iron and steel industry. Gold, low-grade coal, and copper are among other minerals found.

Sweden's relief and climate favor water power development. About one-third of the 60 billion kilowatthour potential is utilized. Approximately 80 per cent of the potential is in the northern half of the country, distant from the southern urban and industrial centers.

Sweden is nearly self-sufficient in food. Infertile soils are offset by hard work, application of fertilizer, and successful plant breeding. Farming is marginal and allied with forestry in the north but intensive in the favored soils of the south. Over three-fourths of the farms contain less than 25 acres and are too small for mechanization.

Industry has increased rapidly since the 1880s and now outranks agriculture as a supporter of Sweden's population. Industrialization is based on high-quality raw materials, abundant water power, technical skill, and the contributions of Swedish inventors, on which 10 per cent of the country's industries are based (Table 7-5).

**Regions.**   Sweden is divided roughly into two parts by the 60th parallel. The sparsely populated northern area is a source of raw materials from the forests and mines; the south embraces most of the agriculture, commerce, industry, and population. The following regions can be distinguished: Skåne (Scania), Småland Highlands, Central Lowlands and Bothnian Fringes, and Northern Highlands (Norrland).

The Skåne is the most intensely cultivated area of Sweden, containing about 12 per cent of the people on only 2.5 per cent of the area. Ninety per cent of the land is cultivated, with wheat and sugar beets grown in addition to the common Scandinavian crops. Dairying is highly developed. Malmö, with ferry connections to Copenhagen, is the main urban center. The islands of Öland and Gottland are geologically similar and are mostly sheep grazing and resort areas.

The Småland highlands are a detached portion of the northern highlands. The forested slopes range from 300 to 1,000 feet above sea level. The thin, infertile soil handicaps agriculture. Handicraft industries such as wood working and glass manufacture are common. Jönköping is famous for safety matches.

The Central Lowlands and the Bothnian Fringes are the agricultural, industrial, and commercial heart of Sweden. The marine clay deposits favor agriculture, especially dairying. Large lakes such as Lake Väner and Lake Vätter cover much of the area. Rolling glacial topography is characteristic with rougher and poorer soils left in forests.

Metal and wood products are leading industries. Iron ore for the high quality steel comes from the Bergslagen district. Industrial special-

### TABLE 7-5.   NUMBER AND PER CENT OF PERSONS EMPLOYED PER INDUSTRY

| Occupation | Employment | |
|---|---|---|
| | Thousands | Per cent |
| Industry and crafts | 1,133 | 38 |
| Agriculture and related occupations | 730 | 24 |
| Commerce | 435 | 15 |
| Civil service and the professions | 307 | 10 |
| Communications | 224 | 8 |
| Domestic work | 123 | 4 |
| Unclassified | 40 | 1 |
| | 2,992 | 100 |

ties are found in many smaller centers such as steel in Eskilstuna and textiles in Norrköping. Uppsala is a university town, Oxelösund, a shipping point for Bergslagen ore. Numerous wood-processing and export centers are found along the Bothnian coast. Luleå exports Lapland ore and has an iron ore and steelworks.

Stockholm and Göteborg are the major cities of Sweden. Stockholm is the capital, cultural center, and chief Baltic port, and has a variety of manufacturing. Göteborg, with a favored west-coast position, is the principal foreign trade port. Its shipyards are a chief factor in placing Sweden second in world shipbuilding. Textiles and metal goods also are manufactured.

The Northern Highlands, covering approximately two-thirds of Sweden, are located north of the 60th parallel. The glaciated topography is crossed by numerous large, fast-flowing rivers with headwaters in long, narrow glacial lakes in the upland valleys.

Forestry is the chief occupation. As the spring thaw moves upstream, logs, cut during the winter, are floated to coastal sawmills. Processing of the logs is largely a summer activity.

Minerals, especially high-grade iron ore, provide a second mainstay of the northern economy. The Lapland and Bergslagen districts are found in the extreme northern and southern portions of the highlands respectively. Isolation, darkness for nearly six months, and severe winter cold hamper workers and production in the area centering around Kiruna and Gällivare. Iron ore can be shipped only during the warm season from Luleå, but leaves the year around from ice-free Narvik. Boliden is the leading European gold mining area.

Climate, soils, and relief are adverse to agriculture. Limited development is found in the valleys and around the edges of the lakes. Jämt-

*Figure 7-5 Shipbuilding in Göteborg, Sweden. The bow of a 10,000-ton freight vessel, having been prewelded, is being swung into place in a modern shipyard. (Courtesy of American Swedish News Exchange.)*

land is the Swedish counterpart of the Norwegian Trondheim area. In the north, 10,000 Lapps make a living by grazing 200,000 reindeer.

**Trade and Problems.**  Forest products, iron ore, iron and steel, and metal products dominate Swedish exports. Coal, petroleum, and raw materials for industry are major imports. England, Germany, the United States, and Scandinavian neighbors are leading trading partners. Invisible exports such as merchant marine earnings generally offset import excesses.

A major question facing Sweden is the ability to continue the so-called "middle way" economically and politically. Sweden experienced a brief period of postwar prosperity but faces trade and economic difficulties along with the rest of Western Europe.

## Denmark

Physically, Denmark is similar to the North German glaciated plains, but culturally it is linked with Scandinavia. The peninsula of Jutland and about 500 islands, mostly in the Baltic, comprise an area less than one-eighth the size of Norway. Denmark, however, has a million more people with about one-fourth of the population living in the metropolitan Copenhagen (Köbenhavn). The average population density reaches 400 per square mile in the fertile eastern islands but drops to 125 in sandy, infertile western Denmark. Approximately 75 per cent of the gently rolling terrain is used for agriculture. The surrounding water and moderating westerly winds result in a mild marine climate with summer temperatures averaging 60° and winter 32°F.

The position of Denmark, controlling the narrow water outlets of the Baltic, is highly strategic. Germany occupied this tiny nation during World War II in order to command the Baltic. Russian expansion in the Baltic gives Denmark's position added significance.

Denmark lacks the mineral, water power, and forest resources of her neighbors. Even the soil is not exceptionally fertile. Nevertheless, intensive agriculture is the basis of present-day Denmark. Small, carefully tended holdings support large numbers of cattle, swine, and poultry, when supplemented by considerable imports of protein concentrates and grains. Dairy products, meats, and eggs are leading Danish exports. Quality production is largely a result of the effort made by the highly developed cooperative movement. About 90 per cent of the milk is marketed cooperatively. Postwar economic problems have stemmed from the austerity program in Britain, the major market, and the difficulty of finding outlets in other Western European countries and the United States.

Agriculture and fishing employ 29 per cent of the working population; industry a slightly higher percentage. Fish, an important food, also contributes 5 per cent of the export value. Much of Danish industry consists of processing domestic agricultural goods. Most other industrial raw materials and all power sources must be imported.

**Regions.**  Western Denmark, the western two-thirds of the Jutland Peninsula, is a sandy, infertile outwash plain (Figure 7-3). Sandy heaths, made productive by great efforts, support grasslands and hardy crops. Poorer areas have been planted with pine trees. Sand dunes, marshes, lagoons, and shallow water are found along the unindented coast. The port of Esbjerg was constructed to carry on trade with England and Western Europe. It and Limfiord to the north are fishing centers.

With better agricultural land, many islands, and an indented coast line favoring harbor development, eastern Denmark has the bulk of the population. The area has the disadvantage, however, of a Baltic orientation when trade and other interests are mostly with Atlantic nations.

Rolling morainic hills and intervening valleys with fertile clay soil replace the flat, sandy terrain to the west. The highest point reaches only 536 feet. The intensive methods of cultivation, favorable temperature and rainfall conditions, and careful plant breeding result in some of the highest yields per acre in the world. Pasture, hay, wheat, sugar and fodder beets, oats, and barley are leading crops. Most of the exports,

*Figure 7-6    Copenhagen, the capital of Denmark, has a large number of beautiful buildings, old and new. The tower of the town hall can be seen in the center of the picture. (Courtesy of Royal Danish Ministry of Foreign Affairs.)*

butter, bacon, cheese, and eggs, originate in this section. The intensive forced feeding of animals based partially on imported feed has been termed factory farming.

Copenhagen dominates the industrial and commercial development of eastern as well as all of Denmark. It is the capital, cultural, and intellectual center, and rivals Stockholm for beauty and charm among north European cities. Shipbuilding, food processing, beer manufacture, margarine (so butter can be exported), textiles, and world-famous silverware, porcelain, and china are the chief manufactures. The excellent port of Copenhagen is the headquarters of Denmark's maritime interests and also contains an international free port. Aarhus, Aalborg, and Odense are the only other cities exceeding 50,000. Small fishing ports are common along the coast. The island of Bornholm, located 95 miles east of Copenhagen in the Baltic, provides kaolin for the pottery industries.

The Faeroe Islands, 230 miles northwest of Scotland, are Danish territory. The 32,000 inhabitants engage primarily in sheep grazing and fishing, along with limited agriculture. In 1948, Denmark granted home rule in all matters pertaining exclusively to the islands.

## Iceland

Iceland, located just south of the Arctic Circle in the North Atlantic, has the smallest total population and lowest density per square mile (3.5) of any European nation with its area. Over 80 per cent of the area is uninhabitable and less than 1 per cent arable. More than one-third of the 149,000 inhabitants live in the capital city of Reykjavik.

Iceland is a mountainous island with active volcanoes and hot springs. Over 13 per cent is permanently covered with snow and ice. Limited coastal lowlands have grass vegetation but trees are rare. The marine location and the North Atlantic Drift combine to give mild winters and cool summers. The average January temperature of Reykjavik is 33°F, the summer mean is 50°.

The waters off Iceland yield abundant cod, herring, coalfish, and ling. The average annual catch is about 7,000 pounds per capita. Fish normally provide over 90 per cent of the exports. Iceland's prosperity fluctuates with the fish catch and world market prices for fish. Fishermen from other nations also exploit Icelandic waters. Grazing of sheep and cattle and limited crops of hay, potatoes, and turnips are found on the coastal lowlands. Iceland must import many daily food and raw material needs.

A strategic position on the great-circle route between the United States and Europe has made Iceland an Atlantic air station of commercial and military significance.

## Finland

Finland has one-fifth of its area north of the Arctic Circle. Despite this position, the climate is tempered by warm westerly winds. The short, warm summers last from June 1 to September 1. The winters are long, cold, and snowy. Hardy crops, aided by long sunlit days, mature in the three-month growing season.

War destruction and peace treaty concessions resulting from World War II were costly. The 12 per cent (17,780 square miles) of its territory on the east and north which Finland lost to the Russians include its Arctic outlet, 13 per cent of the forest resources, one-third of the installed hydroelectric power, 30 per cent of the fisheries, 11 per cent of gross value of industrial production, the Petsamo nickel mines, and some of its most fertile land. The Porkalla Peninsula, a territory of 151 square miles guarding Helsinki, was leased by the Russians for a period of fifty years but returned in 1955. Russia also demanded a staggering 226.5 million dollars in reparations, to be paid in wood products, cables and ships, and metal goods. To meet these demands, the shipbuilding industry increased six times and the metal industry doubled in size, virtually revolutionizing Finland's industrial structure. The debt was paid in September, 1952, despite an annual drain of more than ten per cent of the national income. The problem now is whether Finland can continue this uneconomic production. Another problem, resulting from the territorial losses, was the resettlement of 420,000 people, one-tenth of the total population.

**Physical Setting.** Finland is a glaciated, old crystalline rock platform. Only in the northeast and in Lapland does the generally low elevation reach over 650 feet. Glacial scour and deposition left a large number of swamps and lakes (60,000 lakes cover 10 per cent of the area). Coastal lowlands and lake borders have more fertile recent sand and clay deposits but comprise only 9 per cent of the soils.

Finland's most valuable resource is the 71 per cent forested area which provides over 90 per cent of the gross value of exports. There is a variety of minerals of which copper is the most important. The complete lack of coal and petroleum is partially offset by abundant water power.

**Economic Development.** The population numbers approximately 4 million. Over 90 per cent are found in the southern half, mainly on the south and west coastal fringes. Swedish-speaking people compose about 10 per cent of

*Figure 7-7 Iceland herring fisheries. The rich waters surrounding Iceland provide the principal basis of the Icelandic economy. (Courtesy of Consulate General of Iceland.)*

the population, located primarily in districts nearest Sweden and in the Aland Islands.

Finland's chief livelihood, supporting 52 per cent of the people, is agriculture. The Finns produced 80 per cent of their prewar food needs; dairy surpluses and cereal shortages normally exist. About 21 per cent of the gainfully employed obtain their livelihood from manufacturing, 5 per cent from commerce, 5 per cent from transportation, and 17 per cent from other sources. Forests and hydroelectric power are the two major industrial assets. War reparations forced increased industrial development.

**Regions.**    Lapland, in the northern part of Finland, is a rather rugged area with tundra vegetation in the north and stunted, inaccessible, state-owned forests in the south (Figure 7-8). The climate is too severe for crops. The chief occupation of the 2,350 Lapp inhabitants is grazing 107,000 reindeer.

The Central Lake region is a swamp- and lake-dotted area in which forests are the primary resource. Timber cutting is a winter occupation and the logs are floated out in summer. Dairying is found around the edges of some lakes.

The Baltic littoral, having more favorable clay and silt soils, climate, and accessibility than the other areas, is the principal region of Finland. Hay, oats, rye, barley, wheat, and po-

tatoes are grown, but two-thirds of Finland's arable area is used for fodder production, indicating the predominance of dairying. Commercial fishing is found in the southwest and the Åland Islands.

Helsinki, Turku, and Tampere, the chief industrial cities, have access to transportation facilities, forest resources, labor, and imported raw materials. Water power is abundant where streams break through the Salpauselka, a double moraine located to the south of the lake district. Manufactures include wood and paper, metal, food, drink, textiles, and tobacco products. About 20 per cent of the industry is located in Helsinki, the capital and the cultural, financial, and university center.

**Trade and Problems.**    Finland's postwar trade was dislocated by the burdensome war reparations. Forest products dominate the free exports, with dairy products, especially butter, also important. Metals and metal products, cereal grains, raw textiles, coal, and petroleum are leading imports. Important in Finland's trade are the United Kingdom, the U.S.S.R., Denmark, the United States, and Benelux.

Economically and culturally, Finland faces the West, but politically, though independent, it is within the Soviet sphere of influence. Its future lies largely in being able to reconcile these conflicting interests.

*Figure 7-8   The Finnish lake country near Sovonlinna. Note the rounded glaciated topography, the abundant forest cover, and the clearings on the better soils along the lake edges. (Courtesy of Legation of Finland.)*

## BRITISH ISLES

The British Isles comprise over 5,000 islands of which Great Britain and Ireland are the largest.* This relatively small group of islands has played an extremely prominent role in the development of Europe and the world.

Before the fifteenth century the islands were on the periphery of the known world, but more recently they have occupied a central location among the populated land masses. The people were maritime-minded, and the power of England increased as the country secured colonies, developed its manufactures, and expanded its overseas commerce. Excellent harbors along the indented cost line and the inventions of the Industrial Revolution were significant factors in this expansion. The islands are part of the European platform, yet separated from the mainland by the narrow Straits of Dover. This separation allowed the English to spend much of their energy on trade and commerce rather than in wars. World War II showed that the Straits of Dover are no longer a complete barrier in wartime, but they still help protect England from invasion by a land army.

### Physical Setting

**Relief Features.** Hilly and mountainous terrain dominates the north, west, and southwest of Britain and undulating downs and plains the south and southeast (Figure 7-10). The highlands average between 500 and 2,000 feet in elevation. Rounded peaks and deepened valleys are a result of glacial erosion. Ben Nevis in the Scottish Highlands, 4,406 feet above sea level, is the highest point. Rocks composing the highlands are mostly old granites and schists. Flanking some of the highlands are valuable coal deposits. Young sediments in the south and east are largely limestone, sandstone, and chalk which form resistant ridges called downs. Weak chalk and clay underlie the valleys and plains. Recent glacial drift covers all of the British Isles

* Great Britain includes England, Scotland, and Wales; the United Kingdom includes Great Britain and Northern Ireland.

except Cornwall Peninsula and the remainder of southern England.

Most of Ireland is a low, poorly drained glaciated plain rimmed by low mountains.

**Climate.** The marine climate is free from extremes except in the highlands. Summer temperatures range from a July average of 63°F, in southeastern England to 55° in northern Scotland and 59° on the west coast of Ireland. The winter tempering by the sea is shown in January averages of 44° in southwest Ireland, 39° in southeast England, and 37°F in northern Scotland.

The annual precipitation ranges from 24 to 55 inches, with generally a slight winter maximum. The exposed and higher western portions have the heaviest precipitation. Valencia in western Ireland averages 55.6 inches per year as compared to 24.5 in London. Eastern districts, in the rain shadow of the highlands, have a summer maximum, largely of convectional origin. The cyclonic influence causes dominantly cloudy, humid, rainy, and often foggy weather. Southern England has a cloud cover seven-tenths of the time.

### Natural Resources

Soils range from a leached, moderate fertility type in the rainy western districts to a less leached, more fertile soil in the drier east. The thin, infertile soils of the highlands and limestone escarpments are used mostly for grazing. Glacial soils and those in the clay vales and chalk areas of the southeast are generally good for sown and tilled crops.

Only 4 per cent of Britain is forested—a serious lack in the British economy. Much of the meager natural vegetation remaining consists of lowland marsh and upland moor of limited value for grazing.

Minerals are the principal natural resources of Great Britain. Coal, the outstanding mineral resource, accounts for 90 per cent of the mineral output by value. At present production rates, the estimated workable reserves of 43

# REGIONS OF WEST CENTRAL EUROPE

**BENELUX**
1. Sandy Coastal Fringe
2. Polder Lands
3. Interior Plains
4. Interior Uplands

**FRANCE**
5. Massif Central
6. Pyrenees
7. French Alps
8. Brittany and Normandy
9. Ardennes Plateau and Vosges
10. Northern Lowlands
11. Aquitaine Basin
12. Rhone Valley and Mediterranean Coast
13. Corsica

**GERMANY**
14. Saar
15. North European Plain
16. Central Highlands

17. Ruhr
18. Bavarian Alps and Alpine Foreland
19. Rhine Valley

**SWITZERLAND**
20. Alps
21. Juara
22. Central Plateau

**AUSTRIA**
23. Alps
24. Austrian Lowlands

**GREAT BRITAIN**
25. English Lowlands
26. Wales
27. Cornwall
28. Lake District
29. Southern Scottish Uplands and Pen
30. Central Scottish Lowlands
31. Grampians and Eastern Lowlands
32. Northern Scottish Highlands

NORTH SEA

IRISH SEA

ENGLISH CHANNEL

CHANNEL ISLANDS

BAY OF BISCAY

FRANCE

EAST GERMANY

WEST GERMANY

AUSTRIA

SWITZERLAND

MEDITERRANEAN SEA

CORSICA

SARDINIA

0    200 MILES

billion tons will provide more than enough of all qualities except coking coal for two hundred years. Principal fields include those on the flanks of the Pennines, the Northumberland-Durham (Newcastle), South Wales, Cumberland, and the Scottish Lowlands. All are leading industrial districts.

Some current British economic problems can be traced to difficulties in the coal fields. Production and exports have steadily decreased, and the output is now about 228 million tons. Since the war, coal has provided less than 3 per cent of the total value of exports, as compared to 33 per cent in 1913. Present production supplies only a minimum of domestic needs. Handicaps facing the British coal industry are thin seams, deeps mines, dipping and faulted beds, lack of mechanization and modernization, and labor shortages. The industry has been nationalized since 1946.

Iron ore, the second mineral, has the low average of metallic content of 29 per cent. It is a low phosphorus and high sulfur content ore. The principal fields are east of the Pennines. The iron and steel industry imports 40 per cent of its needs, primarily from North Africa and Sweden. Excluding the U.S.S.R., Britain ranks third in European production.

Nonmetallic minerals such as limestone, chalk, and kaolin are quarried for cement and pottery manufacturing.

Fish abound in the North Sea and adjacent bodies of water. Easy access to nearby banks on the continental shelf and the maritime-mindedness of the people have led to the development of a fishing industry ranking second only to that of Norway in Europe. The postwar catch has averaged slightly over a million metric tons annually. The fishing fleet operates from such ports as Aberdeen, Grimsby, Hull, and Yarmouth. Fish exports have decreased in postwar Britain.

## Economic Development

The large population places considerable pressure upon land area to produce food. Nevertheless, before World War II, much land was extensively rather than intensively used. The United Kingdom imported 70 per cent of prewar food needs, including grains and meat products to supplement home production. Land use was intensified during World War II. Immediately after the war, Great Britain produced nearly half of its own food requirements. Now, however, the country imports approximately 60 per cent of the food consumed.

The plow-up campaign increased the acreage devoted to grain crops and to intensive dairy farming. Scientific grassland cultivation and mechanization also increased production. British agriculture is among the most highly mechanized in the world. Agriculture employs nearly 1.5 million people and utilizes 48 of 60 million acres of land in the United Kingdom. Eire has approximately 50 per cent of its working population engaged in agriculture.

The marked predominance of industry over agriculture is the outstanding feature of the British economy. Manufacturing, accounting for over 38 per cent of civilian workers, employs seven times as many people as agriculture and fishing. Transport and trade activities are another important segment.

Industrial concentrations show marked correlation with the location of coal fields. Industries are often localized as the cotton textile industry is in Lancashire. There has been a definite shift from basic to lighter metal products, and from cotton and wool to rayon, nylon, and other synthetic fibers. In general, the trend has been to utilize Britain's technical skill and ingenuity in making quality consumer goods.

In Ireland, the economy centers primarily upon agricultural pursuits although industry is increasing, especially in Northern Ireland.

*Figure 7-9  The regions of West Central Europe are the result of cultural activities as well as the physical environment. Most land is used intensively.*

*Divisions of Great Britain*

**Scotland.** The Northern Highlands, rising 1,000 to 3,000 feet above sea level, are a plateau strongly eroded by water and glaciers. The western portion is high and rugged with a fiorded coast. Agriculture is handicapped by poor soils, excessive precipitation, and rather severe winters. Approximately 95 per cent is sparsely populated moorland utilized for crofting (limited sheep grazing). Local areas specialize in high-quality tweeds based, in part, on imported wool. Grouse and deer hunting and the scenic country attract tourists.

The Eastern Coastal Lowlands have better soil, less rainfall, and higher summer temperatures. Grass, oats, turnips, and barley are the principal crops. Scottish arable farming is closely associated with raising beef cattle for the English market. Aberdeen, the largest city, ranks third among British fishing ports.

The Orkney Islands are low and similar in land utilization to the Scottish east coast. In contrast, the rugged Shetland Islands specialize in sheep grazing. Lerwick is a fishing port.

The Central Scottish Lowlands are one of the major agricultural and industrial regions of the British Isles. On 20 per cent of the area are 80 per cent of the people of Scotland. This lowland has recent alluvial and glacial soils and a moderate climate. Approximately two-thirds of the eastern portion is in cereal grains, with sheep utilizing the pastures and rougher areas. Grass farming, with emphasis upon the breeding and rearing of dairy cattle, dominates in the rainier western portions.

Scotland produces about 12 per cent of the British coal, much of which is of excellent bi-

tuminous grade, in the central and east portions of the basin, with some coming from the Ayrshire field in the western part. The iron and steel industry, which produces one-seventh of the United Kingdom tonnage, depends mainly on imported iron ore.

Glasgow, with over a million people, Edinburgh, and Dundee are the three major urban centers of the Central Scottish Lowlands. Glasgow, located on the Clyde River, is the fourth port in the British Isles and a heavy industry center specializing in iron and steel, machinery, and chemicals. The famous "Queen Mary" and "Queen Elizabeth" were built in the Clyde River estuary, one of the world's leading shipbuilding centers which annually provides about one-third of the tonnage constructed in the United Kingdom. Edinburgh, the capital, is a cultural, university, printing and publishing, and light-industry center. Dundee is noted for manufacturing imported jute fiber.

The Southern Scottish Uplands, although smaller and less rugged than the Northern Highlands, are a communications barrier between the Scottish Lowlands and England. The uplands are dissected by numerous small river valleys. Over 10 per cent of the hill sheep of Great Britain are found here. A high-quality woolen tweed industry is centered in the Tweed River valley. Cattle grazing, dairying, and crop agriculture were expanded during World War II in the coastal districts, river valleys, and lower slopes.

**England.** The Pennine Chain is a rolling to flat-topped upland averaging between 600 and 2,000 feet in elevation. The western slopes are quite abrupt but the eastern slopes are more

*Figure 7-10   A shepherd and hill sheep in the southern uplands of Scotland. Sheep grazing is suited to the bleak grass-covered slopes. Note the rounded glaciated topography. (Courtesy of British Information Services.)*

gentle. Lower gaps, separating the several highland blocks, are utilized by major east-west railways or highways. Most of the sparsely populated Pennine Chain is heathland, moorland, and rough pasture.

The Lake District consists of a rugged highland core surrounded by gentle slopes and lowlands. Several deep glacial valleys, occupied by lakes, are now a tourist mecca. Dairying is prominent in the lowlands. Extremely heavy rainfall restricts highland agriculture.

A small industrial district is based on the Cumberland coal field and low-quality iron ore. Barrow is a small iron and steel and shipbuilding center. Carlisle is a rail focus leading into Scotland.

The Isle of Man is located 30 miles west in the Irish Sea. Sheep grazing and tourism employ most of its 54,000 people.

The Cornwall Peninsula of southwest England is dominated by several high moors on which sheep are grazed. Luxuriant lowlands furnish grass for beef and especially dairy cattle. The mild climate of the south coast and protected valleys permits the growth of early flowers and vegetables for the London market. Small fishing villages dot the rugged coast. Plymouth is a port of call for passengers and mail steamers. The climate and quaintness of Cornwall, especially Lands End, make it a popular vacation area. Considerable china clay is produced for a local pottery industry and for export.

The English Lowlands, which make up approximately three-fourths of England, are less than 500 feet above sea level. The bulk of the topography is undulating to rolling, but some rough hills and downs reach nearly 1,000 feet. This is the agricultural, industrial, and commercial heart of England and the British Isles.

The agriculture is similar to the mixed farm economy of the European plains. A variety of crops adapted to cool summer temperatures is raised, with considerable emphasis upon grazing. Animal and dairy products are the sources of cash farm income.

Cropland is predominant in the fertile eastern sections of England that have less than 25 inches of rainfall and warm summers. Wheat, barley, oats, and root crops are utilized in the winter fattening of beef cattle. Certain areas specialize in fruits, potatoes, vegetables, and dairy products for the large urban market. Sugar beets are locally important.

The western districts, with wet, cool summers, have extensive rotation grass pastures. Dairying is common, with oats as the major cereal crop. Certain districts ship cattle eastward for fattening; others fatten them locally.

The rougher summits of the chalk downs and limestone escarpments in the south and central portions are generally sheep-grazing areas. The clay soils of the intervening lowlands grow wheat, beans, and oats, with turnips and barley on the chalk soils.

England's industrial concentrations occur in or near the coal fields and iron deposits or contact zones between highlands and lowlands. London is the principal exception. The industrial northeast, which is dominated by the iron and steel industry, normally produces about 20 per cent of Great Britain's steel. Coking coal is obtained locally, but over half of the iron ore must be imported to supplement Cleveland Hills and Northampton ore. Iron and steel manufacturing is concentrated in Middlesborough and surrounding Tees River towns. Shipbuilding on the Tyne and Tees River estuaries normally accounts for one-third of the total British tonnage. The fabrication of iron and steel products and chemical industries based partly on local salt, gypsum, and lime also are important. Exports of coal from Newcastle have declined considerably.

East of the Pennines, industry is based primarily on Yorkshire coal. This field supplies 25 per cent of Great Britain's total and extends over 70 miles in north-south and 15 to 20 miles in east-west distance. The northern part of this district specializes in woolen manufacturing and the southern part in high-grade steel products. The woolen industry was originally based on local raw materials and water power, but now a large portion of the wool is imported and coal supplies most of the power. Soft water for washing the wool also is easily available. Leeds and Bradford are the major woolen centers. Leeds also produces leather products.

Sheffield is the center for high-grade cutlery, hardware, machinery, and other steel products. Some steel is imported from other parts of England or abroad. Sheffield usually accounts for about 15 per cent of British steel.

South of the Pennines, at the southern end of the Pennine Chain, is the leading English industrial complex, often referred to as the Midlands or "Black Country." Though these terms characterize the cities, there is also much green agricultural land. As local iron supplies declined, basic iron and steel production tended to move to coastal areas for import of foreign ore. Some iron and steel is still produced, but industries using steel made elsewhere (such as metal goods, motors, automobiles, and locomotives) are now more important. Birmingham with a population of over one million, the major center, manufactures a variety of materials, especially brass, other nonferrous metal products, leather products, clothing, and pottery. Notting-

ham, Leicester, Stoke-on-Trent, and Coventry are other major urban centers.

Lancashire leads the British Isles in cotton spinning and weaving. Access to nearby coal, early development of water power, plentiful pure water, a mild, moist climate lessening thread breakage, and an advantageous position for import of foreign cotton are leading factors explaining this localization. Great Britain's and Lancashire's place in world cotton manufacturing has suffered because of foreign competition, antiquated machinery and methods, competition from synthetic fibers, and postwar labor shortages.

Though cotton still dominates, textile machinery, engines, electrical goods, glass, chemical, leather, and paper are also manufactured in the district's numerous cities. Liverpool and Manchester are respectively the second- and fourth-ranking British ports; the latter connected with the sea by a deepwater canal.

London, long the world's largest metropolitan district, is rivaled only by New York City. Greater London contains over 8.5 million peo-

*Figure 7-11 View of the House of Parliament, London. The clock in the tower is the famous "Big Ben." (Courtesy of British Railways.)*

ple, and 10 million or nearly one-fourth of the population of Britain live in the city and surrounding area. Although located 65 miles up the Thames, London is a major world port. It collects, processes, and distributes goods from numerous distant points. London is the single leading industrial center of Britain and has a large variety of processing and light industries. It is also a cultural, transportation, financial, and commercial center of British and world importance.

Several isolated port and industrial centers are found along England's coast. Hull, a major fishing port, handles much of the North Sea and Continental trade. Portsmouth is the great dockyard on the south coast; Southampton is the major passenger port servicing North Atlantic and African areas. The western port of Bristol has access to coal and processes tobacco and cacao.

**Channel Islands.** The Channel Islands base their economy on early vegetables for the English market, dairying, and tourism. Guernsey, Jersey, Alderney, and Sark, the four chief islands, contain about 100,000 people. The Jersey and Guernsey breeds of dairy cattle originated here.

**Wales.** Wales consists of a highly dissected central plateau surrounded by narrow coastal lowlands. The highlands culminate in Mt. Snowdon, reaching 3,560 feet. The rugged, isolated character of Wales has handicapped interchange with outside areas and accounts for the persistence of the Welsh language and an intense national feeling.

The grasslands of the excessively rainy highland interior favor sheep grazing. Dairying, along with oats as a major crop, is found on the broader southern coastal lowlands. Small resort towns are located along the northern and western coasts.

The South Wales coal field supports a densely populated mining, industrial, and exporting region. The extensive coal measures vary in quality from bituminous coal in the east to anthracite in the west. The change-over to oil-burning vessels and general decline of British coal trade resulted in large-scale prewar unemployment and poverty in the congested mining valleys. Inability to attract young men into the mines has resulted in postwar labor shortages.

Cardiff and nearby cities account for nearly one-fifth of the steel of Great Britain. Swansea is a tin plate center and processes zinc, nickel, and copper.

## Ireland

Since 1921, Ireland has been divided into Northern Ireland and Republic of Ireland (Eire) which became completely independent

*Figure 7-12 Bleaching linen in Northern Ireland. Linen is spread on fields around the factory for bleaching by the moist air and sun. Linen manufacturing is one of the leading industries of Northern Ireland. (Courtesy of British Information Services.)*

of the Commonwealth on April 18, 1949. Eire occupies about five-sixths of the island's 31,840 square miles and has a population of 2,961,000, as compared to 1,375,000 in Northern Ireland. The average population density, however, is 110 people per square mile in agricultural Eire compared to 260 in the more industrialized Northern Ireland. Eire is predominantly Catholic; Northern Ireland, Protestant.

The long English domination has geared the trade of both areas to that nation—supplying agricultural materials and buying manufactured goods. The protective policy of independent Eire and the continued close political and economic imperial ties of Northern Ireland, however, are causing the economies to become more diverse. As differences grow, unification becomes less likely.

**Eire.** Since 1921, Eire has become more self-sufficient by breaking up many large estates, placing greater emphasis upon raising wheat and sugar beets, and increasing industrialization. Most industries must be based on agricultural raw materials, for Eire lacks coal and iron. Developments on the Shannon River provide some water power. One-third of the exports are live animals to England for fattening. The remainder consists of eggs, dressed poultry, bacon, butter, ham, tobacco, beer, leather goods, and linen. About 86 per cent of the export trade and 51 per cent of the import trade are with the United Kingdom. The steadily declining rural population (60 per cent in the last century) is a problem facing Eire.

**Ulster.** Northern Ireland, or Ulster, the principal area of industrial development, is dominated by linen manufacturing and shipbuilding; both are centered in Belfast and vicinity. The linen industry was a natural outgrowth of the local flax raising, water supply and climate favorable for bleaching, and of the large supply of female labor in families of shipyard workers. Considerable flax is now imported. The linen trade employs one-sixth of the working population of Northern Ireland; two-thirds of this number are women. The shipbuilding opera-

*Figure 7-13   O'Connell Street in Dublin. (Courtesy of Irish Tourist Bureau.)*

tions of Belfast normally account for 10 per cent of the annual tonnage of the United Kingdom. Coal, iron, and steel are easily available from Great Britain.

The value of exports from Northern Ireland is far greater than from Eire. Trade is almost entirely with Great Britain. Imports of food, drink, tobacco, other raw materials, and manufactured products usually are greater than the exports; this deficit is offset by income from tourists, investments abroad, and pensions paid from Britain. Industrial materials such as ships account for 80 per cent of the export value.

**Regions of Ireland.** The Central Plain is largely the poorly drained basin of the Shannon River. It covers most of central Eire and extends into southern Northern Ireland. The limestone soil often is covered by glacial debris and peat bogs. Small farms, with considerable area in pasture and meadow, are characteristic. The amount of cropland decreases westward with the increasing annual rainfall. Livestock and occasional cash crops provide the chief source of income. Sheep raising and fattening, with some cattle raising, is the chief type of farming in the western Central Plain, mixed crops and livestock in the center, and dairying around Dublin and in Northern Ireland. Dublin (Baile Atha Cliath), the chief industrial city of Eire, is the outlet of the Central Plain.

The Highland Rim and associated valleys surround the Central Plain except on the east. The higher parts are rough, sheep grazing areas. Dairying is predominant in the ridge and valley section of the south and around Belfast. Crop farming is predominant in the southeast and in the valleys of Northern Ireland. Oats, potatoes, and turnips are common crops, with flax in the north and barley in the southeast as specialty crops. Animals supply most of the cash income. Fishing is of local importance in the southwest. Cork and Cobh have excellent natural harbors. Shannon is an international airport but is often bypassed by long range transatlantic airliners.

The coast of Ireland is irregular with many broad bays. All of the island has been glaciated and the scenery attracts many tourists.

## Trade and Problems of the British Isles

Despite the increase in self-sufficiency during and after World War II and self-imposed austerity, the British Isles are faced with a serious trade deficit problem. Nearly 60 per cent of the food requirements and a large part of the industrial raw materials must be imported. Exports and income from foreign investments, foreign financial services such as insurance, and the merchant marine are no longer sufficient to offset the deficit. The combined export value of coal and textiles, for example, decreased from 48 per cent of the total in 1913 to 23 per cent in 1948. Markets for manufactured goods have declined because of increased competition from Germany, Japan, India, and other nations. The development of nationalism has also caused former good customers to favor products made at home.

Meat, dairy products, cereal grains, petroleum, timber, wool, cotton, nonferrous metals, and tropical products are the leading imports. Principal exports include machinery, vehicles, iron and steel, cotton and woolen goods, and chemicals. British exports represent quality finished products where technical ability and skill give a competitive edge. The Commonwealth, the United States, the countries of Western Europe, and Argentina are foremost in British trade. Great Britain's trade with the Dominions and Colonies increased from 42 per cent of the total in 1929 to over 50 per cent in the 1950s. The role of the Commonwealth is increasing as the Empire declines.

## BELGIUM, NETHERLANDS, AND LUXEMBOURG

Belgium, Netherlands, and Luxembourg possess a combined area of nearly 26,000 square miles, slightly larger than that of West Virginia. Within this area live 19 million people, nearly half the number found in France, which is eight times larger. The Netherlands, with 769 people per square mile, and Belgium, with 725, are unrivaled in Europe in population density.

The triangle of land occupied by the three countries is wedged between Germany and France. This buffer position is an advantage for peacetime trade but a disadvantage in time of war. The natural funneling of Rhine and West German traffic through Netherlands and Belgium is of tremendous value to their respective economies. Location on the North Sea, whose coastal regions are traffic-generating areas, also aids commercial development. Despite extremely limited natural resources, the industrious inhabitants have made these countries significant in both agricultural and industrial production. Large overseas territories supply valuable raw materials.

These countries are often referred to as the Low Countries or Benelux. The first is partially a misnomer, for interior areas, especially in Belgium and Luxembourg, are quite rugged and reach altitudes of 2,000 feet. The Benelux designation developed during World War II when the governments in exile of these countries decided to form a customs union with the ultimate goal of a free-trade area. In 1948, tariff charges on commodities shipped among the partners were abolished, and tariff rates charged on foreign goods were equalized in the three countries. This provides a larger market for Benelux products.

## Cultural Differences

The people of the Netherlands have a common culture and language. The Dutch language developed from ancient Frankish or Germanic dialects. The people are thrifty, strongly nationalistic, and unified, and have high educational standards.

The Walloons and Flemings, highly diverse peoples, occupy Belgium. The Walloons, short, dark, and French-speaking, populate the southern industrial portions. The Flemings are of a dominantly tall, fair Nordic type. They speak Flemish, a Germanic language, and are largely in agricultural and commercial occupations. Both languages are official. The views of the two groups are often dissimilar. The people of Luxembourg show both French and German influences in their language and culture.

## Natural Resources

In spite of the small size of the Benelux countries there are considerable resources including minerals. Coal is the most prominent in Belgium and Netherlands. The Sambre-Meuse coal fields of Belgium extend into the Limburg province of southern Netherlands. These deposits, especially in Belgium, are deep, faulted, and have thin seams. Mining is difficult and expensive and the output per man is the lowest in Europe. The Campine field in northern Bel-

gium, though 1,500 to 3,000 feet deep, has thicker seams and greater reserves. Belgium produces over 30 million tons of coal a year and the Netherlands 12 million. Luxembourg shares the Lorraine iron ore field with France and produces about 2.7 million tons annually, ranking high in world production.

Other minerals include petroleum and salt in the Netherlands. A petroleum field, developed since World War II in northeast Netherlands, produces 5 million barrels a year, about 30 per cent of the home consumption. Approximately 60 per cent of the salt produced in eastern Netherlands is exported.

Soil is a major resource in all three countries. Much of it has been reclaimed from the sea. Infertile sandy soils have been made productive by great effort and ingenuity. Limited forests are found on rougher and sandy soils of the interior.

## Regions

**Coastal.** The Sandy Coastal Fringe area, a narrow belt of sand dunes, separates the interior lowlands from the sea in Belgium and the Netherlands. In northwestern Netherlands it exists as the Frisian Islands. Some of the higher dunes are forested, and sheep graze on the grassy portions. They are commonly utilized for home and town sites such as The Hague ('s Gravenhage), a Dutch government center. The coast has poor harbors, but Ostende and Hoek Van Holland are crossing points to Britain. The Frisian and Zeeland Islands are important for fishing. The excellent sandy beaches are summer resorts.

The Polder Lands, which form approximately 50 per cent of the Netherlands and nearly 10 per cent of Belgium, are subject to flooding at storm or spring tide levels in the absence of sea and river dikes. Drained and diked lands, called polders, must be constantly drained by power pumps which are replacing former picturesque windmills. In the Netherlands, 2,200 square miles have been reclaimed since the thirteenth century and an additional 538,000 acres are being reclaimed from the shallow Zuider Zee (Yssel Lake) cut off from the sea by a barrier dam in 1932. The completed project will add

10 per cent to the arable land. The flood of 1953, covering one-sixth of the Netherlands, caused the most severe damage in centuries. The dikes have been repaired and the land returned to cultivation.

The polders often are left in grassland as it is uneconomical to lower the water table sufficiently to grow crops. Dairying is predominant, but on higher ground wheat and fodder crops are grown. Cash crops such as seed potatoes, flax, sugar beets, vegetables, and horticultural crops are raised in the north and southwest. Flower bulbs and vegetables are found inland from the coastal sand region on clay and peat soils, especially between Haarlem and Leiden. South of The Hague, horticultural crops are extensively grown in greenhouses.

Amsterdam, Rotterdam, and Antwerp (Anvers) are major commercial and industrial cities. Despite inland locations, rivers and canals give them ocean connections. Antwerp and Rotterdam handle Rhine hinterland trade and transshipments; grain, iron ore, forest products, petroleum, cotton, and oil seeds go upstream, and iron and steel products, coal, and building stones come downstream. Antwerp and Amsterdam are centers for diamond cutting and

polishing. Amsterdam is also the capital and financial center of the Netherlands.

**Interior Plains.**    The Interior Plains in eastern Netherlands and central Belgium are slightly rolling and sandy. The infertile soils have been improved, and when heavily fertilized, produce potatoes, sugar beets, wheat, oats, barley, and hemp. Rye, buckwheat, forest, and heath are found on the poorer soils. Dairy cattle are common. Coal is mined in the Campine field of Belgium and in the Limburg district of the Netherlands. Brussels (Bruxelles), capital of Belgium, has a population of 1 million, and is the commercial, transportation, and industrial hub.

**Interior Uplands.**    The Interior Uplands in the extreme southeast of the Netherlands, southeast Belgium, and Luxembourg vary from 300 to 2,000 feet in elevation. The Ardennes proper is a sparsely populated, dissected, infertile plateau with forests, moors, and dairying, but the fertile loam soils of the foreland are densely populated and intensively utilized. Limburg has many orchards and dairying.

The industry of the Sambre-Meuse Valley

*Figure 7-14   The busy port of Antwerp. Located 53 miles up the Scheldt River, Antwerp serves Belgium, and along with Rotterdam, the Rhine Valley of Germany. Both river barges and ocean freighters are accommodated in this deep-water port. (Courtesy of Belgian Government Information Center.)*

and the adjacent province of Limburg in the Netherlands is based on local coal. Iron and steel, machinery, zinc smelting, textiles, chemicals, glass, and leather products are principal industries in such cities as Liege, Tons, and Charleroi. The Battle of the Bulge was fought in this regi n during World War II.

## Economic Development

**The Netherlands.** This country is an agricultural and commercial nation, with industry increasing in importance. About 20 per cent of the labor force is employed in agriculture, 37 per cent in industry, 24 per cent in trade and transport, and 19 per cent in other occupations. The highest use of fertilizer and the highest average wheat yields per acre in the world indicate how intensive is Netherlands agriculture. Farms are small; 42 per cent are less than 12.5 acres. The land use percentages are as follows: pasture 36, arable 32, built-up 13, woodland 7, horticulture 3, and wasteland 9. Agricultural produce such as vegetables, flowers, bulbs, butter, and cheese is exported. Widespread cooperatives maintain high-quality products; they control 75 per cent of the dairy output. Leading industries include shipbuilding, refining of tin and other metals, textiles, chemicals, and leather goods.

Location, overseas possessions, skill, experience, and necessity have greatly aided the commercial development, including the important transit trade to and from Germany. Besides agricultural goods, Dutch exports include a wide variety of finished and semifinished goods. Imports include coal, timber, iron and steel, textiles, and cereals. The merchant marine of over 4 million tons ranks seventh in the world.

Lack of resources, loss of income from now independent Indonesia, decreased German transit trade, and overpopulation are major postwar problems. The prosperity of Germany is essential to the Netherlands.

**Belgium.** The economy of Belgium places greater emphasis upon industry and less upon agriculture and commerce than that of the Netherlands. Heavy industries, such as basic iron and steel, contrast with the lighter types found in the Netherlands. Using iron ore from Luxembourg and France, Belgium and Luxembourg produce over 7 million tons of steel annually, ranking seventh among world producers. The smelting of Belgian Congo zinc and copper is another leading industry along with textiles, machinery, and chemicals. One of the world's densest transportation networks serves the industrial and commercial centers. Foodstuffs, iron ore, and other raw materials for industry are prominent imports; metal products, chemicals, textiles, and glass are exported.

An earlier liberation than its neighbors gave postwar Belgium a head start in recovery. The fact that a large foreign exchange balance had accumulated from Belgian Congo exports during the war also aided the country. Nearly 40 per cent of the industrial production must be exported to maintain a prosperous economy. German transit trade is also important to the welfare of Belgium.

**Luxembourg.** The smallest of the Benelux countries, Luxembourg, a tiny principality, bases its livelihood almost entirely upon iron and steel. Only limited forestry and agriculture are found. Luxembourg has the highest per capita steel production in the world: nearly 1,300 pounds compared to 1,158 in the United States and 742 in Belgium. Production totals nearly 3 million tons annually. Luxembourg has had an economic union with Belgium since 1919.

All three Benelux countries are placing hope in the Benelux Union, the Coal and Steel Community, and other similar plans. They hope these will offset their small areas and lack of resources and domestic markets, as well as tariffs and trade restrictions imposed by others.

## FRANCE

France, long a cultural and artistic center, is one of the world's great republics. Except for the Soviet Union, France is the largest nation of Europe and one of the best balanced in terms of natural resources. Despite present military and political weaknesses and loss of prestige resulting largely from two world wars, the country is vital to the economies and the defense of all Western European nations.

## Location and Shape

The location of France gives it a dual continental and maritime orientation. Though 1,870 miles of coast line face the Atlantic Ocean and the Mediterranean Sea, the strongest links have been with Continental Europe. Possession of the world's second largest colonial empire and the fifth largest merchant marine indicate French maritime interests. In the east and south, common land boundaries exist with six nations. Much of the border follows the barrier-forming ridges of the Pyrenees, French Alps, and Juras, but the northeast is open to areas of dissimilar language and culture.

The area of France, including the island of Corsica, totals 212,737 square miles, nearly twice the size of the British Isles. This relatively large country includes many regions with agricultural and industrial diversity.

The compact shape gives France a greater degree of cultural and economic uniformity and national consciousness than most European countries. The large amount of lowland area facilitates north-south and east-west communications and results in few isolated areas.

## Population

France's population has been stabilized at 40 million since the middle of the nineteenth century. The resulting labor shortages were partially offset by immigration of Italians, Spaniards, Poles, and Belgians. Since World War II, there has been an annual average excess of 300,000 births over deaths. Thus, in contrast to the prewar period, the population has been increasing. Of the 42,700,000 population, 53 per cent is urban and 47 per cent rural, another indication of the balance in France. Only the Central Plateau, Pyrenees, Alps, Juras, and other mountains of the northeast are sparsely populated; yet with 495 people per square mile France has the lowest average population density among the industrial nations of Western Europe.

The population is remarkably homogeneous although minor regional language dialect and other cultural differences exist. Small minority groups are found on French borders such as the Basques toward the western end of the Pyrenees. All but one million of the people are Roman Catholics.

## Physical Setting

**Relief Features.** The varied topography of France is relatively simple in structure. Three major landform types exist: (1) areas of old rock such as the Massif Central (Central Plateau), hills of Brittany and Normandy, the Ardennes, and the Vosges Mountains; (2) the rugged, young, folded mountains represented by the Alps, Juras, and Pyrenees; and (3) the recent deposits in river basins and valleys. Strategic corridors such as the Belfort between the Rhine and Rhone Valleys and that of Verdun between the Rhine and the Paris Basin are among the connecting lowlands.

**Climate.** The varied climates of France are the result of several factors including relief, lat-

### TABLE 7-6.  CLIMATIC DIFFERENCES

| City | Jan. av., deg F | July av., deg F | Av. annual rainfall, in. | Climate |
|------|-----------------|-----------------|--------------------------|---------|
| Brest | 45 | 61 | 30 | Marine west-coast |
| Paris | 36 | 65 | 24 | Modified marine |
| Strasbourg | 32 | 66 | 27 | Transitional |
| Marseilles | 44 | 72 | 23 | Mediterranean |

itude, and location between the Atlantic Ocean and the Mediterranean Sea. The position of 42° to 51° north latitude, and location on the west coast of Europe places the country in the path of the tempering prevailing westerlies and cyclonic storms. The cities in Table 7-6 illustrate the major climatic differences.

The daily and seasonal temperature ranges and the amount of summer rainfall increase eastward with the lessening sea influences. Paris has a blend between the maritime and transitional climates. The higher mountains generally have heavier precipitation and lower temperatures. These diverse climates give France growing conditions suited to a variety of crops.

## Natural Resources

**Minerals.** Among the world's iron ore producers France ranks third, following the United States and the Soviet Union. Over 50 million tons are mined yearly, 90 per cent in the Lorraine district and 10 per cent in the Normandy and East Pyrenees fields. The Lorraine ore averages 33 per cent metallic content but is self-fluxing. It was not usable, however, until the development of the Thomas-Gilchrist process for reducing high-phosphorus-content ore. The Lorraine ore, occurring on or near the surface in an area 70 by 12 miles, is easily mined. Much smelting is done near the mines as it is uneconomical to ship the low-quality ore long distances. Considerable quantities move freely into Belgium, Luxembourg, and Germany as a result of the Coal and Steel Community. The Normandy ore is of higher quality but less abundant and less accessible.

The coal fields of France normally supply only two-thirds of the country's needs. Especially significant is the lack of coking-quality coal. Over half the 53 million tons mined comes from the Sambre-Meuse field near the Belgian border; scattered fields on the fringes of the Massif Central and the lower Loire River valley provide the remainder. In addition, France has a fifty-year lease on the Saar coal mines which produce 16 million tons a year, even though ownership of the Saar passed to Germany on January 1, 1957. Thin and broken seams, deep beds, antiquated methods, and war destruction account for the fact that coal output per manshift in France is the lowest in Europe except for Belgium. About 245,000 men are employed in the French mines.

In bauxite production, France ranks fourth in the world and first in Europe. Bauxite is mined on the southern flanks of the French Alps, near the Spanish border in the Pyrenees, and just west of the Rhone River near the Mediterranean coast. With hydroelectric power available nearby, much is processed into aluminum; some also is exported.

Potash deposits are located near Mulhouse in

*Figure 7-15   Coal industry in northern France. Coal is one of the keys to the French economy. Here, pressed coal is being transported on a conveyor belt. (Courtesy of French Embassy Press and Information Division.)*

Alsace. France ranks third, behind Germany and the United States, in world production. Potash is used in the commercial fertilizers vital to the intensive agriculture of northwestern Europe. Extensive salt deposits in Lorraine are used along with potash in the chemical industry.

**Other Resources.** The water power resources of France are limited primarily to the highlands of the east, central, and southern districts. Of the approximate 44 billion kilowatthours of electric energy output about half is hydroelectricity and half thermoelectricity.

Forest products are of primary importance in the highland economy. The Alps, Vosges, and Massif Central produce furniture, pit props, and construction timber. Pine trees planted to prevent the migration of sand in the Landes district of southwest France are now a major source of lumber and naval stores (resin, tar, and turpentine). Lumber and wood pulp also are imported.

Fisheries are located in the Atlantic and Mediterranean coastal waters. The Brittany coast and English Channel have the best developed fishing industry. France ranks third among European fishing nations, behind Norway and Great Britain.

The soils of France are productive. The country has large areas of fertile, arable lowlands. Postwar figures show 38 per cent in arable cropland, 22 per cent in meadow and pasture, 19 per cent in forest and woodland, and 21 per cent in other uses. Only one-tenth of France is classified as unproductive.

## Economic Development

The balance in the economy is illustrated by the fact that France accounts for 16.4 per cent of the agricultural and 11.3 per cent of the postwar industrial production of Europe (excluding the U.S.S.R.). Agriculture produces 21 per cent of the national income, manufacturing and construction 38 per cent, trade 14 per cent, transportation and communication 14 per cent, and other activities 13 per cent. Industry is handicapped by raw-material deficiencies, especially coal and petroleum, by labor shortages, particu-

larly of young men to man new industries, by antiquated equipment and organizational procedures, and by the vast physical destruction of industrial capacity during World War II. By 1949, however, French industrial output had reached the previous record high.

**Agriculture.** Employment figures indicate the importance of agriculture, since nearly one-third of the working population are farmers. Agriculture is often called the backbone of the French nation. Diversified agriculture predominates, but specialties have developed based on long tradition and inexpensive, highly skilled farm labor. Examples are wine, cheese, fruit, and vegetable production. Cash income comes largely from the sale of animals, animal products, and certain crops. Wheat is the single most important crop grown. Olives, cork oak, irrigated fruits, and vegetables are found in the Mediterranean region. Corn is peculiar to southern France. Grapes and wine production are widespread over the southern two-thirds of the country, with certain areas of specialization. France leads the world in wine production and consumption. The areas of cool, moist climates or rugged topography encourage livestock production and dairying. Crop yields per acre are generally lower than in Britain or Belgium because of poorer soils and agricultural methods. Farms average less than 25 acres and are rather intensively cultivated, largely by hand. French agricultural production has suffered from lack of mechanization and the loss of labor to French industry.

**Industry.** France ranks behind the United Kingdom and Germany as a European industrial nation. The possession of iron ore and coal is largely responsible for this position despite the necessity of importing one-third of the coal needs and an almost complete lack of petroleum.

The localization in French industry depends upon access to steam and hydroelectric power, transportation facilities, labor, cheap and skilled, and raw materials, especially iron ore. The following areas stand out in French manufacturing: (1) the northern area around Lille and the Sambre-Meuse coal field—wool and linen textiles and iron and steel; (2) northeast (Alsace and Lorraine)—metallurgy, cotton textiles, and chemicals; (3) Paris—diverse manufactured products, with emphasis on quality; (4) Lyon and St. Etienne district—silk and rayon textiles; and (5) the lower Loire River valley and Bordeaux—shipbuilding, metal products, and diversified manufacturing. The latter areas received impetus from the dispersion of industry during World War II, but Paris remains unrivaled in importance.

France has a well-developed rail, highway, and inland waterway transportation system. The Rhone, Loire, Garonne, and Seine are all navigable and connected by canals.

## Regions

**Highlands.** The Massif Central, dominating south central France, averages 3,000 feet above sea level. It is mostly a dissected crystalline rock plateau with some volcanic rock; sedimentary rock is found on the edges and in the lowlands. Except for a few favored valleys, poor soil and a rigorous climate restrict agriculture to hardy crops and grazing. This is the chief rye-growing area of France and contains one-fourth of the cattle and one-fifth of the sheep. The Massif is a barrier to communications within France. St. Etienne is an iron and steel and textile center. Clermont-Ferrand manufactures rubber, textiles, and chemicals, and Limoges is famous for china.

The crest of the Pyrenees, rising to over 9,000 feet, forms the French-Spanish boundary. The inaccessible rugged and infertile slopes are sparsely populated. The climate of the western portion is marine; the eastern is Mediterranean. Grazing of the transhumance type is dominant in the higher grasslands, with some crop agriculture on the lower slopes and in the valleys. Hydroelectric power, iron ore, and bauxite provide the basis of small electrochemical and electrometallurgical industries.

The French Alps and Jura Mountains are thinly peopled and play a minor role in France. Cattle and sheep are pastured on alpine grasslands. Small chemical and metallurgical centers utilize part of the large hydroelectric potential. Grenoble is a rail, university, and glove-manufacturing center. The Juras consist of longitudinal valleys and ridges with some peaks reaching over 5,000 feet. Dairying, forestry, and small workshop industries, especially watchmaking, are predominant.

Brittany and Normandy differ from the Massif Central in that their outcrops of crystalline rocks have lower relief, no volcanic material, and a peninsular shape with numerous offshore islands. The hedgerow landscape is characteristic. One-fourth of France's cattle and some sheep are grazed on the interior uplands. There is little land suitable for wheat; thus buckwheat is the major cereal grown on the poor soils. Apple orchards are common and cider is the usual beverage. More than 2 million tons of iron ore are mined annually, with smelting works in Caen. Laval is a textile center and Rennes the regional capital.

The narrow Normandy coastal strip is densely populated. A rich soil and mild marine climate give rise to vegetable gardening. Nantes and St. Nazaire are metallurgical and shipbuilding centers, with industries based on Swedish and Spanish iron ore and British coal. Ports and naval bases are located also at Cherbourg, Brest, and Lorient. Several smaller villages are fishing and resort centers. Part of the Normandy coast is famous for the World War II invasion.

The Lorraine and Ardennes plateaus and the Vosges Mountains possess a strategic location bordering on Germany. They contain nearly half the iron ore resources of Europe. The iron and steel industry, which is concentrated in Nancy, Metz, and other smaller centers, obtains coking coal from the Ruhr. The chemical industry is based on iron and steel manufacturing by-products and on local salt and potash deposits. The textile industry also is noteworthy. The Vosges have lumbering, dairying, and paper and cotton textile manufacturing based on water power.

The fertile Rhine Valley, a down-dropped block, produces grapes, tobacco, hops, sugar beets, and wheat. Strasbourg, a key rail and water transportation center on the Rhine, has served as the Council of Europe headquarters since 1949.

**Lowlands.** The Northern Lowlands include the Paris Basin, Loire and Saone Valleys, and the industrial North. The Paris Basin is the most productive agricultural as well as industrial region of France. It is formed by saucer-like sedimentary rock layers. The outer layers, consisting of a resistant limestone and chalk, form rugged and wooded outcrops. Transportation lines pass through breaks or gaps in the escarpment faces.

Agriculture is intensive, with wheat, oats, sugar beets, flax, vegetables, and fruits as the principal crops. Cattle predominate in the more

humid west and sheep in the drier, rougher east portion of the northern lowlands. Two important wine areas are found: white wine in the middle Loire Valley, and champagne from grapes grown on the warm, south-facing slopes east of Paris.

Paris, with a population of more than 5 million people, is the cultural, artistic, and leading manufacturing center, the hub of water and rail traffic, and the first inland or river port of France. Over one-fourth of France's urban population is in the metropolitan district. Industry consists largely of finishing types of manufacturing. Luxury goods, for which Paris is famous, play a relatively minor role as compared to automobile assembly, electrical, chemical, food processing, and printing industries.

*Figure 7-16  One of the typical sights in any French city is the book, paper, and picture stall. This one is located near the center of Paris. (Courtesy of French Cultural Services.)*

*Figure 7-17  Mediterranean coast in Nice, France. This is the famous resort area, called the French Riviera, which is protected from cold north winds by the French Alps. (Courtesy of French Embassy Press and Information Division.)*

Lille is the industrial center of northern France. Industry is based on the Sambre-Meuse coal field, and iron and steel and woolen and linen textiles dominate. Rouen near the mouth of the Seine is a cotton-milling center and the deep water port for Paris. Le Havre has transatlantic and trans-channel trade and is important for the refining of imported crude oil. Cherbourg handles the transatlantic liners between France and New York. Resorts are common along the Channel coast.

The Aquitaine Basin is drained primarily by the Garonne River and its tributaries. The Garonne Valley and the central parts of the basin contain wheat, corn, vineyards, and pastures for cattle grazing. The area has one-fourth of the French vineyards; production of red wines predominates. Poor farming methods and the unreliable precipitation result in low yields. Sheep grazing is a leading activity of the infertile sub-Pyrenean northeast and sandy Landes districts.

Bordeaux is the fourth port and city of France. It is the outlet for wine and many other products including those from the forests of the Landes district. The city also refines petroleum. Toulouse controls the narrow gap between the Aquitaine and Mediterranean lowlands. It is an important industrial center, and there is a natural gas field nearby.

The climate of the Mediterranean lowlands and Rhone Valley results in a distinctive agriculture. West of the Rhone River is the leading vineyard and wine-producing district of France. East of the Rhone, where the topography is rougher and soils are poorer, olives, vineyards, and the grazing of sheep and goats are common. Wheat and early irrigated crops such as citrus fruits, rice, and vegetables occur on the better soils. Flowers for perfume are grown. The Rhone Valley has vineyards on the slopes and crops and cattle grazing in the valley bottom. Mulberry trees for the silk industry are found near Lyon.

The large bauxite deposits form the basis of the aluminum industry and bauxite exports. Marseilles, the second city in France and first in ocean shipping, is the major Mediterranean port. It has a wide range of manufacturing activities, including soapmaking and petroleum refining. Lyon, strategically located at the confluence of the Rhone and Saône, utilizes nearby coal and water power for silk and rayon as well as automobile and other manufacturing. Toulon is a naval base and Nice, a Riviera resort town. The Riviera coast, protected from cold north winds by the Alps, has long been a famous resort area.

**Corsica.**   The island of Corsica, a miniature Massif Central, is located about 100 miles southeast of France in the Mediterranean Sea. Mediterranean climate and agriculture prevail, with pastoral activities most important because of lack of fertile arable land.

## Colonies

The French colonial empire, approximately twenty times the size of France, totals nearly 60 million people. The possessions are mostly in subtropical and tropical areas. North Africa, the major producing area, supplies France with wheat, wine, iron ore, phosphate, and pastoral products. In general, the colonial areas are greater importers than exporters. Intense nationalism, especially in North Africa, is causing France trouble. (Most of the French territory outside Europe is discussed in Chapters 11 and 12.)

### GERMANY

Germany is generally recognized as the key to the postwar recovery of Europe, especially

## Trade and Problems

The position of France is favorable for trade with Europe and the world. Although minerals and other raw materials are scarce, the high technical skill of the people is reflected in the making of commodities like clothing and art goods for which the country is famous. Raw cotton, coal, crude petroleum, crude rubber, copper, hides and skins, wool, and wood pulp are the principal raw material imports. Machinery, other manufactured products, foodstuffs, and beverages (coffee and wine) are also among the imports. Wine, iron ore, clothing and textiles, iron and steel products, and many light manufactures, some of luxury category, are the chief exports. The colonies, Western European countries, and the United States are major trading partners.

France faces many problems, social, political, and economic. Although the birth rate has risen during the postwar period, previous declining rates implied a shortage of labor and of military manpower. Two world wars within a generation have drained French resources. Monetary inflation and governmental crises have contributed to political and economic insecurity. Colonial unrest has burdened the French treasury; the unsuccessful war in Indochina and the Algerian rebellion have damaged French prestige. Balanced though the French economy is, there are serious regional disparities. French individualism hampers the introduction of modern mass production and distribution techniques. Hence, despite postwar improvement, French agriculture and industry are insufficiently mechanized. French capital has preferred foreign to domestic investment, and much has been expropriated in Communist countries. The French export structure is weak. French industrial specialization, especially in the production of luxury goods, is precarious in an impoverished Europe. Finally, in its exposed position, France continues to fear a rejuvenated Germany.

Western Europe. United in 1871 after a long period of disunity, Germany has twice risen to the status of a major world power and twice has lost that position in a world war. The countries that defeated her in World War II, especially the United States, have helped revitalize West Germany. Recovery has been remarkably rapid since 1948 and this part of Germany is again emerging as a major agricultural, industrial, and trading nation. Obstacles include war damage, uncertain political prospects, and the perils of being a major instrument in the cold war between the Communist and Western worlds.

The location of the former Germany in Europe was generally advantageous in peacetime and a liability during war. The central location, transitional between Eastern and Western Europe, offers the following advantages: (1) trade relations easily developed with nine bordering countries; (2) ease of development of water, rail, and highway routes for east-west and north-south transit traffic; (3) access to and good harbors on both the North and Baltic Seas facilitates waterborne trade; (4) transitional climate for agricultural development; (5) access to nearby Lorraine iron ore vital to German industry; (6) access to normally important trade with Southeastern Europe via the Danube and rail routes.

The possibility of encirclement by enemies in wartime is a major disadvantage. Other liabilities are the boundaries with Poland and France that have been shifted repeatedly in modern times, the fact that the Rhine outlet, vital to the industrial regions of western Germany, is controlled by the Netherlands, and the vulnerable position of the Ruhr and Berlin. The added distance from the Rhine-Ruhr industrial district to North German ports on the Atlantic is a handicap in competition with other Western European ports like Rotterdam and Antwerp.

## Postwar Changes and Problems

The postwar boundaries, though not established by treaty, considerably change Germany's size, shape, and resources. Major changes are the loss of all territory east of the Oder-Neisse River line. Included are some of the best agricultural land, the important Silesian coal fields, and associated industrial districts. Minor Belgian

and Netherlands boundary shifts also have been made. The resultant postwar Germany has a more compact shape. The economy is much less self-sufficient in food but still has surpluses of industrial goods as the country retained 93 per cent of the former industrial output potential.

Germany, now separated into eastern and western parts, has approximately 70 million people in an area about equal to Minnesota and Wisconsin combined. The population density averages over 500 people per square mile; if one considers only arable area, the density reaches nearly 1,300. The densest zone of concentration is found near the contact between the highlands and plains extending from the Ruhr Valley to Dresden. About 70 per cent of the population is urban and 30 per cent rural.

The German ethnic group is numerically the largest in Europe excluding the Russians. About 13 million ethnic Germans and German nationals have been forced out of East European countries and former German territory now occupied by Czechoslovakia, Poland, the Soviet Union, and Lithuania. The net result is that Germany has nearly her prewar population on three-fourths of the former area. Regional differences in dialect, religion, and group character exist, and this sometimes leads to antagonisms, such as that between Prussians and Bavarians.

## Divided Germany

After World War II, Germany was divided into four zones of occupation. The British, Americans, and French occupied about 94,700 square miles of western Germany which became the German Federal Republic in 1949. In 1955, it became a sovereign state with free and equal partnership in the Western world. West Germany is a member of NATO (North Atlantic Treaty Organization), and Allied forces remain as security forces. A peace treaty and unification remain unsettled.

Dominantly industrial West Germany has a population of 50 million. It contains only 45 per cent of prewar Germany's arable land and must import one-third of its food requirements. The Ruhr mines most of Germany's hard coal and produces a large share of the steel and other industrial products. Potash, salt, and limited quantities of iron ore and petroleum are found. Located here are the two leading German ports, Hamburg and Bremen. Production and trade are oriented toward the West.

The Soviet Union occupied about 41,700 square miles of eastern Germany. In 1949 a Soviet-sponsored puppet Communist government, called the German Democratic Republic, was established. Berlin, well within Soviet-controlled Germany, is occupied jointly by the British, French, Americans, and Russians. Approximately 45 per cent of the city is in the Russian sector.

East Germany, with 20 million people, is nearly self-sufficient in food production. It has valuable lignite, potash, and salt deposits, and large chemical and electrical industries. Production and trade are oriented toward Communist Europe. A unified Germany would benefit from the domestic exchange of agricultural, fuel, and industrial products.

The Saar, an area of 991 square miles, contains nearly a million people. It was controlled by Germany from 1871–1920, the League of Nations 1920–1935, Germany 1935–1945, and France 1945–1956. After the Saarlanders voted for annexation to Germany, it was reunited with that country on January 1, 1957. Coal is the major resource which makes the Saar desirable. It is of good quality for steam power but must be mixed with Ruhr coal to produce coke. Although the Saar has become part of Germany, it will continue to ship coal to France. Easy access to coal and Lorraine iron ore have made the iron and steel industry a natural development. Nearly 17 million tons of steel are produced annually. Saarbrücken is the leading industrial center.

## Physical Setting

**Relief Features.** The two general German landform types—in both East and West Germany—are the glaciated lowlands in the north and the highland complex in the south. The northern lowland, covered with recent unconsolidated glacial deposits, is generally below 600 feet in elevation. The central zone is char-

acterized by the dissected remains of Hercynian mountains, reaching nearly 5,000 feet at their highest point. In the extreme south the rugged Bavarian Alps and their forelands dominate. The Alps average between 6,000 and 7,000 feet; the forelands are lower and strewn with rock debris brought down by the Alpine streams.

**Climate.** Considering the country as a whole, western and especially northwestern Germany has a marine west-coast climate. Eastern Germany has a modified continental type, and the southern portions reflect the altitude and varied relief of the highland areas. The major characteristics of climate for the whole country are cool summers, relatively mild winters, except in highland Germany, and summer maximum precipitation. The marine influence lessens eastward and southward. Most crops raised are suited to cool, moist conditions except the vine, corn, and tobacco found in sheltered valleys of the south and west.

**Vegetation and Soils.** The original vegetation cover of both East and West Germany was largely a mixed coniferous and deciduous forest. Forests still cover more than one-fourth of the country, with a greater percentage in the central and southern highland regions and the poorly drained areas of the lowland north. An efficient conservation program, including replantings of cut timber, normally is in effect. The forests are an important resource for timber, pulp and paper, and locally for wood carvings and toys.

The acid, leached soils which prevail in Germany are generally mediocre to poor except for the loess soils at the southern edge of the North German Plain. They are highly productive only through careful management and fertilization.

**Rivers and Drainage.** Germany has eight river systems of which the Rhine, Elbe, Oder, and Danube are the most important. These rivers, connected by a system of canals, give Germany one of the best waterway networks in the world. Even precipitation plus the melting snows in the Alps give a fairly steady stream flow although at times traffic is handicapped by low water. Normally, 20 per cent of the total rail and water traffic is carried on the inland waterways and of this 50 per cent is on the Rhine. The Oder is now shared by the Germans and Poles, the latter controlling the outlet, and the Elbe, cut by the Iron Curtain, is limited in navigational use.

Poorly drained areas are found principally in the northwest, where glacial lakes are common, and along the North Sea coast.

## Natural Resources

**Coal.**  Germany's greatest mineral resource is coal, all kinds from anthracite to lignite being found. The Ruhr or Westphalian fields are the principal producers of anthracite and bituminous coal. Much of the bituminous coal is of coking quality. Large lignite deposits are important in East Germany. In an average year, West Germany mines 112 million tons of bituminous coal and 76 million tons of lignite, as compared to 3 million tons of bituminous coal and 132 million tons of lignite in East Germany. In addition, West Germany imports considerable coal from the United States. Germany supplied approximately one-half of prewar European coal deficiencies.

**Iron Ore.**  Germany has limited, widely scattered iron ore deposits and must import approximately 70 per cent of its consumption from France and Sweden. The Siergerland deposits south of the Ruhr are the most valuable. Germany benefits from the free flow of iron ore from the French Lorraine fields.

**Potash and Other Minerals.**  Between the Weser and Elbe Rivers on the flanks of the Harz Mountains is a 100-square-mile area estimated to contain 20 billion metric tons of potash. Mining areas are split by the Iron Curtain, with West Germany the larger producer. Potash is essential to the commercial fertilizer and chemical industries.

Insufficient quantities of copper, lead, zinc, pyrites, petroleum, and salt are mined. Petroleum production is increasing, however, and about one-third of the West German needs come from fields within the country.

**Water Power.**  The highlands, especially the Bavarian Alps, supply considerable water power. Germany ranks sixth among European countries, excluding the U.S.S.R., in hydroelectric production. Its importance to industries, railways, and homes as a source of power is generally overlooked because of the prominence of coal.

## Economic Development

Germany is favored by a relatively large amount of arable land (Table 7-7). Much of the North German Plain, a number of river valleys and basins in the central and southern regions, and considerable areas on the lower slopes of the highlands can be cultivated.

Despite setbacks by two world wars, the West German economy still shows a decided industrial emphasis. Industry has surpassed prewar production levels although handicapped by raw material shortages, war destruction, loss of Upper Silesia, and the cold war. Levels in Berlin, however, are much lower. Germany depends on low wage rates rather than mass production techniques to meet foreign competition, although the Volkswagen automobile is a prod-

### TABLE 7-7.  LAND USE OF GERMANY

| | Acres, in thousands | Per cent | | | |
| | | Arable | Meadow and pasture | Forest and woodland | Other |
|---|---|---|---|---|---|
| Germany | 86,806 | 39 | 20 | 28 | 13 |
| Western Germany | 60,307 | 35 | 23 | 29 | 13 |
| Eastern Germany | 26,499 | 48 | 12 | 27 | 13 |

uct of the assembly line. Industry is diversified with both heavy (basic) and light (finished and consumer goods) represented.

In West Germany, nearly half the gainfully employed are in industry and handicraft with only one-fourth in agriculture and forestry, one-sixth in commerce and transportation, and the remainder in public and private service. West Germany, with a production of about 20 million tons of steel annually, ranks fourth in the world. Industry in East Germany is geared to Soviet-sphere needs. The greater emphasis is on agriculture.

German agriculture is characterized by mixed farming, small farms, low income per farm, large families providing labor, and little use of machinery. The inherently poor soils necessitate scientific farming and heavy fertilization for high production. Prewar Germany produced about 75 to 80 per cent of its food requirements; now, less than two-thirds of its needs are grown in West Germany and probably that required for East Germany is insufficient because of droughts, war dislocations, fertilizer shortages, and mismanagement by the communist government.

## Regions

**Northern Lowlands.** The German portion of the central European lowlands extends from the Netherlands to the Polish boundaries with tongues, or lowland bays, protruding southward into the highlands in both West and East Germany. The maximum east-west extent is about 300 miles. Surface materials and relief are largely a result of continental glaciation. The previous drainage system was disrupted, leaving lakes, large areas of bog and marsh, and east-west oriented glacial valleys that facilitated the building of canals connecting the navigable rivers. The topographical differences can be summarized as follows: (1) a poorly drained outwash plain extending inland from the North Sea; (2) a sandy, heath-covered, outwash area between the Elbe and Weser Rivers; (3) a sand, lake, and forest district east of the Elbe with greater relief due to morainic ridges, and (4) the southern transitional zone, largely loess-

covered, bordering on the highlands. Most of the plain is under 300 feet and only rarely reaches over 600 feet.

The agricultural development reflects the differences mentioned above. Dairying and livestock grazing are the predominant uses of the bog, marsh, and sandy heaths of the northwest, with crop agriculture, especially vegetables and sugar beets, in the artificially drained areas. To the east, crops are increasingly important, with potatoes and rye on the poorer soils and sugar beets and wheat on the better soils. Grazing utilizes the rougher grasslands. The sparsely populated northeast normally produces food surpluses. Forestry and resort activities are significant. The transitional zone on the south is one of the best farming areas in Germany and has a dense rural population, growing wheat, barley, sugar beets, and fodder crops for stall-fed cattle.

The North Sea coast is much more favorable than the Baltic for ports and trade. Both coasts are sandy and have shallow water offshore. The Baltic, however, is frozen for several months during the winter, and trade is limited largely to the neighboring countries. The North Sea ports, facilitated by deepened, narrow estuaries, have better access to Atlantic and world trade. Hamburg and Bremen, the leading ports, are located considerable distances up the Elbe and Weser Rivers respectively, with access to rich agricultural and industrial hinterlands. Hamburg, whose population is 1.6 million, is the first port and second city of Germany. Although its free port attracts considerable trade, Hamburg is handicapped by the Iron Curtain which cuts the productive Elbe River hinterland 20 miles upstream. Extensive war damage to harbor facilities has been largely repaired. Hamburg also has engineering, shipbuilding, and other industries. Cuxhaven, Hamburg's outport, is used by large passenger vessels. Bremen, Germany's second port, does not have such a large hinterland but normally has as much ocean traffic. Bremerhaven, important for fishing and Bremen's outport, is the chief port supplying the Allied armies and postwar West Germany. Wesermünde is another leading German fishing port, and Emden is a small North Sea port.

Berlin, the prewar governmental, cultural, and artistic center, is handicapped by the Four-Power occupation, its location deep in Soviet-controlled East Germany, and physical war destruction. Its 1950 population of 3,343,000 was over a million less than in 1939. Varied manufacturing establishments made prewar Berlin the leading German industrial and commercial center. It is the hub of a vast rail and waterway network. Berlin's future is precarious, but it will again become the capital and focal city should Germany be unified. At present it is the capital of Communist East Germany.

**Central Highlands.** A complex of worn-down mountains and dissected plateau, the Central Highlands, extends southward from the Northern Lowlands to the Alpine Forelands. The forested or grass-covered highlands are infertile, but the basins and valleys are generally intensively cultivated and grow sugar beets, potatoes, wheat, and other cereals. Many of the slopes are terraced for such crops as the vine and fruit. Livestock is grazed on the poor, rough grasslands.

The populous contact zone between the highlands and the Northern Lowlands is one of the most intensely developed industrial and agricultural regions of Germany. The minerals of the highlands and the coal along their northern flanks provide the principal basis for industry. The Ruhr coal and the lignite fields near Cologne (Köln) and Leipzig are the major sources of power. From Hannover to Dresden are a number of prominent industrial towns. Lignite, potash, and salt provide raw materials for the heavy chemical and fertilizer industries in cities on the flanks of the Harz Mountains such as Halle, Staszfurt (Stassfurt), Magdeburg, and in the Leipzig area. Lignite is also used in synthetics production to make rubber, plastics, dyestuffs, explosives, and other materials. Textiles, scientific instruments, and watches are among products made in this area. Leipzig, a great commercial and rail center, led in prewar publishing and printing. Dresden, a music and art center, also produced a variety of specialty products such as scientific instruments, china, and optical goods. The latter two cities are in East Germany.

Uranium mining is now of significance in the Erz Gebirge (Ore Mountains). Lumbering, wood carving, and toy and clock making are developed in the Black and Thuringian Forests.

**Ruhr Industrial.** The huge industrial complex based on Ruhr coal is one of the outstanding manufacturing concentrations in the world. Ap-

*Figure 7-18 A part of Hamburg, Germany's second city and major port. The widened Alster River is used for barge and other boat traffic and adds beauty to the center of the commercial and industrial district. (Courtesy of German Tourist Information Office.)*

proximately 6 million people are found in an area about the size of Delaware, which has a population of 240,000. The Ruhr accounts for over 90 per cent of anthracite and bituminous coal and 80 per cent of the steel output of West Germany. The steel capacity almost equals that of the United Kingdom. In addition, it is a leading metal products, coke and coal derivatives, machinery, chemical, and textile manufacturing district. It was the arsenal of both the Kaiser and Hitler and is again rising from the depths of war destruction as a pivotal area in the East-West struggle.

The following factors favor the development

*Figure 7-19　The city of Bad Reichenhall and the cable car leading to the Predigtstuhl peak in the Bavarian Alps. In the distance is the flatter Alpine Foreland. (Courtesy of German Tourist Information Office.)*

of the Ruhr: (1) the most extensive deposits of excellent coking and other qualities of coal in Europe (130 seams, of which 57 are used, occur in succession, with the lowest at a depth of 9,000 feet); (2) good water and rail connections for import of raw materials, especially Lorraine and Swedish iron ore, as well as export of finished products to foreign markets; (3) location at the junction of the Rhine Valley and east-west rail and water routes along the northern edge of the Central Highlands; (4) access to the Sieg Valley iron ore, and (5) an abundance of skilled labor.

The Ruhr in the south is hilly and forested, but the relatively level and fertile agricultural north provides about 50 per cent of the area's food needs. Three cities, Essen, Dortmund, and Düsseldorf, have population of more than 500,-000, 14 cities have more than 100,000 people. Urban districts in the north specialize in coal mining and heavy industry such as iron and steel. High-quality metal industries requiring skill and only small amounts of raw materials such as machine tools, motors, springs, and locks are found in the southern hilly district. Located here and in cities west of the Rhine are textile and clothing industries, whereas chemical, metal, and glass industries are scattered throughout the Ruhr.

Much of the prewar industry was controlled by huge cartels. During the occupation period, many of these were broken up and replaced by a large number of independent concerns in an attempt to initiate competition. The dismantling of plants was stopped because Ruhr production is needed for the defense and recovery of Western Europe.

**Bavarian Alps.**   The northern limestone fringe of the Alpine system, the Bavarian Alps, extends in southern Germany from Lake Constance to the Austrian border. Though not as high as the main Alps, they average from 6,000 to 7,000 feet in elevation and are snow-covered most of the year. Zugspitze, 9,721 feet, is the highest peak. Tourism is a major industry; the wooded slopes and mountain meadows form the basis of lumbering and pastoral pursuits.

**Alpine Forelands.**   Averaging 1,000 to 3,000 feet above sea level, the Alpine Forelands slope northward to the Danube River. They are a relatively level plateau covered with coarse glacial debris. The generally poor soils and swampy areas foster an important dairying industry. The richer soils of the Danube and tributary valleys are most intensively utilized. Wheat, barley, oats, hops, and cattle are common. Lumbering is developed on the forested slopes.

Munich (München), the third city of Germany, is an art and music center. Industries include breweries, textiles, electrical and mechanical goods. The city is located at the intersection of the Berlin-Rome and Vienna (Wien)-Paris routes. Augsburg is of regional importance; Ulm and Regensburg are Danube River ports. Considerable water power is available for industry.

**Rhine Valley.**   The Rhine Valley is divided into three sections: the upper rift valley, the central gorge, and the lower plains. The rift valley is a down-dropped block of rock 20 miles wide and 185 miles long, part of which is in France. Except for swampy meadows near the river, the valley floor produces abundant wheat, tobacco, hops, and fruit orchards. Vineyards and pastures occupy terraced lower slopes; the upper slopes are forested. Karlsruhe and Mannheim are strategic transportation centers.

The Main and Neckar Valleys are tributary to the rift valley. Fertile, terraced fields and a moderate climate result in agriculture similar to that of the rift valley. Frankfurt, on the Main River, and Nuremburg (Nürnberg), on a tributary of the Main, are the chief cities of this region. Frankfurt served as the headquarters of the combined British and American occupation zones. Stuttgart dominates the Neckar industrial region.

From just west of Mainz to Bonn is the picturesque Rhine gorge. The valley, cut into resistant rock, is barely wide enough in places for a railway and highway on each side of the river. Terraced vineyard slopes are prominent. Bonn is the present capital of West Germany. The

Rhine carries a very large traffic by boats and barges.

North of Bonn, the Rhine enters the flat European plain. Cologne, with over half a million inhabitants, has access to large lignite deposits and is a diversified industrial center and important Rhine port. Duisburg-Ruhrort is the chief German Rhine port and the principal river port in Europe. Although the Rhine barge fleet was greatly reduced during World War II, the river has resumed its importance as an international artery.

### Trade and Problems

Individual countries of Western Europe normally purchase up to 40 per cent of their imports and send 30 per cent of their exports to Germany. West Germany exports dominantly coal and manufactured goods—iron and steel, machinery, chemicals, textiles, and wood products. Principal imports are foodstuffs and industrial raw materials such as petroleum, iron ore,

cotton, wool, wood pulp, and paper. The trade of West Germany is predominantly with the United States and Western Europe.

East German imports include primarily coal, iron and steel, petroleum products, and agricultural and forest products. Chief exports are brown coal, potash, cement, chemicals, metallic ores, and various consumer goods. Eastern Europe usually accounts for over three-fourths of East Germany's foreign trade. Lack of interchange of East German food for West German coal and manufactured goods handicaps both parts.

The natural outlet and source of trade with Southeastern Europe is now largely closed to West Germany. West Germany carried on 20 per cent of its trade with Eastern Europe in 1936 but only 5 per cent in 1950. Although severe competition exists for world markets, by the mid-1950s West Germany had regained most of its prewar trade volume. However, other problems exist for a resurgent Germany. War

ruins still dot the German landscape. Unemployment and overpopulation, intensified by millions of displaced refugees and expellees, face a Germany smaller in area and resources. A postwar divided Germany, in its buffer position between the West and the East, is at a disadvantage in dealing with many of its problems. Despite all obstacles including the lack of unification, Germany must recover for a successful, peaceful Europe. By the mid-1950s great progress had been made in West Germany, business was prosperous, exports were expanding, and there was little unemployment. But in East Germany, controlled by the Communists, economic and political conditions were so poor that thousands of people fled into West Germany.

## SWITZERLAND

Switzerland is one of the smallest but most prosperous European countries. Since 1815, the Swiss have maintained a neutrality policy in their landlocked Central European nation. They have avoided the war destruction and disruption so disastrous in much of Europe and have been ready to trade and carry on normal relations with the return of peace.

In 1950, Switzerland had 4,714,992 people within 15,944 square miles, slightly smaller than Denmark. Population is concentrated largely in the central plateau areas, as much of Switzerland is too mountainous for settlement.

Switzerland exemplifies how peoples diverse in race, language, and religion can be welded into one nation. It has four official languages, German dialects, spoken by 73 per cent living in the central and northern districts, French, spoken by 21 per cent in the southwest, Italian spoken by 5 per cent on the southern slopes of the Alps, and Romansch, a Latin-derived tongue spoken in a few southeastern districts by 1 per cent of the people. In religion, 58 per

*Figure 7-20   The Rhine near Koblenz with the castle Ehrenbreitstein. The Rhine, the leading waterway in Europe, has heavy barge freight traffic as well as passenger and tourist vessels. This is the central portion of the Rhine gorge with steep forested or vine-covered slopes bordering the river. (Courtesy of German Tourist Information Office.)*

cent are Protestant, 41 per cent Catholic, and 1 per cent other.

The physical resources of Switzerland are limited. Severe climate, poor soil, and great slope limit agricultural development to favored valleys and the central plateau. Small, low-quality, poorly located coal deposits, building stone, sand, and clay are the only minerals. Mountains are dominant and occupy over 70 per cent of the total area. They are of major significance for defense, grazing and dairying partially based on Alpine grasslands, water power, the greatest natural resource, channeling profit-earning traffic through Switzerland, since major arteries of communication use the low passes in the Alps and Juras, and tourism.

### Economic Development

Since about 1880, industry has emerged as the major segment of the Swiss economy despite almost complete lack of raw materials. Approx-

imately 45 per cent of the working population are engaged in industry, 22 per cent in agricultural enterprises, and 14 per cent in trade. Only Belgium and England have greater percentages in manufacturing. Many of the enterprises are small, scattered, and specialize in high-quality goods such as watches and precision instruments. Swiss industries in order of importance are watchmaking, engineering and metals, chemicals, and textiles. Greater emphasis is being placed upon machinery and chemicals.

Despite handicaps of soil and relief, the Swiss have developed a rather intensive agriculture. Dairying is dominant, supplemented by hay and cereal crops. Sugar beets and tobacco, with orchard and vineyard products, are cash crops.

### Regions

The Alps, Jura Mountains, and the Central Plateau are the three regions of Switzerland.

*Figure 7-21 Transportation systems in all parts of Germany are well developed. Here a railway and a highway wind through the Schwarzwald. (Courtesy of German Tourist Information Office.)*

*Figure 7-22   An alpine pasture near Zweisimmen in the Bernese Alps. Rugged mountains such as these dominate three-fourths of Switzerland. The dairy cattle are transferred from summer mountain pastures to winter quarters in the Swiss Plateau, a procedure termed transhumance. (Courtesy of G. Müller.)*

The rugged Alps cover 60 per cent of the country, with the famed Matterhorn reaching 14,705 feet. Forestry, dairying, and tourism are the major economic activities. Transhumance, the seasonal transfer of animals and caretakers to summer mountain pastures, is practiced.

The Jura Mountains, located on the French boundary, are folded parallel valleys and ridges reaching 5,000 feet. Dairying and forestry are common, with vineyards on south-facing slopes. La Chaux-de-Fonds is a center of the watch-making industry. Basel, a Rhine port and railway hub, is a chemical, machinery, and silk manufacturing city.

The glaciated and stream-dissected Central Plateau covers 29 per cent of Switzerland but contains 70 per cent of the people. It is the heart of Swiss economic activity. Elevation varies from 1,300 to 4,600 feet and the climate is damp and rather severe. Agriculture is intensive with specialization in dairying. Milk is used in the production of cheese, condensed milk, and chocolate. Other scattered industry is based primarily upon hydroelectric power. The silk and cotton textile industries are located in the north around Zürich and St. Gallen. The manufacture of machinery, watches, and textiles is found in Geneva and Bern, the capital. The cities and areas bordering the famous Swiss lakes are tourist centers. About 285,000 people are employed in the Swiss tourist trade.

## Trade and Problems

The prosperity of Switzerland depends upon the export of at least 30 per cent of the industrial production. Machinery, watches, chemicals, precision instruments, and high-grade textiles are the chief exports. Watches and watch movements formed 23 per cent of the value of 1952 exports. Leading imports are iron and steel, chemical products, industrial heavy machinery, coal, wheat, automobiles, petroleum, forage crops, and cotton. Neighboring industrial countries and the United States are the chief trading areas. The adverse balance in trade is offset by transit traffic on Rhine barges and the Swiss railroads, tourism, foreign insurance and investments, and the recently begun merchant marine, which numbers 12 ships and is largely based in Italian ports.

## LIECHTENSTEIN

Liechtenstein, an independent principality of 14,000 inhabitants on the eastern Swiss border, has an economic union with Switzerland. The majority of the people are of German origin and are Roman Catholic. Agriculture is the main occupation. The capital and chief city is Vaduz. The people pay no taxes, the Prince securing his income from fees of foreign corporations that are licensed by Liechtenstein, and from the sale of postage stamps to collectors.

## AUSTRIA

Austria, strategically located in the heart of Europe astride vital modern rail, water, and air routes, forms a link between the West and the East. The 1,648-mile boundary line is shared with seven countries.

The population numbers 6,949,000 with 26 per cent living in Vienna (Wien). Most of the remainder reside in lowlands such as the Danube Valley. The sparsely populated Alps occupy three-fourths of the area. Though nearly 98 per cent of the people speak German, cultural and other differences from the Germans are apparent. About 94 per cent are Roman Catholic.

Present Austria, created from the Austro-Hungarian empire in 1918, possesses the following percentages of former land and resources: area 12.5, labor 30, steam power capacity 20, coal 0.5, and food production 20. Banking, industrial, educational, and administrative facilities, organized for 50 million persons, now serve about 7 million. Psychological adjustment to these losses has been a major problem.

After the forced union with Germany in 1938, Austria was dominated by the Nazis until 1945. It was then divided into four zones of occupation. The 1955 peace treaty restored complete sovereignty to Austria but required heavy reparations payments to the Soviet Union for a period of ten years.

### Physical Setting

Austria is dominated by the Alps; only one-fourth is plains and low hills. The climate is transitional with temperature extremes increasing eastward and with higher altitudes. Soils are varied. The most fertile are found in the Danube Valley and in favored basins. Approximately 21 per cent of the total area is arable; 28 per cent is in meadow and pasture fostering an important grazing and dairying development, and 37 per cent is in forests, making it one of the few European exporters of timber products and paper. Austria ranks high in production of hydroelectric power. Important petroleum fields are located in eastern Austria, but until 1965, a million tons a year must go to the U.S.S.R. as reparations. The Styrian iron ore fields are among Europe's largest. Other significant minerals are coal and magnesite.

### Economic Development

Approximately 40 per cent of the labor force are engaged in manufacturing and 32 per cent in agriculture and forestry. Consumer goods, machinery, and metallurgy are the main types of manufacturing. Mining employs many. Vienna, Linz, Graz, and Salzburg are the principal industrial centers. Industrial levels are now considerably above those of the pre-World War II level.

Agricultural production supplies about 65 to 75 per cent of the Austrian food requirements. Wheat, rye, barley, oats, potatoes, and sugar beets are the chief crops. Dairying and pig raising are very important. There are some areas of fertile valley land, but the average farmer wrests a living from small, rugged farms with hard work and a minimum of machinery.

The severely folded Alps reach their maximum width in Austria. The highest peak is Gross Glockner, 12,461 feet. Grazing and forestry are dominant on the rougher slopes with crops such as rye, oats, potatoes, and hay concentrated in valleys and small basins (Figure 7-23). The Arlberg and Brenner gaps contain important arteries of trade and traffic through Austria. Tourism is also of importance; Tyrol alone attracts 800,000 visitors annually. Salzburg and Innsbruck are the major cities. Northern Austria is a forested plateau.

Limited areas in the east and south and the narrow Danube Valley comprise the lowlands. The more favorable soil and climate of the lowlands result in the growth of wheat, corn, vineyards, and garden crops along with dairying. Lumbering is important on lower slopes. The eastern lowlands contain the valuable oil deposits. Linz, Graz, and Vienna are the leading cities. The industry of Vienna is largely finishing and processing manufactures. Vienna is a major problem as it is too large a capital city for present Austria.

### Trade and Problems

Austria, with its limited resources, must trade or die. Foodstuffs, coal and coke, raw cotton and wool, and heavy machinery are Austria's principal imports. Forest products and paper are the leading exports, along with iron and steel products, textiles, magnesite, and machinery. Trade with Eastern European countries and the U.S.S.R. decreased from over 40 per cent of the total value in 1938 to less than 15 per cent at present. Western Germany, Italy, Switzerland, Great Britain, and the United States are major trading partners. Austria finds it difficult to market in the West manufactured products that formerly found an outlet in the East. In order to pay the peace treaty reparations, Austria will have to export to the U.S.S.R. goods which it previously had sold to the West for cash.

*Figure 7-23  Mariazell in the province of Styria, Austria. The cleared slopes and valley bottoms support dairying. The eastern Austrian Alps are somewhat lower than those in the west and possess a valuable forest cover. (Courtesy of Information Department of the Austrian Consulate General.)*

Increased utilization of existing resources and expansion of industry, agriculture, transportation, and trade are necessary to overcome the lack of resources. The 1955 peace treaty poses economic problems, for Austria must pay the U.S.S.R. 150 million dollars a year in cash for six years, deliver a million tons of oil per year, and assume the burden of maintaining an army. An estimated 50 million dollars a year in income from the United States occupation forces will also be lost.

## IN PERSPECTIVE

### *Importance of Western Europe*

The political expansion and economic growth of Western Europe after the discovery of America and the sailing routes to the Far East was the outstanding geographic development since the fifteenth century. Many European governments emerged from feudalism. Discoveries of new lands and peoples led to the establishment of colonies and trade overseas. Inventions and the increased use of minerals and other resources, especially the application of power to manufacturing, resulted in the Industrial Revolution, with great growth in density of population, particularly in the population of cities. The world was largely dominated by the countries of Western Europe; most of Africa and Oceania, much of Asia, and parts of America was governed from European capitals until World War II. Since 1946, however, many former European possessions have become independent nations.

The culture of Europe spread to distant lands; European languages were used in trade and education; the Christian religion gained adherents abroad, and many backward peoples learned the principles of self-government. Thus, the contributions of Western Europe to the advancement of civilization are great. Even today, weakened by two world wars, most European countries have made great recovery in industrial production and in bettering standards of living for their citizens. Even greater advances can be made by solving political and economic problems that hinder commerce and hamper the exercise of human rights.

Not only is Western Europe the site of huge and varied manufacturing, but the area also has a noteworthy output of agricultural products. Wheat and other bread grains, potatoes, sugar beets, fruits of many sorts, vineyard products, and vegetables, along with dairy products, pigs, beef cattle, and sheep are among the produce of Western European farms. Soil, rainfall, length of growing season, experienced farmers, and closeness of markets are among factors that favor agriculture. Coal, iron, and other minerals are present in great abundance, and forest and fishery resources are locally in large supply. Most important of all the factors affecting the growth of industries are the skill and experience of the factory workmen, the efficiency of management, and the availability of capital. Although exports of manufactures help provide income for the countries of Western Europe, the large local populations constitute a big market within themselves. Europe has much of historic and cultural interest to visitors from abroad, and the more than a billion dollars which tourists spend annually is available for the purchase of foodstuffs, minerals, and other materials and goods not manufactured in sufficient quantity on the Continent itself. Although Western European countries have lost much of their colonial empires and other nations have developed into commercial and industrial rivals, the region remains the most important for its size in the world.

## EXERCISES

*1.* What are the climatic regions of Northwestern and Central Europe? How do they compare in location and area with the same regions in North America? Do they extend a greater distance inland and poleward in Europe or in North America? Why?

2. How do countries in this region compare in area and population density with New York and Texas?

3. Which countries are the most highly developed industrially? What minerals do these countries mine? In what ways has the topography of each country aided or hindered its industrialization?

4. Which countries are the most highly developed agriculturally? What are the chief crops? In what ways have the soils and climate aided or handicapped this development? What adjustments have been made to the physical environment?

5. What are the principal activities in the Sambre-Meuse area? Jutland Peninsula? The Skåne? Ruhr Valley? Lancashire area? In what ways do these activities promote the national welfare?

6. Why has West Germany recovered from the effects of World War II more rapidly than other European nations? What problems now face Germany?

7. What are the principal natural resources of the United Kingdom? Why is the United Kingdom not as effective as a world leader today as in 1900?

8. What are the principal economic problems in France? In what ways are these problems related to the geography of the country?

9. Should the Central European nations form a United States of Europe? What would be its economic advantages and handicaps? Which of these are geographical?

10. Which cities in Northwestern and Central Europe have populations in excess of one million persons? What locational advantages does each possess? Which of the cities are most dependent upon the natural resources of these areas? Why?

11. What are the geographical handicaps of Switzerland and Sweden? How have they been able to overcome those handicaps?

12. In what ways have the people of Denmark and Netherlands made adjustments to their physical environment? Why was it necessary to do so? What are the principal items exported from these countries?

13. Why do so many Americans travel to Europe? What attractions interest them? How does the tourist industry benefit Western Europe?

## SELECTED REFERENCES

Alexander, Lewis M.: "Economic Problems in the Benelux Union," *Economic Geography,* 26:29–36, January, 1950.

Carlson, Lucile: "Luleå and Narvik: Swedish Ore Ports," *Journal of Geography,* 53:1–13, January, 1954.

Goodwin, William F., Jr.: "Scandinavia," *Focus,* 5(1):1–6, January, 1955.

Gottmann, Jean: *A Geography of Europe,* Henry Holt and Company, Inc., New York, 1950.

Hoffman, George W.: *Geography of Europe,* The Ronald Press Company, New York, 1953.

Hubbard, George D.: *The Geography of Europe,* Appleton-Century-Crofts, Inc., New York, 1952.

MacFadden, Clifford H., Henry M. Kendall, and George F. Deasy: *Atlas of World Affairs,* Thomas Y. Crowell Company, New York, 1946.

Miller, E. Willard: "Recent Trends in the Pattern of European Manufacturing," *Journal of Geography,* 53:185–196, May, 1954.

Mitchel, N. C.: "Ireland," *Focus,* 6(4):1–6, December, 1955.

Pounds, Norman J. G.: "France and 'Les Limites Naturelles' from the Seventeenth to the Twentieth Centuries," *Annals of the Association of American Geographers,* 44:51–62, March, 1954.

———: "France," *Focus,* 3(7):1–6, March, 1953.

Van Valkenburg, Samuel, and Colbert C. Held: *Europe,* John Wiley & Sons, Inc., New York, 1952.

# 8. Southern Peninsular Europe

SOUTHERN peninsular Europe—Iberia, Italy, and Greece—is Mediterranean. This statement is full of meaning, for among all the seas the Mediterranean is unique as an element of man's physical environment and as a center of human progress (Figure 8-1).

Though geologically young, the Mediterranean is old historically. Here was an ancient cradle of civilization and a nursery of human progress. The first cultures of the Old World grew up in the Nile and Asiatic river valleys. These civilizations influenced the more backward peoples that lived to their west. The contacts, through trade and migrations, were along two main thoroughfares, the land bridge of Asia Minor and the Mediterranean Sea. The land bridge, a peninsula of plateaus, mountains, and westward-trending valleys, viewed three seas and looked toward Europe from across the Dardanelles and Bosporus. The seaway, long and narrow, landlocked, with little tide, and studded with steppingstones—islands that stretched from Cyprus to the Balearics—was easily navigated. Many promontories provided a long coast line.

Invited by the favorable environment, there arose in the basin of this sea a

282

succession of maritime commercial states—Crete, Phoenicia, Athens, Carthage, and Rome. Continuous intercourse back and forth across the water bound the peoples of the basin together economically and led to an interchange of ideas. As a result, aided by likeness of landscape and climatic environment, Mediterranean culture took on an essentially similar character and something of a Mediterranean civilization arose. Particularly did the pattern of land use develop along nearly identical lines.

In time sequence, the first high civilization was at the eastern end of the Mediterranean in Crete, Phoenicia, and Greece. Civilization moved from there to Italy. Rome, in its prime, reached out to conquer North Africa and the barbarians of Northern Europe. The statement that "all roads lead to Rome" became literally true, for Rome ranged east, north, and south to extend its political and economic influence. But eventually Rome declined. In the Dark Ages that followed, much that had been learned in the past almost disappeared.

During the Middle Ages, Italian Genoa and Venice, her rival, were the great ports of trade. Milan, situated at the foot of St. Gotthard Pass, was a city of wealth and power. Under the Medici, the trading and financial center of Florence became the leader in the Renaissance movement that carried Europe from medievalism into the modern period. It was in the basin of the Mediterranean, then, and particularly in the cities of Venice and Florence in Italy, that the Renaissance—not only a cultural movement, as it is so often regarded, but economic in character as well—had its first and greatest expression.

For nearly 2,000 years, the Mediterranean was dominant. During all that time, European civilization faced south. The ebb of this brilliant period of Mediterranean supremacy came at the beginning of the sixteenth century as control of the spice trade slipped from the hands of the Turks. Hitherto, the products of the East had flowed by caravan through Egypt or by way of Baghdad and Aleppo, the route of the Fertile Crescent, to the Levantine ports. Here they were met by the galleys of the Italian cities and

transported westward. By 1503, however, practically no spices were arriving at the ports of the eastern Mediterranean. They were being carried in Portuguese vessels, by way of the ocean route around Africa and thence to Lisbon, to be picked up there and distributed by the ships of the Hansa League. According to Derwent Whittlesey "Portugal swiftly eclipsed the city-states of the Mediterranean world which for centuries had thrived on the trickle of oriental goods filtering through the deserts of Western Asia. Venice, wealthiest of Italian city-states, received the news of the all-sea route to the Orient with public mourning, well recognizing the inevitable eclipse of its own costly and complicated land-and-sea tradeway in competition with the single lading from India to Europe around Africa." [*]

Dominance moved westward to the two countries of the Iberian Peninsula, Mediterranean lands that faced also upon the Atlantic. It was the Portuguese and Spanish who opened up the highways of ocean transport, for their daring and skill as seamen dispelled the fears that had held much of the Western world captive, and opened the trade routes through discovery. They took possession of new lands far and wide. In 1494, the newly discovered and unknown lands of the entire globe were divided equally between Spain and Portugal. A line, drawn by the Pope, designated the territories of each.

In time they, too, declined. With the dying out of the royal line, Portugal came under Philip II of Spain, and Spanish interests were pushed to the elimination of those of the Portuguese. Though it had its illustrious days, Spanish colonial history is notable not only for the spread of its influence but also for its swift ebb after attaining a glorious climax. Spain went into eclipse, through bankruptcy, at the defeat of the Armada by England.

Power moved north and, for a time, the bypassed Mediterranean became a backwater in the affairs of the world. Though there was a revival of Mediterranean commerce in the first

[*] *The Earth and the State,* Henry Holt and Company, Inc., New York, 1939, p. 399.

half of the nineteenth century, only with the opening of the Suez Canal did that sea return to a place of great prominence as a route of trade. The states that bordered the sea, however, remained in relative obscurity. Not until the past half century have there been indica-tions of recovery. Nevertheless, the lessons in economics, politics, navigation, and culture learned here, in this enclosed basin, carried Western man from barbarism into advanced civilization and forms the base for many of his present-day achievements.

## THE MEDITERRANEAN ENVIRONMENT

What is the nature of the Mediterranean land-scape?

Typically, it is a region of alternating, frag-mented littoral plains and projecting head-lands, backed by lofty mountain ranges toward the Continent and fronted by the waters of the inland sea. Add to this a prevalence of sunny, cloudless skies, with a pattern of precipitation that shows a winter maximum and comes in short, quick, heavy showers; paint in the vine, the olive, the citrus, the cork oak, wheat, barley, and some goats; sketch in a proud people with a great past, and you have the landscape al-most in its entirety. The limits of the Mediter-ranean zone are quite clearly defined, for both the climate and adjustment change as the coastal littoral is left behind and distance from the sea increases.

### Physical Setting

**Relief Features.** The topography is one of mountains, hills, and valleys (Figure 8-2). Large Mediterranean coastal plains are a rarity. The Po Valley and narrow coastal plains in Italy, portions of coastal Portugal and Spain, and the coastal region of southern France are

*Figure 8-1   Mediterranean Europe includes four rela-tively large and four tiny independent nations. Note the relationship of railroads to mountain areas and cities.*

the most important lowland areas. Greece, dissected by mountains and fringed with multitudes of islands, is a jumble of ranges and valleys and promontories thrust into the sea so that the coast is an alternation of forbidding cliffs and deep indentations, with Thessaly being the largest lowland. Offshore, the islands are the tops of submerged ranges that are a continuation of the mountains of the mainland.

**Climate.**   Over most of this southern fringe of Europe there prevails the Mediterranean climate (Figure 8-3). Though this climate takes its name from the Mediterranean Sea region, it is found distributed in other areas in the world, along west coasts of continents in latitudes that range between 30° and 40° north and south. The coast of central Chile, southern California, Cape Province in Africa, and the two tips of southern Australia are thus also "Mediterranean lands." The principal areas in the European Mediterranean region where other kinds of climate prevail include northwestern Spain

which has a marine west-coast type, interior Spain, where semiarid steppes occur, and northern Italy, which has considerable summer rainfall because of its location near the Alps (Figure 8-4). In winter, cold winds from northeastern Europe sometimes blow through the gaps that pierce the mountain barrier north of the Mediterranean. The mistral of the Rhone Valley, and the bora of the Adriatic and Aegean Seas are examples.

The Mediterranean climate has two seasons, a cool winter, with rain usually associated with cyclonic storms, and a hot, dry summer. Rarely does the temperature drop to freezing, for mountain barriers shut out most of the cold winds from continental interiors. Even during the winter, the proportion of sunny days is high. Summer is a period of drought, broken only occasionally by showers, of brilliant sunshine, hot south winds, and, in some places, of dust storms that blow across the sea from the Sahara. This dry season parches the lands so that grass and other vegetation is brown and scorched-

POLITICAL AND RAILWAY MAP
OF MEDITERRANEAN EUROPE

★ Capital of country

0          200 MILES

*Figure 8-2   Mediterranean Europe is a discontinuous and fragmented land. Three great peninsulas reach southward into the sea, each peninsula broken into many separate and distinct regions by hills and mountain ranges so that regionalism is nurtured and communication made difficult. Few plains exist and the uplands are steep and eroded.*

looking. Fields are bare and often plowed in readiness for the planting that takes place with the oncoming of the wet season. Precipitation, averaging between 15 and 35 inches, varies considerably from place to place and from year to year but is dependable for the growing of winter crops. Only by careful water conservation, however, are the people of the Mediterranean able to maintain a supply that satisfies even the minimum requirements. Irrigation supplements rainfall in many vineyards, orchards, and gardens, and is essential where rice is grown.

**Vegetation.**   Plant life shows a high degree of adaptation to these climatic conditions, being of the drought-resistant variety, as maqui. Thorned flora, as cacti and thorny shrubs, are found in great number and variety. Deep-rooted plants, as the grape, fig, and olive, penetrate to the level of permanent ground water for moisture sustenance. In fact, the olive is a classic example of the type of vegetation known as Mediterranean. It is found only within Mediterranean regions. Its long roots help the olive survive drought during the hot, dry period. Another such typical plant is the cork oak, indigenous only to and a part of the Mediterranean landscape. Its thick, pulpy bark acts as an in-

sulator to cut down the evaporation of moisture from its surface.

Because of the extended dry season, pasture is scarce. Hence the goat, sheep, and little donkey are the characteristic animals of the Mediterranean. Only nimble-footed creatures who thrive on poor forage can scramble among the rough scrubby lands and survive.

## Cultural Landscape

The two factors of topography and climate have acted to shape Mediterranean life throughout the ages. Here man has more completely exhausted the possibilities offered him than in most regions (Figure 8-5). Three types of agriculture are carried on side by side: growing winter grains using natural precipitation; terracing and raising tree crops whose deep roots reach down to subsoil water and live through the drought period; and irrigation agriculture.

Wheat and barley are the two Mediterranean grains par excellence. Wheat takes the better-watered and more fertile soil; barley is planted on the marginal lands where wheat will not do as well. The grains are planted in the fall, grow under the moisture of the winter rains, and are harvested in the spring. Even then, in this land of high evaporation, the method of cultivation known as dry-farming must be employed to

LANDFORMS
F MEDITERRANEAN EUROPE

0       200 MILES

BLACK SEA

ADRIATIC SEA

AEGEAN SEA

MEDITERRANEAN SEA

30°

20°

make the most of the uncertain and scanty precipitation that is typical of Mediterranean lands. Under this method, fields are planted in alternate years. During the fallow year they are plowed and frequently reworked to keep the soil loose and free of cracks and weeds, so that the rains can penetrate and the moisture can be stored. By this technique, two years of precipitation is used to grow one crop of grain.

Since the amount of plains area is definitely limited, even intensive use of the lowlands is insufficient to provide a livelihood for the large population. Therefore, hillsides are cultivated. To combat erosion, the slopes are terraced, often from bottom to top. Steps walled with broken stones and filled with soil, frequently carried up from the lowlands, are planted to vines. Fig trees and the gray-green olive crown others. These crops are produced without irrigation.

In a land that is characteristically a nondairy region, the oil of the olive replaces butter and cooking fat in the diet of the people, and also provides a skin lotion against the intense summer heat and sunshine. The vine, another typically Mediterranean crop, supplies not only fruit for eating but the major drink as well. Wine is consumed in place of water, and is served with every meal, even to children. The grape frequently occupies lowlands as well as hill slopes. On the plains, the vines are generally trained on trellises or other supports that extend between trees to keep the plants off the ground. Between the widely spaced rows of trees and trellis there are frequently interplantings of other crops. Land is intensively used, and no amount of hand labor is too great to assure a good yield.

The grains, wheat and barley, depend on the winter rains. The orchard crops of olives, figs, grapes, and even citrus fruits, at times, exist through the drought of summer. Other crops, such as rice, vegetables, small fruits and, in times of great and prolonged drought, the citrus fruits, require irrigation. Wet rice, a somewhat unusual crop in Mediterranean lands, is grown in selected places as the river valleys of the Po, Ebro, and Tagus (Tejo), the coastal plain near Valencia, and on the reclaimed salt flats of Greece, where rice cultivation is a new project. Vercelli, Italy, is the major rice market of Europe.

Because the environment is meager for the large population that is found everywhere in the Mediterranean Basin and, also, because the sea invites, fishing and commerce have become important occupations. Fish ranks high in the diet of Mediterranean peoples. Large quantities of

**TABLE 8-1. SOUTHERN PENINSULAR EUROPE**

| Country | Area, sq miles | Population |
|---|---|---|
| Andorra | 192 | 5,000 |
| Gibraltar | 2 | 24,000 |
| Greece | 51,246 | 7,604,000 |
| Italy | 116,290 | 47,021,000 |
| Monaco | 0.6 | 20,000 |
| Portugal | 35,466 | 8,549,000 |
| San Marino | 23 | 13,000 |
| Spain | 194,945 | 28,306,000 |
| Vatican City | 0.2 | 890 |

dried fish are imported to this area from the North Atlantic fishing countries because the amount caught locally is too small to meet the demand.

In few regions of the world have topography and soil, climate, and even the sea itself had a more direct bearing on human development. It can also be said that there are few areas where man has worked so closely with nature to make a garden of waste places. The development of the techniques of Mediterranean agriculture took centuries. Ellen Churchill Semple states the farmer was "weak in theory, but strong in practice." Through trial and error, by the interchange of ideas, there slowly unfolded the "precocious form of intensive tillage" that characterizes Mediterranean lands today.

## THE IBERIAN PENINSULA: SPAIN AND PORTUGAL

No explanation of the political partition of the Iberian Peninsula into Spain and Portugal can be found in the ethnographic composition of the two countries. The peoples are closely similar, for all Iberia is of very old Mediterranean stock and, though this unity has been modified by the invasion and colonization by Vikings, Moors, and other aliens, the basic character of the people has been little changed.

Because the peninsula lies between Europe

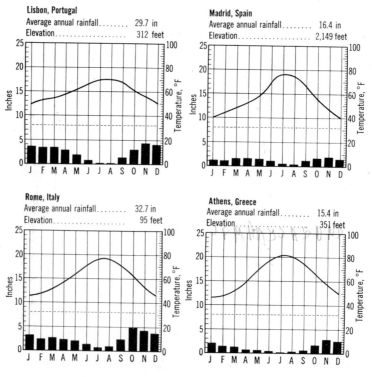

*Figure 8-3   Climate graphs for selected Mediterranean stations.*

and Africa, it was long the battleground of Islam and Christianity, with Nordic and Moor seesawing back and forth across it for many centuries. For a millennium, all Europe seethed with the "turbulence of ethnic commingling." This subsided earlier in Portugal than in most parts of the Continent. Welded together by more than six centuries of struggle with the foreign Moorish civilization inflicted upon them by the Moslem invaders from North Africa, the people of this compact little land were early bound into social and political unity. Two hundred and fifty years before neighboring Spain was liberated and unified, the African Moors had been ejected from Portugal, and the area emerged as a national state.

While the Portuguese were slowly unrolling the outline of coastal Africa, the Spanish were having experiences similar to those of their western neighbor in creating a nation. The original success of the Moorish invasion lay less in the organization or strength of the invaders than in the social and regional disorganization of the people of Spain. From the middle of the fourteenth century, Spanish history relates a long and painful process of unification.

The early division of Iberia into two sovereign and distinct nations can, then, be explained only in historical terms, but once the division had been made, geographic factors tended to perpetuate it. That geography should strengthen trends toward maintenance of national separatism is the more logical when one considers that within Spain itself, according to Isaiah Bowman, "patriotism is a local thing—reflecting the geographical division of the country; a man says he is a Galician, an Asturian, a Castilian, an Andalusian; he rarely thinks of himself as a Spaniard." * Dialects and even languages differ from one localized area to another, for Spaniard is separated from Spaniard by physical barriers, by language, by custom, and by social class. Only the forced collaboration against the Moorish invaders of the half-dozen little Iberian realms, of which Castile and Aragon were the

* *The New World*, 4th ed., World Book Company, Yonkers, N.Y., 1928, p. 215.

most important, brought about coalescence into a nation, a unity that has precariously endured to the present. Separate action by Portugal and its eventual independence arose, in part, as a result of its physical seclusion on the coastal edge of the tableland, for it is separated from the rest of the peninsula by the rough mountain country that features the plateau margin on the western side.

The geologic structure and the physiography of Iberia have much to do with the orientation of the two countries. Portugal faces the Atlantic. The boundary between Spain and Portugal lies along a zone where it is easier to travel downhill to the west coast than to go uphill and across the plateau to the Spanish centers.

Portugal slopes to the sea. The coastal location is enhanced by the fact that the lower reaches of the Douro (Duero) and Tejo (Tagus) Rivers are navigable. Thus the Portuguese are naturally sea-minded. Historically, the Portuguese were among the first great navigators of Europe. Currently, fishing holds an important place in the economy of the country although Portugal's present interest in oceanic trade is negligible.

Spain, largely plateau, is oriented landward. Though it had a brilliant career as an exploring and colonizing nation, this was but an episode, relatively short-lived because the potential of Spain as a sea power is weak. Although half the country's population lives near the coasts, the fine harbors of northwest Spain are not easily accessible from the interior, and much of the coast offers meager opportunity for modern harbor developments. The Castilians, plateau dwellers, show little aptitude for the sea. Recently, however, there has been a revival of interest in trade. At present the Spanish merchant marine amounts to a little over 1 per cent of the world's total.

## Relief Features

The Iberian Peninsula lies between the Mediterranean Sea and the Atlantic Ocean and, cut off from the rest of Europe by the lofty Pyrenees, it acts as a land bridge between that continent and Africa. It is a bulky block of land, the greater part of which is made up of an ancient massif; an eroded stump of old folded mountains whose margins, formed by faulting, are steep and straight. It is tipped higher in the east than in the west so that the longest rivers—the Douro, the Tagus, the Guadiana, and the Guadalquivir—rise near the eastern margin of the block, cross the plateau, and empty into the Atlantic Ocean. Faulting also occurred in the interior of the tableland where huge upthrusts of rock were projected above the surface to form mountain ranges. The greatest of these, the Sierra de Guadarrama, extends through the center of the plateau from Portugal to Aragon. Faulting also explains the Cantabrian Mountains near the northern edge and the Toledo Range to the south of the Sierra de Guadarrama.

To the north and south of the central range are two large basins known respectively as Old and New Castile. Great areas of these basins are extremely flat. They have, however, been dissected in such a way that broad, level tablelands alternate with wide terraced steps and valleys. Though the plateau is over 2,000 feet above sea level, the surface has the character of a plain which, at intervals, is interrupted by steep rises a few hundred feet high ascending to other flat tables.

Young, folded mountains were crushed against the northern, northeastern, and southern edges of the plateau to form highland barriers. In the south, the highest of these, the Sierra Nevada, mounts to 11,660 feet, towering abruptly above the plains of the Guadalquivir. In the north, the plateau is partially rimmed by the Cantabrians and the Pyrenees which rise almost as high as the southern ranges. Though not as lofty as the Alps, the northern mountains form a more formidable barrier to communication than do the mountains that separate Switzerland and Italy.

Between the folded structures and the plateau are wedgelike lowlands. One of these, the valley

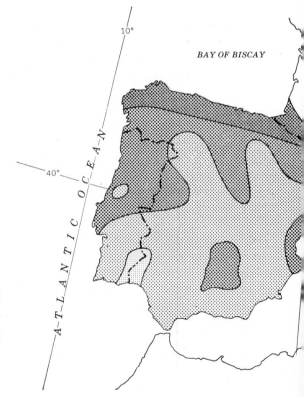

*Figure 8-4  In most parts of the Mediterranean countries the summer season is the period of least rainfall. The Po Valley has more of a continental than a Mediterranean climate, and therefore has a greater rainfall during the summer.*

of the Ebro River, is separated from the Mediterranean Sea by the Catalonian coastal ranges; the other, the plain of Andalusia, drained by the Rio Guadalquivir, opens into the Atlantic through the Gulf of Cadiz. Narrow plains are found along the coast of the peninsula, widest in the west in Portugal and along the Mediterranean shore of eastern Spain. Most of the fertile land of Iberia lies in these lowlands.

## Climate and Vegetation

Iberia is like a miniature continent, for the massive bulk and mountain barriers make the interior an isolated region, very continental, though the sea surrounds it on more than three sides. Latitude, relief, and position with respect to the oceans are responsible for the climatic contrasts found on the peninsula. Because of the direct effects of the westerly winds, especially during the winter months, the climate of Portugal is somewhat moderated. In general, it shows less range of temperature and receives greater amounts of precipitation than does Spain, except along the north and northwestern coasts and in the Pyrenees.

Three types of climate are found in Iberia, marine, Mediterranean, and continental. Although the peninsula is relatively small and the situation seemingly favorable, maritime influences are singularly lacking in the interior, making climatic conditions unexpectedly severe for the latitude and location. Because of the latitude, the Mediterranean pattern of a dry summer and a winter with precipitation holds true. During the latter months, however, the Meseta is dry as compared with most other parts of Spain and Portugal because of local high pressures that form over the plateau. Madrid, most centrally located, averages only 17 inches of precipitation annually, and large areas—about a third of Spain, including portions of the Ebro Valley in the northeast—receive only 12 to 16 inches. Temperatures are likewise more extreme on the plateau than elsewhere, with Madrid, at

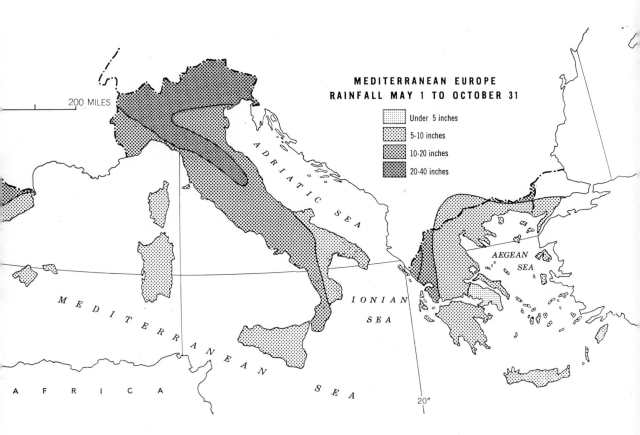

MEDITERRANEAN EUROPE
RAINFALL MAY 1 TO OCTOBER 31

Under 5 inches
5-10 inches
10-20 inches
20-40 inches

200 MILES

ADRIATIC SEA

AEGEAN SEA

IONIAN SEA

MEDITERRANEAN SEA

AFRICA

20°

2,000 feet elevation, averaging 40°F in January, the coldest month, and 77°F in July.

The drought that prevails over the interior is shown in salt flats and treeless steppes, grasslands that are suited to the raising of sheep. In both Old and New Castile, large areas are adapted to the growing of winter wheat, whereas the valleys in the south support Mediterranean vegetation. In the western portion of the plateau, on the borderlands between Spain and Portugal, greater humidity and milder temperatures favor growth of the cork oak, and the region is an important producer of this forest product.

There are two sets of climatic contrast in Iberia, one between the interior and coastal areas, and the other between the east and west coasts. The most marked distinction is found between the northwest (Galicia) and the southeast. In the former area as well as in the mountainous north, a typically marine climate exists, with year-round precipitation, though showing a winter maximum, and with characteristically mild temperatures throughout the year. Mean temperatures range from a low of 45°F, for the coldest month, to not above 70°F, for the warmest month. Precipitation varies from 30 to over 60 inches annually. The result is a rich forest vegetation interspersed with grasslands, and a prosperous agriculture, producing fruits as well as grains. Climatically this is the best part of Spain and, though topographically less favorable than the flatter plateaus and lowlands, it is one of the most progressive. Unfortunately the areal extent of the marine region is small.

Southward along the Atlantic coast from Galicia, the westerly winds continue to moderate temperatures and bring sufficient precipitation so that a view of Portugal presents a land with green and lush vegetation. The dry summer season prevails, but the period of drought is short; rainfall reaches nearly the same amounts as are typical in the lowlands of north-

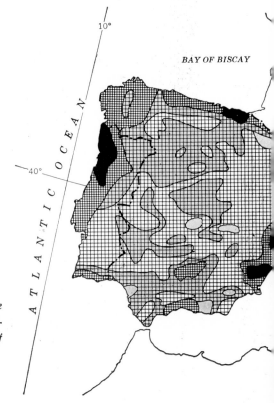

*Figure 8-5  The distribution of population in the Mediterranean area is greatly influenced by the landforms. Notice the greater density along the coast of Italy than in the mountain parts of the country.*

west Spain. For example, Lisbon has more than 29 inches of rain annually.

In southern and eastern Spain, a true Mediterranean climate obtains. Bare hills, maqui-like vegetation, and dry, brown fields characterize these lowlands in summer. Only the gray-green of the drought-resistant olive and the almond, and the green of irrigated crops such as rice, citrus, and sugar cane, break the barren monotony produced by lack of rain.

## Agriculture and Land Use

Iberia is a domain of cultivators and graziers, its culture a product of the land and climate. Land and climate, however, and social conditions which are in part cause and in part result, are not always kind, so that agrarian conditions in Iberia are backward, the levels of living low. Though 45 per cent of the peninsula is cultivated and another 40 per cent grazed, neither Spain nor Portugal is self-sufficient in food. There are several reasons for this. In the first place, methods of cultivation are outmoded. Crude wooden plows prepare the soil for planting. Where irrigation is practiced, the techniques are primitive. Water is generally raised from a well by a mule-driven pump to which is hitched a blindfolded animal, plodding round and round in circular fashion all day long. Seeds are hand-sown, and the grains harvested with hand sickles. The threshing floor, where grains are trodden from the stalks by animals, recalls the methods used in Mediterranean lands during Biblical times.

Most of the farmers till infertile, semiarid soil moistened by rainfall that is erratic in amount, varying at times as much as 50 per cent from one year to the next. The inability to depend upon precipitation means that anticipated yields can never be counted upon. Seriously inadequate supplies of nitrogen fertilizer help keep the gross output unnecessarily low. While it is possible for Iberia to be largely self-sufficient, this goal cannot be reached and main-

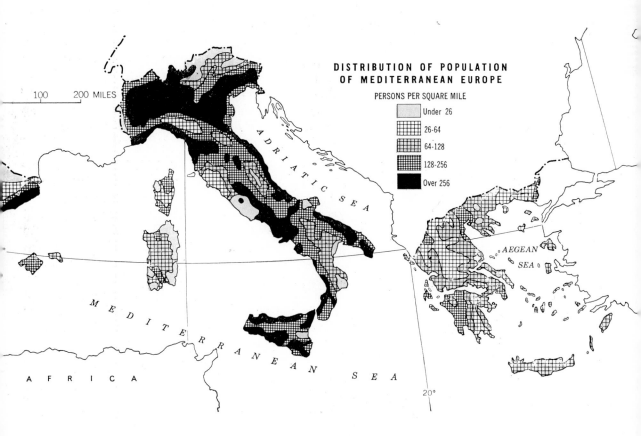

DISTRIBUTION OF POPULATION
OF MEDITERRANEAN EUROPE

PERSONS PER SQUARE MILE

Under 26
26-64
64-128
128-256
Over 256

*Figure 8-6 For a thousand years the Mediterranean peasant and his ancestors, practicing a type of horticulture agriculture that is more akin to manicuring the soil than cultivating it, have been sustained on the patiently terraced slopes and carefully fertilized and irrigated fields. The prickly pear in the foreground and the scrubby maqui on the untilled hillsides in the background are typical vegetation types in the Mediterranean lands. This is a view of terraced fields on Majorca. (Photograph by Burton Holmes, Ewing Galloway.)*

tained until at least double the present volume of fertilizer is put on the land annually. Small crops almost invariably mean poverty and little surplus capital for improvements. These conditions lead to social and often political unrest as evidenced in Spain during the past two decades.

These difficulties are intensified by the system of land tenure. Large estates prevail, especially in the south. Owned generally by absentee landlords, the estates are worked by peasants. They reside in villages and go out each morning from the villages to the fields, traveling on foot or, for those who can afford them, in carts drawn slowly by oxen or mules for distances of as much as five miles. The time consumed in going to and from the fields makes

working hours short. This loss of time, combined with backward techniques of cultivation and climatic handicaps, results in poor crops; an oversupply of laborers keeps wages low and causes unemployment. Even where most of the land is owned by the peasant himself, holdings generally are barely large enough to support a family at even a meager subsistence level.

The pressure of people upon the land is not apparent from statistics, for the density per square mile averages but from 150 in Spain to 249 in Portugal. For the present level of Iberian agricultural technology, however, population pressure is excessive.

Livestock is important in the economies of Iberia. In the humid marine north, dairy cattle and beef animals feed in the mountain pastures; besides those kept in pens, droves of pigs roust about the oak forests of the western plateau, fattening on the acorns; several million goats scramble among the maqui in the rough and scrubby landscape of the Mediterranean sections; oxen, and even cows, as well as horses, donkeys, and mules, draw carts and work in the fields. As in almost all Mediterranean lands, the little donkey is one of the most familiar sights. Always he seems to be burdened beyond his size and strength with carts too heavily loaded or carrying on his back a human whose feet almost touch the ground. Nor does he receive very gentle treatment or care. Although cultivation is infringing on their steppe lands, 24 million sheep are found throughout the peninsula, spreading from north to south. Mainly of the Merino type, they are superior for their wool.

Northern and northwestern Iberia is a wheat-corn country. The humid climate makes possible the growing of maize, not found elsewhere on the peninsula. Apple trees are scattered about the pastures, and potatoes and rye are raised. The Meseta is a sheep and wheat country with a scattering of other crops. Wheat is grown in all parts of the plateau but most extensively on the Meseta to the north of the dividing ranges. It is the principal agricultural crop of both Spain and Portugal, these countries together raising more than Italy and almost equaling the production of France. Yields per acre are low, however, compared with those of most European countries. Barley is produced in the more marginal areas of the upland to the east of the major wheat lands and in the south, where better than average grazing conditions exist but where soil and rainfall are not suited to the growing of the preferred grain, wheat.

*Figure 8-7   Cork trees. This hardy oak tolerates the stripping of its bark every ten years or so. A newly stripped cork forest presents a striking effect, for the inner bark is red in color, making the trees stand in stark contrast to the green of the surrounding grasslands. (Ewing Galloway.)*

The cultivation of the Mediterranean sections approaches horticulture. Rice, grown under irrigation on some of the rich river lands, is a specialized crop. Though limited in area, the yields per acre are among the highest in the world, European Spain frequently exceeding even the famed rice lands of the Asiatic Far East.

The olive tree is almost coextensive with Mediterranean Iberia. Only in the north, northwest, and parts of the Meseta where rainfall and altitude make the climate unsuitable, does the olive tree disappear. Most of the fruit is pressed for its oil, this being the most usual cooking fat for the people of the peninsula. In Spain, however, a considerable quantity is pickled. Table olives are the leading Spanish export to the United States. In Portugal a large share of the oil is used by the sardine-canning industry.

Although grapes are grown over much of Spain and Portugal, the cultivation of the vine is especially important along the sheltered sides of the river valleys, growing on terraces that cover the slopes. Certain localities have become famous for their products of the vine. Among these are the port wine of the Portuguese Douro —named after Oporto (Porto), the city located at the mouth of the river—the sherry of Andalusia, and the table grapes of Almeria. Wine is a leading export from both Spain and Portugal.

It was the Moors who brought the orange to the peninsula and introduced it to Iberian culture. Although citrus fruit is grown all around the southern periphery, it attains the greatest importance in the vicinity of Valencia. Spanish oranges find their market in Northern Europe. Almonds, raised in the south, are becoming an increasingly important item in the export trade.

Portugal is the world's foremost producer of cork, normally supplying about 50 per cent of the cork exports moving into international trade. The major producing area in Iberia is located on the western border of the plateau, in the boundary region between the two countries.

## Fisheries

Fishing nets wreathe the Atlantic coast of the Iberian Peninsula, for the coastal waters off Western Europe are alive with fish. One of the most important sources of national wealth, the fishing industry of Portugal takes in three main fields of activity. The coastal fishery, of which sardines are by far the most important variety taken, also includes catches of tuna, anchovies, mackerel, and chinchards. Trawl fishing on the high seas for such species as whiting, pargo, and sea bream is mainly off the coast of Africa. Cod fishing, by a large modern fleet of Portuguese schooners and trawlers, is carried on in

*Figure 8-8 Fishermen at Nazare, Portugal, mending their nets. (Courtesy of Portuguese Embassy.)*

the Newfoundland Grand Banks and off the west coast of Greenland. Of lesser importance is the whaling carried on off the coast south of Lisbon and in the Azores.

Fishing is vital to Portugal both as a source of food and raw material for a large canning industry. Tinned sardines and tunny are important in the list of exports from the small country. Portuguese sardines are found in markets all over the world. The little fishing villages that send their men out to sea are no less colorful than the fishermen themselves in their traditional wool caps and striped sweaters. The sailing galleys resemble those of the early Phoenicians.

Hardy though the Portuguese fishermen are, the Basques and Galicians of northern Spain, who are famous for their fishing, are the only real seafarers of that country. A spare, mountainous land with many sheltering harbors and a sea rich in fish encouraged them to take to the water. In fair weather or foul, Basque and Galician fishermen set out in their ketch-rigged boats to take the sardines, tuna, and other fish found in the coastal waters. Vigo, La Coruña, and Berneo are the leading fishing ports in Spain.

## Minerals

Iberia has notable mineral resources, most of them concentrated in Spain (Figure 8-9). The famous Rio Tinto deposits of the southwest have been mined for their copper since 1240 B.C. Huelva is the main outlet for these ores. Deposits of lead and silver exist. In the north between Santander and Bilbao is one of Europe's important iron reserves. Exported in considerable quantity, largely to Great Britain and Germany, it is also the basis for a small Spanish iron and steel industry. Coal is found in the northwest and is important for Spain. The deposits could support an expansion of iron smelting and fabrication. At present, the Spanish steel mills generally use imported coal. Mercury is secured from the Almaden mines in south central Spain, and smaller deposits occur in several other regions. Sulfur, potash, and several of the alloy metals are also produced. Although min-

ing has been carried on for centuries, although the variety of Spanish minerals is large and the deposits substantial, the industry is still in its infancy.

Mining is a traditional activity in Portugal, yet the exploitation of mineral resources is relatively unimportant, and exploration and mapping of the deposits far from complete. Portugal does produce small quantities of coal, iron, kaolin, tungsten, lead, and manganese.

## Industry

Manufacturing is not well developed in Iberia. There are, however, three areas of industrial concentration in Spain. One is in Barcelona, the center of a textile industry that was originally based on wool from the Meseta. There is an area of heavy industry around Bilbao. At Madrid, there is a center of diversified manufacturing. Compared with the manufactures of northwest Europe, these are still small. Copper refining, food processing, some shipbuilding at Bilbao and at Barcelona, cotton textiles, a little silk manufacturing, some leather work, wine production, and handicrafts almost complete the list of Spanish manufactures. A recent development has been that of the chemical industries, particularly the production of nitrogenous fertilizer and superphosphates. Spain has latent possibilities for manufacturing. These include not only the resources noted but also water power, in which the country is estimated to have a greater potential than either Switzerland or Sweden.

Food processing, including fish canning, sugar refining, flour milling, and the production of olive oil is an important part of Portuguese manufacture. Lisbon (Lisboa) is the center of a textile industry. Handicrafts, such as embroideries, and the making of wine are widespread, the latter especially notable in the Douro River valley.

## Trade and Transportation

Iberia imports more than it exports. Foodstuffs, raw materials, machinery, and consumer goods are the major imports of both countries. Spain likewise brings in large quantities of nitrogenous fertilizer and phosphate rock for agricultural purposes. Among the exports of Portugal, cork, both in the raw and manufactured form, leads, normally accounting for one-sixth of the total export value. Wine and sardines rank next. Portugal is also an important producer of naval stores and ranks second, though far behind the United States, in the export of rosin and turpentine. The economy of Spain relies heavily on foreign trade, and Spain's exports are ten times as great as those of Portugal.

Though the railroad systems of Spain and Portugal connect with each other, transportation is inadequate and not up to modern standards in either country. Roads have been improved and extended, and commercial air transport has steadily increased since World War II. Because of their geographical position, Lisbon and the Azores are of great importance in international air commerce, Lisbon serving as a major European air terminal and transit point. Fifteen foreign lines, including two

American, make regularly scheduled stops in that city. The Azores airport on Santa Maria Island is a stopover on mid-Atlantic crossings.

*Towns and Cities*

Iberia is a land of many small agglomerations. Along the coasts of Portugal and the Bay of Biscay, numerous picturesque fishing villages can be seen. Nets, stretched for drying and repairing, fish-drying racks, and many small fishing craft, bobbing with the waves, dominate the scene. On the Meseta, as well as elsewhere in the interior, the agricultural villages are scattered about the landscape. Often dull in appearance, and frequently some distance from good highways, the villages reflect the economic condition of their inhabitants.

Madrid and Barcelona are the two largest cities of Spain, each having a population of over a million persons. Madrid owes its size and importance to the fact that it is the political center of the nation. Located on the Meseta in a

*Figure 8-9 The mineral resources of Mediterranean Europe are diversified but generally inadequate for the development of any great industry. This map indicates reserves rather than production. Of the four Mediterranean countries, Spain comes out best, being relatively rich in minerals. Greece has sufficient reserves to meet many of its domestic requirements.*

relatively barren area, the city is handicapped by an inadequate water supply. In spite of the disadvantages, Madrid has become a modern city and has many small industries. Barcelona is the chief industrial center and port for the country. Situated on a good harbor, and in one of the best agricultural areas in Europe, the city has a favorable location for import-export trade. Large textile manufactures—cotton, linen, and wool—have been developed.

Valencia and Seville (Sevilla) are the third and fourth largest cities respectively. Each is an old, historic city located in an irrigated area and surrounded by citrus orchards and gardens. Here, notable churches, narrow streets, historic walls, and ancient buildings are of interest to the numerous tourists. Various industries have also been established.

Bilbao, the principal northern port, lies in a valley surrounded by high and fairly steep hills. Railroads enter the city through tunnels. Nearby iron mines supply the chief item of export.

Modern steel mills, fired by imported coal, are among the heavy industries to be developed in this land of the Basque.

Lisbon and Oporto are the principal urban centers in Portugal. Lisbon, the capital, is one of the principal commercial centers of the world. The city, having the best harbor on the Iberian Peninsula, is important as a center for transshipping and entrepôt activities. Most of its manufactures are consumer goods. Lisbon is also an important tourist center. Oporto, the second city and second port, is noted chiefly for its wines, although the city manufactures numerous other items.

## Overseas Territories

The overseas possessions of Portugal are twenty-three times greater than the mother country, and are, in fact, the fourth largest colonial holdings in the world. Only those of Britain, France, and Belgium are greater. The more important of the territories are Mozambique and Angola in

MINERALS OF MEDITERRANEAN EUROPE

Coal    Tungsten
I Iron    Mercury
Lignite    S Sulfur
Copper    Silver
Z Zinc    Marble
Lead    K Potash
Emery    Salt
Chromium    Bauxite

*Figure 8-10   A typical Mediterranean landscape would include a small town or villa perched on a hill, the gray houses blending so indiscernibly with the gray soil that the buildings seem carved from the eminence. Orchards of citrus and particularly olives and vines cover most of the hills from top to bottom. (Ewing Galloway.)*

Africa. Of her once vast holdings in the Far East, only part of the East Indian island of Timor, Portuguese India (Goa, Damao, and Diu) and Macao in China remain. The population of the colonies exceeds that of Portugal, approximating 20 million as compared with the 8.5 millions for the European nation. Many people besides the Portuguese speak the Portuguese tongue. It is the official language not only throughout the colonial territories but also in Brazil, a former colony, where 55 million people show this former tie with the little Iberian state.

The colonies of Spain, only one-sixth the size of those of Portugal, are inconsiderable as compared with those of her small neighbor. What remains of a world-wide empire is found scattered along the coast of Africa from the northwest to the Gulf of Guinea. The total population is small and, except for the island of Fernando Po, which exports cacao, their trade is insignificant.

## ITALY

Overpopulation and underproduction are the foremost problems facing Italy today. Until just after World War I, the pressure generated by too many people on too little land was partially relieved through emigration. Though the total number of persons departing for other countries is still large, proportionately it is not great enough. Emigrants equal only one-fourth of the annual population increase. The demand for social and economic betterment has become so insistent that the government has been forced to do something about land reform.

Italy, 116,290 square miles in area, is about the same size as the state of New Mexico. On this constricted space live 47 million people. Half of these derive their living from the land, a land that is but 21 per cent plains, 79 per cent being either mountainous or hilly. For centuries, the farmers have been making things grow in the valleys and on the mountainsides. The time comes, however, when even the most intensively worked soil is incapable of supporting more people. With an average density of 390 per square mile, Italy is one of the most heavily populated countries in the world.

Though the Italian feels he should own the land he works, only 38 per cent do own their own farms. Of the rest, more than 12 per cent rent the land they till, 19.5 per cent are sharecroppers, 23 per cent are farmhands who work on a day-to-day or year-to-year basis. The greatest ferment is found in the south, but a deep unrest also exists among the northern workers in the rice fields. Land reform must proceed on three lines: redistribution of land now held by large estates in the south; consolidation of small holdings; technical guidance and, above all, the general elevation of the educational level of the peasants.

Under the redistribution plan, land will be expropriated from the large estates of southern Italy and divided among the peasants. It is significant that the area of concentrated land ownership, the south, is the most depressed in Italy. Yet here, where holdings may run over a million acres in size, where population pressures are greatest and Italian peasants poorest, landlords allow their holdings to lie fallow much of the time. This may occur because owners are unable or unwilling to invest the amounts necessary to develop their estates.

The second problem to be faced is that of the consolidation of holdings. In many areas, the land for miles around the villages has been divided and subdivided for hundreds of years; frequently, a farmer owns as many as a dozen pieces, each a fraction of an acre in size, in different localities. Consolidation can take place only gradually. In places it may not work at all because of the close attachment that the peasants have for their particular pieces of land which, for successive generations, their families have cultivated.

Low standards of living, stemming from inefficient utilization of resources that long have been outstripped by a rapidly increasing population, testify to the need for changes in the structure of Italian agriculture, particularly in the more backward south. Emigration from the farms has overcrowded the cities also, so that conditions among urban laborers, particularly from Naples southward, are no better than among rural workers.

## Physical Setting

**Regions.** Italy falls into four natural regions with apparent simplicity. To the north is the alpine border where the boundary in general follows the crest line. Though the Alps Mountains seem to isolate Italy from the rest of the Continent, the Italian ranges actually provide the natural transit zone between continental Europe and the Mediterranean. In early days passes, like the Simplon, Great and Little St. Bernard, St. Gotthard, and Brenner, situated at the heads of valleys, permitted ranges to be crossed in spite of ice and snow. Today, railroads and tunnels have almost eliminated the Alps as a barrier.

A number of long narrow lakes are interspersed along the frontal zone where the mountains drop to the plains. Occupying valleys deepened by the action of glacial ice and dammed by terminal moraines that impounded the waters, the lakes are of great economic significance to Italy for the development of power and irrigation, especially for the agricultural and industrial Po Valley. The Italian lake district is milder than the plains below for it lies on the warm, sunny south-facing slopes. Foehn winds that descend from the higher Alps also have a tempering effect. This region is, therefore, famous as a winter and tourist resort.

The Po Valley is the northern end of the Adriatic depression that has been filled with alluvium carried down the mountainsides by tributaries of the Po and other streams. An actively building delta is extending the plain still farther toward the east, noticeably encroaching upon the quiet waters of the sea. Fertile soil and level land, combined with a favorable climate and water for irrigation, render this one of the great agricultural plains of the world. Though the political center lies to the south in Rome (Roma), the economic core is focalized on these plains in the north.

The Apennine Mountains, traversing the narrow peninsula, with Sicily constitute the third natural region. The surface configuration is one of a central folded mountain backbone bordered by marginal plains. A zone of active and quiescent volcanoes extends along the western coast from Rome southward through Sicily. In the north, the Apennines are considerably lower than the Maritime Alps with which they merge. Farther south, however, the peninsular ranges become higher and more rugged, with elevations in the central portions reaching over 9,500 feet. As a whole, the Apennine country is difficult of access. Railroads are few and have been costly to construct. Paved highways, built during the Fascist regime, cross the mountains to connect major cities. Though excellent, they are narrow and breathtaking, with many curves.

Slowly and transitionally, geology and geography change the mountain scene from north to south. Where the northern Apennines meet the Mediterranean along the Ligurian coast, steep slopes rise high and shut out the cold winds from the north. Here a narrow strip of land, known as the Italian Riviera, edges the sea. As a resort center, it is a close competitor with the Riviera in France, just across the border.

From the northern mountains, that are relatively green and well covered with trees, with distance southward the hills become barer, the soil grayer, the olive more prominent. Throughout, vines climb hills from base to summit, or run on trellises between trees on the plains. Close-ups in the bordering lowlands reveal hedges of big-lobed cacti growing beside low stone walls, pastel houses—yellow, blue, green, pink—making picture-like compositions in their carefully tended settings, and white oxen, along with other beasts of burden, drawing plows, preparing the land for cropping or fallowing.

The Apennines, with their jutting spurs and foothills, occupy most of the peninsula, leaving few plains. Of importance, however, are the three fertile but isolated lowlands along the western shore, each centered by a commanding city. First, there is Tuscany in the valley of the Arno with Florence (Firenze), the art center of all Italy, and in a strategic position at a major pass through the Apennines. Then there is Lazio in the Tiber Valley focusing on the ancient city of Rome (Roma). Third is Campania, to the south, spread around the beautiful Bay of Naples (Napoli), on which the great port city of the same name is situated. The lowlands of the east are of lesser importance than those of the west, though the largest of the peninsular plains is found here, occupying the heel of the boot of Italy and extending northward along the shore to the Gargano Peninsula. Other areas of level land are small and separated from each other by projections of rough country.

As a result of poor drainage, swamps have infested the plains with malaria so that their development has been retarded. Though an extensive drainage and disease-extermination program was begun under Mussolini, it was not until World War II that malaria was appreciably brought under control by the systematic use of DDT by American troops. More was done to eradicate malaria at this time than at any previous period. There is much land still to be reclaimed, however, and malaria is by no means conquered.

**Climate.** Except for the Po Valley and in the rain shadow of the Apennines, the climate of Italy is true Mediterranean. Summers are hot and dry with blindingly brilliant sunshine; winters mild and rainy but having a prevalence of blue and cloudless skies. The Po Valley, on the other hand, is modified continental, which means that precipitation falls the year round but has a summer maximum, and that the seasonal range of temperature is marked. A comparison of temperature and rainfall statistics brings out the contrasts between peninsular Italy and the

Po Basin. Beginning in the south at Palermo temperatures range from a monthly January mean of 50.0°F, to 76.3° in July, decreasing to 46.8° and 75.6° respectively at Naples to the 34.4° and 74.8° of Milan. More than 50 per cent of the precipitation of Milan falls during the six summer months, April to September; less than one-third of that of Naples and one-fourth that of Palermo falls during the same period.

## Agriculture

Twenty-five per cent of the cultivated land is planted in wheat, a crop of particular importance in Italian agriculture. Grown throughout all of Italy, this typically Mediterranean grain is produced most heavily in the Po Basin, the bread basket of the country. This region is dominated by cereals, with wheat leading and corn ranking second in importance. The upper valley of the Po, with alpine streams providing water for irrigation, is the center of rice production. Grapes for wine are prominent as well as the two industrial crops of sugar beets and hemp. The olive, scattered throughout most of Italy, is not found in the north where cold winters inhibit its growth.

Stock raising and dairying are better developed in the north than elsewhere and a high proportion of the land is in improved pasture and fodder crops. These extend into the mountains, where agriculture takes on an alpine character. In favorable parts of the northern foothills wheat is grown, but in general rye replaces the wheat, corn, and rice of the lowlands. Potatoes are also a major crop and grapes are important in most parts of Italy.

Mediterranean Italy is characterized by two types of agriculture that might be classed as horticultural or nonhorticultural, depending on the intensity of the cultivation and the variety of crops raised. In the former type, intensive methods of land use, including irrigation, terracing, high fertilization, and triple-cropping, produce fruits and vegetables in a garden type of agriculture. Here grapes attain their highest perfection. Olives are especially important in the heel of the boot in southern Italy. Lemons,

oranges, and peaches, along with some vegetables, move from these lands of intensive husbandry into the markets of northern Europe. Sicily is the center of citrus production, especially lemons, though lemon culture extends along the western side of the peninsula to Naples, and oranges grow almost as far north as Rome. In the Mediterranean regions where the less intensive type of agriculture is practiced, five crops predominate, wheat, oats, grapes, olives, and beans. Few cattle are reared in the Mediterranean lands where, because of sparse and poor grasses, sheep and goats typically replace the larger animals.

Sardinia, though a part of Italy, is remote from the rest of Italian life. Rugged, deforested, and eroded, it is a spare land. Although Sardinia produces famous wines and cork and has some areas of intensive cultivation, it is principally a pastoral land. Animals, especially sheep, are grazed on the plateau and mountain country which occupies seven-tenths of the island. The inhabitants are known for their hardy endurance and interest in livestock.

## Resources and Industry

Italy, being geologically young, is naturally poor in mineral resources. Though there are small deposits and a limited production of zinc, lead, iron, and coal, only in mercury, sulfur, and marble is the Italian supply adequate. Lacking coal, except for some small deposits on Sardinia, Italy must import this fuel or substitute others. The country has a large water power potential; that, however, is almost entirely confined to the northern area, where the mountain streams from the Alps supply the power. An interesting development, and one with great promise, is the generation of thermoelectricity produced by tapping the live steam from volcanoes. It is looked upon as a cheap and probably permanent source of energy.

Because of American competition, Italy (Sicily), which formerly held a near monopoly in sulfur, today supplies but 4 per cent of this chemical. The country still ranks as a major world producer of mercury. Loss of Istria to Yugoslavia meant the forfeiture of most of Italy's bauxite deposits and also deprived the country of its former quarries of white sand. Vital to the glass industry, the sands must now be imported from France, Belgium, and the Netherlands.

Possessing only hydroelectric and thermoelectric power and skilled, cheap labor as assets, and lacking the mineral and vegetable resources that are requisite for a major development in manufacturing, Italy has nevertheless established some important industries. Italian heavy industry equals that of the Saar. The metallurgical industries produce such items as automo-

biles, motorboats, roller bearings, sewing and calculating machines, and typewriters. Textiles, produced from the natural fibers of silk, cotton, and wool as well as the synthetics, are important. Textile industries are centered in Milan (Milano), the second largest city and the most important industrial center in Italy. Mechanical products are predominant in the western portion of the Po Valley, in and around Turin (Torino). Food processing, including flour milling, pasta manufacture, sugar refining, and the packaging and canning of other food items, is carried on throughout the country. Chemi-

cals, of which sulfuric acid is the most important, are produced.

In recent years the volume of industrial output has been more than 36 per cent higher than during the prewar period. This has meant jobs for a portion of the excess population. The greater number of Italian manufacturing concerns are small, and handicrafts are a vital part of the industrial economy of the country. Among these, glassmaking ranks high. Large plants concentrate on the manufacture of commercial products having a wide market, such as flat glass, 35 per cent of the total glass output, bottles and other containers, and inexpensive glassware. Most of the artistic and ornamental glass products are produced in many small factories where the artisan adds his individual touch to each piece. Some of the small establishments are internationally known. Other handicraft industries include weaving with straw, raffia, and linen, lacemaking, jewelry production, and cameo carving. Though the number of small establishments far exceeds that of the large manufacturing plants, huge state-owned and private monopolistic corporations dominate every major field of production.

*Figure 8-11   The valleys of northern Italy are intensively farmed. The headwaters of the river shown in this picture are in the Alps. The river is a tributary of the Po.*

Tourism, bringing in several million dollars of income annually, is an industry important to the economy of Italy. Rome, the largest city and capital of the country, is the goal of the thousands of tourists each year who visit Vatican City. Situated on both sides of the Tiber River, the city has a central position on the western side of the peninsula. Well known for its religious and historic associations, its art treasures, and its numerous educational institutions, the city is second only to Milan in industrial activity. Venice (Venezia), Florence, Leghorn (Livorno), and Pisa are also tourist centers, each with its special historical attraction. The lovely lakes that penetrate the Alps in northern Italy, the jagged Dolomite peaks, and volcanoes like Vesuvius and Etna are among the scenic attractions. Many tourists enjoy the blue ocean waters and coastal features of the Italian Riviera and the Bay of Naples.

### Transportation

The Italian state-owned railroads connect all major centers. Schedules are convenient. Six ferryboats are employed for the railway crossing of the Strait of Messina between the peninsula and Sicily. These boats transport up to 1,500 railroad cars daily so that the water barrier between the island and mainland is no longer a bottleneck to traffic.

Highways between the largest cities are paved and in good condition. Passenger bus service is excellent even when compared with that of the United States. Since 1948 both trucking and air transport have shown a marked increase.

According to tonnage, Italy occupies sixth place among the maritime nations of the world. Although commercial shipping was almost totally destroyed during World War II, it has made a remarkable recovery in the postwar period. Italians have drawn sunken vessels from the bottom of the sea, reconditioned ships returned by the Allies, and built and bought new tonnage. As a result the Italian merchant marine has been brought up to about 90 per cent of its prewar level. Income from its shipping partly supplies Italy with funds to help overcome its unfavorable balance of trade. The construction and operation of fine, large ocean liners provides employment and helps attract tourists to the country.

Genoa (Genova) is the principal port of Italy and the second port of the Mediterranean, ranking next after Marseilles. Because of its excellent modern harbor, Genoa serves as an outlet for the industries of the Po Valley and some of the countries of Central Europe. Naples, the second seaport in importance, is the third largest city in the country. Because of the numerous tourist attractions nearby, including the ancient ruins of Pompeii at the base of Vesuvius, the city is an important passenger port. Both Genoa

Figure 8-12   A team of white oxen drawing a modern binder in an Italian wheat field. Oxen—white in Italy, brown or black in Iberia and Greece —are the most usual beasts of burden used for field work. The white oxen of Italy are particularly striking in appearance. At times as many as six will be hitched to one plow. (Ewing Galloway.)

and Naples are old cities, each having many narrow streets connected by steep stairways in its older sections. Both also have modern shipyards and many manufacturing establishments.

## Postwar Italy

Following World War II, the Italian overseas possessions were taken away so that the territory of the country is today confined to the peninsula and the two large islands of Sicily and Sardinia. Of the large but economically unimportant holdings in North Africa—Libya, Eritrea, and Somalia—only the last remains to Italy as a United Nations trusteeship which is scheduled to end in 1960, when Somalia will become independent. The port of Trieste remains with Italy, but adjacent Istria has become a part of Yugoslavia as well as the Dalmatian coastal islands of Cherso, Lussino, and Lagosta, and the city of Zara on the mainland, all formerly Italian territory. Most of the Italians in these places were repatriated to Italy. To Albania went the island of Saseno, small but strategic, in the narrows that control the entrance to the Adriatic Sea; to the Greeks, the Dodecanese Islands in the Aegean and to China, Italy's former concession in Tientsin (T'ienching).

## GREECE

Greece is located at the tip of the Balkan Peninsula. Washed on three sides by seas and indented by many inlets and bays, it has one of the longest coast lines in Europe. Across the northern frontier lie Albania, Yugoslavia, Bulgaria, and on the northeast, Turkey.

### Physical Setting

A rugged mountain country, with four-fifths of the area made up of mountain chains and spurs, it is probably the most barren and sterile among the Mediterranean lands. The Pindus, a series of long continuous ranges, extend southeast through central Greece. East of the Pindus the topography is one of basins separated by southeast- and eastward-trending spurs. The principal plains are in the eastern portions and in central and western Macedonia.

Northern Greece is very mountainous, the central section less so. Here are located Athens (Athenai) and Peiraeus (Peiraievs), the main seaport. To the south lies the Peloponnesus. It is separated from the mainland by the Corinth Canal which was cut through a narrow isthmus to sever the former peninsula from the Continent. The many islands in the bordering seas make up nearly one-sixth of the total area of Greece.

The Mediterranean climate predominates throughout Greece, though the situation relative to prevailing winds, altitude, and continental location causes differences from place to place. The south and east are drier and warmer, generally, than the north and west. The lowlands are warmer and have less rain than the uplands. Corfu, for example, off the extreme northwestern tip of Greece, has 49.7 inches of well-distributed annual rainfall whereas Athens, in the southeast, averages 15.5 inches and shows a marked summer dry period. Salonika (Thessalonikē), on the other hand, receives 21.5 inches of precipitation fairly well distributed throughout the year, though the three summer months get somewhat less than the others. Large parts of Greece have averages that correspond to those of Athens.

### Problems of Land and Population

On an area about the size of North Carolina live 7.7 million people trying to eke a living from the land. Although only 15 per cent of Greece is cultivated, more than 60 per cent of the population are classed as rural. As in Italy, overpopulation and underemployment are the foremost domestic problems. The per capita income is one of the lowest in Europe while, at the same time, living costs are phenomenally high.

Other difficulties face Greece. Mountain barriers isolate one small plains region from another, particularly in the southern part of the country. Of the cultivated area, more than 60 per cent is over 750 feet above sea level with the result that most of the land is steep, rocky, and cut by gullies. The holdings of the Greek farmer are small and fragmented. On well-drained plains, the land is frequently divided into many small units, each peasant holding several of these plots scattered throughout the cultivated area. Although fertile, the lower lands are generally poorly drained.

American economic aid has done much to help the Greeks with problems of land reclamation, drainage, erosion, flood control, irrigation, and soil conservation. Spectacular results have been attained in the reclamation of alkali lands through rice production. Thousands of acres of such areas, which have been considered useless since before the time of Christ, are being sweetened by the steady flow of fresh river water poured in to irrigate the grain. It is expected that within a few years the soils will be sufficiently cleansed to permit the raising of other crops such as wheat and cotton. Since Greece is a large importer of rice, the rice produced on these reclamation projects should meet its needs. Many swamps and lakes have been drained and large areas provided, for the first time, with irrigation through the drilling of new wells and the channeling of rivers which

for centuries drained off unused into the seas.

By constructing a series of new power plants Greece, for the first time in its history, is able to produce electricity from its own resources of water and lignite. Previously, oil had to be imported for this. Mines, not operated in years, have been reopened. Industrial loans have stimulated manufacturing. As in Italy, the spraying of thousands of acres of swampland with insecticide has reduced malaria.

## Agriculture

Agriculture remains the backbone of the Greek economy. The main crops, produced in valleys that nestle between or among mountains, are tobacco, wheat, grapes, and olives.

Tobacco, making up 50 to 60 per cent of the Greek exports, provides Greece with its leading trade item. In spite of its importance the growing of tobacco is on a modest scale. Farms are small and the soils in the tobacco area probably the poorest of the cultivated lands in Greece. Greek tobacco is classed as Oriental. Interestingly enough, the major areas of tobacco production, Macedonia and Thrace, are those that were settled by Greeks repatriated, between 1907 and 1928, from Turkey where they had learned the skill of growing this demanding

*Figure 8-13 Macedonian girls weeding the rice fields on reclaimed land. They must wade in the water, being careful not to injure the tender rice stalks. (Courtesy of Mutual Security Agency.)*

*Figure 8-14 Threshing wheat on Syra Island, Greece. Greek farmers are as primitive in their methods as were those of 500 B.C. Notice the barren landscape and the prevalence of rock fences and buildings. (Ewing Galloway.)*

crop. It is used generally as a blend because of the distinctive aroma. The Oriental tobacco produced in Greece is the highest quality grown in the world. Thirteen and a half per cent of the total value of Greek agricultural products is represented by tobacco.

Cereals, including wheat, corn, barley, oats, and rice, are the most basic and widespread of all crops. Potatoes, pulses, olives, fruits including citrus fruit and grapes, nuts, and cotton also rank high. As in other Mediterranean lands, the vine is extensively cultivated and provides a money crop, many of the Greek grapes being dried and exported as currants and raisins. Together they make up nearly 15 per cent of the export value.

Greece occupies third place in the production of olive oil. Though slow in growth, requiring fifteen to twenty years to mature, the olive is a sturdy plant that lives and produces for centuries. Spreading from Albania southward through the Peloponnesus and north to the Macedonian coast, olive culture extends eastward to within 50 miles of the Dardanelles. Olive and other oils make up 6 per cent of Greek exports and rank third in export value.

### Resources and Industry

**Minerals.**   Beneath the bare and rocky hills of Greece are minerals which, if properly developed, can contribute much toward national solvency and prosperity. Although not rich in natural resources as compared with many countries, minerals are one of the few assets that Greece possesses. Fourteen basic minerals, in quantities and qualities worth mining, are known to exist. They include, among others, iron, lead, zinc, lignite, magnesite, chromite, manganese, bauxite, and emery.

One resource, virtually untouched until recent years, is lignite, the single most important development in the mining field. The largest reserve is that of the Ptolemais field in Macedonia, about 26 miles from the Yugoslav border. These lignite mines have been termed the fuel bin of the nation. Another significant undertaking has been the revival of the extraction of chromite at Domokos in central Greece.

Near Lavrion, at the tip of the peninsula of Attica, important deposits of zinc and lead, yielding by-products of silver and iron pyrites, are being worked. This is the site of the famous silver mines that, over two thousand years ago, supplied Athens with wealth. In the fifth century B.C., the tragedian, Aeschylus, described the mines as a "fountain running with silver, a treasure of the land." North and south of the city are located the two mountains, Pentelicus and Hymettus, from which were quarried the marble for the Greek buildings and statues.

Though Greek rehabilitation has been slow, industry produces electricity, textiles, metals (bauxite and copper manufactures), chemicals, foodstuffs and brewed goods, cigarettes, and leather. The Athens-Piraeus district is the major industrial area.

**Fisheries.**  One of the major occupations in Greece, and probably one of the most ancient, is fishing, though the Mediterranean Sea falls short of some of the requirements of a great fishing ground. A specialty in the warm waters of the Aegean and along the African coast of the eastern Mediterranean is sponge gathering. Greeks bring up 80 per cent of the Mediterranean take and, before World War II, supplied over 50 per cent of the world's sponges. The boats go out in fleets of ten or twelve vessels, fish for the first few weeks in Greek waters and then move on to the sponge fields along the African shores of Libya and Tunisia. With the aid of American funds, about 100 sponge-fishing vessels have been assembled and supplied with diving equipment so that this industry is well on the road to recovery.

*Transportation*

The Greeks are called the carriers of the Mediterranean. Their merchant marine, ranking eighth in the world, is equal to prewar proportions. Greek-owned ships sail not only under the flag of the mother country but also under those of a number of foreign nations—Panama, Canada, Honduras, South Africa, Britain, the United States, Sweden, and Israel.

Because the topography is so rugged, coastwise shipping constitutes a major form of transport. Many passenger and cargo vessels are thus engaged in coastwise and interisland shipping. There are no navigable rivers in Greece al-

*Figure 8-15 Sheep grazing among the olive trees, a typical rural scene on the Greek island of Corfu. The island is covered with olive groves and dark cypress trees. (Ewing Galloway.)*

though, during high water, short stretches of some of the larger rivers, such as the Vardar, may be used by flat-bottomed craft.

Greece has approximately 1,700 miles of railroads. Because of the increasing importance of trucking, the railways now transport about one-fourth less tonnage than previously. Air transport is gaining in importance. Besides two Greek lines, the planes of seventeen international companies make scheduled stops at the Ellenikon airport at Athens.

Greece is not a country of large cities. Rough topography, poor highways, and adverse economic conditions make for small and sometimes isolated settlements. Athens is the political, economic, and cultural center of the country. One of the oldest cities in the world,

established before 1000 B.C., Athens has long been noted for its historic buildings and the early development of democratic forms of government. Modern Athens and Piraeus, the leading seaport of Greece, form a continuously built-up urban area. Within them are located over 60 per cent of the country's industrial facilities. Modern trolley and bus lines connect this port area of Piraeus with the commercial center of Athens.

Salonika (Thessalonikē), at the entrance to the Vardar Valley, is the second largest city and the second port of Greece. Like Athens, it is a very old city, having been founded about 315 B.C. Salonika is the principal commercial, industrial, and transportation center for the Macedonian area.

## TINY MEDITERRANEAN COUNTRIES

Four very small independent countries—Andorra, Monaco, San Marino, and Vatican City —and two British Crown Colonies—Gibraltar and Malta—are located in the Mediterranean area. The nations of Andorra, Monaco, and San Marino are relic nations, the remains of

*Figure 8-16 Boats of the Kalymnos fishing fleet starting for their long voyage to the sponge fields off the African coast where the most important sponge beds of the Mediterranean are located. Fishermen from Greece normally work North African fields for seven months of the year. The boats set sail in the spring and return toward the end of October. (Courtesy of Mutual Security Administration.)*

states established in mountainous areas centuries ago. The Vatican City, as it exists today, was established by the Lateran Treaty of 1929. It has, however, existed for many centuries as the popes have held temporal authority over certain areas in Italy since the establishment of the Roman Catholic Church. The two British colonies are important as military installations because of their strategic locations.

## Andorra

A country of narrow mountain valleys and a few high peaks, Andorra is located in the heart of the Pyrenees. It is an area of cold winters and cool to mild summers. For many months of the year most of the mountain passes are snowbound. In the valleys, during the short growing season, subsistence crops are grown. The principal occupation is sheep raising. Politically the nation is a semifeudal state, being governed by an elective council which rules under a joint suzerainty of the President of France and the Bishop of Urgel. Andorra is the capital and only town of importance.

## Monaco

Near the Italian-French border is Monaco, an independent principality which is in a customs union with France. This country, with an area slightly greater than one-half square mile and a population in excess of 20,000, is, after the Vatican City, the smallest sovereign state in the world. The principality surrounds a good, sheltered harbor. On a rocky promontory facing the Mediterranean is the old capital Monaco. The most noted part of the country today, however, is Monte Carlo, famous for its gambling casino and luxurious hotels which form a primary attraction for Riviera tourists. The country receives its income from the casino, tourists, and the sale of postage stamps.

## San Marino

San Marino is a nation of some 23 square miles, entirely surrounded by Italian territory. It is located on the eastern slopes of the Etruscan Apennines. On the small farms, corn and fruit are grown. Stock raising is also important. The chief source of governmental revenue is postage stamps which are issued for collectors. San Marino, the capital and principal city, with its castle and fortifications, is located on the precipitous side of Mt. Titano.

## Vatican City

The smallest nation in the world is the Vatican City, its total area being only slightly more than 100 acres. The city-state, located on the west side of the Tiber River, is entirely surrounded by Rome. St. Peter's Church, the largest Christian church in the world, the Vatican, and the pontifical palaces are among the important buildings located within the area. As the home of the pope, this small nation is an ecclesiastical state with world-wide influence out of all proportion to its physical size.

## Gibraltar

Gibraltar occupies a narrow peninsula which is connected to Spain by a low isthmus. Located at the northeast entrance to the Strait of Gibraltar, it is ideally situated for controlling the western entrance to the Mediterranean Sea. Much of the peninsula is covered by a huge rock which attains an elevation of approximately 1,400 feet. Natural caves within the rock aided in making it a very strongly fortified naval base. Securing fresh water is one of the principal problems confronting the people. Large areas of the very steep eastern slopes of the Rock have been cemented to prevent water from soaking into the shallow soil and to direct the rapid run-off into underground storage basins. Most of the people living in Gibraltar are military personnel. Almost all civilians are employed by the various military departments. Many shopkeepers and laborers come in daily from Spain.

## Maltese Islands

Malta, Gozo, and Comino are the three principal islands of the Maltese group, which is a part of the British Empire. Although the total area is only about 122 square miles, the islands have a population of about 316,000. Population pressure causes each bit of the poor, shallow, rocky soil to be kept in as intensive production as the annual rainfall of about 17 inches will allow. Large churches, rock-walled fields, and the small, rock, flat-topped homes of the rural dweller dominate the landscape. Malta, the largest island, is an important British naval base. Malta derives most of its income from the naval establishments and the tourist trade. Valletta, the capital and principal city, is built around the old walled fort and churches established by the Knights of Malta. The people of Malta send elected representatives to the British Parliament.

## IN PERSPECTIVE

### European Mediterranean

Three peninsulas, Iberia, Italy, and Greece form much of the northern shores of the Mediterranean Sea, with Iberia also making the chief bordering land on the west. These lands and associated islands are called Southern Peninsular Europe. The regional unifying characteristics include mountains that dominate the landscape, the Mediterranean climate, closeness to the ocean except in interior Spain, similarities in crops, the drought-resistant natural vegetation except that growing in the higher mountain areas or along the rainy west coast, the preponderance of the Mediterranean race, and a culture that stems from that of Greece and Rome.

Although manufacturing is important in northern Italy and at Barcelona, in general the most common occupation is farming, mostly done on small holdings with simple implements, often by hand methods. The same grains—wheat, barley, and rice—are grown and vineyards, fruit and nut orchards, and olive trees are important. The chief animals are the goat, sheep, and donkey. Even cattle and pigs are scarce in some sections. Houses are mostly built of stone and brick, and the people prefer to live in villages and cities. Standards of living are generally lower than in Western and Northern Europe. The fishing industry is common along many of the coasts. Italy and Greece are important in ocean shipping. The scenery and historic monuments in the region are major attractions to visitors, and especially in Italy is the tourist industry an important source of income. Both Italy and Spain have developed large amounts of hydroelectricity which is a partial substitute for the small output of coal and petroleum. Italy also generates a little power from steam tapped from underground by wells.

## EXERCISES

*1.* Why is the Mediterranean area unique as an element of man's physical environment and as a center of human advancement?

*2.* What are the chief characteristics of the Mediterranean climate? How does it differ from the climate of the British Isles? What other areas in the world also have a Mediterranean type of climate?

*3.* What are the principal mineral resources of southern peninsular Europe? What important minerals are lacking? How has this handicapped industrial development in these countries?

*4.* What are the physical advantages and handicaps of Spain, Italy, and Greece? Where, in each country, is the greatest amount of level land? In what ways has local topography influenced land use?

*5.* What four tiny independent countries continue to exist in the Mediterranean area? In what ways are these countries alike? How do they differ? Why are they in existence?

*6.* What are the principal agricultural products of the Mediterranean area? Which of these are exported? What advantages does this region have for the production of these crops?

*7.* How does the population density of Italy and Greece compare with that of Belgium, France, and the United Kingdom? How does the producing power of these countries compare? What are the chief handicaps for successful manufacturing?

*8.* In what ways does Portugal differ from Spain? What factors have probably prevented the two countries from forming a single nation? What locational advantages does Portugal have?

9. Which part of Italy has the greatest industrial development? What physical advantages does it have for this type of economy? What are the leading products of the area?

10. What are the chief handicaps to the development of a modern Greece? Why is Greece not as important a nation today as it was two thousand years ago?

11. Why do many tourists visit Southern Europe? What does Italy do to attract tourists?

12. Where is Malta? Gibraltar? Of what importance are these to the United Kingdom?

## SELECTED REFERENCES

Cahman, Werner J., and Alice Taylor: "Spain," *Focus,* 5(3):1–6, November, 1954.

Hainsworth, Reginal G.: *World Agriculture,* U.S. Department of Agriculture Miscellaneous Publication No. 705, Washington, 1949.

Houston, J. M.: "Irrigation as a Solution to Agrarian Problems in Modern Spain," *Geographical Journal,* 116:55–63, September, 1950.

McNee, Robert B.: "Rural Development in the Italian South," *Annals of the Association of American Geographers,* 45:127–151, June, 1955.

Newbigen, Marion I.: *Southern Europe,* E. P. Dutton & Co., New York, 1949.

Pounds, Norman J. G.: *Europe and the Mediterranean,* McGraw-Hill Book Company, Inc., New York, 1953.

Semple, Ellen Churchill: *Geography of the Mediterranean Region,* Henry Holt and Company, Inc., 1931.

Van Royen, William, and Oliver Bowles, *Atlas of the World's Resources: Mineral Resources of the World,* Prentice-Hall, Inc., Englewood Cliffs, N.J., 1952.

Vouras, Paul P.: "Greece's Means of Livelihood," *Journal of Geography,* 52:89–98, March, 1953.

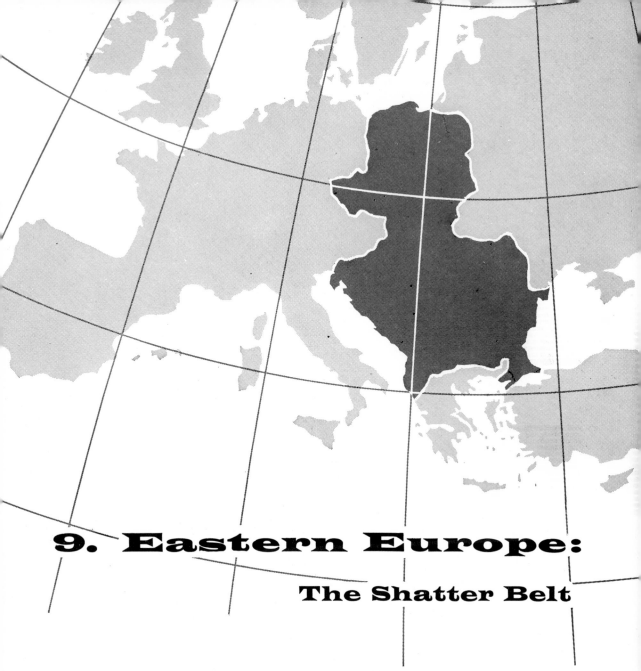

# 9. Eastern Europe:

## The Shatter Belt

THE Shatter Belt of Europe is a broad zone stretching from the Baltic Sea to the Mediterranean and comprising the central core of the European Peninsula with its Baltic and Balkan fringes (Figure 9-1). It is an area of transition between the three dominant geographic features of Europe: the Atlantic coastal lands, the Mediterranean region, and the great central lowland extending westward from the Asiatic heartland. In it are represented the Alpine System with its arcing mountains and large enclosed basins, the old worn-down mountains and plateaus of the Central Uplands, and the Great European Plain.

Historically, the area has always been the scene of conflict, armed or cultural,

315

POLITICAL AND RAILWAY MAP
OF THE SHATTER BELT

★ Capital of country
▬ ▪ ▬ International boundaries
── Major railways

0                    200 MILES

BALTIC SEA

Gdyna  Danzig
Stettin
Bydgoszcz
Berlin
Poznan
Vistula River
Warsaw
P O L A N D
Lodz
Lublin
Oder River
Krakow
Kiev
U. S. S. R.
50°
E. GERMANY
Prague
Pilsen
C Z E C H O S L O V A K I A
Brno
Danube River
Kosice
Bratislava
Vienna
Miskla
Tisza River
Budapest
Debrecen
A U S T R I A
H U N G A R Y
Iasi
Odess
Cluj
Ljubljana
Szeged
Pécs  Subotica
R O M A N I A
Zagreb
Drava River
Timisoara
Galati
35°
Belgrade
Ploesti
Y U G O S L A V I A
Bucharest
Constanta
Sarajevo
Moraua River
Danube  River
A D R I A T I C   S E A
Split
Varna
Dubrovnik
B U L G A R I A
B L A C K   S E A
Rome
Sofia
I T A L Y
Skoplje
Plovdiv
A L B A N I A
Vardar
Istanbul
Tiranë
SEA OF
Durres
G R E E C E
MARMARA
T U R K E Y
Salonika
Vlone
40°
AEGEAN SEA

15°        20°              25°              30°

15°

religious or political. Few have been the times of tranquillity in this region. The last was during the turn of the century when Austria-Hungary, Turkey, and Russia dominated the scene. World War I witnessed the collapse of these political structures. The nearsighted jealousies of the fragmentary Succession States were a constant threat and an unsurmountable obstacle to real peace in Europe. In their turn the Great Powers of Europe took full advantage of the situation and used these nations as pawns in their game of power politics.

From the human point of view it is an important area. It is inhabited by over 100 million people on 516,835 square miles of land. In this area lie 8 of Europe's 32 independent countries —Albania, Bulgaria, Czechoslovakia, Hungary, Poland, Romania, Yugoslavia, and the European part of Turkey. It includes some of the most highly developed industrial areas of the Continent as well as some of the poorest farmlands in Europe. Culturally, the area shows a gradation from famed cosmopolitan centers of art and refinement to small hamlets of illiterate, superstitious peasants. All three forms of Christianity, Catholic, Orthodox, and Protestant, are represented among the people. Other religions, such as Mohammedanism and Judaism, form strong local nuclei or widespread minorities. Ethnically, the Slavs predominate but a strong non-Slav core of Germans, Magyars, and Romanians divides the Slavs into the northern group of Poles, Czechs, Slovaks, and Ruthenians and the southern group of Slovenes, Croats, Serbs, and Bulgarians. In addition there are the Albanians, the Turks, and finally the controversial Macedonians.

In all this heterogeneity, it is significant that most of the people in the area belong to the Western phase of Europe's economic, cultural, and religious life. Only in the Balkan states did the Eastern way of life gain dominance. This way of life, racial kinship among Slav and Orthodox Eastern Christianity, tied the latter area strongly to Imperial Russia. After the fall of Czarist Russia the ties between the Balkan States, including non-Slavic Romania, and the young U.S.S.R. became weak. After the Nazi conquest or Fascist misrule, the U.S.S.R. was able not only to reestablish the Russian influence but to dominate the scene completely until the Titoist defection of Yugoslavia altered the political picture.

This Shatter Belt of Europe, though not the most prosperous or populous part of the Continent, has great complexity. If it can be said that diversity is a typical characteristic of Europe, then the Shatter Belt is most typically European.

## PHYSICAL SETTING

### Relief Features

The great diversity of topographic features is clearly attested by the large number of physiographic regions into which the area can be subdivided (Figure 9-2). All three of the dominant physiographic types of Europe are present in the Shatter Belt. The young, rugged Alpine Mountain system with its associated lowlands occupies the larger, southern half of the area. Similarly, much of the northern sector is occupied by the great European Plain, and much of the land between belongs to the Central Uplands.

**Alpine System and Associated Lowlands.** The Alpine System consists of young, rugged mountains with towering, often snow-capped

*Figure 9-1   The Shatter Belt includes seven nations and the European part of Turkey. With the exception of Turkey, each is a Communist nation. Note the importance of the capital of each country as a railroad center.*

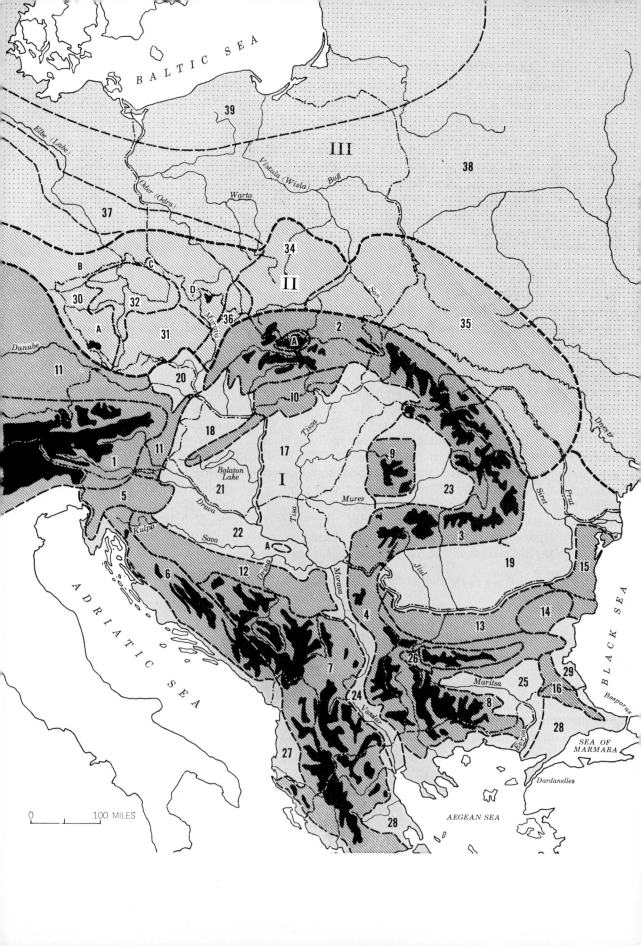

# PHYSIOGRAPHIC REGIONS
# OF THE SHATTER BELT

## I. THE ALPINE SYSTEM

### A. MOUNTAINS AND PLATEAUS
1. Alps
2. Carpathians: A. High Tatra
3. Transylvanian Alps
4. Balkans: Stara Planina
5. Karst Plateau
6. Dinaric Alps
7. Central Yugoslav-Albanian Highlands
8. Rhodope Massif
9. Bihar Mountain
10. Central Hungarian Hills
11. Alpine Forelands
12. Yugoslavian Foreland
13. Danubian (Balkan) Foreland
14. Deli-Orman
15. Dobrogea (Dobrudzha) Platform
16. Pontic Hills

### B. ASSOCIATED LOWLANDS
17. Great Hungarian Alföld
18. Little Hungarian Alföld
19. Walachian Plain
20. Vienna Basin
21. Transdanubian Lowland
22. Slavonian Lowland: A. Fruska Gora
23. Transylvanian Basin
24. Morava-Vardar Valley
25. Maritsa Valley
26. Sofiya Basin
27. Adriatic Littoral
28. Aegean Lowlands
29. Pontic Lowlands

## II. THE CENTRAL UPLANDS
30. Bohemian Rim: A. Bohemian Forest,
    B. Ore Mountains, C. Giants Mountains,
    D. Sudeten Mountains.
31. Moravian Hills
32. Bohemian Basin
33. Sudeten Foreland
34. Lysogóry Gora
35. Poldolian Plateau
36. Moravian Corridor

## III. THE EUROPEAN PLAIN
37. Southern Morainic Hills
38. Glacial Valley
39. Baltic Moraine

—·—·— Political boundaries
▬ ▬ ▬ Regional boundaries
— — — Sub regional boundaries
⬛ Elevations over 3,000 feet

*Figure 9-2 The Shatter Belt is an area of rugged topography. In this area there are 39 physical regions which makes for isolation and the lack of progress in many regions.*

peaks, and deeply cut V- or U-shaped valleys carved by running water or by former mighty mountain glaciers. In spite of its high elevation the system has a large number of low, easy-grade passes which have played important roles in the human development of the region. In addition to the passes, mountainous units are often separated by stretches of narrow lowlands, known as gates or corridors. These have been of great help in the movement of people and the development of trade routes, railroads, and motor roads.

The Alps (1) * proper terminate in the Alpine Forelands (11) in Austria. They are separated by the Valley of the Upper Danube and the Vienna (Wien) Basin (20) from the great double horseshoe arc of the Carpathian-Transylvanian-Balkan system. Although the Carpathians are the lowest as a whole they include the snow-covered High Tatra (2A), which is one of the highest ranges in this system. The Transylvanian Alps (3) are the highest unit on the average, and the Star Planina of the Balkan unit (4) contains not only the highest peak but forms the most serious barrier in the entire mountain system. Though low and well-provided with passes, the heavily forested Carpathians and Transylvanian Alps form definite barriers; for more than a millennium they have served as one of the more stable and obvious political boundaries of Europe.

The southern unit, Karst Highlands and Plateaus (5), is dominated by soluble limestone rock with all the accompanying Karst features of sinkholes, underground drainage, large springs, and disappearing lakes. The Dinaric Alps (6) rise abruptly from the narrow Adriatic Littoral (27) with its many elongated islands and narrow coastal plain. Once heavily forested,

* The figures in parentheses which occur in the following discussion refer to the code which appears on the physiographic map (Figure 9-2).

the dazzlingly white, rocky mountains are, to-day, bare of vegetation and soil because of the merciless cutting of forests.

The Central Yugoslav–Albanian Highlands (7) comprise one of the most complicated systems of inaccessible mountains, valleys, and basins in Europe. Geologically, the dominant rocks are of ancient crystalline origin although considerable outcrops of limestone occur. The polyes (basin meadows or large sinkholes) are often completely surrounded by mountains and have internal drainage. Though often marshy and malarial, they contain most of the arable lands of the area. The small villages and hamlets are usually on the slopes rather than in the valleys in order to get away from the mosquitoes, thus leaving the tillable lowland available for crops. Furthermore, by not living in the main valleys the people avoid the avenues of marauding armies of invaders. Isolation characterizes the valleys and basins where many ancient tribes and rites found their last refuge. The political immaturity, the survival of illiteracy, superstitions, and such outmoded social traits as clan organization and blood feuds amply illustrate the backwardness caused by age-old isolation. Empires came and empires vanished, each leaving some imprints on the people, but none was able to bring them completely into its own cultural community.

In addition to the mountains of the Alpine System there are a number of forelands, isolated mountains, and hilly areas (11 to 16). The forelands, generally speaking, are usually level to gently rolling low plateaus or lowlands and are well populated. In contrast to these conditions the mountains and hilly areas are, as a rule, heavily forested, rather empty regions. The Rhodope Massif (8) is the most important

*Figure 9-3   About 100 miles west of Zagreb, Yugoslavia, is a forested, hilly region of lakes and waterfalls. Part of this area has been made into a national park. (Courtesy of Consulate of Yugoslavia.)*

unit in the latter group. The Massif forms a triangular, rugged and high, mostly crystalline mountain system which is older than the Alpine System. At the western end of the Massif are the hills and mountains that form the heart of Macedonia and much of the almost insolvable Macedonian problem has its origin in the isolation caused by the rugged relief. Here, side by side yet almost completely separated, live Serbs, Bulgars, Pomaks (Mohammedan Bulgars), Greeks, Turks, Jews, and Macedonians, speaking different languages, using different scripts, having different social organizations and mores, and always ready to fight each other.

The lowlands associated with the Alpine System are the most important units as far as the people are concerned. In them are found most of the people, most of the arable land, the densest network of roads and railroads, and the most intensive economic activities.

All but one of these lowlands are closely associated with the great central nerve of the area, the Danube River. Running through all save three nations of the Shatter Belt—Albania, Poland, and Turkey—its name changes from Donau in Germany to Duna in Hungary, only to be called Dunav in Slavic tongues and Dunarea in Romania. Danube is the only name never used along the river in spite of the fact that it is the form nearest to its Latin name, Danubius. The Danube, which is either green or muddy brownish-yellow, depending upon the season, but never blue, has over 300 tributaries and drains approximately 320,000 square miles of territory. It receives all but one of its chief tributaries within the Shatter Belt. The Danube has served as a waterway for a long time. Its effectiveness was greatly increased by the blasting of a navigable channel through the rapids of the Iron Gate. Upstream from the Iron Gate is the picturesque Kazan (Klisura) Pass by which the mighty stream breaks through between the Transylvanian Alps and the Balkan Mountains. It is used by a highway, but the railroads avoid the tortuous pass and use one farther to the north.

The Great Hungarian Alföld (17) is the most important of the Alpine-Danubian lowlands. It occupies the large central basin of Eastern Europe, surrounded by the great arc of the Carpathians and the Transylvanian Highlands. To the west the low, broken Central Hungarian Hills or Bokony Forest (10) separate it from the Little Alföld (18) which is dominated by the large alluvial fan (biggest in Europe) of the Danube as it leaves its upper course in the Alpine Foreland (11) and Vienna Basin (20).

The Danube, which so far has flowed in an easterly direction, makes a sharp turn toward the south as it cuts through the Central Hungarian Hills (10) and enters the Great Alföld which has a flat topography, here and there broken by sand dunes. Besides the Danube, the Tisza River crosses the plain in a winding, tortuous channel. The Tisza has caused serious floods and is responsible for large tracts of marsh. To remedy these conditions, the Hungarian government has straightened the river's course, built levees and provided spillways.

West of the Alföld is the Transdanubian Lowland (21), a rolling plain on which is the long, narrow Lake Balaton, Central Europe's largest fresh-water lake. To the south between the Drava and Sava Rivers lies the Slavonian Lowland (22). Separated from the Alföld by the Bihar Mountain (9) is the moderately high, enclosed Transylvanian Basin (23).

The Walachian Plain (19) dominates the lower course of the Danube as the Alföld does its middle section. In many respects these two lowlands are quite similar. One major difference, however, is that the Danube, flowing at the outer border of the Walachian Plain and facing the bluffs of the Balkan Foreland (13) and the Dobrugea Platform (15), has developed excessive marshes along the lowland side of its course. This marshy border was and still continues as an important barrier to human settlement. It has rendered the Danubian boundary between Bulgaria and Romania the most stable political line in the Balkan Peninsula. North of the Dobrugea, the Walachian Plain reaches out to the Black Sea and includes the large delta of the river with its intricate pattern of channels, islands, and marshes.

Two important corridors lead into the Danubian lowlands. The one lying west of the eastern Carpathians separates the Alpine region from the Central Uplands and is known as the Moravian Corridor (36). This narrow strip is dominated by the northward flowing Oder (Odra) River and the southward flowing Morava River. The Moravian Gate, a low gap between the Sudeten Mountains (30D) and the Carpathians, connects the two river valleys and offers a connection from the European Plain (III) to the Vienna Basin.

The second corridor is the Morava-Vardar Valley (24), which gives easy access to the Aegean Lowlands (28) to the south, and through the Valley of the Nisava River, an eastern tributary of the Morava, to the Sofia (Sofija) Basin (26). Besides the Nisava Valley, the Iskur Gorge connects the Basin with the Balkan Foreland (13), and a high pass leads into the Struma Valley. The most important, however, is the gentle, broad valley of the Maritsa River (25), famed for the rose gardens in its tributary, the Tundza River, which gives access to the Strait of Bosporus and to Istanbul (Constantinople).

**Central Uplands.** The Central Uplands, as the name implies, occupy a central location between the great Alpine Folds to the south and east and the European Plains to the north. They form an elongated, somewhat narrow belt of worn-down mountains, enclosed basins, and marginal low plateaus caused by the erosion of old crystalline rocks, especially in Bohemia. The mountains are well covered by forests which fact is shown by the name Bohemian Forest for one of the ranges. In spite of their general low elevation, they are considerable barriers mostly because of their forested character. The region is rich in mineral wealth, especially in coal. As a result, the greatest industrial development of the Shatter Belt is concentrated in the Bohemian Basin (32) and the Sudeten Foreland (33).

The Elbe River, which dominates Bohemia, rises in the Giant Mountains (30C), flows through a wide valley, the core of the Bohemian Basin, and cuts the Ore Mountains (30B) to enter the European Plain and empty its waters

into the North Sea. The fortress character of Bohemia has been an important factor in the history of the Czech people. In the millennial struggle between the eastward-pushing Germans and the westward-moving Slavs, the mountain rim, with its dense forests and few passes, gave some protection to the Czechs who were able to maintain themselves in the Basin and the Moravian Hills (31). Nevertheless, Germanic elements encroached upon them from three sides.

The Sudetenland Foreland, dominated by the Oder River, contains the important Silesian coal fields. Long an area of conflict among Poland, Austria, and Prussia, it is now controlled by Poland. A rolling, hilly region occupies the area between the Oder and Vistula (Wisla) Rivers. On its periphery are some of Poland's most important cities. With Krakow, the ancient capital of Poland, this region was once the core of the nation; now it is known as Little Poland. The low Podolian Plateau (35) now belongs almost entirely to the U.S.S.R.

**European Plain.** Beyond the highland areas of Central Europe stretches the vast European Plain. Starting from the Atlantic coast, it extends north and eastward, widening into the monotonous plain of Russia and beyond, toward the heartland of Asia. The Shatter Belt occupies that part of the plain which lies between the Oder River and the Pripet (Pripyat) Marshes. This part belongs to the glaciated portion of the plain and is dominated by three important features, two hilly belts and a wide, marshy depression between. The hilly belts are the remnants of ancient moraines, marking the fronts of the huge continental glaciers which covered the plains during the ice ages. At one stage as the ice retreated, a strong westward flow of the waters issuing from the melting ice created the broad Glacial Valley (38). This depression is clearly marked by the sharp westward turn of the northward tending streams of the plain. The southern Moraine Hills partially deflect the Oder where it breaks through the hills entering the valley.

The presence of the Glacial Valley rendered it a relatively simple task to connect the rivers with canals, enabling bulky products to be moved in barges over the streams and canals in an east-west direction. The Baltic Moraine is the most poorly drained of the group. Its marshy character and infertile glacial till are largely responsible for the region's retarded development. Generally speaking, the area is a barrier separating the Baltic coast from its hinterland. Thus, it came about that the German settlers of the coastal strip were confined there, and the hinterland beyond the marshes remained inhabited by Slavic people.

Toward the Baltic Sea, the hills give way to a low, sandy coast, which has large barrier beaches enclosing shallow lagoons. Often there are wide stretches of sand dunes along the shore. Generally, the coastal margin of the moraine offers no more advantages than the hills themselves. Only where the rivers reach the sea have people concentrated.

The Vistula is the largest stream in this part of the European Plain and is the great artery of Poland. The lower Oder, together with its tributary, the Neisse, has risen to political significance lately as the temporary western boundary of Poland. At the mouths of the rivers developed important ports which, during medieval times, were members of the Hanseatic League. Desire to control these ports now causes international intrigue and strife.

*Climate*

The climate of the Shatter Belt displays the same diversity as its physiographic makeup. The area comes under the influence of all three major climatic controls of Europe, the Atlantic Ocean, the Eurasian continent, and the Mediterranean Sea (Figure 9-4). Proceeding from west to east, the influence of the Atlantic becomes less and less marked. The precipitation steadily decreases from 24 to 15 inches or less along the Dobrugea shore of the Black Sea. As the amount of precipitation decreases eastward, it also becomes increasingly concentrated during the summer half of the year. In addition, the variability of rainfall increases considerably along the eastern margin of the area, showing distinctly the continental effect of the large land mass. The influence of the Mediterranean can be traced by a fall maximum or at least a secondary maximum during the fall. These conditions are dominant along the shores of the Balkan Peninsula and penetrate as deeply as southwest Hungary.

As far as temperature conditions are concerned, continental influences are strongest during the winter. The area as a whole, with the exception of the narrow coastal strip around the Balkan Peninsula, lies north of the 32°F January isotherm. The continental high-pressure belt extends from the heart of Asia westward to Transylvania and the eastern half of the Alföld, dividing the northern area from the Mediterranean region. Cyclonic activities are less frequent than in Western Europe and are mainly confined to the northern sector of the region. Along the narrow coastal strip of the Balkan Peninsula, the winters are wet and mild. During the summer, the southern half of the area is the warmer. The presence of mountains

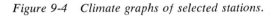

*Figure 9-4   Climate graphs of selected stations.*

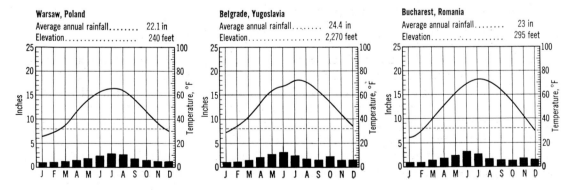

causes the July 68°F isotherm to swing far south along the mountains of Yugoslavia and around Transylvania. Thus, actually only about one-third of the area has over 68°F for its summer average temperature.

The Shatter Belt area can be divided into three main climatic provinces: Central European, continental, and Mediterranean. The mountains, in general, are areas of great variation.

**Central European.** The Central European province results from the combined influences of the three major climatic controls and is transitional to the true continental type. Precipitation ranges from 20 to 25 inches. It is marked by a summer maximum. As much as 58 per cent of the rainfall may occur during the summer half of the year. The continental influence is shown by the dryness of winter. This season accounts for only 19 per cent of the precipitation which is mainly snow brought by occasional cyclonic disturbances. Another typical feature, especially on the Alföld, is the early May-June maximum of rainfall caused by the great number of thundershowers occurring then. During the month of June, 61 per cent of the rain in Hungary comes in the form of thundershowers.

The temperature regime shows well-defined seasonal characteristics, with cold winters and hot summers, the mean temperatures ranging from 25°F for January to 74° for July. Continental influences make spring warmer but autumn colder than in Western Europe. The growing season is long enough for grapes, and, in Hungary, for corn. From its core, the Alföld, the area shows gradual transition toward the major climatic types.

**Continental.** The Continental province occupies the northern and eastern portions of the Shatter Belt. There are two distinct phases of the continental climate represented: the humid phase, where the precipitation is between 20 and 24 inches, and the dry phase, where precipitation falls below 20 inches. Both types have cold, dry winters (January, 25°F) and

moderately warm, humid summers (July, 65°F). Not only are the summers just moderately warm, but also the growing season is short. This combination of factors, together with the precipitation factor, places definite restrictions upon the types and development of agriculture in the area.

**Mediterranean.** The Mediterranean province occupies the least area in the Shatter Belt and is mainly confined to the Adriatic shores of the Balkan Peninsula. The summers are dry and hot, the winters moderate and wet. Along the Adriatic coast, 36 per cent of the rainfall occurs during the autumn months. Winter accounts for 56 per cent of the rain, while summer has only 8 per cent. Principally because of topographic conditions, the amount of rainfall varies from 20 to 60 inches.

Though during the winter a cold north wind, the dreaded bora, often causes frost to occur in the northern sectors, yet the January average temperatures are above 32°F. They vary from 40°F, in the north, to 50° on the southern islands. During summer the inland places are hot, average temperatures in July being as high as 80°F. Along the coasts the July average ranges between 73 and 75°F.

**Mountain.** Mountain climates represent exceptional conditions within all three major provinces. In general the mountains have the highest amount of precipitation, are colder than the surrounding areas, and, in a few places, are high enough for a tundra type of climate to prevail. Unlike the Alps, in the Shatter Belt just a few peaks reach up into the realm of eternal snow.

### Vegetation and Soils

Outside of some highly isolated mountains and extensive marshes, hardly any areas in Eastern Europe are covered by natural vegetation. Man has lived in the area too long to leave any but the least attractive lands unused and unchanged.

Originally most of the area was forest-covered. Only the Alföld and the eastern third of the Walachian Plain, together with the Dobrugea, were park lands, where the woods were mainly confined to the river courses, forming gallery forests, steppes, or grasslands devoid of tree forms. The dominant trees are the beech and oak mixed with conifers like spruce and pine. In the mountains and on some poor, sandy, glacial soils the conifers occur in pure stands. Where mountains rise above the timber line, between 6,500 and 7,000 feet, the forest gives way to alpine meadows.

Along the Adriatic and Aegean fringes the Mediterranean maqui vegetation covers the ground. This is a thorny, bush type of dense vegetation that comes brilliantly to life following the winter rains only to dry up into a grayish mass during the rainless summer.

A narrow strip along the Baltic coast, covered with sand dunes, is barren. Where some stability has been reached, typical coastal vegetation of drought-resistant plants cover the dunes. In the glacial morainic areas, extensive marshes occur.

Man and forests seem always to be in competition for the use of the land. Man learned, however, that wood is needed; therefore, he reforested part of the cutover lands as in Poland. In many instances he is practicing tree farming rather than forestry. The most extensive natural forests are in Romania, Bulgaria, Yugoslavia, and Albania. One mountain range that bounds Czechoslovakia on the west is named the Bohemian Forest. It is still a source of timber.

Though man could change the soil less than its vegetative cover, he has radically altered the chemical composition, texture, and productivity of his soils through cultivation. Under the prevailing climatic conditions, and under forest cover, the brown forest soils and the gray podsols have developed. Both are leached soils which have lost, to a varying degree, the plant nutrients. Locally there are great variations in accordance with the structural conditions of the soils, such as sandy, loamy, or clayey types. The sandy soils are apt to be dry; conversely, clays may become waterlogged. The best structure is displayed by the loams, which result from the half-and-half mixture of sand and clay.

Under the grass cover there have developed deep, fertile soils of the black earth type. These occupy the two Alfölds and part of the Walachian Plain. In the Mediterranean portions the soils are of the reddish-colored terra rossa type. These are clayey, rather poor soils ranging from shallow pockets on mountain slopes to deep layers in bottomlands and along the coasts.

## HUMAN RELATIONSHIPS

### Population

As in the case of the natural aspects, the Shatter Belt is a complex region from the ethnic, cultural, and economic points of view. The area lies at the human crossroads of language, religion, social organizations and mores, and economic activities.

The 100 million people of Eastern Europe live on half a million square miles of land (Figure 9-5). If the population were spread out evenly there would be about 200 people on each square mile. Such, however, is not the case. Hungary, with 250 persons per square mile, has the highest density of population; Albania, with 106, has the lowest. Mere figures, however, are misleading because the character of the land must be considered. For example, almost all of Hungary is arable or productive land; most of Albania is covered by high, rugged mountains which lower capability to support people.

Generally speaking, the population is dominantly rural, living in villages and other rural settlements. Even some of the good-sized towns are in reality overgrown villages, inhabited almost solely by peasants. There is, of course, a small group of middle-class people, merchants, white-collar workers, teachers, and administrative personnel, even in this sort of town. They constitute, however, so small a proportion that they do not change the character of the settlement.

Because of topography, mineral resources, and stages of economic development, the distri-

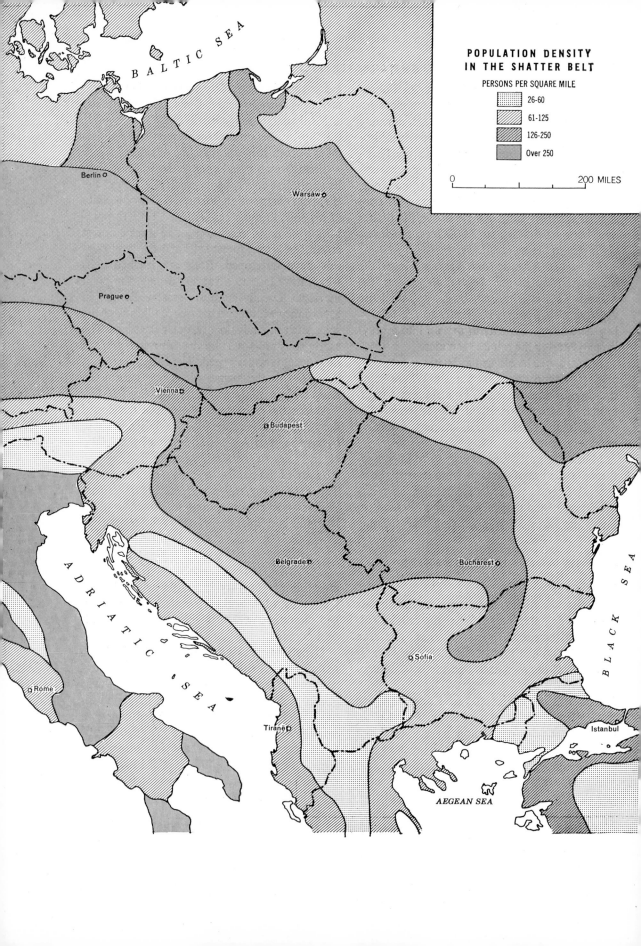

POPULATION DENSITY
IN THE SHATTER BELT

PERSONS PER SQUARE MILE

26-60

61-125

126-250

Over 250

0                    200 MILES

BALTIC SEA

Berlin

Warsaw

Prague

Vienna

Budapest

Belgrade

Bucharest

ADRIATIC SEA

Rome

Sofia

BLACK SEA

Tiranë

Istanbul

AEGEAN SEA

bution of population is uneven. In the great industrial sections of Poland and Czechoslovakia, the density of population is over 500 per square mile, a sharp contrast to the most empty areas of the Alps–Carpathian–Balkan Mountains, much of the Baltic Moraine, and parts of the Balkan Peninsula where the density of population falls below 100 per square mile.

The small number of cities further shows the lack of concentration of population. Europe is the typical example of an urbanized continent. In the Shatter Belt, urbanization is below the European level. Poland, with 21 cities having over 50,000 population, 11 of which have over 100,000 people each, has the greatest number of large cities, but it has no real metropolis. Budapest, Hungary, with over a million people, is the only metropolitan city, with Prague (Praha), the capital of Czechoslovakia, following. Again Albania is on the other end of the scale; Tiranë, its capital and largest city, has only 80,000 inhabitants.

## Cultural Aspects

Two major cultural forces influence in its attitudes the Shatter Belt toward life: the Western, individualistic, free, and democratic, as contrasted to the Oriental, collectivistic, fatalistic, and autocratic. These two ideologies can be seen in all cultural expressions and aspirations of the people. The conflict of these ideas is the real battle, which actually overshadows the significance of the wars and campaigns fought over them in this region. Only in the light of this basic conflict between Occident and Orient one can understand the cultural, economic, and political development of the area.

**Religions.**   The Western forms of Christianity dominate. Roman Catholicism is the strongest and most widespread religion in the Shatter Belt. Poland is almost entirely Catholic. In Czechoslovakia, three-fourths of the people are Catholics. In Hungary, that proportion diminishes to two-thirds. The largest number of Protestants, over 2 million, representing more than one-quarter of the population, live in Hungary. In the Balkan states, the Greek Orthodox Church is the established church. Only in Yugoslavia and Romania are there sizable Roman Catholic minorities.

Albania is a Moslem country. Two-thirds of the Albanians are followers of the Prophet. Of the remainder, two-thirds are Greek Orthodox, the rest Roman Catholic. Yugoslavia and Bulgaria also have sizable groups of Mohammedans. In both cases, they represent about 10 per cent of the population.

Before World War II there was a rather large number of Jews, especially in Poland, and also in Romania, Hungary, and Czechoslovakia. The Nazi terror in all countries of the Shatter Belt resulted in the slaughter of millions of Jews, reducing their numbers from approximately 5 million to about half a million.

**Languages.**   Linguistically, the Slav languages predominate. The Poles, Czechs, Slovaks, and Ruthenians belong to the North Slav group. All of them use the Latin script. The Slovenes, Croats, Serbs, Montenegrins, and Bulgars belong to the South Slav group. Of these, the Slovenes and Croats use the Latin alphabet, the others the Cyrillic script. All Slavic languages are closely related, especially those belonging to the same group.

Romanian, Hungarian, and Albanian are the three major non-Slavic languages used in the area. Lesser languages are German, Italian, Turkish, Yiddish, and Gypsy. The Romanian, known also as Vlach, is a Latinized form of the ancient Illyric; modern Romanian contains

*Figure 9-5   The most densely populated part of the Shatter Belt is in the more highly developed industrial areas of Czechoslovakia and southern Poland. Note the density of population in relation to landforms.*

many other linguistic elements. The Albanian languages are mixtures of an ancient base upon which some Slavic and Turkish has been superimposed. The Hungarian language does not belong to any of the three European language groups. Its basis is Finno-Ugric with a strong admixture of Turkish modified by long contact with German and Latin.

**Growth.** The population of the Shatter Belt since 1914 has suffered heavy losses from wars and racial and political persecutions. Even now, political deportations and forced recruitments into labor camps are a factor to be taken into consideration. Another important factor was the so-called repatriation of various minority groups, especially by Poland and Czechoslovakia. Actually this meant the expulsion of unwanted elements.

Although, since the outbreak of World War II, the population is increasing in the area as a whole, in three countries—Czechoslovakia, Hungary, and Romania—losses in population have occurred. Birth rates in the area are relatively high, but since the middle 1930s there has been a decline in all but two countries of the region, Czechoslovakia and Poland. The death rate is decreasing over the area, but it is still relatively high.

## Economic Development

The region is well endowed with resources and, in certain lines of economic endeavor, it has assumed world importance. There are, however, great contrasts in the area's economic development. Southwestern Poland, Bohemia, Moravia, and western Hungary show the highest types of resource utilization. Proceeding from this area toward the eastern and southern periphery, industrialization decreases at an accelerating rate.

**Agriculture.** The dominant form of economic activity in the area is agriculture. Under normal circumstances, the Danubian countries produce an important food surplus. The most important crop is wheat, followed by corn in the southeast sector and rye and potatoes in the north. Barley is raised throughout the region, oats mainly in the cooler areas, especially in the mountains and on the glacial sands of Poland. Rice cultivation has been attempted with some success in Hungary and the Balkan states.

The sugar beet is the most important intensively cultivated crop. Its production is confined mainly to the northern half of the region. Czechoslovakia and Poland are the chief producers of sugar for export; Hungary is a minor exporter. Tobacco, hops, hemp, and flax are other important industrial crops. Fruit orchards and vineyards are numerous in Czechoslovakia, Hungary, and parts of Poland and Yugoslavia.

Animals are important in the agricultural economy of the area. Cattle dominate in the central and northern sectors. Hungary is noted for its beef production. In Bohemia and western Poland, dairying is well developed. In the mountainous, drier, southern part of the Balkan Peninsula sheep and goats replace cattle. Horses and oxen are the chief draft animals in the better farming areas, mules and donkeys in the poorer areas. Poultry production is on the increase, especially in the western sections.

Agricultural practices, even in the most progressive parts of the region, depend chiefly upon animals. The yields are lower than in Western Europe, and farm labor productivity is considerably below that of the American farmer. These conditions are caused by natural and human factors. With the exception of Hungary, the Walachian Plain, the basins of Czechoslovakia, the loess area in Poland, and certain valleys in Yugoslavia, the soils of the region are weak or outright infertile. The land has been under cultivation for centuries, which intensifies the poverty of the soils. Over much of the area the climate, if not actually marginal, is capricious enough to limit agricultural production. The peasants, trying to eke out a living on their small holdings, especially in cases where the land is poor, fare well when they can feed their families. There is little opportunity to accumulate capital to be used for improving the soils.

The human factor is equally important. Frequent wars in the area have drained its resources. Prolonged Turkish rule over the

Balkan states and Hungary and the Russian wars and rule over Poland retarded agricultural development in most of the Shatter Belt. This was one of the last areas in which landless peasants operated huge estates for the benefit of the aristocratic absentee owners. Land hunger of the peasantry, who form the majority of population in all these countries, was one of the strongest socio-political forces shaping the destinies of Eastern Europe. How breaking up the large estates, parceling out the land among the peasants, and the collectivization of farms that is being tried in many countries since World War II have affected the agricultural production of the region is yet to be determined.

**Forestry and Mining.** Forestry is most important in Poland and Czechoslovakia where the mountains of the latter and much of the glacial till areas of the former are best suited for forest use. Under German influences, the large tracts of forests are well managed. In Hungary the area suited for forests is small. What there is, is well managed, but it is insufficient even for domestic consumption. In the other countries, forest management must be improved to a considerable degree if sufficient supplies are to be available.

With few exceptions mining is not fully developed. This results more from the general low level of economic development than from lack of mineral resources. Except for Hungary, which has only bauxite and limited reserves of coal, lignite, and petroleum, the countries are well endowed with minerals. Coal, petroleum, iron, copper, zinc, lead, bauxite, salt, potash, graphite, kaolin, and glass sands are among the mineral resources. All except flat Hungary have great hydroelectric potentials, which are hardly used even by those countries most industrially advanced. Czechoslovakia and Poland show the greatest development of mining. Considerable quantities of Polish coal are exported. In Romania, outside interests developed the Ploesti oil field, an important source of petroleum. Otherwise Romania, like Yugoslavia, Bulgaria, and the others, has great but undeveloped mineral resources.

**Transportation.** Effective transportation is the first essential for modern economic life. Much of the retarded development of Eastern Europe, both cultural and economic, can be attributed to isolation and the lack of efficient means of transportation in large areas. It is true that much of the region is mountainous, which is a handicap. Yet the Danube offers an excellent waterway which is little used, when compared with the Rhine, because it flows to the east instead of the west; also there are several boundaries where custom duties and restrictions harass traffic.

Only the three western states have adequate rail facilities. Even here, eastern and northern Poland and Slovakia have few railroads. Hungary's railroad system lost effectiveness when the territorial changes after 1918 left the country with railways that radiated outward from Budapest but gave the peripheral connecting lines to the Succession States. In one instance, the town was left in Hungary but the tracks and the railroad station were adjudged to Czechoslovakia. Controversies over such matters have greatly embittered the participants and increased the region's willingness to go to war. The Balkan states have few railroads. The most important ones form a link in the great international routes of Europe like the Orient Express, London-Paris-Istanbul route, or the ill-famed Berlin-Baghdad line.

Highway transportation facilities are poorer than the railroads. Many present highways were built for military rather than economic reasons. Poland inherited some good roads in Silesia and has constructed others. Western Czechoslovakia has a fair network of motor roads. There are a few good trunk roads and a fair net of motorable roads in Hungary. In the other nations, however, highways are poor. Some development has occurred in air transport, but the present political situation is a serious handicap for its full development.

**Industry.** Manufacturing is little developed in the region although most of the governments are striving to increase industrial production. Only in Czechoslovakia, and to a lesser degree in Poland, does manufacturing rise to significance. In these countries, coal and iron ore form the base for heavy industries. In addition there are textiles and other light industries. Some, like the Czech glass industry, have achieved an international reputation. In Hungary, food industries are important, especially flour milling. Romania and Yugoslavia have some heavy industries but little else of importance. Bulgaria has a few factories; Albania is practically without modern manufacturing.

## COUNTRIES OF EASTERN EUROPE

As a result of the geographic and historic conditions described, countries of the Shatter Belt can be divided into two groups, the northern group consisting of Poland, Czechoslovakia, and Hungary, and the Balkan group of Romania, Yugoslavia, Bulgaria, Albania, with the small area of European Turkey. The countries of the first group have belonged to the West for over a millennium; they accepted Western culture and the Western form of religion. The Balkan states, on the other hand, received the Greek Orthodox form of Christianity and the Byzantine autocratic political organization. Superimposed upon these conditions came centuries of Turkish misrule. Although Turkish influence shrank during the second half of the last century, its power in the Balkans did not completely disappear until 1912. These facts, coupled with the mountainous character of the countries and the resultant high degree of isolation, should amply explain their retarded development.

marcation, illustrates better than any other existing European country the troubled fate of a buffer state. The original core of the country lies in the upper valley of the Vistula around the ancient capital, Krakow. While Germany was disorganized and Russia limited to Muscovy, Poland flourished. As German power on the west and Russian power on the east asserted itself, Poland's fate became sealed by the three partitions during the eighteenth century, when the country ceased to be an independent state until revived in 1918. By defeating a Bolshevik army, Poland won the historic boundaries of 1772 including a large area east of the Curzon Line which had a Russian population. The Curzon Line was a proposed boundary between Poland and Russia which would have included only Polish people within the nation. The Polish Corridor, leading to the Baltic Sea, and the Wilno district were other acquisitions which ultimately caused the fall of Poland and led to its partition between Nazi Germany and the U.S.S.R.

Poland, today, is smaller than before World War II. The eastern Polish territories were transferred to the Soviet Union. Pomerania, Silesia, and the southern portions of former East Prussia which were transferred from Germany to Poland as compensation for the loss, are so much smaller in area that Poland lost almost 29,000 square miles of territory. Her losses in population were proportionately greater. With 25 million people in 1950, she had almost 9 million fewer than before the war. Besides losing people to the U.S.S.R., Poland lost population by war devastation and by the expulsion of Germans from Poland and the newly acquired territories. But the Poles are rallying; the birth rate is making up for war

### TABLE 9-1. EASTERN EUROPE

| Country | Area, sq miles | Population |
|---|---|---|
| Albania | 11,100 | 1,200,000 |
| Bulgaria | 42,796 | 7,235,000 |
| Czechoslovakia | 49,354 | 12,340,000 |
| Hungary | 35,912 | 9,313,000 |
| Poland | 120,359 | 24,976,926 |
| Romania | 91,700 | 16,094,000 |
| Turkey (in Europe) | 9,257 | 1,627,000 |
| Yugoslavia | 99,181 | 16,850,000 |

### Poland

Poland, situated on the Great European Plain with no well-defined north-south lines of de-

losses, and the expelled Germans have been replaced by repatriated Poles from the lost eastern territories.

The Polish state came out of the war with better boundaries than it had had before. Based upon the Oder and Neisse (Nysa Luzycka) Rivers, the western boundary is straight and presumably defendable. The southern boundary lies on the mountains of Bohemia and the Carpathians. The eastern and northern lines were established in treaties with the U.S.S.R. to mutual satisfaction. Through these new boundaries, although none except the eastern is recognized as a *de jure* boundary by the United States, the new state acquired a helpfully compact shape. By the exchange of population, Poland achieved a national homogeneity instead of its insecure majority of prewar days. In resources Poland gained greatly for it acquired (1) Europe's largest and second best coal field in exchange for most of its oil fields and potash mines; (2) the industrial capacity of Silesia; (3) the navigable Oder River; and (4) the Baltic seaports of Stettin (Szczecin) and Danzig.

Before the war, agricultural practices were primitive; yields per acre and labor productivity both were low. Poland had a serious agrarian problem since most of the land was in large estates operated by landless peasants. Since the war, the estates have been divided, but productivity has remained low.

The chief subsistence crops, rye and potatoes, are the two best suited for the sandy soils and the cool, short growing season. About half the land used for cereals is in rye. The acreage of potatoes is almost as large as that of rye. In the south, where the glacial till gives way to the rich loess soils, wheat becomes important but barely supplies the domestic demand. Barley and oats complete the list of cereals. Sugar beets and flax are the two most important export items.

Animal industries, including horses for work animals, are important. Beef, dairy cattle, and swine are raised. Before the war, meat and butter were exported.

The main problem confronting Poland is industrialization, Communist style. To what extent this industrialization will succeed, under the present circumstances, is difficult to estimate, although basic requirements are present. Mineral resources, especially coal and zinc, are plentiful. The large coal production and iron ore from both local sources and from Sweden have favored the development of iron and steel

*Figure 9-6 Tractor and disk plow in operation to prepare land for planting on a state farm near Ciezkowice, Poland. (Courtesy of Embassy, Polish Peoples Republic.)*

industries, including machinery and shipbuilding. Glass, cement, textiles, tanneries, and chemicals are also important manufactures.

Hand in hand with industrialization goes urbanization and Poland is becoming thoroughly urbanized. Next to Czechoslovakia, Poland has the highest percentage of urban dwellers. Warsaw (Warszawa), the political and commercial center of the country, is located on the Vistula River. It has water transportation as well as rail, highway, and air connections. Many bridges span the Vistula to link the industrial area east and northeast of the river with the rest of the city. Metal-working industries, electrical appliances, and the making of tractors and automobiles are among the important manufacturing activities. Much of the city is new, for it was necessary to rebuild large areas which were destroyed during the Nazi invasion of 1939.

Lodz, Krakow, Danzig, and Stettin are the chief cities in their respective areas. Lodz is the youngest of the large Polish cities although it was established during the early part of the fifteenth century. It is a city of contrasts where many large, modern buildings stand adjacent to old frame or rock structures about to fall. The city is the principal Polish center for the manufacturing of textiles, clothing, and leather goods. Krakow is the important trading and commercial center of southern Poland. Before 1595 it was the capital of the country. Danzig and Stettin are the two chief ports. Danzig is a transshipment point for places on the Vistula; Stettin serves the Oder and the canals connected with it. Each also has numerous industrial activities.

For the future, as in the past, Poland faces great problems. Under the tyranny of an alien ideology the country seems to be making industrial progress. In 1956 the country reorganized its government and, although it remained Communist, a greater degree of home rule apparently resulted.

## Czechoslovakia

Czechoslovakia was carved out of Austria-Hungary in 1919. The boundaries, drawn with-

*Figure 9-7    The market place in Krakow. This city, once the capital of Poland, is located just north of the Carpathian Mountains. (Courtesy of Embassy, Polish Peoples Republic.)*

*Figure 9-8 The central part of Bohemia and Moravia is flat and the soil is fertile. This picture shows a power-driven planting machine in use. (Courtesy of Fotoddeleni Ctk.)*

out considering the nationalities of the inhabitants, included Moravia, the ancient Kingdom of Bohemia, and Upper Hungary, part of which was renamed Slovakia and part Carpatho-Ruthenia. In Upper Hungary the division was made without a plebiscite, contrary to the Wilsonian principle of national self-determination. As a result, when the solidly Hungarian fringes of the two Alfölds were included in the new state almost three-quarters of a million Magyars found themselves under Czech rule. In addition, over 3 million Germans and almost half a million Ruthenians and Poles were also included in Czechoslovakia. Thus, the new country had all the makings of a troubled future. During Hitler's regime in Germany, Czechoslovakia was torn apart. The German fringes were joined to Germany and the Czech coreland of Bohemia and Moravia was taken over by Hitler as a subdivision of the Reich. Slovakia, shorn of her Magyar areas which were returned to Hungary, became an independent pro-German republic.

At the war's end the Allies reestablished the *status quo,* with the exception of Carpatho-Ruthenia which was added to the U.S.S.R. As partial compensation for this loss, Czechoslovakia received a few square miles of additional Hungarian territory near Bratislava (Pozsony) and, like Poland, gained the right to expel the German and Hungarian minorities.

From the topographic point of view, the country does form a homogeneous area. The heavily forested Carpathian arc definitely separates Slovakia from the strong Bohemian fortress and its foreland in Moravia. All the natural ways through Slovakia's river valleys lead to the Alföld and Budapest, not Prague. The mountainous, mineralized, forested but food-deficient Slovakia is the natural complement to the treeless food basket of Hungary. Yet during the interwar period, political tensions made a sensible economic integration impossible; instead a senseless rivalry prevailed, detrimental to both countries.

Czechoslovakia is well endowed with natural resources. Its population is industrious and progressive. Bohemia is the westernmost and most Westernized unit of the Shatter Belt. It has the most intensive agriculture, the highest yields, the best animals, and the highest ratio of tractors on farms. Czech industries are world famous. The great Skoda Iron and Machinery Works near Pilsen (Plzen) is outstanding. Czech glass and Pilsen beer have world renown. Textile, shoe, earthenware, and china factories are also important.

Slovakia, even on the border of the plain, is not as well developed as Bohemia. But as Bohemia served Austria so Slovakia started to develop basic manufacturing processes which served the people of Hungary. The finishing industries were concentrated in Budapest. After 1918 these ties were broken, bringing hardship

*Figure 9-9  Czechoslovakia is an industrialized country with plants that manufacture many types of machinery and a wide variety of other products. (Courtesy of Fotosluzba Ctk.)*

to all concerned and forcing an industrial re-alignment.

Agriculture in the Bohemian Basin is highly intensive and productive. In the mountainous areas, especially of Slovakia, agriculture becomes extensive, yields low, and the crops limited in variety. The chief crops are rye, barley, potatoes, sugar beets, wheat, oats, and tobacco. Czechoslovakia is a leading world producer of the first four crops enumerated. In addition, hay, hops, and deciduous fruits are grown. Some corn is grown in southern Slovakia. Barley and hops supply the raw materials for the Czech breweries, sugar beets for the sugar mills. Hops and beet sugar are also exported.

The animal industries are significant, cattle and pigs being the leading animals. Czechoslovakia is the second producer of milk in the Shatter Belt. The Czechs have developed a method of curing which makes the Prague ham highly esteemed. The number of horses is declining because of the increased use of tractors.

Lignite and bituminous coal are the two chief mineral products of the country. Czechoslovakia produces almost half of the northern region's lignite and holds second place in this area for coal production. This prominence it owes mainly to control of the southernmost extension of the great Silesian coal field. The country

mines about four-fifths of the iron ore produced in the Shatter Belt. Crude petroleum, silver, gold, uranium, pyrites, kaolin and clays, glass sand, and construction materials are also produced.

Iron and steel manufactures, together with machinery, form the leading branch of industry in Czechoslovakia. The industry has two centers, one in the Silesian coal field at the confluence of the Oppa and Oder Rivers near the Moravian Gate and Corridor. In addition to being the most important iron and steel center, it is also an important traffic node. The second center is Pilsen where the Skoda works, which manufacture munitions, locomotives, airplanes, and electric motors, are located.

The textile industry centers mainly on Brunn (Brno) the second largest city of the country. The city boasts also of breweries, the Brenn machine gun factory, chemical plants, and machine shops.

The capital city, Prague, the largest Czech city, of almost a million inhabitants, is located on both banks of the Moldau Vltava River. Prague is a bridge city on the main route from Germany through the Elbe to the Vienna Basin. This historic city is today the political, cultural, and commercial center of the republic. Textiles, chemicals, paper, glass, and machinery are manufactured there.

Bratislava, besides being the provincial capital of Slovakia, is also the principal Danubian port of Czechoslovakia. The city is a bridge city and rail and road center as well. For a century and a half it was the capital of Hungary. During the short life of the Slovak Republic, the city served as its capital.

Though Czechoslovakia has direct access to three large navigable waterways—Danube, Elbe, and Oder—only a relatively small proportion of its foreign trade clears by water. Overland transportation, especially rail, is the most important. Bohemia and Moravia have excellent rail and good road facilities. The Hamburg-Prague-Vienna line brings the railroad from the North Sea to the Vienna node. The north-south line between the Adriatic-Mediterranean region and the Baltic utilizes the

Moravian Corridor and fans out from there to the Baltic ports, Warsaw, and the Soviet Union. As a result Czechoslovakia has a large transit trade. The republic has the largest foreign trade of the seven countries of the Shatter Belt. The exports normally consist of textiles, machinery, iron and steel products, glass and chinaware, shoes, sugar, and munitions. Cotton, iron ore, and foodstuffs are among the chief imports. Before World War II Czechoslovakia had considerable trade with Western Europe, but at present its main trade alignment is with the U.S.S.R. and its satellites.

## Hungary

The Hungarian People's Republic is a residual state of the ancient kingdom of Hungary which later, combined with the Hapsburg lands, formed the Austro-Hungarian empire until its collapse at the close of World War I in 1918. The Magyars moved into the central basin of the Danube at the close of the ninth century, coming originally from the Middle Volga region. The Great Alföld, with its rich pasture lands and open landscape, suited the Magyars, who accepted the Latin form of Christianity. St. Stephen was crowned first king of Hungary in 1001.

Peace was not the portion of Hungary. Situated on the main route between the North Sea and Western Europe on the one hand and the eastern Mediterranean and Asia Minor on the other, first between Byzantium and the Holy Roman Empire, later between the Hapsburg and the Ottoman Turk empires, Hungary faced a constant struggle to maintain its independence. In addition to defending its homeland against Tatars, Turks, and Russians, Hungary also had to defend its constitutional liberties against the absolutism of its Hapsburg kings, who acquired the crown during the sixteenth century when the Turks occupied most of the Alföld and the capital city, Buda. After the Turks were finally expelled, the country was in ruins. During the nineteenth century, the Hungarians tried to rebuild their domain. Peace was badly needed but instead conflict arose with the reactionary government of the Haps-

*Figure 9-10 Budapest, the capital of Hungary, is located on both sides of the Danube (Duna) River. The two parts of the city are connected by numerous bridges. (Courtesy of Ambassador of Peoples Republic of Hungary.)*

burgs. About the time these differences were adjusted World War I started. Then, by the Treaty of Trianon, Hungary lost about two-thirds of its territory and population.

Between World War I and World War II, Hungary asked for a revision of the Treaty of Trianon. When these pleas went unheard, the country became an ally of Italy and was involved in Axis politics. What the democracies had not done for Hungary the Axis Powers did. Between 1938 and 1940, the Hungarian-inhabited territories of the Succession States were returned to Hungary, increasing its size to 66,-000 square miles, and its population to over 15 million people. In 1945, these territories were ceded by Hungary to Czechoslovakia together with a small additional area at the Bratislava bridgehead. These last territorial changes were accompanied by a large-scale repatriation of Hungarians, especially from Czechoslovakia.

*Figure 9-11  Harvesting Tokay grapes in Hungary. These grapes are a superior table variety and are also used for making wine. (Courtesy of Ambassador of Peoples Republic of Hungary.)*

For centuries Hungary has been the granary of Central Europe, and agriculture is still one of the major industries of the country. The loss of southern Hungary has, however, reduced the country's importance as a corn and wheat producer. Nevertheless wheat is the chief crop. Winter wheat is dominant in the western areas whereas spring wheat is grown mostly in the east. Both are high-quality wheats yielding excellent flour. In the sandy areas, rye replaces wheat. The Hungarian rye production is significant, and the country is one of the principal producers of this cereal. The central Danubian lowlands are the northernmost areas where corn is produced on a large scale in Europe, yet Hungary is one of the principal producers of corn in the world. Corn is the second cereal crop of the country. Barley and oats are also grown. Since World War II, wheat production has somewhat declined. It has been more than balanced, however, by the increased production of other cereals, especially corn.

Sugar beets, potatoes, and tobacco are the chief crops. Hungary ranks second in tobacco and third in sugar beet and potato production in Eastern Europe. Truck crops, some under irrigation, are produced for domestic urban markets as well as for limited exports. Deciduous fruits and grapes are important, especially in the Transdanubian area and on the southward-facing slopes of the Central Hills. Especially fine wine is produced in the volcanic Tokaj mountain area and the region along Lake Balaton.

The extensive herding of the Hungarian long-horned cattle has given way to field crops and the intensive pasturage of Western types of beef cattle. Only in a few areas in eastern Hungary, are there remnants of the old type of cattle raising. With the improvement of beef cattle came also the expansion of dairying. Pigs form the second most important animal group. The sheep contingent of Hungary is small in comparison to that in other nations within the region, especially the Balkan countries. The ravages of war were felt to a great extent in the animal industries, and the number of livestock is still at least one-third less than before World

War II. Insufficient sources of power and mineral resources handicap manufacturing. Hungary has some bituminous coal and lignite deposits, but neither in quality nor in quantity are they sufficient for large-scale industrialization. With its low relief, Hungary has hardly any water power potential. Under the present regime, however, coal and lignite production is strongly emphasized. Although the production of 1.4 million metric tons of bituminous coal per year makes Hungary a poor third after Poland and Czechoslovakia, its production of 12 million metric tons of lignite ranks second in the northern region. Hungary is the second producer of petroleum and third in the production of natural gas in Eastern Europe. These resources, however, are of relatively small importance. Some iron ore is produced for local use. Hungary is the chief producer of the manganese used in steelmaking in the region. Bauxite is the most important metallic ore mined in the country. Depending upon circumstances, Hungary is the second or third European producer of this important source of aluminum.

Except for the iron and steel plants in the Miskolc area, most of the manufacturing establishments are concentrated in and around Budapest. Manufacturing started with flour milling and sugar mills at the turn of the century. Food and tobacco industries are still important. The textile industry has been fostered by tariff and general economic policies.

Hungary has few real cities. Budapest, the capital, is a cosmopolitan metropolis. Located on both banks of the Danube, it is an important bridge city, river port, and the cultural and political center of Hungary. Buda, on the hilly west bank of the river, is the historic city with its fortress, royal palace, and other monuments. Pest, on a low platform rising above the floodplain on the east side of the Danube, is the modern commercial and industrial center. Badly damaged during World War II, much of the city has been rebuilt.

Szeged on the Tisza River, though an important river port and commercial center, still bears the imprint of an overgrown village agglomeration. The same is true of Debreçen, the commercial center of the northeastern part of the Alföld. Miskolc, though smaller than either

*Figure 9-12   City square in Szeged, Hungary. The city is located on the Tisza River in the southern part of the country. (Courtesy of Ambassador of Peoples Republic of Hungary.)*

of the two cities mentioned, is a true city with manufacturing, trade, and commerce being the dominant economic activities. The great iron and steel plants at Diosgyör, seven miles west from Miskolc, are tributaries of the latter's economy.

## Romania

Romania forms the easternmost wedge separating the northern from the southern Slavs. Though linguistically the Romanians belong to the West, culturally they are of the East. Thus, Romania forms a transitional link between the two cultures. Romania arose from the unification of Walachia and Moldavia in 1861 and became an independent kingdom in 1881. Since then it has gained and lost territories several times. The greatest gains followed World War I when Transylvania and the border of the Alföld, together with the major share of the Banat, were transferred from Hungary to Romania. Bessarabia also became a part of the country when it was occupied by the Romanians, pushing the eastern boundary to the Dniester (Dnestr) River. During World War II, Romania had to yield half of Transylvania and the Alföld border to Hungary but regained it again in 1945. The Soviet Union reoccupied Bessarabia and incorporated it into the Moldavian S.S.R. Bulgaria regained southern Dobrugea.

There is some resemblance between Romania and Czechoslovakia. Both are newly created countries, both are rent apart by the Carpathian Mountains, both have within their boundaries large minority groups, both have rich mineral and forest resources and the best water power potentials in the Shatter Belt. Here the likeness ends. Whereas the Czechs were the most highly developed group in their country, the Romanians of the Old Kingdom were generally on a low level of culture. Transylvania showed higher development in all fields of human endeavor than did Old Romania. These cultural discrepancies expressed themselves in the checkered political development of the country.

The Romanian state is based upon the Lower Basin of the Danube as Hungary is upon the Central Danubian Basin. Transylvania is a mountain-surrounded upland between the two lowlands. Its approaches toward the Alföld are more open and gradual than toward the Walachian Plain or Moldavia, thus for centuries its orientation was toward Hungary. Hungarians and Germans settled in the valleys and in the open basin of Transylvania. The Romanians occupied the high valleys and alpine meadows of the mountains, thus enclosing the Hungarian and German elements. Based upon such distribution of people, Transylvania was adjudged to Romania in 1918. The area then became tributary to the Lower Basin of the Danube.

The Walachian Plain, like the Alföld, has rich, dark-colored, deep soils which form the basic asset of the country. Wheat, corn, and other cereals are grown in almost unbroken continuity. In recent years, Romania has reached its prewar level of wheat production with 2.6 million metric tons, about 10 per cent of a year's wheat production in the United States. Romania is the largest wheat producer in the Shatter Belt. The most important crop, however, is corn, Romania ranking among the first producers of corn in Europe and holding fourth or fifth place in the world. Corn is the main staple of the Romanian peasantry, which enables the country to export a considerable proportion of its wheat crop. Barley, oats, rye, and potatoes are also grown on a limited scale, mostly in Transylvania. Fruits, especially plums, hemp, sugar beets, and tobacco are also produced. The principal handicaps are the poor farming methods used by the Romanian peasants and the low crop yields per acre.

The country has numerous cattle, relatively few pigs, and a large number of sheep. Sheep are found mostly in the mountains, where a strong transhumance movement has developed, and on the dry steppes of the east. Romania produces about 1 per cent of the world's wool. The importance of sheep, the low yields per man and per acre are all typical earmarks of the Balkan countries.

Romania is rather well endowed with mineral resources, petroleum and natural gas being the most important. Outside of the Soviet Union, the Ploesti field is the largest in Europe, and

Romania is the chief European producer of both petroleum and natural gas. In addition, Romania has important salt deposits, bituminous coal and lignite beds, iron ore, manganese, lead, and zinc deposits. With so much of its territory being mountainous the water power potentials are great. Yet with all these advantages, Romania's industrial development is slight.

City life in Romania is confined to the capital city of Bucharest (Bucuresti), the cities of the former Hungarian territories, Ploesti, and the Danubian–Black Sea ports of Braila and Galati. Bucharest, on the Dambovita River at an important east-west route, is a modern westernized city. It is not only the political, economic, and railroad center of Romania but also an important manufacturing city. Its industries include machinery, textiles, chemicals, leather, and metal goods. Cluj (Kolozsvar, Clausenburg), the capital of Transylvania, is the cultural and industrial center of the region. Braila and Galati are deep-water ports on the Danube accessible to seafaring vessels. Their chief exports are wheat and timber. Constanta on the Black Sea, though smaller than the Danubian ports, is the chief port of Romania. A pipeline connects it with the Ploesti oil field; thus it is the principal oil port of the country.

## Bulgaria

Bulgaria antedates both Hungary and Poland. The original Bulgars were kin to the Magyars, Finns, and Estonians. Unlike their kinsmen, the Bulgar overlords were completely absorbed by the Slavic element they conquered and ruled. Today, only their name remains as a memento of their glorious but dim past. They were converted by the Byzantines to the Oriental form of Christianity. This cultural tie, however, did not prevent frequent warfare between Byzantines and Bulgars.

The Bulgarian conquest by the Turks was completed by 1371, and for the next five hundred years the Turks ruled the country with an iron hand. Unlike their practice in other conquered European areas, the Turks moved into Bulgaria and Thrace in rather large numbers. The significance of modern Bulgaria, resur-

rected in the 1870s, does not lie in its size, or number of inhabitants; rather it hinges upon the strategic location of the country. The Sofia (Sofija) Basin, sandwiched between the arc of the Balkan Mountains and the apex of the Rhodope Massif, controls the most important routes of the peninsula. Thus, the basin, due to its nodality and easy access, is one of the most strategic areas of the peninsula. The Turks early realized its significance and so, at a later period, did the Germans and the Russians. The present government is a Communist republic.

The economy of the country is dominated by the simplest type of peasant agriculture. Deep loess deposits on the Danubian Foreland and fine alluvium in the river valleys provide good, fertile soils in the restricted areas of level or nearly level terrain. The climate south of the Stara Planina is mild enough for fruits, grapes, and roses. On the Foreland, which is open to the influx of winter colds from the Russian steppes, cereals are grown. Sheepherding dominates in the dry Deliorman, the Dobrugea, and the mountainous districts of the country.

The chief crops are wheat, corn, barley, and millet. Some sugar beets, oats, potatoes, and rye are also grown. Bulgaria is the sole producer, in this region, of attar of roses which is the finest base for perfume. It is sold, almost exclusively, to France. From 3,000 to 5,000 ounces of petals are required to produce one ounce of attar. Normal annual production is about 2,000 ounces valued at a million dollars. Before World War II, Bulgaria was the region's largest producer of tobacco; since then, however, she has regained neither her prewar level of production nor her leading rank in the industry. Rice, cotton, truck, and orchard production show intensive forms of cultivation. Sericulture, based upon the mulberry orchards, flourishes in the warm southern valleys. The Bulgarian peasant, though lacking capital, modern tools, and machinery, through industry and perseverance makes the country productive. He uses much of his spare time, and the off season, for home crafts and industries, the products of which are often exported.

Sheep grazing is the chief animal industry.

Cattle, horses, goats, and pigs are all comparatively few. Cheese-making is well developed; both ewe's and goat's milk are used. Yoghurt, made originally from ewe's milk, has become a well-known commodity even in American supermarkets. Mules and asses number high in Bulgaria; together with water buffaloes and oxen they are the most important work animals in the country. Poultry raising and egg production are important. Millet, rather than the expensive corn or barley, is used to a great extent as a poultry feed.

Bulgaria has rich mineral deposits but only a few of the resources are actually being worked. What little manufacturing is done is based, mainly, upon agricultural resources. Since manufacturing is still in an incubation stage, manufactured goods form the most important items among Bulgaria's imports.

The population being 80 per cent peasant, there are only a few cities. Sofia (Sofija) has the largest population. It is the capital of the republic and the economic and cultural center as well. The city is the most important traffic node on the Balkan Peninsula. Plovdiv, the classical Philippopolis of King Philip of Macedonia, is the commercial and industrial center of the Maritsa Valley. Varna is the chief Black Sea port of the country. In addition to commercial activities, it supports also a few manufacturing and processing plants such as cotton and woolen mills, tanneries, flour mills, and chemical plants.

## Yugoslavia

Yugoslavia, like Czechoslovakia, is also a newly created country. It is composed of several distinct cultural and political units which more or less coincide with its natural regions. Six related yet competing groups of Slavic people form the Yugoslav nation. The division between these groups is the result of historical developments which placed these diverse groups under different cultural influences following their geographic distribution in the area. The westernmost are the Slovenes who were under German influence from the tenth century and were ruled by the Hapsburgs after 1335. The Croats in-

habit the lowlands of the Drava and Sava Rivers. In 1102, Croatia united with the kingdom of Hungary but maintained a large degree of autonomy. Both the Croats and the Slovenes became thoroughly Westernized. They are Roman Catholic in religion, use the Latin script, and have developed, especially the Croats, in a constitutional, parliamentary atmosphere.

The third Westernized group of people are the townspeople along the Adriatic coast, politically a part of Croatia. During the flourishing days of the Venetian Republic and the great Levantine trade, these cities were either held by Venice, or were allied city republics, usually with an Italian ruling class. Several of them maintained their freedom even against the Turkish onslaught. Facing the Adriatic Sea and backed by the abruptly rising Dinaric Alps, Venetian and Italian influence did not penetrate beyond the immediate vicinity of the coast.

In contrast to the Western influences of the German, Hungarian, and Venetian cultures, the rest of the people of Yugoslavia developed under the shadow of Constantinople. The Serbs became converted to the Greek Orthodox Church, accepted the Cyrillic alphabet, and remained under Oriental influence. The Turks conquered and ruled them for five hundred years. Islam made many converts among the people, especially the Bogomils who were numerous in Macedonia and Bosnia. As a result of these conversions, and actual settlement of Turkish families in the area, among the Bosnians and the Macedonians there is a large Mohammedan element today which represents the third cultural influence. The people of Montenegro (Crnagora) maintained their independence during the Turkish invasion at the expense of constant fighting with the Turks. This left them free but impoverished and isolated. The Macedonians present a difficult problem. They speak a separate language and live in scattered groups divided among Greece, Bulgaria, and Yugoslavia. They are too few in numbers to organize themselves into a nation. Perhaps the simplest way to describe the Macedonians' attitude is to say that they never feel part of the ethnic group which rules them at the moment.

In addition to these related Slav groups, Yugoslavia has large foreign minority groups of Germans, Magyars, Romanians, and Albanians along the border zones. Jews are a minority group in the eastern cultural areas. Their number was sharply reduced during the Nazi occupation. Two nomadic groups of rather small numbers are the Gypsies and the mountaineer herdsmen.

This diversity of cultural, political, and economic backgrounds and conditions is the main weakness of the new state, the original name of which was the Kingdom of the Serbs, Croats, and Slovenes. The political traditions and ambitions of the various groups were in such conflict that the democratic parliamentary system failed to work and the king assumed a personal dictatorship. The country was reorganized; historic units were broken up, a policy of forced unification adopted, and the country's name was officially changed to Yugoslavia. After eighteen years of smouldering unrest a new, more liberal constitution was promulgated in 1939, but soon afterward Yugoslavia was overrun by the Germans. After the war ended and Marshal Tito's Communist regime was firmly established, Yugoslavia was reorganized into six People's Republics and two autonomous areas administered by the Serbian People's Republic. These form the Federated People's Republic of Yugoslavia.

There are vast variations in the economic development as in the cultural conditions of Yugoslavia. Agriculture is the dominant economic activity of the people. In the western areas, especially on the fine, rich loessal soils, heavy yields of wheat and corn are harvested. In normal years the corn yield in the Backa is, if not the highest, at least among the highest in Europe and better than that of the United States. Sugar beets, mulberry orchards, some rye, barley, and oats are also produced. Corn is the most widespread crop, but as one leaves the Vojvodina, the yields drop off. Poorer soils, primitive cultivation, and the vagaries of weather account for the lower yields. The rainfall is highly variable and dry years are frequent. Corn

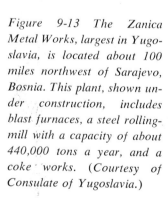

*Figure 9-13 The Zanica Metal Works, largest in Yugoslavia, is located about 100 miles northwest of Sarajevo, Bosnia. This plant, shown under construction, includes blast furnaces, a steel rolling-mill with a capacity of about 440,000 tons a year, and a coke works. (Courtesy of Consulate of Yugoslavia.)*

is mostly grown in the more humid Danubian–Northern Morava section; in the dry southern area, wheat takes the lead.

In the sheltered valleys, on favorably exposed slopes, orchards and vineyards produce a variety of fruits and grapes. Plums are especially important in Bosnia and Slavonia. The dry weather assists in drying the fruit; prunes are a valuable addition to exports of fresh fruit. Much fruit goes to distilleries for the production of fruit brandies. Wine production is also important. Wherever the growing season is long enough, and summer temperatures are high enough, rice and cotton are grown for home consumption. Tobacco is widely cultivated. At present, Yugoslavia is the chief producer of this crop in the Shatter Belt and exports considerable quantities of tobacco and tobacco products.

The Adriatic coast and the lower Vardar Valley support a Mediterranean type of agriculture. Walnuts, olives, and grapes are abundant. The mountains present almost insurmountable problems for agriculture. Generally they are better suited to forest and grazing economies than to crop production.

Isolation, which is a key to understanding Yugoslavia, breeds conservatism and an attitude of "what was good for grandfather is good enough for me." To overcome this inertia takes education and time; hence agricultural practices are still primitive over most of the country.

Animal industries, especially sheepherding, are of eminent importance. Yugoslavia, with almost 12 million sheep, has the greatest number among the countries of the Shatter Belt. It also leads in wool production. Transhumance is well developed but on the wane at present. Pigs are also numerous. Many of them are herded and fattened, mostly on acorns, in the great oak and beech forests. This, too, is a diminishing form of resource utilization.

Except for coal and petroleum, Yugoslavia is well endowed with mineral resources. Though the country is mountainous, the climate places restrictions upon the development of Yugoslavia's water power. These limitations of energy supplies are serious handicaps to industrialization. Most of the manufacturing is simple processing. There is a growing iron and steel production. Sugar manufacture, flour milling, paper and pulp industries, cementmaking, and some textile mills round out the picture of manufacturing. Most of the rich ores are exported from the country either in the original or in concentrated form. Among these, antimony, bauxite, copper, chrome, iron ore, lead, and zinc are important. Because railroads and roads are all but lacking in the mountainous areas, increased mining activity must await the development of an adequate transportation system.

Yugoslavia, like the other Balkan states, is a country of peasants living in small, scattered, often isolated, communities. Of its five cities with over 100,000 inhabitants only Belgrade (Beograd), the capital, is in the eastern cultural area of the country. Belgrade occupies a most strategic site. Its origin goes back far into history. At the confluence of the Sava and Dan-

*Figure 9-14 Public buildings in Belgrade, capital of Yugoslavia. (Courtesy of Consulate of Yugoslavia.)*

ube Rivers, a few miles west from where the Morava empties its waters into the master stream, Belgrade, a bridge city, is a transportation center of first order in the Balkan Peninsula. Not only has it control over rail and road transportation, but it is an important river port as well. It is also an industrial center and the only really Western-appearing community in the eastern cultural region of Yugoslavia.

The other large cities are all located in the former Austria-Hungarian territories of Yugoslavia. Zagreb (Zagrab, Agram), the capital of Croatia, is located on the Sava River where it emerges from its narrow upper valley. The city has a nodal position with reference to north-south and east-west routes leading from Vienna and Budapest to Fiume and from Belgrade to Trieste. Ljubljana (Laibach), the capital of Slovenia, is situated on the Upper Sava River. The important Vienna to Trieste railroad passes through the city. In contrast to these cities Sarajevo, capital of Bosnia-Herzegovina, is an Eastern city with a number of mosques and graceful minarets and an architecture which bears the undeniable imprint of a Mohammedan world.

Despite the numerous towns along the Dalmatian coast, Yugoslavia, until recently, did not have a good harbor. When Fiume was taken over from Italy the country acquired a rather well-equipped port. Even though it is the least handicapped of any port, Fiume has a difficult approach from the hinterland.

The greatest value of the Adriatic coast, especially its Dalmatian portion, may lie in its natural beauty and delightful climate. Tourism was an important source of income for a few internationally known resort towns and islands even before World War I. With the tremendous development of tourism since then, the Yugoslav coast can offer the wild beauty of the Dinaric Alps, a string of picturesque islands, the impressive ruins of the ancient past, the graceful cities of the near past, and a pleasant climate.

## Albania

Albania is the smallest country in the region and the most underdeveloped of all the European

*Figure 9-15   The Adriatic coast of Yugoslavia has many old towns of which Korcula, on an island of the same name, is an example. The tower was built in the thirteenth century and is a tourist attraction. The palm trees show that the climate is of the Mediterranean type. (Courtesy of Consulate of Yugoslavia.)*

nations. Its government is Communist, affiliated with the U.S.S.R. Geographic handicaps are numerous. High, rugged mountains separate it effectively from the rest of the peninsula. Although Albania has the widest stretch of coastal plain along the Adriatic shore of the peninsula, its recently filled surface is dotted with shallow

*Figure 9-16   Istanbul, the former capital of Turkey, has a strategic location on the Bosphorus. Within the city are many historic buildings such as Soldiers Mosque shown here. (Courtesy of American Export Lines.)*

lagoons and marshes, breeding mosquitoes and malaria, which seems to be a more serious handicap than the mountains.

The Albanian people, speaking the Gheg dialect in the north and the Tosk in the south, antedate all other inhabitants of the Balkan Peninsula. In their mountain fastness they have successfully preserved their entity. Conquered with difficulty by the Turks, Albania was ruled by them for five hundred years. During this time the majority of the people accepted Islam as their religion. In the north dwell Roman Catholic, in the south Greek Orthodox minorities, with the Mohammedans occupying the central region.

The economy of the country is based upon a simple, self-sufficient agriculture. Because of the increased ameliorating influence of the sea, cit-rus fruits can be produced on the low coastal areas. Corn and wheat are the two chief crops. Tobacco, cotton, and rice are also grown. Sheep form the backbone of the animal industries. Transhumance is well developed.

With practically no roads and without railroads, the country is in no position to advance in its economic development. Albania is not as well mineralized as most of the other countries of the Shatter Belt. Petroleum and copper ore represent the mineral industries in the country's small exports; the rest is made up of limited quantities of foodstuffs, hides and skins, and lumber from the magnificent forests in the mountainous interior.

There are few towns in the country. Tiranë (Tirana), the capital, is located almost in the geographic center of the coastal plan opposite the chief port Durazzo (Durrës). Scutari (Shkoder), between the lake of the same name and the Drin River, is the center of the northern part of the country.

Small and insignificant as Albania may be, the country has a locational significance which caused it to loom important in the eyes not only of its immediate neighbors but of the Great Powers of Europe as well. Albania lies just opposite the heel of the Italian boot, where the Adriatic Sea terminates in the Strait of Otranto. The sea here is only 47 miles wide, which explains the strategic importance of Albania. Finally, in 1912 the powers agreed upon the creation of an independent Albania since none wanted to see another controlling the coast.

### European Turkey

Most of the Republic of Turkey is in Asia, but an area of 9,237 square miles lies in the southeast corner of Europe. This part has a population of over 1.6 million persons most of whom live in the city of Istanbul, formerly called Constantinople. This city is situated on the Bosporus between the Black and Marmara Seas at a narrow land crossing between Europe and Asia. Istanbul is a seaport and cosmopolitan metropolis. For many centuries it was the capital of the Eastern Roman empire and later, for nearly five hundred years, served as capital of the Turkish empire. Outside of the city most of the people are farmers.

### IN PERSPECTIVE

#### The Shatter Belt: An Unsolved Problem

Between the powerful Soviet Union and the countries of Western Europe is a zone of conflict occupied by weak and often disorganized nations that usually have been dominated alternately by Germanic and Slavic peoples. Currently, East Germany, Poland, Czechoslovakia, Hungary, Romania, Bulgaria, and Albania are satellite countries controlled by Communists. Finland and Austria are independent but are compelled by circumstances to remain on friendly terms with the U.S.S.R. Yugoslavia is an independent Communist nation. The Baltic states, once independent, have been annexed by the Soviet Union along with territories that, before World War II, belonged to Poland, Czechoslovakia, and Romania. The peoples and industries of the satellite nations are managed for the benefit of the Soviet Union. The region has some areas of excellent soils and important mineral resources, but the share of the inhabitants in these resources and in the products of their factories is reduced by the great quantities of goods sent to the U.S.S.R. Many of the inhabitants are dissatisfied with this condition of affairs as was shown by strikes and warfare in Hungary in 1956. Until the late 1950s, except for Poland, the people were unable to make effective protests to their Communist-dominated governments.

In the past, there have been many wars and frequent boundary changes among the nations in the Shatter Belt. Intense nationalism and the fear with which the varied peoples regard their neighbors have made cooperation among the diverse countries very difficult. No immediate solution of the problem of the Shatter Belt is in sight and the region is likely to remain a world problem well into the foreseeable future. A United States of Eastern Europe would be one solution, but the conflicts of interest between the countries in the Shatter Belt have prevented union or concerted action. Improvement in living standards and democratic progress both will probably be slow so long as the Shatter Belt countries are dominated by puppet Communist governments controlled by the U.S.S.R.

## EXERCISES

*1.* What countries are included in the Shatter Belt zone? Why is the region referred to as the "Shatter Belt"? How does the historical background justify this name?

*2.* In what ways has the topography aided in the development of many national groups? Has the development of these groups aided or hindered the development of strong nations? Why?

*3.* What are the principal cities of the region? Which ones are seaports or river ports? What are the chief activities of each city? How do they compare with each other in population? Why is there such a great variation?

*4.* What do the many small nations in the region gain from their separate existence? What disadvantages arise from separatism? How do these nations compare in area with each other? How do they compare with such nations as France, Germany, Sweden, and the United Kingdom?

*5.* Why is the climate of the region so varied? What is the relationship between the climate, soils, and vegetation of the region? Which areas were originally park lands?

*6.* What are the chief cultural aspects of the region? Why is there a greater variety of religions in this region than in Western Europe? In what ways does religion influence what the people do?

*7.* What are the chief minerals of the region? Where are they mined? Why are such large quantities exported? Why is the production of many minerals not developed?

*8.* Which country do you consider the best developed? What are its physical and economic handicaps and advantages? What cultural advantages does it have? What must it do to become a world leader? Can it develop as such?

*9.* Which country do you consider the least progressive? What are its physical and economic handicaps and advantages? Is its cultural background a handicap? Why? What does it need in order to become a nation with at least regional influence?

*10.* What has been the influence of World War I and World War II on this region? How has the political geography been changed? What nations have come into existence since 1914?

*11.* Why is grazing an important activity? Where is it of special importance? Which country leads in agricultural production? What animals and crops form the base of the agricultural economy?

*12.* Why has the Soviet Union wanted to make satellite countries of most of the nations in the Shatter Belt?

## SELECTED REFERENCES

Beynon, Erdmann D.: "Budapest: An Ecological Study," *Geographical Review,* 33:256–275, April, 1943.

Boyd, Louise A.: *Polish Countryside,* The American Geographical Society, New York, 1937.

Cahaman, Werner J.: "Frontiers between East and West in Europe," *Geographical Review,* 39: 605–624, October, 1949.

Doukas, Kimon A.: "Bulgaria's Modes of Transport," *Economic Geography,* 19:337–346, October, 1943.

Hoffman, George W.: "The Shatter Belt in Relation to the East-West Conflict, *Journal of Geography,* 51:266–275, October, 1952.

Johnston, W. B., and I. Crkvenčić: "Examples of Changing Peasant Agriculture in Croatia,

Yugoslavia," *Economic Geography,* 33:50–71, January, 1957.

Kish, George: "Yugoslavia," *Focus,* 1(6):1–6, March, 1951.

Moore, Wilbert E.: *Economic Demography of Eastern and Southern Europe,* League of Nations, Geneva, 1945.

Roberts, Henry L.: *Rumania,* Yale University Press, New Haven, 1951.

Spubler, Nicholas: "The Danube–Black Sea Canal and the Russian Control over the Danube," *Economic Geography,* 30:236–245, July, 1954.

Steers, J. A.: "The Middle People: Resettlement in Czechoslovakia," *Geographic Journal,* 112:28–42, July, 1948.

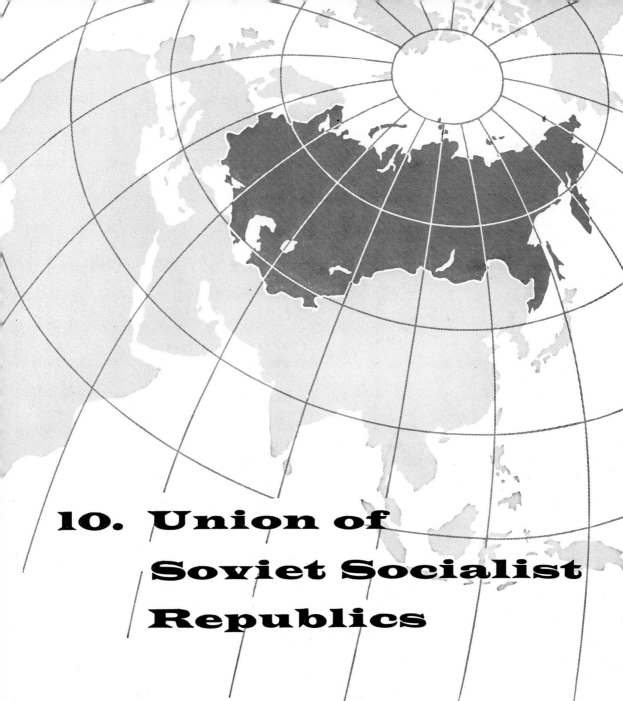

# 10. Union of Soviet Socialist Republics

SINCE World War I, the form of government, planned economy, expansionist policies, and frequent strained relationships with other powers have made the U.S.S.R. an enigma to many people. The Soviet Union's 200 million inhabitants include many diverse races with varied language and cultural backgrounds, conditions which would appear to make national unity difficult. The country has great agricultural, mineral, and forest resources, but it is handicapped by several factors. Among these are a northern location that causes long, cold winters and a short growing season, extensive deserts, and transportation difficulties.

347

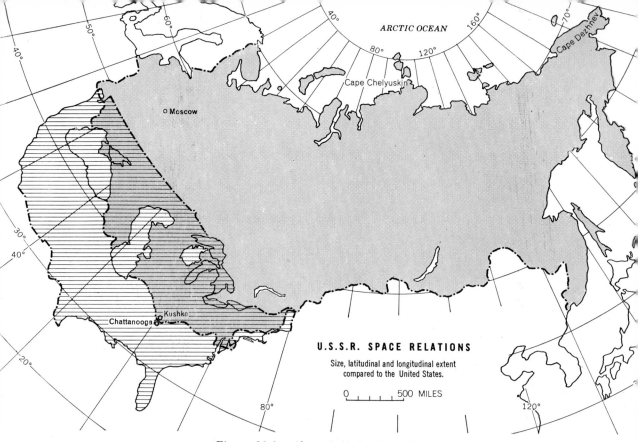

ARCTIC OCEAN

Cape Dezhnev

Cape Chelyuskin

o Moscow

Chattanooga  Kushke

**U.S.S.R. SPACE RELATIONS**

Size, latitudinal and longitudinal extent
compared to the United States.

0 _____ 500 MILES

*Figure 10-1   About half the United States is south of the latitude of the
Soviet Union. In area the Union is almost three times as large.*

## SPATIAL FACTORS

### Location

Situated in Eastern Europe, Central Asia, and
Northern Asia (Siberia), the Soviet Union occupies about 45 per cent of Asia and 40 per
cent of Europe. Longitudinally, the Union extends from 19°30′ east longitude, just west of
Kaliningrad (Königsberg) on the Baltic Sea,
to 169°30′ west longitude, on the Bering Strait;
nine degrees short of extending halfway around
the globe. This longitudinal spread approximates 7,000 miles, or as far as from Tokyo to
Washington, D.C., and makes a time difference
of eleven hours between Moscow (Moskva)
and eastern Siberia. Latitudinally, the U.S.S.R.
extends from 77°35′ to 35°15′ north latitude at
its most southerly point in the Turkmen Republic, a distance of about 3,000 miles. The southernmost point in the Union has the same latitude as Chattanooga, Tennessee. Except for the
Caucasus region, the southern Ukraine, and the
southern part of the trans-Caspian area, Soviet

Russia is located north of the 49th parallel
which forms most of the northernmost border of
the United States (Figure 10-1). Moscow, capital of the Union, is located a few miles north
of the latitude of Ketchikan, Alaska. Climates
vary from the humid subtropical and Mediterranean regions to the polar zone, with the largest part of the country lying in the cool, intermediate belt with long winters.

Within the Arctic Ocean the U.S.S.R. possesses several islands including Franz Josef
Land, Novaya Zemlya, and Wrangel Island.

### Size and Postwar Expansion

In size the U.S.S.R. ranks first among the nations, having 8,615,000 square miles or roughly
one-seventh of the world's land area. This is
more than two and one-half times larger than
the United States. Naturally within such a
large area are found great topographic variety
and climatic continentality. The Soviet Union

faces three oceans, the Atlantic, Arctic, and Pacific; the Black Sea provides access to the Mediterranean. The country has land boundaries with 12 different nations, a fact which, together with its great size, makes Russia an interested party in the political and economic events of Europe and Asia.

As a result of World War II the Soviet Union annexed over 261,000 square miles between 1939 and 1945, including the Baltic states of Estonia, Latvia, and Lithuania, the Kaliningrad and Memel (Klaipeda) areas of East Prussia, a segment of eastern Poland, and portions of Finland. The Soviet Ukraine also acquired part of Poland, the Ruthenian part of Czechoslovakia, and the Bessarabian area of northern Romania. Along the Siberian border, Tannu Tuva was absorbed as an autonomous oblast (province) in 1944. After the defeat of Japan in World War II, the Union annexed the southern half of Sakhalin Island (Karafuto), and the Kuril Islands which stretch from northern Japan to the peninsula of Kamchatka.

The U.S.S.R. is compact in form. At no time in Russian history since the Czardom of Muscovy was established has its form greatly changed. The expansion of Russia has always been by territorial accretion about its periphery. The most recent territorial acquisitions, after World War II, have been accomplished in the same manner. Russia has never seemed interested in an overseas empire or a fragmental state. Alaska was sold to the United States when it was found to be disadvantageous to hold this territory. Compactness has been a stabilizing and unifying factor for the U.S.S.R. Besides its territorial gains after World War II, the Union has followed a policy of establishing satellite states, or Communist-governed allies along its borders wherever it was politically feasible.

## RELIEF FEATURES

### Plains

Plains occupy over half the area of the U.S.S.R. (Figure 10-2). The principal plain, the one in which most of the population live, extends from the western frontier to the Central Siberian Upland, a distance of 3,000 miles; from north to south it spreads out for 2,000 miles. On the northeast it merges into river lowlands and the north Siberian coastal plain. Along the southern frontier and in eastern Siberia, high mountains circumscribe this vast plain, but the Ural Mountains that form part of the boundary between Europe and Asia are not a prominent barrier and are cut by low passes through the central portion. On the country's great plains has been played the historical, economic, and human drama of Russia for over four hundred years. These lowlands are subdivided into the East European Plain, Ob-Khatanga Plain, Lena Plain, and the Caspian-Turan Lowland.

**East European Plain.** A syncline (broad structural basin), the East European Plain occupies almost all of European Russia, and in turn is divided into several smaller basins. It is predominantly comprised of sedimentary rocks, although very old ones outcrop especially toward Finland and in a few uplands that jut through the lowlands. Hilly deposits, called moraines, made by prehistoric continental glaciers generally form the divide that separates the rivers emptying into the Baltic, White, and Barents Seas from the Don, Dnieper (Dnepr), Volga, and other tributaries which flow south to the Black, Azov, and Caspian Seas. The glaciated plains have deranged drainage, being dotted with hundreds of lakes, many bogs, and marshes that were the sites of former lakes resulting from the irregular deposits made by the continental ice sheets. Ladoga and Onega are the largest lakes, with the Pripet (Pripyat) or Pinsk the largest marshland. South of the areas affected by glaciation there is, in many places, a veneer of fertile "loess," a fine soil carried by the wind and derived from glacial outwash materials. The loessal soil is the best land in the Ukraine for raising wheat and other grains.

The East European Plain has a rolling surface and is interrupted by numerous uplands and hilly areas. In the northwest is the Kola-Karelia Upland, a remnant of ancient worn-down mountains with relief that rises to over 4,000 feet in the Kola Peninsula. The surface here has been so scoured and smoothed by gla-ciation that large parts either consist of bare rock or have soils too thin for agriculture. An-other area of ancient rock is the Azov-Podolian Upland near the Black Sea. Where the great bend of the Dnieper River crosses this hilly zone of hard rocks, rapids occur. A series of uplands that extend in a north-south direction —the Valdai Hills, the Smolensk-Moskva Ridge, and the Central Russian Upland—di-vides the Russian plain into two parts. In some places the uplands are caused by resistant stra-

*Figure 10-2  Because of its great size the U.S.S.R. has all kinds of relief features. Note the dominance of plains in the western part of the nation, uplands and mountains in the eastern part.*

ta; in other locations the hills are part of a glacial moraine. The Central Russian Upland is an uplifted low plateau with rolling surface that reaches an elevation of slightly over 1,000 feet. Among other areas that rise above the plain is the Donets Ridge, just north of the Sea of Azov, and separated from the Central Russian Upland by the Donets River. Another is the pre-Volga Upland, a plateau that slopes gently westward; toward its southward continuation is a topographic saddle, only 300 feet in elevation, where the bends of the Don and Volga Rivers come within 62 miles of one another. The Timan Ridge is a worn-down mountain over 1,000 feet in height in northeast European Russia; it separates the Pechora River lowland from the

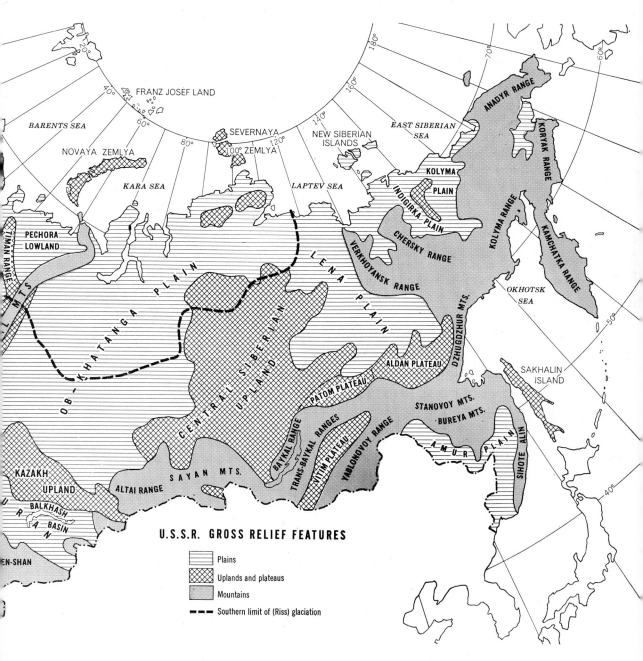

**U.S.S.R. GROSS RELIEF FEATURES**

Plains

Uplands and plateaus

Mountains

- - - Southern limit of (Riss) glaciation

main portion of the East European Plain. The Pechora region is too cold for agriculture but contains important deposits of coal.

**Ob-Khatanga Plain.** In western Siberia, the Ob-Khatanga Plain measures 1,200 miles from east to west and 1,500 miles from north to south. The plain occupies a basin of sedimentary rocks. The northern part has been glaciated and once contained a glacial lake that during glacial time drained southward into an enlarged Caspian and Aral Sea. This old, featureless lake bed is one of the flattest and largest areas of its kind in the world. The slope of the land toward the Arctic is so gradual that it drops less than 100 feet from south to north for every 500 miles. The divide between the Yenisey and Ob Rivers is barely 35 feet above the plain. The Ob River and its tributaries which drain this plain meander back and forth, testifying to the very gentle gradient of the plain and the river bed. Along the central part of the Ob River there is a vast waterlogged area, called the Vasyuganye Marsh. East of the lower Yenisey River is the Khatanga Plain, an extension of the Ob Plain, drained by the Khatanga River and its tributaries.

**Lena Plain.** Situated between the Central Siberian Uplands and the highlands of northeast Siberia, the Lena Plain is drained by the Lena River and its tributaries. The Lena rises in the Baykal Range near Lake Baykal and empties into the Arctic, where it has built a delta three times larger than that of the Volga in the Caspian Sea. Inland there are extensive marshlands. To the eastward are coastal plains along the Arctic whose surfaces resemble those found in the Lena Plain. The coastal plain is drained by the Indigirka River in the westward portion and the Kolyma River in the eastern part.

**Caspian-Turan Lowland.** This lowland has a basin structure. Throughout most of geologic time the lowland was a part of an ocean which included the present Aral, Black, Caspian, and Mediterranean Seas. Finally, the Black and Caspian Seas were separated from the Mediterra-

nean to form a single sea and later they in turn were separated from each other. During the glacial epoch the Aral and Caspian Seas were united and drained into the Black Sea by way of the Manych Lowland. It was into this sea that the overflow from the glacial lake in the Ob Plain drained via the Turgai Pass, which affords the most convenient route across the uplands.

The Caspian Lowland is a flat and monotonous plain, occupying the ancient floor of the Caspian Sea. One-third of this plain is below sea level and slopes gradually toward the Caspian, which is about 85 feet below sea level. The lowest point on the lowland is 426 feet below sea level in the alkaline depression of Lake Batyr. Chief rivers flowing through the lowland are the Volga and Ural. For a distance of 280 miles, from the Caspian Sea to Stalingrad, the Volga is below sea level. Because it has no outlet the Caspian has become somewhat saltier than the ocean.

The Turan Lowland surrounds the Aral Sea. It is an area of internal drainage, drained by two principal rivers, the Amu Darya and the Syr Darya. It includes the desert, dune-covered plains of the Kara Kum and Kyzyl Kum, and minor uplands like the Ust Urt Plateau between the Aral and Caspian Seas. East of the Syr Darya River, but within the area of internal drainage, is the Bet-Pak-Dala or Hunger Steppe. Rivers entering this steppe disappear beneath the desert sands before reaching the Syr Darya. The Lake Balkhash Plain, with internal drainage, forms the only exit into China from central Asiatic U.S.S.R. The Turgai Pass in the north is the only lowland route into Siberia.

*Uplands*

Besides the previously mentioned minor uplands that disturb the surface of the plains, there are the larger areas of the Ural, Kazakh, and Central Siberian Uplands.

The Ural Upland is comparable in elevation to the Appalachian Mountains of the United States. The Urals were folded and uplifted and then subjected to a long period of erosion that reduced them to old worn-down mountains or high rounded hills. They are highest in the northern and southern parts where elevations exceed 5,000 feet. In the central part there is a low saddle between the cities of Chelyabinsk and Nizhni Tagil, a distance of about 225 miles, where elevations do not exceed 2,600 feet, too low to be a physical or transportation barrier. In the intrusive granite found in the southern half of the Urals are deposits of iron, copper, chrome, gold, and platinum.

The northern extension of the Urals form the mountains of Novaya Zemlya. On the west, the Urals are flanked by the rolling Molotov-Ufa Plateau, and on the east by a piedmont zone which rises abruptly above the Ob-Khatanga Plain.

The Kazakh Upland between the Ob-Khatanga Plain and Turan Lowland was once a rugged mountain range but has been eroded to high rolling hills that reach elevations of over 4,500 feet. Deposits of copper, coal, lead, zinc, and gold are found in this upland.

The Central Siberian Upland is a large, relatively undisturbed, stable region of sedimentary rocks that overlie ancient rocks. These old rocks come to the surface to form hills in the north and the Baykal-Aldan Plateau in the south, the latter being located on both sides of Lake Baykal. Erosion has given much of the region a mountainous appearance. Much of the upland is well forested.

## Mountains

Mountains surround the wide Russian plain and the Central Siberian Upland. The oldest mountains are nearest to the plains, with progressively younger ranges farther out toward the perimeter of the U.S.S.R.

The oldest mountains bordering the plains include the Baykal and trans-Baykal Ranges, the Yablonovoi Range, the Yenisey Range, and the Sayan Mountains. In the latter are the Kuznetsk and Minusinsk Basins, which contain large coal deposits.

Mountain folding at a somewhat later time produced, besides the Ural and Kazakh uplands, the Altai Mountains and the Tien Shan, from both of which long spurs, often having individual names, extend. The former range is southeast of the Ob Plain, and the latter borders the Turan, Bet-Pak-Dala, and the Lake Balkhash Plain. Other mountains chiefly in eastern Siberia are shown on the map (Figure 10-2).

The outermost mountains in southern U.S.S.R. are those in the Crimea Peninsula, the Caucasus, the Kopet Dag, and the Pamirs. These are geologically youthful, very high and rugged. In the Caucasus, the highest peak is Mt. Elbrus, 18,481 feet and in the Pamirs, Mt. Stalin, 24,584 feet, and Mt. Lenin, 23,377 feet, the highest peaks in the U.S.S.R.

## CLIMATE

Most of the climate of the U.S.S.R. is continental, with severe winters and hot summers. The rainfall varies from dry to humid, but large areas of the country are semiarid. These characteristics are due to the fact that much of the country is far removed from the Atlantic; only in western Russia do mild oceanic winds slightly temper the extreme cold of winter or the heat of summer. This factor also limits the amount of precipitation the Union receives throughout most of its extent. The mean annual precipitation decreases from west to east and toward the southern interior (Figure 10-3). Riga, on the Baltic Sea, and Moscow both receive 23 inches

of precipitation; Yakutsk on the Lena River receives 14 inches, and Verkhoyansk in northeast Siberia, 4 inches.

Low temperatures over most of the Union are the result of its latitudinal location, its great distance from the warm Atlantic, and the large size of the land mass in high latitudes that permits cold Arctic air masses to build up in winter. From these cold, stationary air masses the cold air invades Eurasia over the broad plains as far south as the Turkmen Republic. High mountains along the southern frontier do not permit tropical air from the oceans to enter the U.S.S.R., but when dry air from Iran blows north in summer it helps cause droughts on the Russian steppes. The moderating influence of the Atlantic Ocean is evident in the increase of the mean annual range in temperature from west to east. At Moscow the mean annual range is 54°F. At Tomsk in western Siberia it is 69°F, and at Verkhoyansk it is 119°F. The growing season varies from about 60 days in northeast-ern Siberia to more than 120 days in north-western Russia. In the Ukraine the growing season may reach 180 days as compared to 200 days in the southern part of the Turkmen Republic.

Winter is the longest season and January, the coldest month, shows strikingly low mean temperatures for most of the U.S.S.R., with the min-

*Figure 10-3  In the Soviet Union the area of greatest rainfall is in the Caucasus Mountains, east of the Black Sea. Note that the amount of yearly rainfall decreases from west to east until nearing the Pacific.*

0            500 MILES

imum reached in the northern interior. In European Russia the January mean varies from 25°F at Odessa to 7°F at Archangel (Arkhangelsk). In Siberia the January mean falls to −3°F at Tomsk, −5°F at Irkutsk, and to −59°F at Verkhoyansk. Snowfall is light throughout the Union, but it covers the ground most of the winter because thaws are uncommon and thus snow accumulates with the passing of the season.

Over much of the Union summers are warm to hot. The hot areas are in the steppe and desert, and the warm areas stretch across the northern part of the country. Even in the lands north of the Arctic Circle the mean monthly temperatures of summer are 50 to 60°F, which results

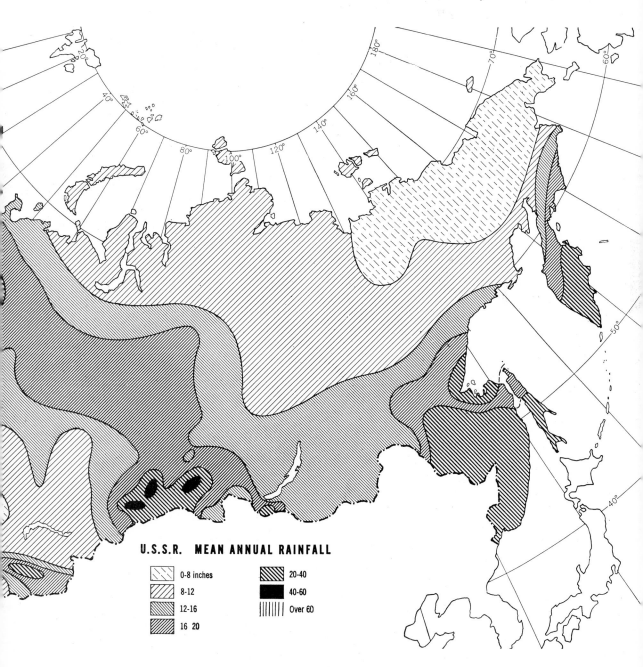

U.S.S.R. MEAN ANNUAL RAINFALL

| | | | |
|---|---|---|---|
| 0-8 inches | | 20-40 | |
| 8-12 | | 40-60 | |
| 12-16 | | Over 60 | |
| 16 20 | | | |

from the long days with sunshine during that season. Kharkov, Semipalatinsk, and Irkutsk, roughly in the same latitudes, have mean July temperatures varying from 65 to 75°F. In the deserts the July mean temperatures rise to over 80°F. During the short summer season storms move in predominantly from the west, and rainfall during the summer diminishes from the west

toward the east and south. The map (Figure 10-3) shows a wedge of heavier rainfall enclosed roughly by a line extending from Karelia (Russian Finland) to Lake Baykal and back westward to the southern Ukraine. This heavier rainfall is associated with the frequency of storms moving eastward from the Atlantic Ocean. Summer conditions in western Siberia

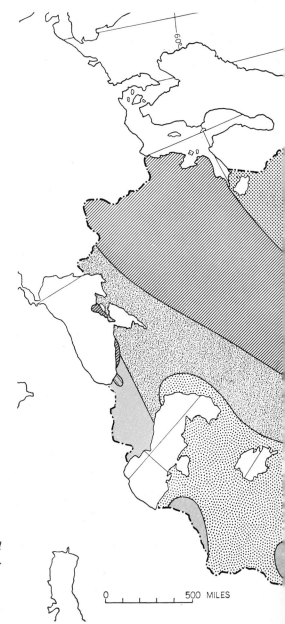

*Figure 10-4  In general the climatic zones extend from west to east across the nation. Note the relationship of these belts to latitude.*

are as warm as those of European U.S.S.R., and scattered localities receive as much rain. In eastern Siberia, along the Pacific Coast, onshore winds cause a rainy summer season although mountains prevent the rainfall from reaching the interior. Everywhere mountains show increased precipitation compared to the adjacent lower lands.

An important factor in the climate of the Union is the distribution of atmospheric pressure over the continent of Eurasia. During the cold months, cold air masses become established over Siberia, and cold winds from this high-pressure area blow toward the areas of lower pressure situated over the north Atlantic and adjacent parts of Western Europe, the north

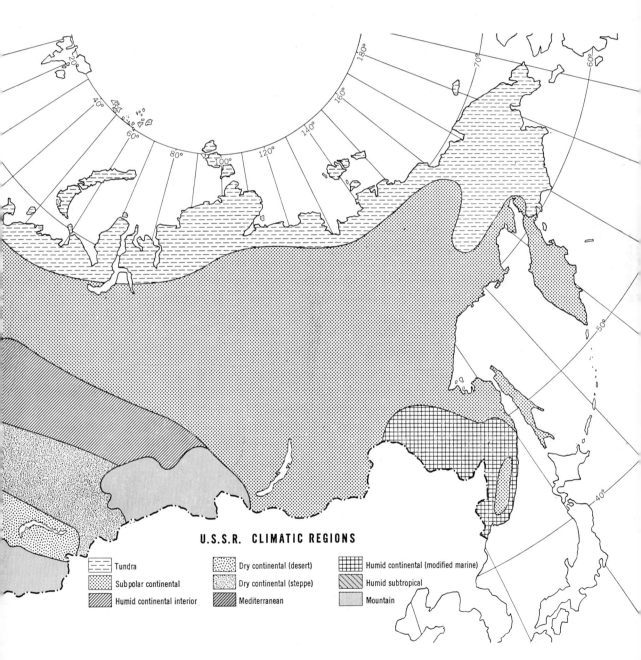

**U.S.S.R. CLIMATIC REGIONS**

| | | |
|---|---|---|
| Tundra | Dry continental (desert) | Humid continental (modified marine) |
| Subpolar continental | Dry continental (steppe) | Humid subtropical |
| Humid continental interior | Mediterranean | Mountain |

Pacific Ocean, and middle Asia. This cold winter air mass limits the eastward influence of the relatively warm and humid Atlantic to western Russia, as is evident in the isotherms which trend from northwest to southeast in European Russia during the winter months. In Siberia, where the high pressure is best developed, the weather during the winter is dry, calm, and sunny, but continuously cold. The winter climate along the Pacific Coast is cold and rather dry because the cold winds from the interior prevent the warming influence of the Pacific Ocean from being felt.

## Climatic Regions

In spite of its great size, only a few of the earth's climatic regions occur in the U.S.S.R.; because of its poleward location, the country has no tropical climates and only insignificant areas of the subtropical types. The climatic regions are polar or tundra, subpolar continental or taiga, humid continental, semiarid continental or steppe, arid continental, Mediterranean, humid subtropical, and mountain (Figure 10-4).

**Polar or Tundra.** Situated along the Arctic, the tundra has severe winters, although less severe than those in the interior of Siberia; the European part is warmer than the Siberian. This is a result of the warming influence of the North Atlantic Drift which makes Murmansk an ice-free port. At Archangel (Arkhangelsk) the mean January temperature is 7°F and at Port Tiksi, at the mouth of the Lena River, −33°F. The lower temperatures farther east are associated with cold winds blowing from the interior of Siberia during the winter. Summers of the tundra are warm to cool but too short for agriculture. The mean July temperature at Murmansk is 54°F. Precipitation is low, averaging about 12 inches annually, and comes chiefly in the form of snow.

**Subpolar Continental or Taiga.** This region is the largest and coldest climatic area in the Soviet Union. It covers half the country, extending from Karelia on the northwest to the Pacific Ocean, and is characterized by long, severe winters and short summers. The European portion is milder and has more rainfall, about 20 inches annually, than Siberia. Average January temperatures vary from 5 to 12°F, with the temperatures decreasing to the east and north. In the vicinity of Verkhoyansk, in northeastern Siberia, is located the "cold pole" of the world. At Verkhoyansk a minimum temperature of −90°F has been recorded. Here the mean January temperature is −59°F, and the July mean is 60°F, giving an annual range of 119°F. The low winter temperatures in Siberia are caused by the high pressure and cold air masses that develop there, and the cold air drainage from the mountains. Precipitation in Siberia diminishes from west to east; for example, Tobolsk has about 18 inches a year, Irkutsk 14 inches, and Verkhoyansk 4 inches. Although rainfall is low, it is sufficient for plant growth since low temperatures check evaporation. The climate of the Pacific shorelands is modified by onshore winds from the ocean and has summers that are cool, foggy, and raw, with drizzling rain. Winter precipitation is negligible because of the cold, dry west winds that then blow out from the interior.

**Humid Continental.** This climate is roughly coextensive with the rainfall wedge which extends eastward into Siberia from western Russia. This region is under the influence of the Atlantic Ocean during both winter and summer, receiving rainfall as well as moderating effects on temperatures in both seasons. The region has cold winters and warm summers. The average January temperature is about 12°F, the average July temperature about 66°, although averages as high as 80° have been recorded. Precipitation varies from over 30 inches in the west to less than 20 inches in the east. Agriculture is helped by the fact that much of the rain falls during the summer months. Snow is abundant, and when the spring thaws arrive, the melting provides moisture for agriculture but makes the dirt roads impassable.

A similar climate, modified by its coastal location, is situated on the lowlands facing the Sea of Japan in the Amur-Ussuri region of far eastern Siberia. The mean annual temperature, about 40°F, and the average summer and winter temperatures for this area are similar to those in the European humid continental climate. Another similarity is that winter temperatures decrease toward the interior of the continent, and summer temperatures increase in that direction.

**Dry Continental or Steppes.** This climate has uncertain and limited rainfall, diminishing from 16 inches a year in the west to 7 inches in the east. This is moisture enough for grass but not for trees. Most of the precipitation comes during the summer months when high temperatures cause excessive evaporation, which is bad for wheat and other grains grown without irrigation. Summer temperatures average well over 70°F throughout the entire area, but winter extremes are greater toward the east away from the warming influence of the Black Sea.

**Dry Continental Deserts.** Located in the interior of the country, the dry continental deserts are largely east of the Caspian Sea, and far removed from any major source of water. No place receives more than a yearly mean of 10 inches of rain. Many places receive no rain for months at a time. The summers are hot and dry, and temperatures of over 120°F are common, especially in southern Turkmen Republic. The diurnal range in temperature is extremely great; 100° or more from day to night may occur. The winters, especially in the northern half of the deserts, are cold. Only the extreme southern Turkmen Republic is mild during the winter. In the north, Irgiz has a mean January temperature

of 3.4°F and Mary (Merv) in the Turkmen Republic 34°F.

**Mediterranean.** This region is limited to the southern coast of Crimea and the northeast coast of the Black Sea. Rainfall comes mainly during the winter months, the yearly total at Yalta being 20 inches. The mean annual temperature is 56°F. Winters are mild but frosts are not uncommon, and the summers are hot. The Yaila Range, north of the coastal zone, protects it from the freezing north winds that in winter sweep across the steppes from the Arctic. Southern Crimea, with a climate like southern California, is the year-round resort area of the U.S.S.R.

**Humid Subtropical.** A small area of humid subtropical climate is located at the western end of the Black Sea, around Batum. The winter is mild, the January mean being 43°F, and the summers moderate with an August mean of 74°F. The rainfall at Batum is 93 inches annually and there is no dry season.

**Mountain.** High mountain climates of considerable variety occur. Usually the mountains have more rainfall with lower average temperatures than the lowlands, and at equal elevations the climates are more rigorous the higher the latitude of the ranges. East-west trending mountains protect their south slopes from cold air masses from the north. North-south trending mountains often have a rainy and a dry side when rising in the westerly winds. Snow and ice fields are found in the higher mountains. Alpine meadows occur below the snowline.

## VEGETATION AND SOILS

The natural vegetation types of the U.S.S.R. usually occur as broad bands extending west to east (Figure 10-5) and reflect the climatic, topographic, and soil regions of the country.

### Tundra

This vegetation type occupies 13 per cent of the Soviet Union, and is coextensive with the cli-

matic region of the same name. The tundra has extremely cold winters, summer frosts, constantly frozen subsoil, and harsh winds, making tree growth impossible. Mosses and lichens predominate farthest north, with shrubs, dwarf willow, birch, and linden interspersed with peat bogs next. The wooded tundra of scattered, small spruce, larch, and birch trees follows, and inland this blends into the taiga. The true tundra is treeless, and all other vegetation is perennial. In the transition zone to the taiga the first shrubs and trees that appear are stunted and the plants spread quite wide and close to the ground. The tundra has a brief summer when bright flowers and green grass add color to the landscape. There is grazing for reindeer but

farming is impossible. The thin surface soils contain very little decaying plant matter since the cool summers are too short for much decomposition to occur. Furthermore, these poor tundra soils rest on a permanently frozen subsoil, or permafrost, that limits drainage and makes the surface, during the summer, very wet in flat locations.

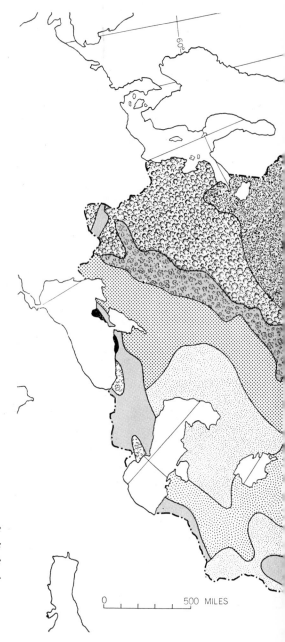

*Figure 10-5 The vegetation bands follow closely the climatic zones across the Soviet Union. The taiga is one of the great forest regions of the world. Note the similarity of these vegetation zones to those of Canada.*

0      500 MILES

## *Taiga*

The taiga is a coniferous forest; in area it approximates the subpolar continental climate, and occupies 52 per cent of the Union. This is significant because it forms the largest untouched virgin forest in the world. Trees cover most of Siberia and much of European Russia.

Spruces, firs, larches, and pines predominate, with the pines occupying the arid sandy soils. The lowlands of western Siberia have in addition vast marshes and bogs, but these are not prevalent in eastern Siberia. The taiga has a sandy and acidic podsol soil. This comprises about a fourth of the cultivated soils of the U.S.S.R. Because of their low fertility, podsol

**U.S.S.R. VEGETATION REGIONS**

- Tundra
- Taiga
- Mixed deciduous
- Mediterranean
- Humid subtropical
- Steppe
- Wooded steppe
- Semi-desert
- Mountain vegetation
- Desert

soils need large amounts of lime to counteract the acidity and improve production of crops.

## Mixed Deciduous

Two mixed deciduous forest areas are found in the U.S.S.R.; one is in Europe and western Siberia, and the other the Amur-Ussuri region of eastern Siberia. Both of these occurrences are rather narrow and at their northern margins the deciduous trees are mixed with conifers. Along the southern border of the European portion there is a transitional zone with the steppe, called the wooded steppe. Trees in the European section of the mixed deciduous forest include oak, maple, elm, ash, and linden. In western Siberia birch and aspen occur, but marshes and bogs in the beds of old glacial lakes occupy half of the total area in this Siberian vegetation belt. The Amur-Ussuri mixed deciduous forest consists of Mongolian species, but otherwise the trees resemble those of the European area. The hardwood forests have been cut over, resulting in a deficiency of hardwoods and the substitution of softer woods from the taiga for buildings and furniture.

Soils in the mixed forest are podsolic, generally gray-brown forest soils that, along the southern margin, grade into the chernozem or black prairie soil. Although the topsoil is thin, gray-brown forest soils contain more humus and are more productive than the true podsols of the taiga.

## Steppe

The true steppe grass belt lies south of the wooded steppe and extends from the Ukraine into western Siberia. Except for woods along the rivers, it is treeless because of the limited rainfall, 7 to 16 inches annually. The chernozem is the characteristic soil of the steppe lands. It is a black to chocolate-brown calcareous loam with a high per cent of humus. The humic material is derived from the decaying roots and stems of the grasses; the lack of heavy rainfall prevents leaching. Chernozems are among the most fertile soils in the world and constitute the basis for the largest amount of good farmland

in the Union. The transition zone from the tall-grass steppe with chernozem soil to the desert with gray soil supports short grass and clumps of herbage.

## Desert

This region, with its low rainfall and little or no vegetation, includes the lowland east of the Caspian Sea, the Turan Lowland to the foothills of the mountains in the south, and the Tien Shan on the east. Where the steppe grades gradually into the desert, forming a transitional semidesert, steppe grasses are lacking, and are replaced by patches of wormwood, feather grass, bushes, and tamarisk, interspersed with salt marshes. This is the home of the wandering nomad with his cattle, horses, sheep, and camels, who depends on deep wells and water holes.

The gray desert soils, which are rich in carbonate of lime and other fertilizing salts, can be very productive if irrigated, even though the humus content in the topsoil is low. Salt marshes have alkaline soils, that often contain so much salt that a white incrustation is formed on the surface. Shifting sand dunes are found in the Kara Kum and Kyzyl Kum deserts, the southern Bet-Pak-Dala, and the Balkhash Basin.

## Humid Subtropical

The forests of the humid subtropical region of the western Caucasus near the Black Sea consist of a dense mixture of deciduous and coniferous trees, with a thick undergrowth that includes ferns and bamboo, the plants being favored by the heavy rainfall and mild winters. The soils of the humid subtropical forest region are red-yellow earths, resembling the laterites of the rainy tropics. They were formed under conditions of high temperatures and heavy rainfall that leached out most of the humus and lime.

## Mountain

Soils in the mountains are generally thin and highly variable but the vegetation in mountains shows a vertical zonation corresponding to the climates found there, with vegetation belts resembling those occurring with increasing latitudinal change. For example, the wetter, lower and intermediate slopes of the Caucasus support a forest of deciduous trees; higher areas have pines and firs, and above them are alpine meadows and snow fields. Mountains of Central Asia adjacent to deserts are treeless on the lower slopes. With more rainfall come patches of maple, ironwood, and fruit-bearing trees. Above these is a zone of conifers, followed by alpine meadows and permanent snow fields. Alpine meadows of the Caucasus, Tien Shan, and Altai Mountains support millions of head of cattle, reared on the plains in winter, and fattened on the high grassy meadows during the summer.

## THE PEOPLE

### National Development

Four groups of people—the Slavs, Norsemen, Tatars, and Teutonic Knights (Germans)—spread into the area that became western Russia, and each ruled large parts of the region for a time. Novgorod and Kiev were the Norse centers of trade and culture; Moscow, of the Slavs. The Tatars controlled the lower Volga and Ukraine from A.D. 1224 to 1480 when they were overthrown by Ivan the Great, who established the Czardom of Moscovy that expanded into Russia. About 1200 the Teutonic Knights entered the Baltic region and became traders and landlords there. During the last five or six centuries, the Russians have expanded from their center at Moscow to the Black Sea, the Baltic Sea, and eastern Poland, across Siberia to the Pacific, and well into Central Asia. Russia even expanded into North America and secured Alaska for a colony, but finding this difficult to govern and defend because of its vast distance from St. Petersburg, sold it in 1867 to the United States. Soon thereafter Russia became greatly interested in northern China.

Vladivostok is not an ice-free port. This caused Russia to center attention on Port Arthur (Lushun) in Manchuria toward the close of the last century. After the Trans-Siberian Railroad was built to Chita, Russia constructed the Chinese Eastern Railroad, with Chinese approval, through Manchuria to Vladivostok. In 1898, a branch line was built to Port Arthur; this expansion led to the Russo-Japanese War of 1904–1905 and the defeat of Russia. The Japanese took over the port and the branch railway line to Port Arthur, and renamed it the South Manchurian Railway. Other losses by the Russians included the south half of Sakhalin Island and the Kuril Islands. These events led Russia to complete the Trans-Siberian Railroad in 1917 from Chita to Vladivostok, Russia's only important port on the Pacific Ocean. The possessions lost in 1905 were regained by the U.S.S.R. through the Yalta agreement in 1945. This provided port facilities at Dairen and a joint Sino-Soviet naval base at Port Arthur.

The outermost frontiers of Russia were definitely set by World War I. After that conflict she lost Estonia, Latvia, Lithuania, eastern Poland, Bessarabia, and Finland. All of these territories after World War II were returned to the U.S.S.R., with the exception of Finland, where only minor acquisitions were made along the Russo-Finnish border. In Poland Russian acquisitions do not extend as far west as before World War I.

The U.S.S.R. is a conglomeration of peoples. There are about 185 nationalities and over 150 racial groups who speak more than 150 different languages and several hundred dialects (Figure 10-6). The cultures vary from those of migratory hunters and reindeer breeders to those of advanced agricultural and industrial peoples. This variety is significant from the standpoint of developing a common social level, national spirit, and economy, as well as a unified program of national and international relations. Variations in language and custom make it difficult to find a single solution to the numerous internal problems that arise in the U.S.S.R.

## Nationalities and Political Divisions

The many nationalities of the U.S.S.R. in a political sense are called Russians. In a cultural sense this is a misnomer. It was the Czars who applied the name, Russian, to all the peoples of Russia. For the Czars, who conquered the minor nationalities, made every effort to Russify them according to the principle of one czar, one language, and one religion.

The nationalities are intimately associated with the political units, since the latter are based on nationality and economic factors. The basic political units are the *okrugs* (districts or circuits), *oblasts* (provinces), *raion* (area, or a division of an oblast), autonomous areas which

*Figure 10-6   The U.S.S.R. is divided into 15 unions of varying sizes. Each union in turn is also subdivided. The largest of the unions is Russia. Of the ethnic groups within the nation, the Great Russians are by far the most numerous.*

are grouped into *krais* (territories for administration), and autonomous republics, which are federated into the Union of Soviet Socialist Republics. There are 16 republics and each represents a major national group. The political boundaries are not permanent but can be altered for political expediency or to accommodate economic changes. Republics in the Un-

ion can be abolished for security and military reasons, as was the case of the Crimean and other republics during World War II.

The Russian Soviet Federated Socialist Republic (R.S.F.S.R.) is very large, occupying three-fourths of the Union, and is politically complex. This republic is the home of the Great Russians and numerous smaller nationalities.

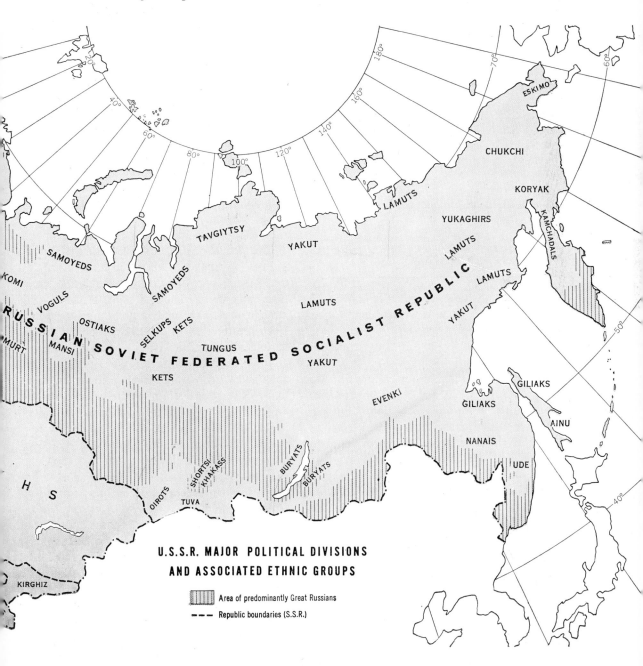

U.S.S.R. MAJOR POLITICAL DIVISIONS
AND ASSOCIATED ETHNIC GROUPS

Area of predominantly Great Russians
--- Republic boundaries (S.S.R.)

## TABLE 10-1. REPUBLICS OF THE U.S.S.R. 1956

| Republic | Population, in millions | Area, sq miles |
|---|---|---|
| Armenian S.S.R. | 1.6 | 11,500 |
| Azerbaidzhan S.S.R. | 3.4 | 33,100 |
| Byelorussian S.S.R. | 8.0 | 80,100 |
| Estonian S.S.R. | 1.1 | 17,400 |
| Georgian S.S.R. | 4.0 | 29,400 |
| Karelo-Finnish S.S.R.* | 0.6 | 68,900 |
| Kirghiz S.S.R. | 1.9 | 76,100 |
| Kazakh S.S.R. | 8.5 | 1,061,000 |
| Latvian S.S.R. | 2.0 | 24,600 |
| Lithuanian S.S.R. | 2.7 | 31,200 |
| Moldavian S.S.R. | 2.7 | 13,100 |
| Russian S.F.S.R. | 112.6 | 6,501,500 |
| Tadzhik S.S.R. | 1.8 | 54,900 |
| Turkmen S.S.R. | 1.4 | 187,200 |
| Ukrainian S.S.R. | 40.6 | 220,600 |
| Uzbek S.S.R. | 7.3 | 157,400 |
| U.S.S.R. | 200.2 | 8,570,600 |

* Incorporated into Russian S.F.S.R., 1957.

SOURCE: *The National Economy of the U.S.S.R.: A Statistical Compilation,* State Statistical Publishing House, Moscow, 1956.

Most of the autonomous republics in Soviet Europe and in the Caucasus were formed for national minorities of Mongol, Tatar, and other origin, but the largest autonomous republic is the Yakutsk in Asia.

In the Karelo-Finnish Soviet Socialist Republic (S.S.R.) Finns and Karelians predominate over Russians. The three Baltic Republics are lands of the Esths, Letts, and Lithuanians.

The Byelorussian and Ukrainian republics are lands of the Byelorussians (White Russians) and Ukrainians (Little Russians), respectively. Byelorussian, Ukrainian, and Great Russian are dialects of the same Slavic language. The cradle or origin of the Great Russians was in the deciduous forest of the Moscow region. The Ukrainians originated on the southern steppes around Kiev, and the Byelorussians in the Pripet Marsh area between Poland and the R.S.F.R. The three Russian groups are not a homogeneous ethnic stock since their languages differ, but they do have some physical

characteristics in common, being mostly short and stocky, with broad heads, blond to reddish hair, blue eyes, and fair skin.

The Moldavian people, a Romanian language group, make up 65 per cent of the population of the Moldavian S.S.R.; Ukrainians, Russians, and Gypsies form the principal minorities. The U.S.S.R. acquired this area of rich farmland after World War II.

Nationalities of the Caucasus region are extremely diverse for geographical and historical reasons. In its numerous isolated mountain valleys the area has provided many places of refuge for minority groups. Historically, this region has undergone numerous invasions, with mountain passes used as avenues of penetration. Despite the diversity of peoples, Georgians, Armenians, and Azerbaijani form the predominant national groups. Within Georgia are the Abkhasian and Adzharian Autonomous Republics, and the South Ossetian Autonomous Province, created for groups who speak different Armenian dialects.

The peoples living in the Central Asian republics—Turkmen, Uzbek, Tadzhik, Kazakh, and Kirghiz—are of mixed nationality, but they have in common yellowish skins, broad heads, straight dark hair, and slant Mongolian eyes. They are referred to as Turkic peoples, speak various dialects of the Turki language, and have adopted the Mohammedan religion. The Kazakh and Kirghiz were formerly horsemen, and many of them are still nomadic pastoralists.

The complex political and national minority problem of the U.S.S.R. is being solved by requiring that each minority learn the national language which is Russian, but by allowing each to have its own schools and (at least in theory) to conduct its own business and government.

The official population census of 1939 placed the number of people in the U.S.S.R. at 170,467,000. Despite the estimated loss of 10 million lives in World War II, the total has increased. The birth rate is said to have made up for the loss, and the population, in 1956, was estimated at 200.2 million.

Part of the population increase between 1939

and 1945 came as a result of acquisition of new territory during World War II. The figures in Table 10-2 show that the Union's population increased by slightly over 24 million inhabitants as a result of her acquisitions. It is interesting to note that about half this increase comprises White Russians, formerly in Poland, and Ukrainians (Ruthenians), largely in Ruthenia, the former eastern province of Czechoslovakia. The total increase in population from these territories represents about a 15 per cent addition to Soviet manpower. The new territory improves the maritime position of the U.S.S.R., shortens its border between the Baltic and Black Seas, gives it a flanking position with reference to Poland, and places its border in contact with Hungary, Czechoslovakia, and Norway.

For the entire area of the U.S.S.R. the average density of population is about 24 persons

## Population

### TABLE 10-2. POPULATION OF U.S.S.R. AND ACQUIRED TERRITORIES, 1945

| | |
|---|---|
| U.S.S.R. | 170,467,000 |
| **Baltic States** | |
| Estonia | 1,120,000 |
| Latvia | 1,950,000 |
| Lithuania | 2,575,000 |
| **East Europe** | |
| Eastern Poland | 13,000,000 |
| Ruthenia (Trans-Carpathian Ukraine) | 850,000 |
| East Prussia | 600,000 |
| Memel Land | 147,000 |
| Northern Bucovina | 500,000 |
| Bessarabia | 2,400,000 |
| **Finland** | |
| Petsamo Oblast, Kuolayarvi area at "waist" of Finland between the White Sea and Gulf of Bothnia, and the Karelian Isthmus | 454,500 |
| **Far East** | |
| Karafuto | 339,000 |
| Kuril Islands | 6,000 |
| Tannu Tava | 70,000 |
| Total | 194,478,500 |

*Figure 10-7   The Park of Culture and Rest in Tashkent. Note the variant characteristics—features, expressions, clothing—of the persons shown. (Courtesy of Embassy of the U.S.S.R.)*

per square mile. In Soviet Europe, the average density is about 70 per square mile, with concentrations as high as 260 and more per square mile in the Ukraine and around Moscow. In Siberia large areas of less than 2 persons per square mile are common, with densities along the Trans-Siberian Railway varying from 25 to 65 to the square mile. The desert of Central Asia varies from uninhabited regions to areas of 130 to 260 per square mile on the oasis, and over 260 per square mile in the Fergana Valley. In general, the distribution of population in the Union reflects the fertile soil triangle, the most favorable climatic area, and the oasis areas (Figure 10-8).

From 1939 to 1956, the major shifts in population were from rural to urban areas, eastward
into Siberia, and south into Central Asia. During this period, the urban population increased
greatly, from about 56 million in 1939 to 87
million in 1956, a rise from 33 to 43 per cent of
the total population. Urban increases resulted
from industrialization of the Union, and many
new industrial cities were founded, especially in
Siberia. In 1926, there were only 12 cities with
200,000 or more inhabitants, all in European
U.S.S.R. and including Moscow and Leningrad. In 1939, 39 cities in the Union had more
than 200,000 people; by 1956, this number had
increased to 62. In 1956, two cities, Moscow
and Leningrad, each had populations of more

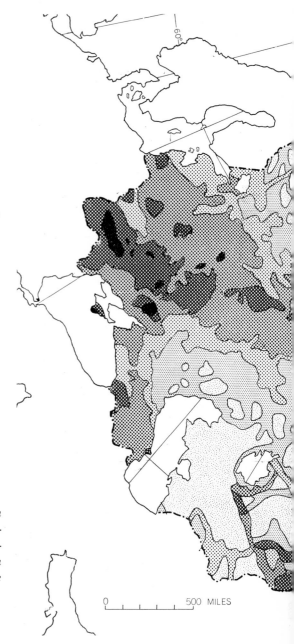

*Figure 10-8   The European part of the Soviet Union
has the greatest population. In Asia climate and landforms have limited activities somewhat. Note the location of population in relationship to the Trans-Siberian
Railway, the irrigated areas in Central Asia, and the
river valleys in Siberia.*

than three million and the population of Kiev was almost a million. Nineteen cities have populations between 500,000 and 800,000; another 113 range in size from 100,000 to 500,000 persons each. Many of these cities are located in the Ural Mountains and in Siberia. Population has shifted into Siberia because of the development of new industrial areas in the Urals, the Kuznetsk and Minusinsk Basins, the Irkutsk region, and the Amur Valley. This shift was particularly evident during World War II, with the advance of German armies toward Moscow, the Volga, and the Caucasus region.

Between 1926 and 1939, the rural population dropped from about 120.7 million to 114.5 million. This tendency has continued to the

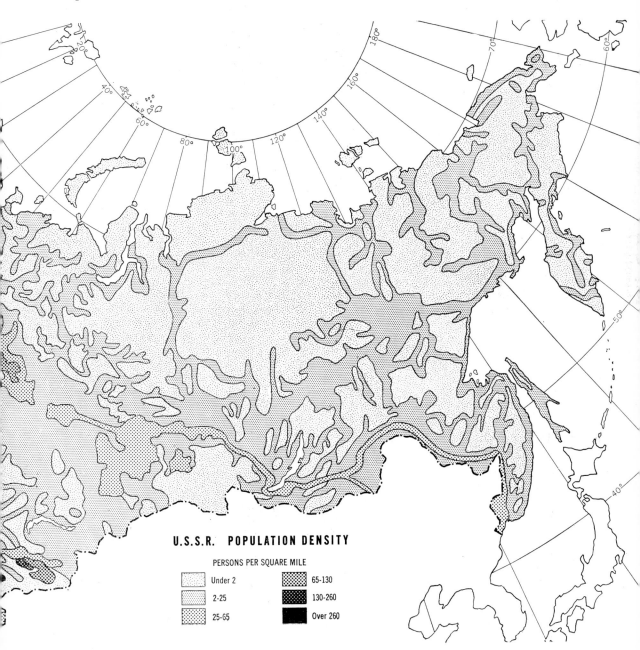

## U.S.S.R. POPULATION DENSITY

PERSONS PER SQUARE MILE

| | | | |
|---|---|---|---|
| Under 2 | | 65-130 | |
| 2-25 | | 130-260 | |
| 25-65 | | Over 260 | |

present, the 1956 estimated rural population being 113.2 million. Improvement and mechanization of agriculture enable fewer farmers to feed the growing population of the urban centers. However, sometimes dry seasons occur; then crops fail or yields decrease.

## ECONOMIC DEVELOPMENT

### The Planned Economy

It was possible to impose the present planned economy on the people of the U.S.S.R. because of the chaotic conditions and famines which prevailed in the country after World War I and the Revolution that followed. The initiator of the new economic system was Lenin who built his doctrines on the philosophy of dialectical materialism, laid down by Marx and Engels. According to this philosophy man is the initiator, planner, and controller of material changes, and can even modify nature by developing and expanding the wealth of a nation through state planning to increase production and control its distribution. Upon Lenin's death in 1924, Stalin took over the reins of the government, and, to carry out the Marxist-Leninist philosophy, created the First Five-Year Plan in 1928, to expand industry and continue the collectivization of agriculture started under Lenin. Under state planning, the U.S.S.R. is trying to conquer nature by increasing agricultural production through expansion of the farming frontier into areas of uncertain environmental conditions. It is attempting to discover new sources of minerals and increase their output. The plans call for expanded industrial production, development of transportation facilities, and even the redistribution of population into new areas of production in order to attain these increases.

To date there have been five Five-Year Plans in operation. The First Five-Year Plan (1928–1933) was completed in four years and three months, despite the fact that certain goals were not reached. In agriculture the plan fell short because of crop failures from droughts in 1931 and 1932. Production fell short also in steel and consumer goods. The Second Five-Year Plan (1933–1937) fell short of its goals in pig iron, petroleum, and textile production, but in steel the output was above the quota, and in railroad construction the goals were reached before the five years had passed. World War II and the German invasion in 1941 halted the Third Five-Year Plan (1936 to 1942) and necessitated substitution of a war plan. The Fourth Five-Year Plan (1946–1950) called for postwar reconstruction of the Union and continued interest in heavy industry. The Fifth Five-Year Plan (1951–1955) was short of consumer goods, in part because heavy industry was favored. Farm reorganization, completed in 1953, showed inefficiency and shortage in farm produce. The plan called for increases in all forms of production, but the goals set for 1955 were about half of the over-all United States production. During each plan heavy industry was favored over consumer goods, which were in short supply. Although agriculture, discovery of resources, and industrialization did advance, advances were made at the expense of human welfare.

The goals set constantly exceed production attained. Plans call for an annual output by 1960 of 50 million tons of pig iron, 60 million tons of steel, 500 million tons of coal, and 60 million tons of oil. Despite all the planning, Soviet production is a poor second to that of the United States, and except for coal, the proposed goals, even if attained, would leave it in that place.

### Transportation

**Railroads.**  In the U.S.S.R., railroads for the most part are in Soviet Europe. The pattern reflects the area of early historical settlement, which led to the building of rail lines in the west, where most of the people lived, where minerals were being produced, and where agriculture was best developed. The pattern of the densest railroad net is that of the old wedge-shaped area of Soviet Europe, with its base along the western frontier and its apex extending toward the Urals (Figure 10-9).

With the expansion of agriculture and new locations of mining and industry, the rail system has been extended toward the north, south, and east. The densest rail concentration is in the Donets coal basin, followed by the Moscow industrial area and the central Ural mining and industrial region. Northern Russia has railways from Leningrad to Murmansk, an ice-free port, from Moscow to Archangel on the White Sea, and from Moscow to the Pechora coal and oil fields. East of the Urals is the Trans-Siberian Railroad with spurs leading into the Kuznetsk and Balkhash Basins. Central Asia is traversed by two lines; one goes from Novosibirsk to Krasnovodsk on the Caspian Sea with a branch into the Fergana Valley, and the other runs from Saratov to Tashkent with a spur to Astrakhan. The great length of the railroads that cross the country from east to west, and from north to south, is shown by the fact that it takes ten days to travel from Kaliningrad to Vladivostok, and three days from Odessa to Murmansk. Soviet isolation is displayed by the fact that only five rail lines cross the southern frontier, one each into Turkey, Iran, and Mongolia, and two into Manchuria. The length of the railroads in 1955 was about 70,000 miles, 30 per cent of which is double tracked. Although second among countries of the world in railroad mileage, the Soviet Union has only one-fourth that of the United States, a mileage disproportionate to the size of the Union. Although railroads are insufficient they are the most important transportation medium in the Union, for they carry 83 per cent of the total freight of more than half a billion tons annually, and are usable the year round regardless of climate.

**Water Transportation.** The U.S.S.R has the longest navigable waterway system of any country in the world. Its length is estimated at 248,-000 miles (Figure 10-10) although only about 65,800 miles are used. The usefulness of most rivers is lessened by the fact that they are frozen over during three to nine months of the year, and flow either in the wrong direction or through unpopulated regions of small economic importance. Nevertheless, the rivers carry about 80 million tons of freight yearly.

The Volga River is the most important waterway because it has ample depth, drains a large and populous region, and passes through diversified economic areas. Products carried upstream include oil from Baku, coal from the Donets, salt and fish from the Caspian, and grain; wood is sent downstream. The Volga had the disadvantage of draining into the landlocked Caspian Sea. Now a 62-mile canal, opened in 1952, connects Stalingrad on the Volga with Kalich at the elbow on the Don River, extends the Volga's economic influence into the industrial Ukraine, and makes Moscow a port on five seas. Canals also link the White and Baltic Seas with the Caspian and Black Seas, and Lake Ladoga with the Volga.

The Ob, Irtysh, Yenisey, and Lena Rivers in Siberia, although long, carry very little freight, and transportation is confined to the brief summer months. The Amur has the greatest transport possibilities and is the leading river in Siberia for carrying cargo, since it is navigable by ocean-going vessels as far upstream as Khabarovsk.

The northern sea route between Murmansk and Vladivostok is shorter (6,800 miles) than navigating via Suez (over 13,000 miles). It transports a million tons of cargo annually and would be used more were it not frozen over most of the year.

**Highways.** Road construction in the Union lagged until about 1940, because of the paucity of vehicles and gasoline. The strategic purpose of slowing down invasions by mechanized equipment may also have influenced government policy. Motor vehicles in the U.S.S.R. total about one million, a small number for so large a nation. Dirt roads predominate over paved; spring thaws and summer downpours often make them impassable. The length of roads totals about 850,000 miles; 150,000 miles are called year-round roads but only a third of these are hard-surfaced. Three-fourths of the roads are so little improved that seasonally they are lost in mud. Winter is an advantage because sleighs pulled by horses can travel easily over the frozen ground.

**Air Transport.**    This is needed in a country as large as the U.S.S.R. There are approximately 140,000 miles of air routes, with Moscow and Leningrad being the principal air centers. Main routes extend from Moscow to Tbilisi Tiflis in Transcaucasia, to Vladivostok, and Uelen, the latter located on the north Siberian coast. There are many secondary routes where railroads are absent—chiefly in central Siberia, Central Asia, the Caucasus, the Far East, and the Far North.

*Figure 10-9   The most highly developed system of land transportation is by rail. Moscow is the principal railroad center.*

## Agriculture

The U.S.S.R. is an agricultural country; more than half its people are farmers. Yet much of the nation is not suited for farming; about 75 per cent consisting of deserts, mountains, swamps, tundra, and forest, with 90 per cent of the latter classed as nonagricultural. Of the total area of postwar Russia, only 10 per cent, about 610 million acres, is tillable. Including permanent meadows and pastures, about 25 per cent, or 1,590 million acres, can be called farmland. The 1950 acreage in crops was 363 million; 40 per cent of the tilled land was in Soviet Europe. This total compares with about 320 million acres in crops in the United States.

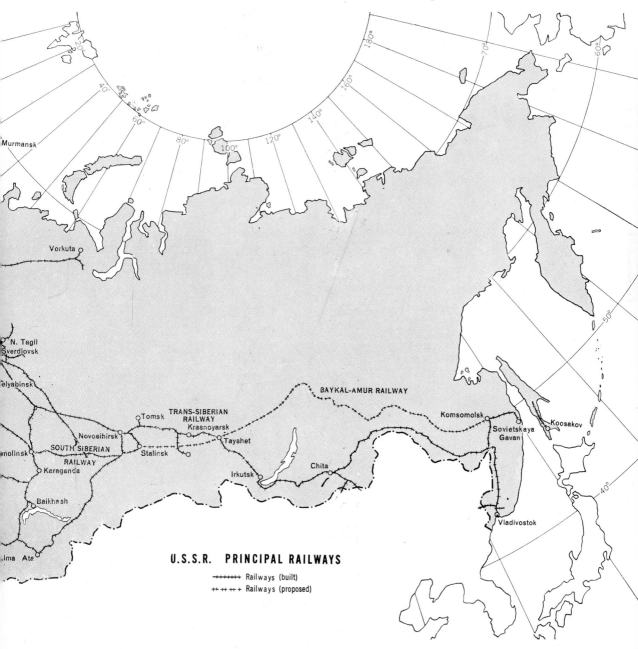

**U.S.S.R. PRINCIPAL RAILWAYS**

++++++ Railways (built)

++ ++ ++ + Railways (proposed)

Because of natural limitations of rainfall not all the tillable land in the U.S.S.R. can be cultivated annually. Some land lies fallow every other year or one year in three, and in many instances droughts, irregular rainfall, and early frosts ruin the harvest.

The major drought areas are along the lower third of the Volga and contiguous regions in Europe and Asia. Between 1891 and 1939, there were twenty-two years of partial drought in these sections, fifteen years of total drought, and only eleven years of sufficient rainfall. In the 1921 famine, 5 million people perished. In the 1931–1932 famine, half the livestock in the country was lost partly because of drought but also because of deliberate slaughter by owners

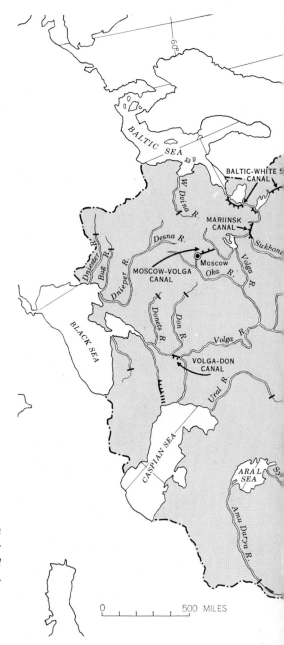

*Figure 10-10   Where possible, rivers are used as a means of transportation. Note that many of the longer ones flow either into the Arctic Ocean or into inland seas. In Europe many canals have been built to connect the various rivers.*

who objected to collectivism. Peasant resistance against collectivization, for which thousands of kulak (well-to-do-farmers) families were exiled to the Far North, produced general demoralization in agriculture. After World War II, droughts prevailed in 1946 and 1948.

Besides the use of the fallow system and other practices intended to conserve soil moisture,

the Soviets in 1932 began to plan for the irrigation of the lower Volga region, part of which was to be used for crops and part for pasture. In 1948, the program began with special emphasis on afforestation. Under this policy, trees were planted on watersheds and river banks, with tree shelter-belts for protecting crops on collective and state farms. When completed in

**U.S.S.R. NAVIGABLE WATERWAYS**

Upper limit of navigation
Canals: completed
Canals: proposed

1965, these tree belts will cover 14 million acres and will help control erosion by water and wind, reduce evaporation from hot winds, and increase the retention of snow that supplies water for winter grains. Large swamp drainage projects are in progress for 667,000 acres in the Pripet Marsh of Byelorussia and eastern Poland, and 500,000 acres have been drained in Georgia, and near the Azov and Black Seas.

Agriculture is being carried into lands with lower rainfall in the trans-Volga and northern Kazakhstan areas by dry farming, strip planting, and contour plowing—practices designed to conserve moisture and lessen wind erosion as was done on the wheat lands of the Great Plains in the United States. In rainy years like 1956, crops are good on such land, but in dry years crops fail with resulting embarrassment to the government.

Irrigated farmland in Central Asia and the Caucasus totals about 17.8 million acres. In Central Asia, irrigation is carried on along the Amu Darya, Syr Darya, and other rivers, as well as along the foot of the mountains where alluvial soils and water are available. Plans for

extending irrigation include dams on the Dnieper River to divert water into southern Ukraine and northern Crimea to irrigate 3.7 million acres, and dams on the Volga near Kuibyshev and Stalingrad to serve 2 million acres in the Caspian and trans-Volga regions.

To secure more production, the Union is trying to push cultivation to the Arctic Circle. New varieties of quick-maturing plants and seed selection are being stressed, but success seems doubtful because of poor yields on the acidic podsol soils and the shortness of the growing season. New areas opened for farming in Siberia are on virgin steppe soils, adjacent to the fertile agricultural triangle. Such developments encourage a large influx of people and the growth of old cities or of newly founded ones. Such population shifts will continue for many years.

The cultivated area has been increased from 342 million acres in 1938 to 360 million acres in 1950 as a result of drainage of marshes; irrigation in Central Asia, along the Volga, and in the Caucasus region; the opening of over 17 million acres of new steppe lands in Siberia; plowing of pasture and meadow lands; and the

*Figure 10-11 Homes on a collective farm in the southern part of the Soviet Union. (Courtesy of United Nations.)*

fertilization and reclamation of poor land within the fertile triangle.

Agriculture is organized into collective farms (kolkhoz) and state farms (sovkhoz). In 1928, collective farms accounted for about 1 per cent of the total area sown to crops. By 1940, collectivization had forced 97 per cent of the peasant households into 236,000 farm units. In 1955, the number was reduced to 93,000 units, with an average size of about 4,182 acres. A unit averages about 1,600 acres in crops, or roughly 16 acres per household, with about 87 households per collective farm. On these farms, all land and capital goods, once held by peasants, are pooled into a cooperative enterprise which is controlled in all phases by the government. Each family unit usually has an acre or two for a kitchen garden. Workers on a collective farm receive a share of the harvest proportionate to their work after the state has taken its share of the production.

The state farms are owned and operated by the government. In 1955, there were 4,857 state farms with an average size of about 3,250 acres. These farms are operated by hired labor, which is directed by farm managers. The workers are paid wages. State farms are scattered throughout the Union in all types of climatic regions, and specialized agriculture and experimentation are their primary purpose. State-owned farms have their own equipment. Collective farms, however, rent their tractors, trucks, combines, threshing machines, and other mechanical equipment, from the more than 8,000 machine and tractor stations owned and operated by the government. In this way the government furthers the mechanization of agriculture.

The U.S.S.R. has an average of about 2 acres

**TABLE 10-3.  MAJOR CROPS OF THE U.S.S.R.**   (*Area, Yield, and Production, 1949*)

| Crop | Area, in thousand acres | Yield per acre | Production, in thousand bu |
|---|---|---|---|
| Wheat | 103,000 | 10.7 bu | 1,100,000 |
| Rye | 75,500 | 12.6 bu | 950,000 |
| Oats | 37,000 | 20.9 bu | 775,000 |
| Barley | 21,500 | 14.4 bu | 310,000 |
| Corn | 8,500 | 16.5 bu | 140,000 |
| Potatoes | 23,400 | 120.0 bu | 2,800,000 |
| Sugar beets | 2,850 | 6.0 tons | 17,100 tons |
| Beet sugar * | | | 1,980 tons |
| Sunflower seed | 8,200 | 460  lb | 1,870 tons |
| Cotton | 5,880 | 284  lb | 2,700 bales |
| Flax fiber † | 3,700 | 200  lb | 760,000 lb |
| Flaxseed † | 4,400 | | 19,300 |
| Tobacco † | 509 | | 380,000 lb |
| Soybeans ‡ | 42 | | |
| Castor beans ‡ | 565 | | |
| Tea † | 120 | | |
| Citrus fruits | 54 | | |

* Based on postwar boundaries.
† Data for 1948.
‡ Figure for 1938.

SOURCE: Compiled from estimates in Lazar Volin, "A Survey of Soviet Russian Agriculture," U.S. Department of Agriculture, Office of Foreign Agricultural Relations, Agriculture Monograph 5, 1951.

in crops per capita; in the United States, the average is about 2.5 acres. Though the acreages in crops approximate one another, the rural population of the Soviet Union exceeds 114.5 million; more than half the nation's people are needed to produce food enough for themselves and the urbanites, indicating poor yields and inadequate mechanization. In the United States, the farm population is less than a fifth of the country's people, yet the farmers feed themselves and the rest of the nation and produce a large surplus besides. Average yields in Russia are low; for example, wheat yields average only 11 bushels per acre because of uncertain rainfall and poor farming. Grains occupy 75 per cent of the plowed land in the Union (Table 10-3). Wheat is the most important crop, occupying 30 per cent of the tilled land. Both winter and spring wheats are grown, mostly on the chernozem soils, with the former planted mainly in the Ukraine, and the latter predominating east of the Don and farther north where the long winters are unfavorable for the winter variety. Although the acreage of spring wheat is twice that of the winter variety, winter wheat yields are larger. By the development of new, hardier varieties, wheat production has been pushed northward toward Moscow and Leningrad.

In production of rye, barley, oats, potatoes, flax, and sugar beets, the Union leads all other countries. Rye is the second most important grain, being a staple food of the people. Russia accounts for about half of the world's rye. It is grown north of the chernozem belt on poorer soils and in more severe climates. Barley stands drought well and is grown in the southern Ukraine, near the Volga, and in Kazakhstan. It is used both as a feed and a food crop. Oats rank next to wheat and rye in acreage, and are grown especially in the north. There is a heavy concentration of potato growing in humid western and central European Russia. In Byelorussia 20 per cent of crop acreage is in potatoes, and potatoes are also important in the Ukraine. As a food potatoes rank next to wheat and rye, yet one-fourth of the crop is fed to livestock, mostly pigs that are grown more for lard than for meat. Maize is relatively unimportant and grows best in Bessarabia, southwestern Ukraine, and Georgia. Plans call for increased emphasis on corn production and the setting up of a corn-hog economy like that in the Middle West of the United States, but its success seems questionable because the growing season is short for corn north of the southern Ukraine and because experience is lacking in raising both hybrid seed corn and the field crop.

The leading industrial crops are flax, sugar beets, cotton, and sunflower seed. Growing of flax is concentrated in the Baltic republics, Byelorussia, around Moscow and Leningrad, and in the northern Volga area. Normally over 4 million acres are in flax grown for fiber, and nearly 1 million acres in flax are grown for seed to be processed into linseed oil. The

TABLE 10-4. DISTRIBUTION OF SOWN CROP AREA, U.S.S.R., 1952

| Crop classification | Area, in thousand acres | | Per cent | |
|---|---|---|---|---|
| Grains and legumes | | 265,100 | | 68.9 |
| Wheat * | 114,200 | | 29.7 | |
| Industrial crops | | 31,600 | | 8.2 |
| Potatoes and other vegetables | | 24,500 | | 6.4 |
| Fodder crops | | 63,500 | | 16.5 |
| Total sown area | | 384,700 | | 100.0 |

* In 1953, area sown to wheat increased 2 million hectares (4.9 million acres), and total sown area increased 1.4 million hectares (3.5 million acres).

SOURCE: Lazar Volin, "The Malenkov-Khrushchev New Economic Policy," *The Journal of Political Economy,* 62(3):197, June, 1954.

**TABLE 10-5. LIVESTOCK, IN MILLIONS OF HEADS: 1938, 1946, 1951,\* 1953†**

|                     | 1938 | 1946 | 1951 (goals) | 1951 (rpd.) | 1953  |
|---------------------|------|------|--------------|-------------|-------|
| Cattle, incl. cows  | 59.8 | 46.9 | 65.3         | 57.2        | 56.6  |
| Cows                |      |      |              |             | 24.3  |
| Sheep and goats     | 75.0 | 69.4 | 121.5        | 99.0        | 109.9 |
| Hogs                | 32.3 | 10.4 | 31.2         | 24.1        | 28.5  |
| Horses              | 19.9 | 10.5 | 15.3         | 13.7        | 15.3  |

\* Lazar Volin, "A Survey of Soviet Russian Agriculture," U.S. Department of Agriculture, Office of Foreign Agricultural Relations, Agriculture Monograph 5, 1951, p. 155.

† Lazar Volin, "The Malenkov-Khrushchev New Economic Policy," *The Journal of Political Economy,* 62(3):198, June, 1954.

U.S.S.R. produces about 75 per cent of the world's flax. Cotton has been important since the turn of the century. It is grown by irrigation in the Turan Lowland along the Amu Darya, Syr Darya, especially in the Fergana and other valleys, and near Astrakhan, in Crimea and the southern Ukraine. Despite efforts to become self-sufficient in cotton, Soviet Russia imports the fiber from Egypt, Iran, and Turkey.

Sugar beets are chiefly grown in the Ukraine. Sunflower seeds are a source of vegetable oil for food, and the crop is widely planted in the Ukraine and eastward beyond the Volga.

Other crops include rice, hemp, buckwheat, millet, fruits, tobacco, soybeans, and a rubber-producing plant that resembles the dandelion. Of these, rice is the most important, occupying about 400,000 acres in Central Asia and Transcaucasia, with a production of 700 million pounds.

Cattle, sheep, goats, and horses have not reached the goals set by the government. Poor management, poor shelter, and shortage of feed on the collective and state farms have contributed to the shortage as did the effects of World War II. In 1946, recovery of livestock was retarded by drought, and conditions remained bad for four years; it was not until 1953 that there was an appreciable increase in numbers of livestock. Even in the late 1950s meat production was less than that of the 1930s.

## MINERAL RESOURCES AND INDUSTRY

### Power Resources

**Coal.** The greatest power resource of the Soviet Union is coal, but it is supplemented by petroleum, water power, wood, and peat (Figure 10-12). Coal production is about 390 million tons annually, a total exceeded only by the United States during the 1950s. The target for 1960 is 593 million tons. The coal reserves are estimated to be 1,654 billion tons, second only to the 3,500 billion tons in the United States. Almost 90 per cent of this coal is in Siberia, far removed from the leading centers of industrialization.

The Donets Basin lying north of the Sea of Azov is the leading source of coal in the country, producing nearly 100 million tons a year, over one-fourth of the national output. Approximately one-half is anthracite; the remainder is bituminous coal of various grades. The bituminous coal is used for power in industry, coke for the iron and steel furnaces, for chemicals, gasification, domestic heat, and the railways. Donets coal is shipped west to blast furnaces at Krivoi Rog, where iron ore is mined.

The Kuznetsk (Kusbas) coal field is second in importance. Located south of the Trans-Siberian Railway in the upper basin of the Ob

River, this field produces about 35 million tons a year, and its reserves are estimated at 496 billion tons, five times larger than the Donets reserves. The coal is of high quality with few impurities. It is used by the iron and steel industry at Kuznetsk and Stalinsk, and by railways. Some is used in the furnaces of the Ural region, and in return cars bring iron ore back to the Kuznetsk industrial centers as a part of the Ural-Kuznetsk Combine.

Important coal fields in Russia are the Moscow, Tula, Ural, and Pechora, which together produce about 90 million tons a year. Tula is about 100 miles south of Moscow; its coal is lignite but suitable for steam-driven electric power plants, locomotive use, and home fuel.

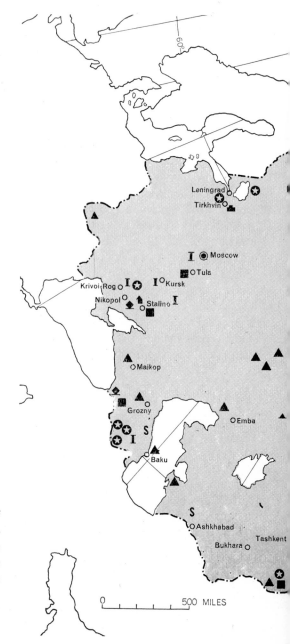

*Figure 10-12   The U.S.S.R. has a wide variety of mineral resources. In the production of many minerals it is self-sufficient. The Ural Mountains and the area between the Black and Caspian Seas are sources of many metals. Coal and petroleum are available in large quantities.*

The Urals have rather poor bituminous coal and lignite on both flanks of the range. Some coking coal is imported for use in the blast furnaces of Magnitogorsk and Chelyabinsk. The Pechora field in the far north was developed during World War II to offset coal production lost when Germany occupied the Donets Basin.

In Siberia the Kazakh coal lies between Lake Balkhash and the Urals; it is chiefly mined at Karaganda. The coal is excellent and is shipped to the Urals for use in copper smelters and iron furnaces there. Other large reserves of coal occur in Siberia and are mined in several localities that include deposits near Irkutsk, near Khabarovsk in the Amur Valley, and near Vladivostok. The Lena and Tunguska Basins are esti-

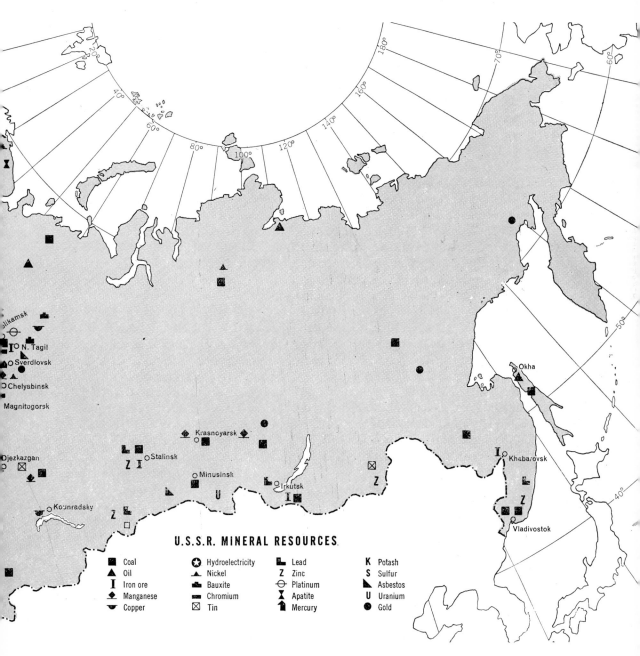

U.S.S.R. MINERAL RESOURCES.

| | | | |
|---|---|---|---|
| ■ Coal | ✪ Hydroelectricity | ▙ Lead | K Potash |
| ▲ Oil | ▴ Nickel | Z Zinc | S Sulfur |
| I Iron ore | � Bauxite | ⊖ Platinum | ◣ Asbestos |
| ◆ Manganese | ▬ Chromium | ✗ Apatite | U Uranium |
| ▽ Copper | ⊠ Tin | ⚑ Mercury | ● Gold |

mated to contain over 500 billion tons of coal, but production is small because of the sparse population and lack of industries. The new industrial development in eastern Siberia lays heavy stress on the Kuznets-Minisinsk, Kansk, and other coal fields.

**Petroleum.** Production of petroleum in the U.S.S.R. totals more than 500 million barrels annually, about 10.5 per cent of the world's output, but is insufficient for the demands of industry, farm tractors, and motor vehicles. Oil reserves are difficult to establish for the Union, but are estimated to exceed 80 billion barrels.

The Baku fields in the Caucasus region near the Caspian Sea produce about half the Union's petroleum. Baku production goes by barge up the Volga River and by two pipelines to Batum on the Black Sea. Batum has a refinery from which oil products are shipped to various ports on the Black Sea. North of the Caucasus, a pipeline connects Baku with the Donets industrial area. The Grozny and Maikop fields, on the northern flanks of the Caucasus, produce about 9 per cent of the Union's output. Northeast of the Caspian Sea are the Emba oil fields, and others are east of the Caspian. A 500-mile pipeline runs from the Caspian at Guryev to the Urals. Several new fields, in what is called the Second Baku, have been discovered between the Volga River and the Urals. Natural gas is produced in large volume near Saratov, and is carried by a pipeline to Moscow, a distance of 500 miles. In the Arctic regions, oil is produced in the Pechora Basin and further east on the shore of the Khatanga estuary. Oil from Sakhalin Island supplies needs in the Soviet Far East.

**Hydroelectricity.** This has great possibilities for development in the U.S.S.R. Many large rivers with steep gradients could supply much power, such as the Lena, Yenisey, upper tributaries of the Ob, and those of the Kola Peninsula. Some big rivers like the Volga and Dnieper have moderate drops but carry such large volumes of water that it is possible to generate much power. However, some of the Union's rivers are so far from centers of industry that

large-scale developments are impractical at present.

The largest hydroelectric dam is on the lower Dnieper River at Zaporozhy'e; it has a capacity of 900,000 kilowatthours. Most electric power in Russia is generated by coal, but several large hydroelectric plants are under construction. To provide energy for the Kuznetsk industrial district an installation is nearing completion on the Irtysh River, a tributary of the Ob, which will create a reservoir of 12,000 square miles to provide storage for irrigation and the electric plant. Four hydroelectric plants and dams are being built on the Volga River and its tributary, the Kama—Kuybyshev with 2 million kilowatts capacity, and north of Stalingrad, with 1.7 million kilowatts, Gorki, and Molotov.

*Metallic Resources*

The U.S.S.R. is well endowed with iron deposits; proven reserves total 9.9 billion tons of ore, and the estimated probable reserves exceed 18,000 billion tons. Over 44 million tons of ore are mined annually.

The chief center of iron ore production is at Krivoi Rog in the Ukraine, where the ore is high grade and accounts for two-thirds of the national output. On Kerch Peninsula, which separates the Black and Azov Seas, are extensive but low-grade iron deposits. In the Urals, high-grade ore is mined at Magnitogorsk, Nizhni Tagil, and other centers. On the basis of these ores the Kuznetsk-Ural Combine was formed, with Kuznetsk coking coal being hauled to the Urals, and iron ore shipped back to the Kuznetsk from the Urals, so that iron and steel mills were located at both ends of the haul of about 1,250 miles. Coal from Karaganda is now replacing Kuznetsk coal in the Ural district, and iron ore has been found in the south Kuznetsk, which eventually will eliminate shipments from the Ural region. Discovery of low-grade ores around Kursk, halfway between Moscow and Krivoi Rog, has caused the development of iron and steel works at Tula, Moscow, and Stalingrad. Several iron deposits are known in Siberia and the government has developed some of these to further national defense, the plants being far from the borders of the U.S.S.R., for instance near Irkutsk on Lake Baykal and at Komsomolsk in far eastern Siberia.

With an annual output of approximately 18 million tons, the Soviet Union is the world's leading producer of manganese, a metal used in making good steel. Manganese is mined at Nikopol in the Ukraine, Chiaturi in Georgia, in the Urals, and in central Siberia. Copper is mined in the Lake Balkhash area, and in the Urals; production is about 255,000 tons a year. About 100,000 tons of lead and 80,000 tons of zinc are produced annually; leading areas are in the Caucasus, Kazakhstan, Altai Mountains, and the Far East. Nickel deposits are located in the Urals, on the Kola Peninsula, and in the lower Yenisey region. In world production of nickel the U.S.S.R. is third, with about 27,500 tons a year.

Aluminum totals about 132,000 tons annually, making the Soviet Union a leading world producer, despite inferior deposits of its ore, bauxite. This is mined east of Leningrad, in the Urals, and on the Kola Peninsula. Electricity is required for aluminum extraction and this is supplied either by coal-fired plants, or electric power from the Dnieper and other dams.

In gold and platinum, the Union vies with the world's leading producers. The gold output is second only to that of the Union of South Africa, the total for the U.S.S.R. averaging 7 million ounces annually, worth nearly 250 million dollars. Gold comes mostly from the Urals and the Lena Basin. Platinum is mined in the Urals near Nizhni Tagil, and the production amounts to a third of the world's supply.

## Nonmetallic Resources

Nonmetallic resources include clay products, cement rock, fertilizer, and asbestos. Phosphate fertilizer is manufactured from a mineral called apatite found in the Kola Peninsula, the Ukraine, and Kazakhstan. Annual output is over 2 million tons, and reserves are estimated at 2 billion tons, or 60 per cent of the world's supply. The chief potash deposits are found west of the Urals and are associated with magnesium salts and bromine. Annual production

of salts is about 1.5 million tons. Asbestos is mined in the Urals, and in the Altai-Sayan Mountains of Siberia; output is 100,000 tons a year, second to that of Canada.

The U.S.S.R. has perhaps the greatest variety of mineral resources of any country in the world, to a considerable extent because of the great number of different minerals found in the Urals. Despite the great variety of minerals, in many cases they are insufficient in amount, or very far removed from markets or industrial districts.

## Industry

The industrial pattern of the U.S.S.R. reflects the distribution of mineral resources. The shift eastward after World War II is for security reasons, and in line with the location of newly discovered resources. Based on the production of iron ore at Krivoi Rog and Kerch and coal and

### TABLE 10-6. PRODUCTION OF INDUSTRIAL COMMODITIES IN THE U.S.S.R., 1955

| Commodity | Output |
|---|---|
| Pig iron, in millions of tons | 33.3 |
| Crude steel, in millions of tons | 45.3 |
| Rolled steel products, in millions of tons | 35.3 |
| Coal, in millions of tons | 391.0 |
| Petroleum, in millions of tons | 70.8 |
| Mineral fertilizers, in thousands of tons | 9,629.0 |
| Steam locomotives | 654 |
| Diesel locomotives | 134 |
| Electric locomotives | 194 |
| Tractors, in thousands | 163.4 |
| Cotton fabrics, in millions of meters | 5,904.0 |
| Linen fabrics, in millions of meters | 305.4 |
| Woolen fabrics, in millions of meters | 251.0 |
| Silk fabrics, in millions of meters | 525.7 |
| Leather shoes, in millions of pairs | 274.5 |
| Paper, in thousands of tons | 1,862.0 |
| Butter, in thousands of tons | 459.0 |
| Vegetable oils, in thousands of tons | 1,156.0 |
| Sugar, in thousands of tons | 3,419.0 |

SOURCE: *The National Economy of the U.S.S.R.: A Statistical Compilation,* State Statistical Publishing House, Moscow, 1956, pp. 40–49.

limestone in the Donets, such cities as Stalino, Makeyevka, Ordzhonikidze, Voroshilovsk, Kramotorsk, Stalingrad, Zaporozhy'e, Dnepropetrovsk, Krivoi Rog, and Kerch have developed into iron and steel manufacturing centers, each with a population of 100,000 to 500,000. Iron ore is shipped to the coal centers in the Donets, whereas coal moves west to Zaporozhy'e, Dnepropetrovsk, and Krivoi Rog, and east to Stalingrad. Kerch uses local ores and Donets coal. The machine-building town of the Donets basin is Kramatorsk, which produces turbines, textile machinery, rolling mills, blast furnaces, and sugar and oil refineries.

Chief iron and steel centers in the Urals are Magnitogorsk and Nizhni Tagil; they are based on iron ore mined nearby and coal shipped from the Kuznetsk and Karaganda. The Ural region is second to the Ukraine in production of iron and steel and other metals. In the Urals, Chelyabinsk and Sverdlovsk are important for tractors, munitions, machines, tools, trucks, and blast furnaces. In the Moscow area, some iron and steel is produced at Tula, but the region is primarily important for machinery, tools, and automobiles, with Moscow, Gorky, and Yaroslavl, the chief centers. Leningrad and nearby cities manufacture generators, machine tools, and instruments. In Siberia, Tashkent and Irkutsk are new centers for the steel industry. Total pig iron

production in 1954 was about 33 million tons, while steel output was about 45 million tons.

Chemical works in the Union are located around waterpower sites in the Ukraine at Dnieper Dam, on the Kola Peninsula, and in the Caucasus.

The shipbuilding industry is located chiefly at Leningrad, Sevastopol, and Vladivostok. River boats are built at Gorky and Molotov on the Volga and Kiev on the Dnieper. The lumbering industry is spread throughout the northern forest, with sawmills usually located on the rivers and bays. Pulp and paper are also manufactured in the taiga region.

Cotton textiles are manufactured around Moscow, Yaroslavl, and Leningrad, whereas cotton is grown in Central Asia, a highly uneconomic scheme from the transportation point of view. Recently mills have been built at Tashkent and Fergana in the cotton-producing areas. Linen mills are located at Ivanovo, Moscow, Yaroslavl, and Kalinin near the flax-growing region.

Sugar refining has spread from the Kiev-Kursk region to Fergana in Central Asia and to Vladivostok. Fish canning is concentrated at Murmansk, Vladivostok, and Sovetskaya Gavan, a port in the Far East. Astrakhan on the Caspian and Rostov on the Azov Sea are important in the south.

*Figure 10-13  Many kinds of farm machinery are made in the U.S.S.R. This tricycle tractor is in use in the tea-garden of the Tea Collective near Makharadze, Georgia. (Courtesy of United Nations.)*

## GEOGRAPHIC REGIONS OF THE U.S.S.R.

### Tundra

The large tundra region has been of small use to the U.S.S.R. in spite of efforts to improve its economy (Figure 10-14). Many natives inhabiting the region live in wigwams and engage in fishing, hunting, trapping, and reindeer herding. Agriculture is found only near small commercial settlements or outposts, and consists of experimental plots and greenhouses to provide fresh vegetables. Most settlements, on the margin of the Arctic or adjoining the taiga, process fish, collect furs, and serve as summer river-ocean transhipment points for lumber, pulpwood, and furs. More important are the ports of Murmansk and Port Tiksi, the latter on the Lena Delta. These centers grew as a result of interest in the Arctic as a route of navigation under the Northern Sea Route Administration, especially since 1932 when a vessel completed a summer voyage from Murmansk to Vladivostok. The purpose of the Northern Sea Route Administration is to find new resources along the Arctic, to explore new territory, and to set up meteorological stations in the Arctic. Travel over the tundra in summer is next to impossible because the surface thawing forms swamps and lakes. In summer, travel is mainly by small river boats; in winter it is by dog or reindeer sled on land or frozen rivers. Airplanes are also used occasionally.

### Taiga

The Russians are greatly concerned with the development of the taiga which occupies over half the area of the Union but supports only a minority of its population. Severe climate, inferior soils, and poor drainage are among the handicaps that limit growth.

The European taiga in Kola, Karelia, and northern R.S.R.S.R. was glaciated, giving rise to numerous lakes and deranged drainage. Rivers, the glacial lakes and marshes, and the soil are frozen 180 to 200 days of the year. In Kola and Karelia, the rivers are short and swift, like the North Dvina that is used primarily to float logs during summer to Archangel, a sawmill

center. Leningrad and Petrozavodsk are the chief lumber centers in the south. The European taiga contains 370 million acres of forest, two-thirds of it classed as exploitable. In the time of the czars, forest products constituted the country's second largest export.

Agriculturally the region is poor, its short summers and acid podsol soils limiting farming. Northward expansion of agriculture is being attempted by Soviet optimists, but thus far has had little success. The people live in inferior wooden dwellings located in clearings along the rivers and raise only a few vegetables and a hay crop for their cattle. Along the southern margin of the forest, some barley, oats, rye, hemp, and flax are grown. The cities and villages are usually located along rivers, or on ridges to avoid marsh areas. Land transport in the European taiga is handled by railways leading from Moscow and Leningrad to northern ports; the railways are supplemented by canals and poor roads.

The vast Siberian taiga resembles the European portion but is even more poorly drained, the Vasyuganye Marsh covering about one-third of the area. Timber is the chief resource, either moving downstream to the ocean and there loaded on freighters going to Archangel, or upstream to cities located on the Trans-Siberian Railway. Because of marshiness large parts are uninhabited. Western Siberia's chief contact with the rest of the Union is up the Ob River and its tributaries to the cities on the Trans-Siberian Railway which crosses these rivers.

The east Siberian taiga is drained by two main rivers, the Yenisey, 2,800 miles long, and the Lena, 2,860 miles. These are the chief regional transportation arteries, and their drainage divide coincides with the Central Siberian Upland. Permanently frozen ground underlies most of this area. Virgin forests cover most of eastern Siberia, with the exception of several thousand acres cleared in the Lena Valley, where some barley, wheat, and vegetables are grown for local consumption. Remoteness, poor, high-cost transport, and the location of better farming regions closer to the industrialized consuming centers preclude much agricultural expansion at present. Natives live by lumbering, fishing, fur gathering and reindeer breeding. Gold is mined along the Aldan River, a tributary of the Lena. Lumbering, the chief occupation, gave rise to the important sawmill city of Krasnoyarsk on the Yenisey where it is

crossed by the Trans-Siberian Railway, and to Igarka and Dudinka. Yakutsk, largest city on the Lena, is the capital and transportation hub of the Yakut A.S.S.R.

## Baltic Soviet Republics

By their location adjacent to each other, the republics of Estonia, Latvia, and Lithuania form

*Figure 10-14   The geographical regions of the Soviet Union are based on both physical and cultural activities. Compare this map with the other maps in this chapter and note the similarities and differences.*

a convenient national unit. This area is exposed to marine influences by its position east of the Baltic Sea, and the climate is, therefore, characterized by quite moderate temperatures. Principal crops on the better soils are rye, oats, barley, flax, and a little wheat. On the poorer soils, where grain farming is unprofitable, dairying, poultry, and stock breeding are important. The lack of industrialization is shown by the fact that only 25 per cent of the population live in urban centers. The principal seaports and manufacturing cities are Riga and Kaliningrad (Königsberg), the latter connected with the Bay of Danzig by a ship canal. Wood products, like lumber and paper are among the manufactures. Each of the Baltic states speaks its own lan-

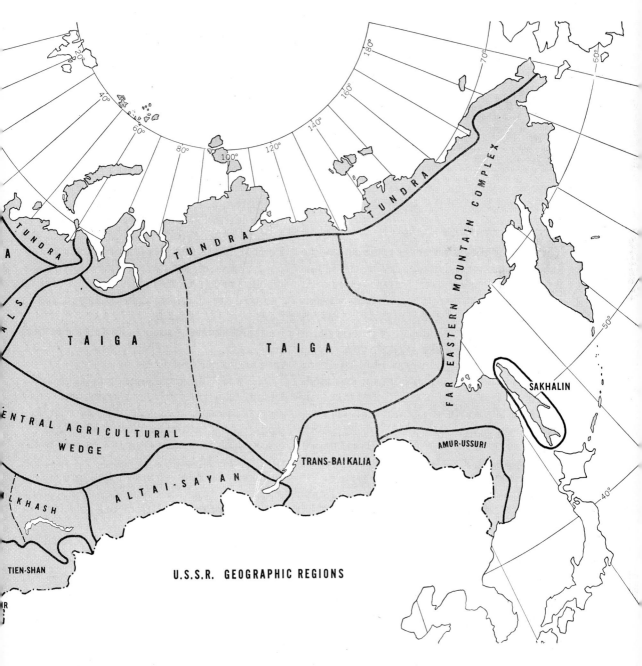

U.S.S.R. GEOGRAPHIC REGIONS

*Figure 10-15   Manezh Square and Okhotny Ryed in Moscow. In the background left to right are the House of the Council of Ministers and the Hotel Moskva. (Courtesy of Embassy of the U.S.S.R.)*

guage or dialect, and the three republics were independent between the two World Wars.

### Central Agricultural Wedge

The central agricultural wedge is the core of the U.S.S.R.'s economy, both in farming and industry, its most populous area, and the region most important in its history. It begins on the western frontier, exclusive of the Baltic states, and is bounded by an irregular line drawn on the north from Leningrad to Lake Baykal, and on the south from Lake Baykal westward to the Black Sea. In the western portion of this wedge modern Russia had its beginnings. Even the colonization of Siberia, in the seventeenth century, took place along the agricultural wedge or within the open forest on the northern margin of the steppe in order to avoid conflict with the tribes on the grasslands.

Climatically, this region is quite homogeneous and has favorable rainfall for crops. The chief soil, chernozem, is deep, black, and fertile. Principal crops are wheat, rye, barley, oats, flax, potatoes, sugar beets, and sunflower seed. Associated with crop agriculture is dairying and the raising of hogs and poultry.

Industry is concentrated in three areas, the Donets Basin, the Tula-Yaroslavl-Gorky triangle, and Leningrad. The Donets has coal, iron, manganese, and limestone deposits besides hydroelectric power, and this section leads in iron and steel and other heavy industry. The Tula-Yaroslavl-Gorky area has some coal and iron ore, but its factories primarily manufacture finished articles, such as machines, tools, automobiles, and tractors. Industries based on iron and coal are also located in Stalingrad and in cities near the Black Sea. The Leningrad area has shipbuilding, and manufactures electrical equipment, paper, lumber, chemicals, textiles, furs, and other products.

The wedge has the densest population in the Union, with parts of the Ukraine and areas around Moscow having densities of over 260 people per square mile. West of the Urals the density is usually more than 100 persons to the square mile. In Siberia, around Omsk and Novosibirsk, densities approach 250 per square mile as the result of expansion of agriculture and industry eastward from the homeland of Russia.

Within the agricultural wedge is located the majority of the large cities of the U.S.S.R. Of these Moscow, with a population of over 5 million and the capital of the country, is the largest. It is the nerve center for all decisions made for the Union by the Communist Party leaders. Moscow is the hub of transportation; eleven railways, seven major highways, the chief canals, and most rivers important for transportation are focused on the city. The Kremlin is at the center of the city and the main streets radiate outward from the gates which once pierced the wall that surrounded the structure. Circular boulevards have replaced two other outer walls built as the city expanded. The Russians are very proud of the Moscow subway, called the "Metro," that has 20 miles of underground track and beautifully built stations. Besides its other functions Moscow manufactures agricultural machinery, foodstuffs, clothing, automobiles, leather goods, electrical goods, and machine tools.

Leningrad, a city of over 3 million population, located at the eastern end of the Gulf of Finland, owes its origin to Peter the Great, who defeated the Swedes in 1703, and in the same year began constructing the city he called St. Petersburg. It is built on low, marshy islands in the Neva River, and might be called a Russian Venice, as hundreds of bridges are required to span the many winding channels among the islands. Leningrad commands a large hinterland, is the former capital of Russia, and is an important historic and cultural center with beautiful palaces, public buildings, churches, and museums.

Kiev, the capital of the Ukrainian S.S.R. and third largest city in the Union, is on the Dnieper

*Figure 10-17  Principal business section of Kharkov. (Courtesy of C. W. Grant.)*

River. Other Ukraine cities include Kharkov, the fourth largest city in the U.S.S.R., Odessa, a port on the Black Sea, Dnepropetrovsk, Stalino, Zaporozhy'e at the Dnieper Dam, the largest in Europe; Makeevka, and Krivoi Rog. On the Sea of Azov are the ports of Mariupol and Rostov-on-Don. The Ukraine is the most urbanized part of the Union, with one-third of its 31 million people living in cities; 17 of these have more than 100,000 inhabitants each.

On the Volga River are Stalingrad and Kuybyshev. East of the Urals in the agricultural wedge are Novosibirsk, an administrative center, Omsk, and Tomsk, both of the latter with large sawmills and with processing plants for farm products, and Krasnoyarsk with sawmills, flour mills, and a locomotive works. All are located on the Trans-Siberian route and are growing commercial and manufacturing cities.

## Ural Region

The Ural region extends 1,500 miles from the Arctic coast south to the Aral Sea. It is important for mining, and for steel, smelting, chemicals, and heavy industry. Iron, coal, nickel, manganese, oil, copper, aluminum, lead, zinc, chromium, potash, salt, building stone, gold, silver, and platinum all come from the Urals. This part of the Union is second only to the Donets in industry. Chief industrial cities of the Urals are Sverdlovsk, Chelyabinsk, Molotov, Ufa, Magnitogorsk, and Nizhni Tagil. They are well served by railroads.

*Figure 10-16  Under the large cities of the Soviet Union great subways have been built. This picture shows a part of the Leningrad subway. (Courtesy of C. W. Grant.)*

## Caucasia

Caucasia lies between the Black and Caspian Seas and includes the Greater and Lesser Caucasus Ranges, the Suram Mountains that connect them, and southern Crimea with the Yaila Mountains, together with the associated lowlands. The climate is subtropical and suitable for citrus fruits, cotton, tea, tobacco, and vineyards; even cork oak and bamboo are grown. In western Georgia tea covers 100,000 acres, and lemon and orange groves about 25,000 acres. Expansion of agriculture is being accomplished by draining the Kolkhiz Lowlands and by irrigation of the Kura River valley. Minerals include oil, coal, manganese, and chromite. Hydroelectric possibilities are great.

There is a large number of racial groups in Caucasia who speak many languages and dialects and who have different customs, religions, and cultures. Cities include Baku, fifth largest in the Union and the capital of Azerbaidzhan, Erevan, the capital of Armenia, and Tbilisi (Tiflis), the capital of Georgia. On Crimea are Yalta, a famed resort, and Sevastopol, a seaport. At the east end of the Black Sea is the port of Batum, terminus for pipelines and railroads from Baku. Many of the people of Caucasia are herdsmen and farmers, living in small villages.

## Caspian-Turan-Balkhash Region

This region is one of internal drainage and desert climate, with irrigation necessary for agriculture. The Amu Darya and Syr Darya Valleys are the foci of the regional life. The upper Syr Darya irrigates 2 million acres in the Fergana Valley, where are located the cities of Fergana, Kokand, and Andijan. The Amu Darya irrigates more than a million acres, and sustains Khiva and other centers. The Zeravshan River waters 980,000 acres which support Samarkand and Bukhara, ancient cities dating to the time of Alexander the Great. A tributary of the Syr Darya, the Chirchik, irrigates 480,000 acres near Tashkent, capital of the Uzbek S.S.R. and a steel milling center. In the Turkmen S.S.R. are oases, in one of which is the old city of Mary

*Figure 10-18 Settlement at the base of a denuded hill near Tbilisi. A reforesting project is to be carried on at this site. (Courtesy of United Nations.)*

(Merv). Within the Turan Lowland are the unproductive Kara Kum and Kyzyl Kum Deserts, areas of shifting sand dunes and the homes of a few nomadic herders.

The chief irrigated crops are cotton, which occupies 60 per cent of the cultivated land, wheat, rice, barley, sugar beets, fruits, and melons. Much of the cotton production of about 750,000 tons annually is shipped to Moscow, although textile mills have been started in Central Asia. Fruits include grapes, apricots, peaches, cherries, apples, and plums, mostly grown by irrigation but with some planted on the intermediate slopes of the mountains where rainfall is adequate. In connection with irrigation, there are possibilities for development of hydroelectric power, since many of the streams rise in the high mountains bordering the desert.

There are several sources of employment in addition to agriculture and livestock. Coal is mined at Karaganda and petroleum comes from the Emba Valley. Much general manufacturing is done in the cities. Caviar is prepared from the eggs of sturgeon caught in the Caspian Sea. Borax and soda are extracted from alkaline lakes. The Caspian-Turan-Balkhash region is served by railways that lead into the agricultural wedge; one connects with the Trans-Siberian at Novosibirsk, and the other with the Volga lines.

Outside of the big irrigated valleys, human use of the deserts consists of oasis farming and collectivized grazing. Cattle number about 9 million in the Balkhash Basin alone, and in the southern uplands sheep are an important source of wool.

Astrakhan, a seaport on the Volga, is the largest city in the area. It processes fish and lumber, the timber being rafted down the Volga, and transships oil from the Caspian tankers to barges for movement up the Volga. Other cities are Karaganda, important for coal, Alma Ata, capital of the Kazakh S.S.R., and Frunze, capital of the Kirghiz S.S.R.

## Pamir–Tien Shan Highlands

The Pamir Knot, a dissected plateau over 12,000 feet high, is referred to as the roof of the world. The Tien Shan trend east-west and

*Figure 10-19   Entrance to the Pedagogical Institute located in Tashkent, Uzbekistan. (Courtesy of Embassy of the U.S.S.R.)*

the range lies north of the Pamirs. Between the two is the Syr Darya, and south of the Pamirs is the Amu Darya. North of the Tien Shan is the Ili River and the Dzungarian Gate. The mountains have snow fields and glaciers that help to maintain the flow of the rivers. Ancient caravan routes cross this region. One is via the Terek Pass into the Tarim Basin; a second leads into Kashmir, a province adjoining India and Pakistan, and the third into Afghanistan. Other routes are up the Ili River or through the pass called the Dzungarian Gate into Sinkiang in western China. Automobile roads of a sort cross this region but there are no railroads. There are no cities; only a few villages and a very sparse population, mostly of herdsmen, can be found in these highlands.

*Figure 10-20    Irrigated vegetable gardens separted by pole fences in the Irtysh River valley near Krasnayanska in the dry steppe area. (Courtesy of United States Department of Agriculture.)*

### Altai–Sayan Mountains

This region extends from the Irtysh River to the south end of Lake Baykal in Siberia. It includes the Altai and Sayan Ranges, their northern slopes, and the Tannu Tuva Basin, the latter being surrounded by the West Sayan and Tannu Ola Mountains. The ranges attain elevations of over 10,000 feet, with Mt. Belukha, 15,153 feet, in the Altai being the highest. On the northern flanks of the Altai is the Kuznetsk coal basin, and on the slopes of the Sayan Ranges is the Minusinsk coal field. Other minerals mined are gold, iron, lead, zinc, and manganese.

The headwaters of the Yenisey River drain the Tannu Tuva Basin. Formerly this basin was a part of China, but since 1944 it has been an autonomous republic of the Union.

The northern slopes from the mountains include some good farmland, used for grains and livestock. The rough mountains and dry basins supply grazing. The coal deposits are actively worked, and iron and steel and other industries are expanding in the Kuznetsk district. Chief cities are Novosibirsk, Stalinsk, Kemerovo, and Prokopyevsk.

### Transbaykalia

Transbaykalia includes ranges both west and east of Lake Baykal, the Yablonovoy Mountains to the southeast and the Vitim Plateau between the latter and the Transbaykal Range, together with the upper parts of valleys that flow to the north and east. The ranges average about 5,000 feet in height. Lake Baykal occupies a downsunken block and has the greatest depth, 5,822 feet, of any lake in the world. It is the largest fresh-water lake in Eurasia, covering 13,197 square miles. The lake drains into a tributary of the Yenisey, called the Angara. Water power development possibilities are very great and several plants are to be built on the Angara near Irkutsk. Coal and iron are mined near Petrovsk, east of Irkutsk, and account for an iron and steel industry there. Other minerals include gold, tin, zinc, tungsten, and molybdenum. Transbaykalia is largely covered by forests, and only about 1.5 million acres are farmed. Cattle raising is more important than crops.

The principal cities are located on the Trans-Siberian Railway. Irkutsk is important for making mining and dredging equipment and other machinery besides having a large meat-combine (packing house). Ulan Ude also has a meat canning and processing plant and manufactures machinery. Chita, a railroad junction point, is farthest east, in an area suited to wheat and oats, the two crops which occupy 75 per cent of the tilled land. Flour milling, sawmills, and coal mining are among its industries.

## Amur–Ussuri Lowlands

The Amur and Ussuri Rivers form most of the boundary between the Soviet Union and Manchuria. The region has made great strides in agriculture to make it independent of the rest of the Union. Crops are wheat, barley, rye, oats, sugar beets, and some rice north of Vladivostok. The minerals include coal, iron ore, lead, and zinc, and their development has led to manufactures at Komsomolsk that supply regional needs. Khabarovsk, located at the head of ocean navigation, where the Trans-Siberian Railway crosses the Amur, is the commercial center. Vladivostok is a port on the Bay of Peter the Great. Although the harbor freezes in winter, it is kept open by icebreakers.

## Far Eastern Mountain Complex

A complex array of mountain systems and ranges forms the surface features of far eastern and northeastern Siberia (Figure 10-2), but few minerals have been discovered or other resources developed in the whole large area. Human habitations and effective land use are lacking throughout most of the entire region, except for scattered locations on the coasts of Kamchatka and the Okhotsk Sea, where fishing is carried on, or on the coast of the East Siberian Sea, where small scientific outposts are located. The largest settlements, with 50,000 to 90,000 inhabitants, are Magadan on the Sea of Okhotsk and Petropavlovsk on the Kamchatka Peninsula. Both are seaports and engage in whaling and the handling and processing of salmon, herring, cod, and crab. For years Japan and the Soviet Union have disputed over these fishing grounds. The acquisition of the Kuril Islands that stretch between Kamchatka and Japan gave the Union additional fishing bases.

## Sakhalin

Sakhalin Island lies parallel to the coast of the Siberian mainland, and is separated from it by the Tartar Strait. Before the Russo-Japanese War of 1904–1905 the island was in Russian hands, but after that only the northern half, north of the 50th parallel, was retained by Russia; the southern half was ceded to Japan and renamed Karafuto. After World War II the U.S.S.R. was given full control of the island again.

The oil fields of Sakhalin are important because they are the only ones belonging to the Union on the Pacific coast. Fishing is the oldest industry, and the catch includes cod, salmon, herring, trout, and crab, but in terms of value lumbering is more important. Pulp is the most valuable forest product. There is a railroad in the southern half, but only dirt roads are available for transportation in the northern half of the island.

## IN PERSPECTIVE

### The U.S.S.R.

The Union of Soviet Socialist Republics holds a vast land area larger than the continent of North America. The country is preeminently a land power and occupies what has been called the heartland from which it has been probing for weak spots and acquiring contiguous territories for several centuries. Although much of the Soviet Union is so cold, arid, or mountainous that in those places only a sparse population can exist, there are also very extensive fer-

*Figure 10-21　A group of schoolgirls in Leningrad on a study trip to one of the museums. (Courtesy of C. W. Grant.)*

tile plains, large forests, and a great variety of fuels, metals, and other minerals. Under the czars, Russia exported grains, lumber, pulpwood, animal products, and a few metals; there was little industrial development, and manufactures were the principal imports. After the Revolution in 1917, the Communists obtained control of the government and began a series of Five-Year Plans intended to increase production of foodstuffs, wood products, coal, petroleum, iron, and other minerals, and especially to industrialize the nation. Peasants were forced onto collective farms; workmen were shifted wherever they were needed, dozens of new manufacturing cities were founded, and thousands of industrial plants were established. Many of the planned goals were not reached, but one should not underrate the accomplishments. Many people perished from famines and purges but production grew, even if not as quickly as planned. The net result is that the U.S.S.R. has become a powerful state, and whether or not its methods can be approved, its power must be recognized. Furthermore, the Soviet Union has large undeveloped resources, and these constitute the base for additional industrial and population growth.

## EXERCISES

*1.* What is the area of the Soviet Union? How does it compare in size with the United States, China, Canada, France, and North America? About what per cent of the land area of the world does it cover?

*2.* What is the population of the Soviet Union? How does it compare with that of China, United States, India, and the United Kingdom? About what per cent of the population of the world lives in the U.S.S.R.?

*3.* What is the dominant physical feature of the Soviet Union? Which part of the nation is covered by it? What are the principal divisions?

*4.* Why does the U.S.S.R. have such a variety of climate? In which climatic region do most of the people live? What are the principal handicaps of each region?

*5.* Where are the chief manufacturing areas of the Union? What minerals are found in or near these areas? What are the chief cities of each? What are the principal handicaps of each? Why have the manufacturing areas developed so rapidly during the past forty years?

*6.* How does agriculture in the Soviet Union differ from agriculture in the United States? What are the principal crops of the U.S.S.R.? In which part of the nation is each produced? Why is production per acre usually lower than that of other European countries?

*7.* What are the chief mountain areas of the country? How do they compare in elevations? What do these mountains contribute to the economy of the nearby areas?

*8.* What are the principal political divisions of the U.S.S.R.? Which two are the most important? Why? What does U.S.S.R. mean?

*9.* Why is the eastern Asiatic part of the Union not as well developed as the European part? Why is the Asiatic area important? What is being done to improve the economy and increase the usefulness of the area?

*10.* Why is transportation an especially important problem in the U.S.S.R.? What are the handicaps of the largest rivers? Where have the most railroads and highways been developed? Why? What are the disadvantages of the chief seaports?

*11.* What cultural advantages or disadvantages do the people of the U.S.S.R. have? How does their form of government influence the economic life of the nation?

*12.* What are the principal minerals produced in the U.S.S.R.? How is the variety of minerals an advantage in the development of manufacturing?

## SELECTED REFERENCES

Balzak, S. S., V. F. Vasyutin, and Ya G. Feigin: *Economic Geography of the U.S.S.R.*, The Macmillan Company, New York, 1949.

Berg, Leo S.: *Natural Regions of the U.S.S.R.*, The Macmillan Company, New York, 1950.

Cressey, G. B.: *Asia's Lands and Peoples*, McGraw-Hill Book Company, Inc., New York, 1951.

———: *How Strong Is Russia?*, Syracuse University Press, Syracuse, 1954.

Field, Neil C.: "The Amu Darya: A Study in Resource Geography," *Geographical Review*, 44:528–542, October, 1954.

Goodall, George: *Soviet Russia in Maps*, Denoyer-Geppert Company, Chicago, 1942.

Gregory, James S., and D. W. Shave: *The U.S.S.R.*, John Wiley & Sons, Inc., New York, 1944.

Grigoryev, A. A.: "The Reclamation of the Forest Belt of the U.S.S.R. in Europe," *Geographical Journal*, 119:411–419, December, 1953.

Harris, Chauncy D.: "The Cities of the Soviet Union," *Geographical Review*, 35:466–473, July, 1945.

———: "U.S.S.R. Resources: I—Heavy Industries," *Focus*, 5(6):1–6, February, 1955.

———: "U.S.S.R. Resources; II—Agriculture," *Focus*, 5(9):1–6, May, 1955.

Rodgers, Allan: "Changing Locational Patterns in the Soviet Pulp and Paper Industry," *Annals of the Association of American Geographers*, 45:85–104, March, 1955.

Schwartz, Harry: *Russia's Soviet Economy*, Prentice-Hall, Inc., Englewood Cliffs, N.J., 1950.

Shabed, Theodore: *Geography of the U.S.S.R.: A Regional Survey*, Columbia University Press, New York, 1951.

———: "Political Divisions of the U.S.S.R.," *Geographical Review*, 36:303–311, April, 1946.

Volin, Lazar: "A Survey of Soviet Russian Agriculture," U.S. Department of Agriculture, Office of Foreign Agricultural Relations, Agriculture Monograph 5, Washington, 1951.

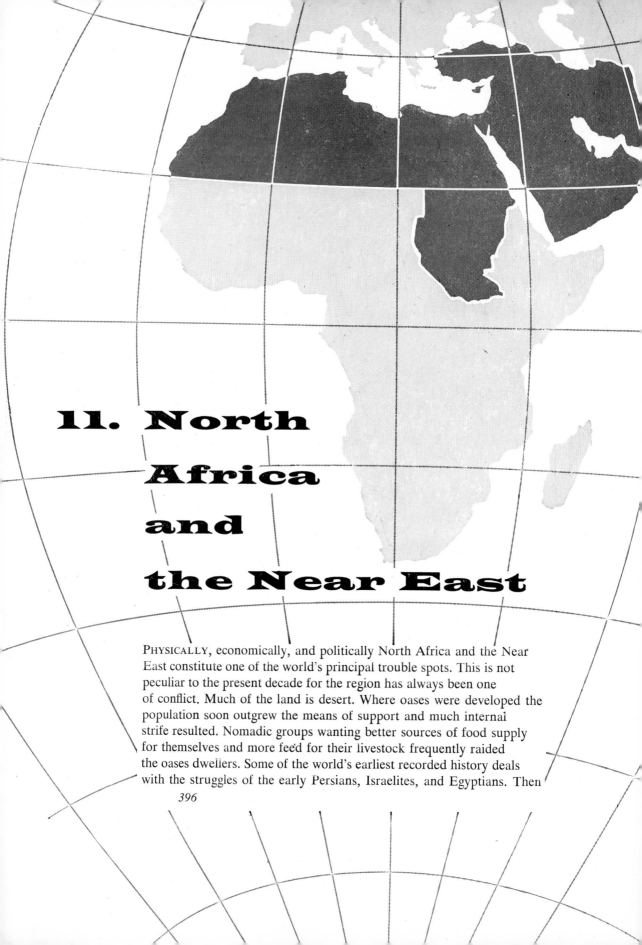

# 11. North Africa and the Near East

PHYSICALLY, economically, and politically North Africa and the Near East constitute one of the world's principal trouble spots. This is not peculiar to the present decade for the region has always been one of conflict. Much of the land is desert. Where oases were developed the population soon outgrew the means of support and much internal strife resulted. Nomadic groups wanting better sources of food supply for themselves and more feed for their livestock frequently raided the oases dwellers. Some of the world's earliest recorded history deals with the struggles of the early Persians, Israelites, and Egyptians. Then as now, their political and economic condition was one of conflict, strife with each other, struggle with the meager resources. From this hot, dry desert and semidesert area have come numerous religions. Three—Judaism, Christianity, and Islam—have influenced the thoughts and beliefs of millions of people as well as the actions of numerous nations.

Until recently, France, Italy, and the United Kingdom have controlled large areas or strategic locations within the region. Italy lost her claim in North Africa as a result of World War II, and Libya has been formed from the former Italian territory. During recent years Britain has released her claim on the Sudan, and her influence has been reduced in several of the Arab countries of the Near East. France has released all claims to lands in the Near East and, for several years, has been having considerable difficulty with her possessions in North Africa. The desire for complete political independence is strong.

After World War I the Turkish Empire was divided to revive old nations or to form new ones; thus Syria, Iraq, the Transjordan now called Jordan, Palestine, and Lebanon came in-

## TABLE 11-1. POLITICAL DIVISIONS OF NORTH AFRICA AND THE NEAR EAST

| Country | Area, sq miles | Approximate population, 1955 |
|---|---|---|
| Morocco | 159,000 | 10,360,000 |
| Algeria | | |
| (*departments of Oran, Algiers, Bône, and Constantine*) | 81,000 | 8,100,000 |
| (*incl. the Territories of the South*) | 846,000 | 9,000,000 |
| Tunisia | 48,000 | 3,500,000 |
| Ifni (Spanish) | 700 | 45,000 |
| Spanish Sahara (Dio de Oro, etc.) | 115,000 | 50,000 |
| Mauritania (part of Fr. West Africa) | 450,000 | 500,000 |
| French Sudan (part of Fr. West Africa) | 470,000 | 3,800,000 |
| Niger (part of Fr. West Africa) | 500,000 | 2,200,000 |
| Chad (part of Fr. Equatorial Africa) | 490,000 | 2,250,000 |
| Libya | 680,000 | 1,200,000 |
| Egypt | 386,000 | 20,000,000 |
| Sudan | 967,500 | 9,000,000 |
| Turkey | 296,000 | 22,000,000 |
| Cyprus | 3,572 | 515,000 |
| Iraq | 171,000 | 5,000,000 |
| Iran (Persia) | 630,000 | 19,000,000 |
| Syria | 73,000 | 3,500,000 |
| Lebanon | 4,000 | 1,300,000 |
| Israel | 8,000 | 1,700,000 |
| Jordan | 37,000 | 1,500,000 |
| Saudi Arabia | 700,000 | 6,000,000 |
| Oman, Qatar, Kuwait, and Bahrein (Br. Prot.) | 92,000 | 900,000 |
| Yemen | 75,000 | 4,500,000 |
| Aden and protectorate (Br.) | 112,000 | 730,000 |

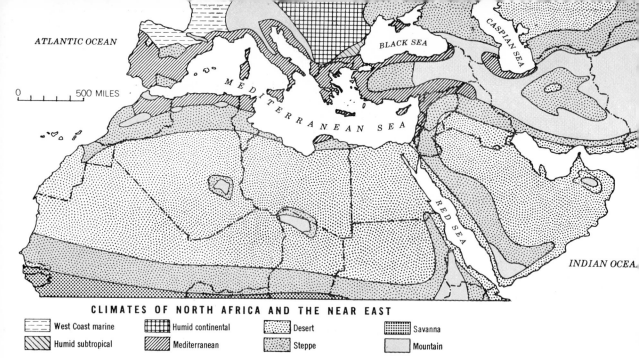

ATLANTIC OCEAN

BLACK SEA

CASPIAN SEA

0 500 MILES

MEDITERRANEAN SEA

RED SEA

INDIAN OCEAN

CLIMATES OF NORTH AFRICA AND THE NEAR EAST

West Coast marine    Humid continental    Desert    Savanna

Humid subtropical    Mediterranean    Steppe    Mountain

*Figure 11-1    Deserts dominate the climatic regions of North Africa and the Near East. Note that in most places steppes surround the desert.*

to existence. France and England, under the direction of the League of Nations, at first directed the activities of these new nations. Later, however, both withdrew from the area. In the meantime many of the small countries of the Arabian Peninsula were united as Saudi Arabia. Since World War II the nation of Israel has been organized in the old Palestine area, the na-

tion of Libya founded, the former Anglo-Egyptian Sudan has declared itself to be the independent country of Sudan, and Morocco and Tunisia have achieved self-government (Table 11-1).

North Africa and the Near East is indeed a trouble spot, and region of conflict, where political changes frequently occur.

### REGIONAL CHARACTERISTICS

*Climate*

North Africa and the Near East have many similarities in physical features and in the culture of the inhabitants. Sunny skies and light rainfall are typical. Coastal areas like the Barbary states of northwest Africa, the shores of the Black Sea, and the eastern Mediterranean have enough rainfall to support agriculture without irrigation. In such places the natural vegetation is the Mediterranean scrub forest, a scattered open woodland of cork oaks, cedars, or bushes with a sparse covering of grass between. These lands of light to moderate winter rainfall and the great irrigated valleys of the Nile and the Tigris-Euphrates are the most favorable for agriculture and human settlement, and in them live the

vast majority of the inhabitants of the region (Figure 11-1).

Between the coastal Mediterranean lands and the true deserts of the interior are the steppes. The steppes have a semiarid climate with occasional rain storms, usually in winter. These grass-covered plains and plateaus are much better grazing lands than the deserts, and support herds of sheep and goats. Certain favored areas produce wheat, barley, or alfa grass. Some of the nomads of the deserts migrate to the steppes to avoid the terrific heat and prolonged drought of the desert summers.

The great deserts of inland North Africa and Arabia have only rare and scattered rains. In some places where rivers run from the mountains or from moist tropical areas into the desert there are strings of oases which produce dates, barley, cotton, and vegetables. For the most part, however, the oases are small dense settlements clustered about wells or springs. Between the oases the desert usually supports a very sparse population of nomads who travel almost constantly in search of pasturage for their flocks.

## The People

The major cultural links among the countries of North Africa and the Near East are language, religion, social customs, and economic life. Arabic is the predominant language from Morocco to Iraq; Turkish, Persian, and Hebrew are related tongues (Figure 11-2). Literary Arabic as used in the Koran, the Mohammedan Bible, is the same throughout the Moslem lands. Spoken Arabic, however, varies from place to place. An educated Arab of Algeria or Tunisia, through his study of Arabic literature and the Koran,

learns the same written language as the literate people of Egypt or Syria. The Bedouins (nomads) are often illiterate, however, and the spoken Arabic dialects of Morocco and Algeria are as different from the colloquial speech of Arabia as Portuguese is from Spanish. Literary works published in Cairo can be read by Arab scholars everywhere, but the talking motion pictures for the masses of Arabs are produced in one dialect for Morocco, and in another for the Iraqui Arab. Despite the colloquial differences in Arabic and the presence of other languages like the Berber tongues in northwest Africa and the Hamitic dialects in the Sudan, the Arabic language, history, and literature are such a powerful unifying force that North Africa and a portion of the Near East are often called the Arab world.

Islam, the Moslem faith, reinforces the unifying power of the Arabic language. Mecca and Medina, the chief holy cities of Islam, are in

*Figure 11-2   Arabic is the common language over much of North Africa and the Near East. The location of the Berbers can be noted in the Atlas Mountains. In Asia the Turkish and Iranian languages are spoken over wide areas.*

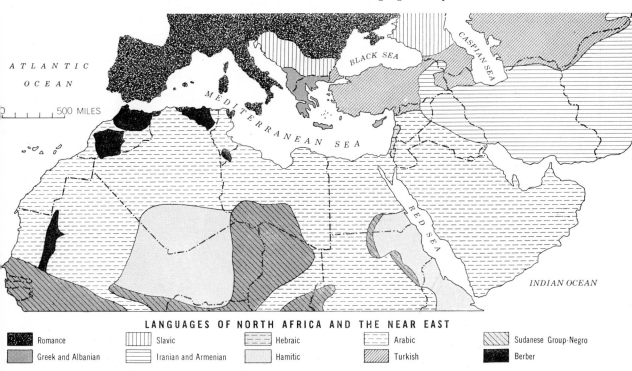

LANGUAGES OF NORTH AFRICA AND THE NEAR EAST

| | | |
|---|---|---|
| Romance | Slavic | Hebraic | Arabic | Sudanese Group-Negro |
| Greek and Albanian | Iranian and Armenian | Hamitic | Turkish | Berber |

Arabia. The religion requires five prayers daily while facing toward Mecca, and those who are able must make a pilgrimage to Mecca, for which the title of Hadj is awarded. The Koran and other religious writings were originally in Arabic. Moslem countries like Turkey and Iran (Persia) are populated by people who are Arabic neither in origin nor language, but Mecca is the center of their religion and they adhere to the main tenets of the faith. Islam has united peoples to such a degree that North Africa, the Near East, and additional Moslem areas in Asia are sometimes described as the Moslem world (Figure 11-3).

Islam provides not only a religion but also a system of social customs, economic attitudes, and government rule. If they are strict Moslems, men use no intoxicating beverages, eat no pork, wear the turban or fez as a head covering, and perform their prayers daily, regardless of locality or occupation. Moslem women live a secluded life in a separate portion of the house

or tent (the harem) and are ordinarily not introduced or even mentioned to guests. On the rare occasions when they leave the women's quarters, they are, in many areas, wrapped in a combined hood and robe that covers them from head to foot with only a narrow opening for the eyes. In Turkey, and in cities elsewhere, this attire for women is being replaced by Western clothing. Although Islam permits a man to have four wives, and under certain conditions, additional concubines, economic conditions usually limit a man to one wife at a time. The custom of having several wives is becoming less and less common.

Giving alms to the poor is prescribed by Islam. Among the desert Moslems hospitality is traditional, and the well-to-do provide for the less fortunate. Tribal chiefs have religious as well as governmental responsibility and leadership. They are legal authorities and official advisers to their people on economic and social matters. Thus, Islam provides for all phases of

*Figure 11-3   Islam is the dominant religion of North Africa and the Near East. It should be noted, however, that like most other religions this one is divided.*

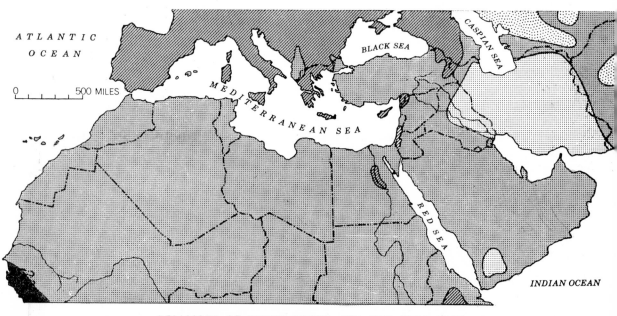

RELIGIONS OF NORTH AFRICA AND THE NEAR EAST

Christianity        Judaism        Tribal        Islam: Sunni Moslems        Islam: Shiah Moslems         Undifferentiated religion

life, and religion is closely associated with government, business, and daily routine. In Turkey, however, government decree has modified the situation, and church and state are separated as in Western countries.

Since early times, herding of sheep, growing of olives, wheat, and dates, and exchanging pastoral products for oasis goods have been typical economic activities. Local travel by donkey and camel has been supplemented by the train, automobile, and airplane; but customs, clothing, foods, and buildings are often strikingly like those described in the history of ancient Egypt and Mesopotamia, in the Bible, and in the Koran. The geographic setting of deserts, oases, and Mediterranean climate partially explains the life of these peoples; for fuller understanding one must also consider history, politics, and religion.

The major themes of the cultural geography of North Africa and the Near East are Mediterranean and oasis agriculture, nomadic herding and caravan trade across the steppes and deserts, Arabs and the Arabic language, and the Moslem religion. Variations upon these themes,

or the complete absence of one of them, are factors that often distinguish one place from another. The separation of the Moslem faith from civil law and government in Turkey has been mentioned as one example. Lebanon is an Arab country where Christianity is the dominant religion. The new nation of Israel is almost an island of Jewish people and religion in a Moslem ocean. Egypt is a desert country dominated by the people and agriculture of the gigantic Nile oasis, and Libya is a Saharan country with only minor oases.

Modernization of agriculture, the construction of Westernized cities, and the development of mining are activities that have changed localized areas so that they contrast with the rest of the region. These Westernized spots, usually on or near the Mediterranean coast, are not yet large or numerous enough to convert any considerable areas into outliers of European culture. The modern European sections of cities like Casablanca, Algiers, Cairo, and Baghdad, are impressive, but they are only exotic settlements in lands that are predominantly Arab and Moslem.

## CONTRASTS WITH ADJOINING REALMS

North Africa and the Near East differ greatly from Europe, tropical Africa, and the Far East. Europe is primarily a Westernized Christian region with Germanic, Romance, and Slavic languages. Mediterranean Southern Europe is closely linked with the culture, language, trade, and politics of the humid and industrialized lands farther north. Nomads, camel caravans, the Arabic language, and oasis agriculture are outside the cultural experience of most Europeans, and the Mohammedan religion is common only in transitional Southeastern Europe.

Although the Arabic language and Islam extend into parts of the grasslands and forests of tropical Africa, there are such important changes in climate, peoples, agriculture, and customs that a traveler soon realizes that he has entered a new geographic realm. The savanna and rain forest replace the Mediterranean and desert lands of the north. Colored peoples predomi-

nate instead of white Semites or Hamites. New features appear, like circular villages of mud and brush huts, Sudanese cattle, savanna grassland, tropical forests, and hoe agriculture. Africa south of the Sahara has no roving Bedouins or historical association with the coasts of the Mediterranean Sea. The barren southern Sahara is an effective barrier between two culture worlds.

Dry lands and the Moslem faith continue eastward across Turkey, Iraq, Iran, Afghanistan, and Pakistan, but Arab people and the Arabic language predominate only as far as Iraq. Iran is a transitional country with historical, religious, and cultural similarities to the Arab world. Afghanistan and Pakistan are Moslem countries but they lack the Mediterranean climate, Arabic influence, and historical association with the Mediterranean Sea. They have been more involved with the history of India and are beyond the recent culture or conquest of Turkey or Arabia. China, Japan, and other areas of the Far East are, of course, far different in human geography from North Africa and the Near East.

## THE BARBARY STATES

The moderate winter rainfall of the Atlas Mountains of northwestern Africa provides a much more favorable setting for agriculture and human settlement than the adjoining regions of the Sahara. This populated western island of Morocco, Algeria, and Tunisia (Figure 11-4) is surrounded by the sea and the desert. Historically, it has often been linked to Europe or other Mediterranean lands. The Phoenicians founded the city of Carthage near the present site of Tunis and it controlled most of Barbary until

destroyed by the Romans. Under the Romans, Barbary became "the granary of Rome." After the decline of Rome, a number of peoples alternated in controlling parts of Barbary—the Vandals, Byzantines, Arabs, Portuguese, Spanish, and Turks—before the modern French conquest.

The original inhabitants were the Berbers, white people of ancient and obscure origin who resemble Italians and Spaniards rather than the peoples of Africa and Asia. The Berbers, from

*Figure 11-4  North Africa is a land of new independent nations. Morocco, Tunisia, Libya, and the Sudan have all become independent since World War II. Each nation has serious transportation problems.*

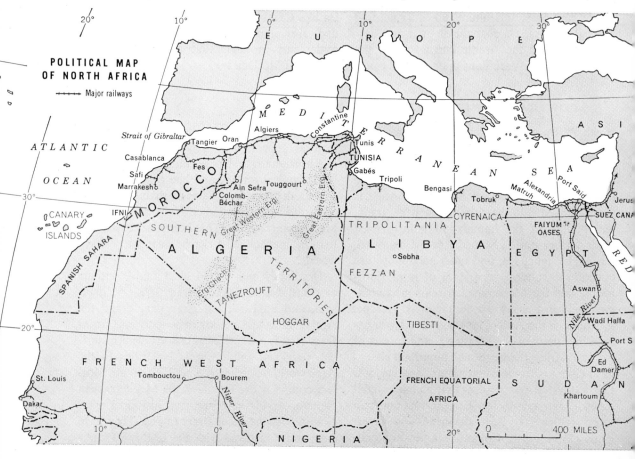

whom the word Barbary was derived, have mixed with their captives and conquerors for many centuries, but comparatively pure groups of Berbers are still found in humid, hilly, and mountainous areas.

The Arab conquest of the seventh century had great and lasting effects upon Barbary. The Arabs converted the region to the Moslem religion, and also introduced the camel, which made possible caravan trade across the Sahara. Although united under one religion, the Berbers and Arabs can often be distinguished by appearance, dress, or language. The Berbers still preserve their spoken dialects without having a written language or literature. They are most numerous in Morocco, but also inhabit the high mountains and some other parts of Algeria. Sometimes without regard to Arab or Berber origin, the peoples of the cities and farmlands of Northwest Africa are called Moors and the nomads of the deserts Bedouins.

## Relief Features

The Atlas Mountains and associated ranges extend east-west across northern Barbary. The coastal hills, plateaus, and mountains are called "the Tell." This is the main agricultural region of northwestern Africa, although the plains areas are small and many of the fields of wheat and grapes are on hilly land. Morocco has the highest mountains, one peak attaining 13,665 feet. There are three east-west ranges, the Rif Atlas (part of the Tell), the Great Atlas, and the Anti-Atlas. The mountains of Algeria consist of two major east-west chains, the Tell Atlas along the coast and the Saharan Atlas farther south. Between these two ranges lie the High Plains and Plateaus, semiarid lands that are used for grazing and for producing grain and alfa grass. The two Atlas Ranges come together in eastern Algeria, extend for a way into Tunisia, and then become lower and disappear before reaching the eastern coast of Tunisia.

## Transportation

When Barbary was a part of the Roman Empire, the production of grain was increased. New areas were opened to agriculture, and the Ro-

mans built hard-surfaced roads to haul grain to seaports in what is now eastern Algeria and northern Tunisia for shipment to Italy and other parts of the empire. Towns of moderate size developed along the coast, with smaller ones at interior crossroads and in the more fertile grain areas. Many of the present cities of North Africa can trace their origin to the Roman era.

The Romans stopped construction at the margins of the Sahara. Their roads were wide and numerous in the more populated areas. Farther south there was only a sparse network of narrow roads, while the routes to the forts in the edge of the desert were little more than trails. Thus agriculture, settlement, and roads declined from north to south in rough correspondence with the zones of Mediterranean, steppe, and desert climates.

When the Roman Empire declined, North Africa passed into the hands of less competent rulers. Cities, aqueducts, wells, and roads fell into a state of disrepair. The Vandals, Arabs, and Turks largely ignored the Roman roads, constructed for wheeled vehicles and legions of foot soldiers. Pack animals, pastoral nomads, and foot travelers used paths instead.

When France conquered Algeria during the 1830s there were no improved roads left. The army constructed short wagon roads from the coast toward the interior, and civilian agencies expanded them into a network. Railroad construction occurred later, and after France acquired Tunisia, during the 1880s, and Morocco, in 1912, all three countries were joined together by highways and railways. The present transportation system covers more area and has much more traffic than the old Roman system of roads, but there is the same general correspondence between resources, the density of settlement, and trade routes.

The railway network has standard gauge lines for the main strategic east-west route and for the important farming areas of the Tell (Figure 11-5). Interior agricultural areas of secondary importance and the mining regions of Algeria and Tunisia are usually served by narrow gauge lines. The railways of Morocco were construct-

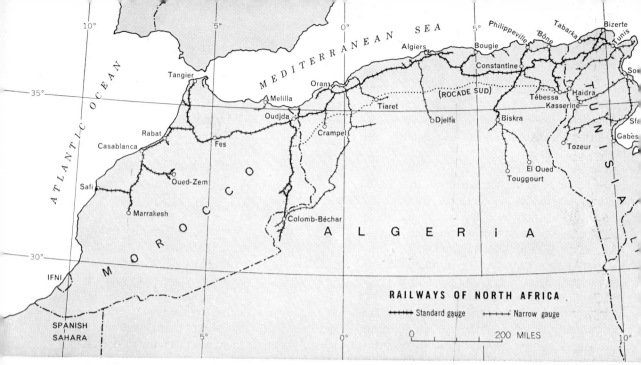

*Figure 11-5   The greatest railway mileage in North Africa is in the Atlas Mountain area of Algeria. These railroads serve the productive coastal plain and the mountain valleys. Deserts limit rail extension in most parts of the area.*

ed more recently than the others. Standard gauge lines connect the more important regions, and highways serve the secondary areas. Since the main routes run across the mountains and hills of the productive coastal areas, the railways have many sharp curves and steep grades, especially in Algeria.

## Cities

All the larger cities of Barbary are on or near the coast. In Morocco, the city of Casablanca has grown so rapidly in recent years that it is now the largest settlement of Northwest Africa. It is a port and trading center for the grain producing plateaus of western Morocco. Marrakech, farther south, is a religious capital of the Moslems and a market town for the agricultural and pastoral products of the region. It was the northern terminus for the old caravan trail that ran to Timbuktu (Tombouctou) in the Sudan. Rabat, near Casablanca, is the capital of Morocco. After Morocco became independent it assumed control over Tangier, which for many years was in an international zone on the southern shore of the Strait of Gibraltar. Its strategic location and the rivalry among Britain,

France, and Spain largely explain this political status.

The settled Tell of Algeria is a long, narrow, hilly coastal zone. Each part ships agricultural or mineral products to Europe through its ports and receives manufactured goods in return. There is little trade in an east-west direction; thus Algeria falls into three parts, each of which forms a separate economic and political area. In the west is the department of Oran, named after the dominant agricultural center and port of Oran. Algiers is the administrative center and seaport of the central department. Constantine, an interior trade center, is the chief city of eastern Algeria. It is served by the ports of Phillippeville and Bône. Both Constantine and Bône are capitals of departments. Algiers is the cultural focus of French North Africa and in size ranks second only to Casablanca. Algiers is the capital of all Algeria—the departments of Oran, Algiers, Bône, and Constantine and the Territories of the South, or Algerian Sahara.

Tunisia has only one large city, Tunis, the major seaport, capital, and cultural center. The towns of Sousse and Sfax, on the east coast, are local markets and outlets for the interior phosphate mines.

The cities of Barbary have much in common. The large seaports have European sections with hotels and stores similar to those in France. The typical native section, or Medina, however, has narrow streets with tiny shops where Moslem clothing, slippers, jewelry, brassware, and similar articles are sold. The souks, or native markets, also have stands for fruits, vegetables, and pastries as well as shops where goods are made by hand. These shops and their trading customs are similar to those of Damascus, Baghdad, and other cities of the Near East.

A North African city often has a Mellash, or Jewish quarter, and a Casbah (Kasba), or native fort. In Algiers the name Casbah has been extended to include both the fort and the native quarter. It is world-famous for its dark, narrow streets and mixture of peoples—Arabs, Berbers, Maltese, Jews, and others. With the establishment of Israel many North African Jews left for that country.

## Economic Development

The areas favorable for agriculture are largely restricted to the Mediterranean and steppe climates, but even there agriculture is not continuous. Many places are too mountainous, and a few, especially in coastal Algeria, are poorly drained. Algeria is world-famous for its wine and typical Mediterranean products like barley, wheat, olives, grapes, and oranges. A variety of vegetables and fruits are grown in scattered spots throughout the Tell. Some of these are small coastal plains and hill lands; others are sheltered and well-watered inland valleys. Corn and oats are among the minor products of Morocco and Algeria, and tobacco has become important in eastern Algeria.

Much of the original Mediterranean forest has been cut for firewood, but the less accessible mountains are still forested and are now being carefully conserved by the French. The cork oak forests of Algeria and Morocco, among other uses, supply stoppers for wine bottles.

The interior semiarid steppes with their nat-

ural growth of short grass or scattered bushes are most suitable for sheep and goats, which far outnumber the cattle. Mules, donkeys, horses, and camels are also raised, and used by the natives for riding and pack animals. The High Plateaus of Algeria produce alfa or esparto grass which is used for making paper.

The fishing industry yields sardines, anchovy, and tuna along the west coast of Morocco, and the canning of sardines is an important indus-

*Figure 11-6 Picking oranges in Morocco. The citrus industry of the Barbary states has increased greatly in importance in recent years. (Courtesy of Press and Information Division.)*

try of the ports of Casablanca, Safi, and Mazagan. In Tunisia, Sfax is the main fishing port. Mullet and whiting come from deep-sea fishing, tuna and sponges from inshore fishing.

Barbary has considerable mineral wealth, especially phosphate rock and iron ore. The phosphate is mined in southern Tunisia, in Morocco, and to a lesser extent, in eastern Algeria. Rich deposits of iron ore occur in a band extending from the Rif of Morocco across Algeria and into western Tunisia. Lead and zinc are mined in Morocco as well as in eastern Algeria and Tunisia. Small amounts of antimony, cobalt, and copper have also been produced. The only coal mines of importance are in western Algeria, near Colomb-Bechar. They provide only a portion of the fuel needed by the Barbary states. In recent years the manganese mines of eastern Morocco have greatly increased their production. Discovery of petroleum in 1957 in the Algerian Sahara about 350 miles inland, may lead to important production from fields where exploratory drilling is being done. Both France and Algeria would benefit greatly from the finding of oil in this area.

## Differences among the Countries of Barbary

Morocco, Algeria, and Tunisia are similar in that each is a strip of Mediterranean, steppe, and desert country that exports raw materials and imports processed goods. Likewise, all have been controlled by France. But there are important variations in landforms, peoples, trade, and government, so that each division has its distinct personality.

In Morocco, there are a few French settlers in the former French portion, and Spaniards in the area formerly controlled by Spain. The Berber elements in the mountains form a large

*Figure 11-7 Arabs approaching the oasis of Gales in Tunisia with produce for the local market. Donkeys carry heavy loads of grain, vegetables, firewood, and water and often their masters as well. (Courtesy of French Embassy Press and Information Division.)*

cultural and political group. Morocco is ruled by a sultan; under international agreements the country is open to trade of all nations. The United States is interested in the manganese mines of eastern Morocco, and has spent considerable sums for the construction of air bases in the Casablanca area. France is the most important source of Moroccan imports, but American sales of motor vehicles, machinery, and petroleum products have also been important.

The major export of Morocco is phosphate rock, followed by fish, fruits, vegetables, wheat, barley, and manganese ore. Moslems do not ordinarily produce or consume wine, which accounts for its absence from the list of major exports. But like other peoples of the region, the Moroccans demand sugar and tea. Neither is raised in the country; they rank high among the imports.

Algeria has many more French settlers than Morocco. There are also moderate numbers of Spaniards in western Algeria, and Italians in the east. Cities like Algiers, Oran, Bône, and Philippeville have well-developed European sections. The European population amounts to about 1 million of the total of 9 million.

The French farmers and Mediterranean climate account for the large production and export of wine, in which Algeria ranks high among the countries of the world. Following wine, the other major exports are fruits and vegetables, cereals, and iron ore. These products, of course, are sent mainly to France. Machinery, textiles, petroleum products, and sugar are the major imports. Politically, the longer period of direct French control in Algeria contrasts with the French protectorates in Tunisia and Morocco which ended in 1955 and 1956.

Tunisia, located just across the Mediterranean Sea from Sicily and Italy, and next to the former Italian colony of Libya, has almost as many Italian settlers as French. The Tunisians, although Moslems of Arabic language and culture, differ from the Algerians and Moroccans in that the Berber element is almost entirely missing. Increasing Tunisian nationalism has led to self-government. Adjoining Libya, although less advanced, culturally and economically, achieved independence at an earlier date.

Tunisia exports olive oil, phosphate rock, wheat, barley, lead, and wine, mainly to France, England, and Italy. The manufactured imports —textiles, machinery and automobiles, petroleum products, refined sugar, and many other products—come chiefly from France and the United States.

## THE SAHARA

The Sahara, or Great Desert, extends from the Atlantic Ocean across the widest part of Africa to the Red Sea. It is larger than the United States. All parts of the Sahara have dry climates, and most of its peoples use the Arabic language and follow the Moslem faith. The tremendous size and the great variations in landforms and water supply, economic development, and settlement give rise to the expression "The Sahara is a land of a hundred landscapes." Population is, on the average, very sparse, but varies from the absolute emptiness of the barren and level Tanezrouft of southern Algeria through the oases of moderate size in the sand dunes of northern Algeria and southern Tunisia to the gigantic oasis of the Nile in Egypt with its 20 million people. All are parts of the Sahara, but Egypt is so important and so different from the other oases that it will be described as a separate region. Politically, parts of the Sahara lie in Morocco, Algeria, Tunisia, Spanish Sahara, French West Africa, French Equatorial Africa, Libya, Egypt, and the Sudan (Figure 11-4).

At first the Sahara was believed to be an endless expanse of sand dunes without vegetation. Although some dune regions, or ergs, are larger than Pennsylvania or Illinois, the total sandy surface is only 10 or 15 per cent of the total. Most of the desert is a low plateau with a gravel or stony surface. A very sparse and withered vegetation of small bushes with weeds and grass is most common. Some areas, like the Tanezrouft, are level and without vegetation, whereas the rocky hills and mountains of the Ahaggar (Hoggar), Air, and Tibesti have scrubby bushes and stunted trees.

Although rainstorms are rare, they may occur suddenly and fill the shallow valleys (wadis) to overflowing in a few minutes. After the storm, the dried-up shrubs and the dormant seeds and roots of grass spring to life as if by magic, and the locality turns brown, gray, or green, depending upon the season and the variety of plants. The interior nomads move almost constantly in search of such pasturage for their goats, sheep, and camels. In the north, the herds are often moved to the Atlas Mountains for the summer, and onto the nearby desert during the period of winter rains.

## The Evolution of Transportation

Before the Arab conquest in the seventh century the oases and mountains of central and western Sahara were occupied by Negro farmers. Water was then, as at present, obtained from streams that ran into the desert from the more humid mountains, from springs at the edges of plateaus and rocky hills, or from shallow wells that tapped underground sources. Travel between oases was rare and generally on foot or by donkey.

The Arabs spread the Moslem faith and the use of the camel to all parts of the Great Desert. The Negroes were driven from some of the northern oases; in other places they were allowed to remain as slaves or workers for the conquerors. Some of the Berbers, especially the proud and warlike Tuaregs, turned nomad and gained control of parts of the Sahara. They rarely became farmers, but often controlled oases which they used as bases for their raids upon camel caravans and hostile settlements.

Despite the danger of raids and the necessity for camels to halt for long periods of rest at intermediate oases, a number of trans-Saharan caravan routes developed. In the west, one ran from Marrakech to Timbuktu in the Sudan. Other routes connected Timbuktu with Algeria, and led from Kano, Nigeria, to Tunis and Tripoli on the Mediterranean Sea. Such long trips required many months. Silk, weapons, tea, sug-ar, and manufactured goods were hauled southward, and the return trips carried ivory, gold, leather goods, ostrich feathers, and cotton cloth. Salt was also a commodity of great importance. It was mined in several places in the Sahara and distributed to the more humid lands on the north and south. Numbers of Negro slaves were also taken across the desert for sale in the cities of Barbary.

Suppression of the slave trade by European nations, the exhaustion of Sudanese gold mines, and the falling demand for wild ostrich feathers, caused a decline in trade across the Sahara. Recent construction of railways and roads from the west coast of Africa into the Sudan made it accessible from that direction, and most of the remaining long trans-Saharan caravan routes were abandoned.

The camel, however, is still used by wandering nomads for transport in areas of sand dunes and for the declining salt trade. Donkeys serve local needs in oases and farming areas, and horses are used on the margins of the desert. Since about 1930, both air lines and bus lines have furnished commercial transportation across the Sahara. The buses operate only during the cooler months (Figure 11-8). The summers are too hot for either Europeans or motor vehicles, but European tourists visit many of the northern oases during the winter.

## Economic Development

The peoples of the desert may be divided into nomads and oasis dwellers. Nomads are most numerous on the steppes and more habitable northern and southern margins of the Sahara. Their herds provide milk, wool, mutton, and hides which are often traded to the subservient oasis people for dates, grain, fruits, and vegetables. Nomads may also carry on trade between oases or serve as professional soldiers.

Oases vary considerably in appearance. Huts may be constructed of brown mud, of red or yellow clay, or rarely of blocks of salt. Sometimes the buildings are whitewashed a brilliant white. The site may be a stream valley lined with palms, a flat-topped hill, a vale between gigantic red sand dunes, or a flat dusty plain—

wherever springs or wells can provide water. The larger oases are urban in character with cafés, shops, and market places to serve the desert travelers. The town may be walled for protection against raids. Irrigated gardens usually provide barley and dates, and less commonly, wheat, millet, tobacco, onions, apricots, and other fruits and vegetables. Some oases, like those visited by tourists in the northern Sahara, are veritable Gardens of Eden and have modern hotels, curio shops, and cafés, but others are hot, dusty, miserable collections of mud huts. High-quality dates are an export of importance in Algeria and have justified the extension of several rail lines to the more productive oases.

## The Nation of Libya

Libya, almost entirely Saharan in character, has recently joined the world family of independent nations for reasons stemming from geography, history, and politics. France was established in Barbary, and England had special interests in Egypt and Suez before Italy became a world power. The desert between, being less valuable, was left under the control of weak Turkey and fell to Italy when that country sought colonial possessions.

In Libya the desert restricts agriculture and animal husbandry to the three inhabitable islands of Tripolitania, Cirenaica, and the Fezzan. The main agricultural products are barley,

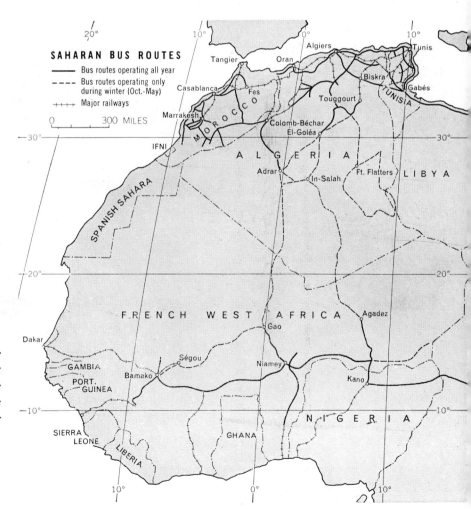

*Figure 11-8  Bus routes have been developed to supplement and connect rail lines. Note that the buses operate across the Sahara during the winter*

dates, and olives; sheep and goats provide wool, meat, and skins. There are very small exports of animals, wool, and skins, also sponges and tuna from coastal fisheries. With the defeat of Italy in World War II, the administration of Libya was at first taken over by Britain and France. Then, in 1952, Libya became an independent nation in accordance with decisions of the United Nations, although the population is small and the three habitable areas are separated from each other by hundreds of miles of barren desert. American and British financial support, in return for the right to maintain military bases in Libya, is an important element in the economy of the country. Possibilities exist also for the discovery of petroleum.

## EGYPT, THE NILE, AND THE SUDAN

Civilization in the Nile Valley began several thousand years before the time of Christ. The desert climate provided dazzling sunlight, and the Nile River brought both fertile silt and water for irrigation during the regular floods of the late summer and autumn. The productive delta

and narrow plain along the river were joined by the navigable stream and had protection from invasion. On the north, the Nile Delta (downstream or Lower Egypt) has numerous distributaries and marshy land—a difficult area to cross. Along both sides of the fertile Nile Valley are barren zones, the Arabian and Nubian Deserts on the east and the Libyan Desert on the west. The Nile Valley narrows in Upper (southern) Egypt until the river has only a gorge through the desert plateau, and there is a series of rapids which prevents navigation. Thus nature provided a suitable habitat for this early cradle of civilization, and man has occupied the land through a succession of dynasties and other governments, cultures, and religions. Worship, as one might expect, has often been associated with the sun or with the Nile.

## Nile River

For centuries the farmers of the Nile Valley regulated their lives according to the floods of the river, without knowing its source or the reasons for its fluctuations. The Nile, one of the longest rivers in the world, has its sources on the equator, 2,000 miles south of the Delta (Figure 11-10). The longest tributary is the White Nile, which rises in Lake Victoria. This large body

*Figure 11-9   A caravan crossing the Sahara near the Atlas Mountains. (Courtesy of Morocco Tourist Office.)*

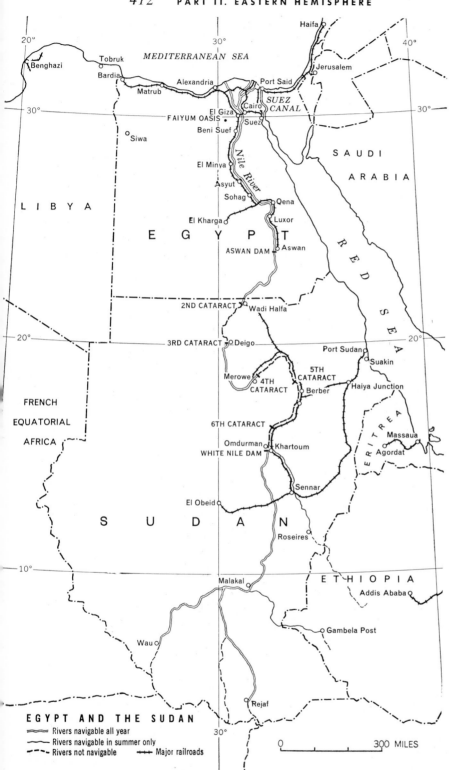

EGYPT AND THE SUDAN
- 〰️ Rivers navigable all year
- —— Rivers navigable in summer only
- –‐–‐– Rivers not navigable   ┿┿┿ Major railroads

0 ⊢————————⊣ 300 MILES

*Figure 11-10   The Nile River is the lifeline of Egypt and the Sudan. Note the vast amount of vacant land away from the river and the use of railroads in conjunction with the river.*

of water has a constant supply from the heavy rains of the wet equatorial climate. The flow of the White Nile is also stabilized farther north in passing through Lake Albert and the Sudd region of floating vegetation. There the channel of the river was completely covered with masses of papyrus, bulrushes, tall grass, and weeds until British engineers opened a path for navigation in 1904. The gentle gradient and widespread swamps result in a very slow flow of water. Evaporation is high and only about half of the water finally escapes from the swamps. The flow is steady, and if it were not for the other tributaries, there would be no great floods on the Nile.

The Blue Nile and the Atbara Rivers start in the Ethiopian Plateau, where the climate is an upland savanna type. Rainfall is heavy in summer and light in winter. In summer the flooded streams flow swiftly from the highlands into the Sudan, bringing large quantities of silt. The Blue Nile joins the White Nile at Khartoum, and from that point northward the river has its seasonal floods. The Atbara adds to the height of the floods, and makes them last longer into the fall. By January the Ethiopian tributaries are at the low level of the dry season. The White Nile continues to supply water from the lakes of the equatorial region during the critical low-water period from January to June. The British constructed the great dam at Aswan, in 1903, and others, to store water during the flood season and release it during the low stage of the river, making possible a great expansion of cotton growing in Egypt.

In the Sudan, a dam at Sennar on the Blue Nile, completed in 1925, regulates the flow so that large-scale cotton production has become possible in the Gezira area at the junction of the White and the Blue Nile. Despite the great success of these and other dams, many problems remain. The silt is trapped by the dams so that it no longer adds new fertility to the irrigated fields; commercial fertilizers must now be used. Complete regulation of the Nile should include Lake Tana at the source of the Blue Nile in Ethiopia, but Ethiopia objects to interference by either Egypt or Britain.

The population of Egypt is growing rapidly, but the Nile remains the same size. During the four low-water months, dams close the mouths of the river and all the water is used for irrigation; none reaches the sea. By international agreements originally sponsored by Britain when she had full control of Egypt, the priority rights on Nile water belong to Egypt. Irrigation water for the Sudan is taken with Egyptian permission and only at the flood season when Egypt can spare the water. Nile water is a strict limiting factor on agriculture in both countries. The present dams hold water during the wet months and release it during the dry ones, but this is only annual storage. The recently completed Owen Falls dam has raised the level of Lake Victoria by three feet and added to the amount of stored water. A proposed second dam near Aswan would make possible a further extension of agriculture in Egypt. However, American and British offers of financial support were withdrawn in 1956, when Egypt obtained military materials from the Soviet nations, on the grounds that the added financial obligation impaired Egypt's ability to repay the proposed loans. Egypt then seized the Suez Canal, leading to complications that will be discussed later.

## People

In the Sudd region of the southern Sudan the primitive peoples are mostly of Negro origin with small amounts of white, Hamitic blood. The Dinka, Shilluk, and Nuer groups are known as Nilotes. They wear little or no clothing and gain a living mainly by herding cattle, hunting, or fishing. To the northwest, in the hill lands of Darfur and Kordofan, Negroid peoples like the Nuba live by raising millet or gathering gum arabic from acacia trees.

The central part of the Sudan and the northwestern deserts are inhabited by nomadic Arabs who raise camels and sheep, and in the more humid lands farther south, cattle and horses. There are also Hamitic tribes between the Nile and the Red Sea. Because of their bushy hair these people are commonly known as "Fuzzie-Wuzzies." They are remembered for their fight against Britain and Egypt when the two countries combined to conquer the Sudan, 1881–

1898. In the northern Sudan most of the farmers of the Nile Valley are Nubians of mixed blood. Some of them engage in native crafts like pottery-making and basket-weaving.

### Economic Development

The major export of the Sudan is cotton, followed by gum arabic, which is used for glue, and hides and skins. Most of the people live by raising livestock, but millet, peanuts, corn, and oil seeds are food products or minor exports.

In Egypt the mass of the people comprise the fellahin or sedantary peasant class. In Upper Egypt some are descended from the ancient Hamitic peoples and belong to the Christian Coptic Church. Several centuries of Arab influence, however, have resulted in a racial mixture, and Moslems now outnumber Christians about ten to one for the country as a whole. The nomadic population of Bedouin Arabs is very small.

Cotton is the main product and export of the densely settled valley and delta of the Nile. Wheat, corn, and rice are major foods, but overpopulation and specialization on cotton result in a shortage of cereals. Wheat, tea, and coffee, manufactured goods, and fertilizers are major imports. Concentration on the cash crop of cotton gives the largest monetary return and makes imports possible. Farming methods are primitive. The use of large amounts of labor without mechanization results in high yields per acre but low yields per individual. The fellahin live in mud huts and on very meager diets. Egypt hopes to provide a better living for her dense and increasing population through the expansion of industries such as cotton weaving and food processing. Meanwhile, the growing of berseem, or Egyptian clover, in rotation with cotton and cereals, increases the nitrogen content of the soil and helps maintain its fertility.

Oxen, buffaloes, and donkeys are used as draft animals, and sheep and goats provide milk and wool for the farming population. The Fayûm Oasis, irrigated by canals from the Nile, is the most important farming area outside the Nile Valley and Delta. Western Egypt has a few scattered oases, some of them served only by camel caravans.

### Trade Problems

The Nile is the main artery of trade in Egypt. There are hundreds of small sailing vessels and dozens of shallow draft steamers plying the river between Cairo and Aswan, at the first cataract. Above Aswan, the Nile is again navigable to Wadi Halfa at the Sudan border. Railways, as well as roads and airlines, parallel this route. From Cairo northward, the delta has radiating distributaries and rail lines to the mouths of the river.

Cairo benefits as the converging point at the head of the delta. East-west commercial and pilgrim traffic along the southern shore of the Mediterranean swings southward through Cairo to avoid crossing the many streams and swamps of the delta—an important factor in the city's early growth. With a population of 2 million, Cairo is the largest and most important commercial center of North Africa and the Near East. Although Mecca is the holy city for the Moslems as Rome is for the Roman Catholics, Cairo is the cultural hub of the Arab world, as Paris is for much of Western Europe. In recent years Cairo has become a great focus of air traffic, and the political center for rising nationalism among the Arab peoples. The modern portion of Cairo is in European style, reminding one of French cities, while the older sections—Arab, Jewish, and Coptic—have the narrow streets, bazaars, shops, and crowded living quarters of other Near Eastern centers. The ancient mosques and palaces, like the pyramids near the city, attract thousands of tourists yearly. Cairo has several suburbs in European style.

Alexandria is the second largest city and chief port of Egypt. Through it pass about ninetenths of the exports, cotton, and small quantities of rice, and onions.

### The Suez Canal

The Suez Canal was built by the French under the direction of Ferdinand de Lesseps, and opened to traffic in 1869. At that time Egypt was technically a province of the Ottoman (Turkish) Empire, but actually a semi-independent area under strong British influence. Britain at first opposed the canal, but both Egypt and Turkey supported the Suez Canal Company, and became shareholders in it. In 1875 Britain made an opportune purchase of the shares of the Khedive of Egypt, and became an important shareholder. The administration, however, remained predominantly French, even after World War I when Egypt was detached from the Ottoman Empire and placed under British protection. The strong interest of Britain and France in the canal has continued to the present.

The Suez Canal is a 100-mile-long sea-level route. Port Said and Suez are the northern and southern terminals. The canal forms a link in the ocean route between Europe and the Far East. In recent years it has become even more important to the countries of Western Europe and the Middle East as a passageway for oil tankers on their way from the Persian Gulf around the Arabian Peninsula to the Mediterranean Sea.

After World War II, rising nationalism in Egypt led to riots against the British and demands for the evacuation of British troops from all of Egypt, including the canal zone. Britain finally agreed to remove its troops from the canal bases in 1954, but the British- and French-dominated company continued operating the canal. Two years later, in 1956, Egypt seized the canal facilities in retaliation for British and American refusals to continue support for the high Aswan dam. France and Britain withdrew their personnel from the canal zone but insisted on continued international control of the waterway. A few weeks later Israel attacked Egypt. Britain and France occupied portions of the canal zone and demanded that both

Israel and Egypt cease hostilities. Britain and France justified their action on the ground that the canal required protection and should remain in operation under international control regardless of Middle Eastern disputes. The United Nations then sent an international police force to the area to maintain order. In 1957 the canal, which had been blocked, was cleared and reopened to traffic under the control of Egypt.

## The Sudan

The Sudan has been independent since 1955. The country has much less trade than Egypt. A rail line starts at Wadi Halfa, the second cataract, and extends southeastward to Abu Hamed instead of following the great bend of the Nile. From Abu Hamed through Khartoum to Sennar, however, the railway parallels the Nile and the Blue Nile tributary. A branch line extends westward from the main trunk to tap the oil seed and gum arabic region around El Obeid; others connect Sennar and Berber with Port Sudan on the Red Sea. Additional lines are under construction, or planned for the future.

The largest settlement of the Sudan is ancient Omdurman near the junction of the White Nile and the Blue Nile. It was the capital of the dervishes, a fanatical sect of Moslems who followed the Mahdi, a supposed descendant and successor of Mohammed. Omdurman is still a center for native trade in camels, cattle, ivory, and gum arabic. The British built the nearby town of Khartoum which soon became the center for railways, steamer traffic, administration, and the cotton trade. In early days the Arabs shipped slaves from Suakin on the Red Sea, but the harbor has silted and declined to a minor port for small sailing vessels. The newer center of Port Sudan, built by the British, is now the major outlet for the country.

## THE STRATEGIC NEAR EAST

The lands of the Near East, extending from Turkey to Iran and southward to include Egypt and Arabia, play a prominent part in the strategy of the modern world. The area forms a land bridge that connects Europe, Asia, and Africa. Since ancient times it has been a crossroads for traders going from Eastern Europe to India, and from Asia to North Africa.

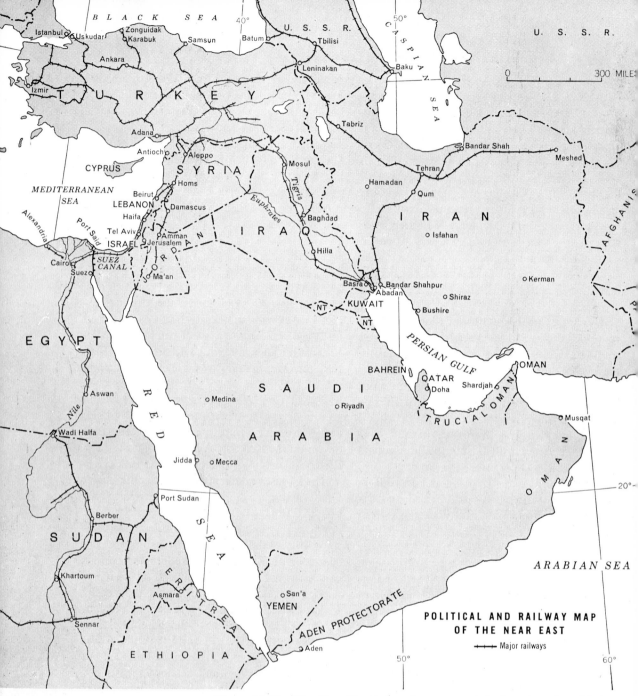

*Figure 11-11  The Near East is largely an area of Arab nations, Israel being the only non-Arab one in the group. Much of the area is desert or semidesert. The Fertile Crescent is the most highly developed part of the area with its large cities and developed transportation routes.*

The shape of this land bridge gives it control over the connections between important bodies of water (Figure 11-11). The Dardanelles, the Sea of Marmara, and the Bosporus link the Mediterranean Sea with the Black Sea, thus providing a possible outlet for the southern part of the Soviet Union and the Balkan countries. For thousands of years traders and invading armies have used the land route from India and Persia to Europe by way of the narrow straits. The physical geography, however, makes it possible for Turkey to close the Dardanelles and defend it against superior forces, giving the nation added weight in power politics.

Another traditional east-west route is that from the Persian Gulf across Iraq and Syria to the eastern end of the Mediterranean Sea. It was first used by pedestrians and caravans, and later was associated with railways, airlines, and oil pipelines. When Britain obtained a sea route to the East by way of the Mediterranean, the Suez Canal, and the Red Sea, Germany countered with plans for a railway from Berlin to Baghdad. Construction was started in 1888, but the railway was not completed until 1940. By this time airplanes had come into commercial use, and Baghdad was also a center for airlines. British, French, German, and Dutch planes connected the city with Europe, and certain lines continued toward the Far East.

Since World War II both land and air traffic across the U.S.S.R. have been blocked. The Near East, therefore, controls the shortest land and air routes between Europe and Asia, as well as the Suez sea route. Baghdad, Cairo, and Suez are strategic points in transport and politics.

## Nationalism, Oil, and Pipelines

In recent decades, oil has played a large part in the politics of the Near East. Two factors, world petroleum supply and Arab nationalism, are basic causes of tension. The United States produces about 55 per cent of the world's petroleum and the Near East about 15 per cent. Until after World War II, the United States was a large exporter of petroleum products. Increased consumption caused this country to import from Caribbean America and the Near East. Western Europe has almost no petroleum, and therefore must import from the Near East, or elsewhere. The Soviet Union produces from 7 to 10 per cent of the world's oil but needs more, for which the closest source is Iran, Iraq, or Arabia. Thus, Western Europe, the United States, and the Soviet Union are all vitally interested in petroleum. The steadily increasing demand for petroleum in Europe and America draws attention to the vast reserves and potential production of the Near East. When ranked according to reserves instead of present output, the Near East assumes first place among the petroleum regions of the world.

*Figure 11-12 Saudi Arabs and their camels stop to rest alongside a portion of the trans-Arabian pipeline system near Badanah, Saudi Arabia. (Courtesy of Arabian American Oil Company.)*

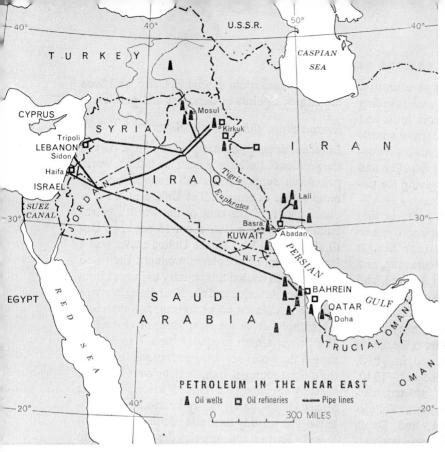

PETROLEUM IN THE NEAR EAST

▲ Oil wells    ▢ Oil refineries    ━━ Pipe lines

0 _____ 300 MILES

*Figure 11-13  The Near East has the greatest reserves of petroleum in the world. The importance of this area is in its mineral wealth. Great pipelines have been built to transport petroleum across the deserts to the Mediterranean coast.*

North Africa as yet produces little petroleum, but several Near East countries rank high among producing nations. In 1950 Iran ranked fourth, after the United States, Venezuela, and the U.S.S.R., with 6 per cent of the world's total. Iranian production practically ceased from 1951 to 1954 because of a dispute with Britain over nationalization of the holdings. Saudi Arabia normally produces almost as much oil as Iran; Kuwait, on the Persian Gulf, produces about 3 per cent of the world total, and Iraq about 1 per cent.

Some of the oil from Iran and Saudi Arabia is piped to terminals on the Persian Gulf (Figure 11-13). Since the oil is destined for Western Europe and the United States, it is more economical to transport the oil by pipelines to the Mediterranean Sea. The lines from Iran and Saudi Arabia, as well as from Iraq, therefore, cross the countries which lie between the oil fields and the eastern Mediterranean—Syria, Lebanon, Israel, and Jordan. In times of serious disputes, or warfare, these countries can close the pipelines.

Securing and keeping concessions for drilling wells, building refineries, and operating pipelines is often a difficult task. The Near East countries all desire independence and higher standards of living, but politics and economy vary from place to place. In several Near East countries the strong desire for complete freedom from foreign influence conflicts with the pressing need for income from oil fields which local capital and technical skill cannot effectively develop.

*Cultural Features*

The Near East is not only a strategic crossroads; it is the seat of several early civilizations and the birthplace of three of the world's great religions, Christianity, Judaism, and Islam. Jerusalem is still a holy city for Moslem, Christian, and Jew; also each year large numbers of Moslems make the pilgrimage to Mecca in Saudi Arabia.

The Moslem religion and the Arabic language and culture have spread from Arabia to distant lands like Morocco, with consequences that have been mentioned earlier in connection with the Barbary states. The Jewish faith and Christianity also have spread from the eastern Mediterranean to all the inhabited continents, together with cultural traits like Christian ethics and the Hebrew language. Modern civilization has been built of many elements that had their origins in the ancient civilizations of Egypt, Mesopotamia (now Iraq), Persia (Iran), Syria, and Palestine (now Israel and a part of Jordan).

The Fertile Crescent is a discontinuous belt of cultivated land which starts at the head of the Persian Gulf and extends in a great arc up the Tigris and Euphrates Valleys and across Syria to Israel. Since early times the Fertile Crescent has been famous for its green pastures and its trade centers. The cities of Basra, Baghdad, and Mosul in Iraq, Aleppo and Damascus in Syria, Antioch in Turkey, Beirut in Lebanon, and Jerusalem, divided between Israel and Jordan, are well-known exchange places for the products of fertile fields, nomadic herding, and local handicraft. Damascus claims to be the oldest continuously inhabited city in the world. The Fertile Crescent was the seat of many ancient empires. Among the earliest were those of the Assyrians, Babylonians, Phoenicians, Hebrews, and Hittites. Persians and Kurds came later, and these in turn were followed by Greeks, Romans, Mongols, Arabs, and Turks.

Aridity, or light winter rainfall, characterizes much of the Near East as well as North Africa. Population is concentrated in the few areas where water is available. In modern times, petroleum has come to dominate the economies of several countries, but aside from this, the main products are from farming and grazing. As in North Africa, cultivation is restricted to the areas of Mediterranean climate, and the oases. There is a great contrast between these spots of green fields and the dry steppes and deserts.

Since the spread of Islam by the Arabs, most of the Near East has been linked by the way of life which that religion imposes, as well as by common pursuits followed by people of similar racial and cultural origin in lands of Mediterranean or arid climates. Resemblances among

*Figure 11-14   Huge under-inflated sand tires enable exploration trucks in the Rub' al-Khali desert to travel through the softest sand. (Courtesy of Arabian American Oil Company.)*

the countries are many, but variations in landforms, location, economic products, and local culture are sufficient to give each unit a personality of its own.

### The Plateau Countries of Turkey and Iran

Turkey and Iran are somewhat alike in general structure; both are large plateaus with bordering mountains as well as interior highlands that divide the land into a number of basins. Small streams flow from the high rugged mountains onto the dry plateaus, but there are no large fertile river plains like those of the Nile in Egypt or the Tigris and Euphrates in Iraq. Settlements are widely scattered in favorable valleys, but the total populations place these countries in the same class as Egypt. Turkey has about 21 million people, Egypt 20 million, and Iran 18 million. The other countries of the region have much smaller populations.

Like Iran, Turkey has its own language instead of using Arabic. Although the Arab conquest included much of both countries, the Arabs did not settle on the highlands. They converted the people to Mohammedanism, but chose to settle mainly in lowland areas like Iraq (Mesopotamia). This is a parallel to the Arab settlement in lowland Barbary, with the original Berbers, converted to Islam, still using their own language in mountainous regions. Thus Persian remained as one language; in

Turkey several groups of Turkish peoples later invaded the region from the north and further modified the language.

Turkey and Iran are not only somewhat similar in general structure but both possess large interior dry areas with nomadic populations. Iran depends upon petroleum exports instead of agricultural products and has a strategic frontage on the Persian Gulf instead of control of the Dardanelles. Both countries are intensely nationalistic, both block possible southern outlets for the Soviet Union, and both have been anxious to avoid falling within the Soviet orbit.

**Turkey.**    During the fifteenth century the Ottoman Turkish nation rose to a place among the Great Powers and conquered most of the territory which had previously been dominated by the Arabs. The empire then declined. In the nineteenth century, France and Britain took the provinces of Algeria and Egypt, and the remaining parts of North Africa soon fell to France, Spain, and Italy. The Balkan Wars deprived Turkey of most of her European territory, and World War I resulted in the loss of Iraq, Syria, and Turkish influence on the Arabian Peninsula.

The freeing of the Near East from Turkish and then from European control was accompanied by a great upsurge in nationalism, an Arab awakening which has spread to parts of North Africa. Most of these areas, so long dominated by foreign powers, now have a strong desire to be rid of all foreign interference.

In Turkey, however, the new nationalism has taken a surprising and distinct form. The Turkish awakening had its origins in earlier movements, but the effects came to the attention of the world soon after World War I. Shorn of former Arab possessions and reduced to a core of Turkish peoples with Greek, Armenian, and Kurdish minorities, the reborn nation made a strenuous effort to reform and modernize its political, economic, and social life. The capital was moved from the metropolis of Istanbul (Constantinople) to the interior town of Ankara. The Moslem faith was modified by gov-

ernment decree and separated from the government. Religious leaders no longer have economic, legal, social, and political control of their followers as is traditional in the Moslem Arab countries. Against great opposition, women were given legal, economic, and political rights, and the custom of wearing the veil was abolished. Men were forbidden to wear the traditional Moslem cap, the fez.

To replace customary Moslem law and the inefficient Turkish legal structure, the rejuvenated nation borrowed a complete new system from Western Europe. In place of law based upon the Koran and upon sayings attributed to Mohammed, the new nation adopted its commercial code from Germany, and its criminal code from Italy. Still more important was acceptance of the Swiss civil code, because that replaced the many complex and ancient rules of the old Turkish law. Thus it is now illegal for a man to have slaves, or more than one wife. Personal liberty is guaranteed regardless of religious belief. National patriotism replaces the Moslem faith as the central principle of the state. The Moslem religion has not been abolished, but merely separated from economy, government, and law, like the churches in Switzerland and the United States. Nevertheless, the customs of centuries cannot be changed overnight, and the struggle to bring practice into accord with written law is still in progress.

The Turkish language has been reformed and simplified. Latin letters are now used instead of the Arabic script, so that the printing resembles that of the Romance languages. In agriculture, industry, education, construction, and most other phases of economic life Turkish policy is to modernize and Westernize. This imitation of Western Europe, however, is sponsored by a small group of leaders and the country is in transition. Progress is made each year, but many old beliefs and practices still exist, especially in remote areas. The reaction of other Near Eastern peoples to modern Turkey varies, but perhaps to most of them, Turkey is a mystery. The Moslem religion is still a strong link, but the close political cooperation of Turkey with the West and the adoption of European customs have aroused suspicion and irritation among conservative Moslem elements.

After World War I, Turkey exchanged much of its Greek population of the west for Turkish people in Greece. In old Turkey the Armenian and Kurdish populations of the east were often persecuted and there were massacres in putting down revolts. Relations with minorities are now much better, although the Kurds would still like to have autonomy for the region of Turkey, Iran, and Iraq which they occupy.

Agriculture has been aided by the use of tractors and machinery. The coastal margins on the north, west, and south have a Mediterranean climate with mild winters and 20 to 30 inches of rainfall. Olives, wheat, tobacco, nuts, grapes, figs, and barley are raised in the narrow coastal zone, but the mountain-rimmed interior plateau, with an average elevation of 3,000 feet, is dry, with cold winters. Large areas are grazed by sheep, goats, and camels, and much of the population is nomadic.

The major exports of the coastal areas are tobacco, figs, raisins, olives, and olive oil. Animals, hides and skins, and mohair wool from the renowned Angora goats are typical products from the interior plateau. Besides the traditional manufacture of tobacco products, rugs, and carpets there is a newly established iron and steel works at Karabuk and small industries have arisen in the major ports of Istanbul and Smyrna (Izmir). Turkey has important deposits of chromium and coal, and lesser resources of iron, copper, and petroleum.

Many roads and railways have been constructed by the new Turkey, but the network is still a loose one. Also, it must be kept in mind that the mechanization of agriculture and establishment of industry are impressive only when compared to former conditions or to undeveloped areas of the Near East. By the standards of Western Europe, Turkey has just begun to modernize and industrialize. Most people have low standards of living, and the country still depends largely on imports of petroleum products, machinery, vehicles, and other processed goods. Modern irrigation projects are rare; pastoral industries still support a considerable part of the population.

Istanbul serves the rolling farmlands and forests of European Turkey and other nearby areas, but is best known as a cosmopolitan and picturesque city of world importance. It is the financial, cultural, and commercial center for a large area. In North Africa and the Near East, only Cairo is larger. Istanbul has many famous mosques, and important Greek, Armenian, and Jewish sections. Ankara (Angora), in the rugged interior uplands, is the capital and trade center for Angora wool and grain. It has grown very rapidly, and now has wide streets with many modern and impressive buildings. Smyrna is presently the major exporting center for Turkey.

*Figure 11-15 Tractor being used to operate a pump on a farm in Turkey. Both the dress of the people and the use of the tractor are symbolic of the great changes that have been made in Turkey since World War I. (Courtesy of Turkish Information Office.)*

**Iran.** Petroleum is by far the most important product of Iran. The export of oil, by value, is normally several times that of all other exports combined and the Iranian government largely depends upon the income from oil for its expenses and for foreign exchange. Usually the industry employs almost as many industrial workers as all other industries together. The refinery at Abadan, in the southwest, is one of the largest in the world. All of the oil fields lie near the head of the Persian Gulf.

The great majority of Iranians are farmers. The main crops of wheat, barley, rice, dates, cotton, and tobacco are mostly consumed locally. Only moderate quantities of dried fruits and cotton, and a few other agricultural items are exported. Except for refined sugar and tea, the country is self-sufficient in food. The more productive farmlands of the north make up for the deficit in the drier sections.

The deserts and mountains of Iran occupy most of the surface. Only about 10 per cent of the land is cultivated. Methods of farming are often ancient and primitive, irrigation facilities are inadequate, and productivity is low. Approximately 90 per cent of the people are illiterate. As in Egypt, there are large numbers of tenants or sharecroppers who work on the estates of wealthy landlords. The main industrial products, aside from petroleum, are handwoven rugs and textiles. Persian rugs have been well-known since ancient times, and rank next to petroleum as an export.

The major centers of Iran lie in the interior. Tehran is the capital and largest city. It is in an important irrigated district and is the focus for several caravan routes and rail lines. Growth has been rapid since World War I and the modern buildings contrast sharply with the older sections. Tabriz is the main commercial center

*Figure 11-16   An aerial view of a tank farm and refinery at Ras Tanura on the Persian Gulf. (Courtesy of Arabian American Oil Company.)*

for the farmlands of the northwest, and manufactures carpets, textiles, and leather goods. Isfahan is noted for its textiles, cotton, silk, and wool. It is also a center for animal products and dried fruits. In northeastern Iran the oasis town of Meshed lies on the caravan route to India and is connected to Tehran by railway. Products of the region include fruits, cotton, grain, sheep, and goats. All the large centers of Iran have colorful bazaars and ancient and famous mosques. Many of these cities were the capitals of past empires.

Bandar Shahpur, at the head of the Persian Gulf, is the most important seaport of Iran. In 1938 a railroad was built to connect it via Tehran with Bandar Shah on the Caspian Sea. Over this route the Allies, especially the United States, shipped supplies to aid the Soviet Union against Germany in World War II.

## Syria, Lebanon, and Iraq

Unlike Turkey and Iran, the countries of Syria, Lebanon, and Iraq are dominated by the Arabic language and culture. Furthermore, the religion of Syria and Iraq, but not of Christian Lebanon, is controlled from the Arabian holy cities of Mecca and Medina. The Turks in former times often carried the brunt of Moslem opposition to Christianity in southeastern Europe with Constantinople as their religious capital, but a number of Arab groups refused to recognize the authority of Constantinople. Modern Turkey, of course, has its own modified Moslem church. In Iran most of the Moslems are of the Shiah sect, which differs from the Sunni Moslem group of Arabia and Africa (Figure 11-3). Thus, in language and religion, as well as in government, the southern margins of Turkey and Iran form a significant border zone.

**Syria.** Syria consists of a Mediterranean coastal belt with interior bordering highlands, the valley of the Euphrates in the northeast, and the central and southern deserts. It is primarily an agricultural country. The seminomadic tribes of the steppes and deserts are tending more and more to settle upon farmlands.

Agricultural population is densest in the fertile western valleys. The largest cities, Aleppo and Damascus, are also located in the west.

Most of the people are Moslems who use the Arabic language. A minority, about 10 per cent, are Christians, but they offer no challenge to the dominance of Arabic culture. Agriculture is largely of the Mediterranean type, with about nine-tenths of the farmlands dependent upon rainfall rather than irrigation. Wheat, barley, melons, olives, and grapes are typical products, although cotton production for local industries is increasing. Sheep and goats are raised both in the farming areas and in the dry sections; cattle are of moderate importance in the more humid regions. The pastoral industries are restricted by inadequate pasturage during drier years, and by lack of places for watering animals in the grazing areas.

Although modern methods have been introduced in canneries and in some textile plants, the total output is low. Small factories and hand workers make such articles as slippers, rugs, brassware, baskets, and pottery. Cereals and textiles are the leading exports. Syria has no important deposits of petroleum, but oil lines from Iraq and Saudi Arabia extend across Syria to the Mediterranean terminals (Figure 11-13).

Throughout history the Syrians have been known as farmers, traders, and artisans, rather than as nomads. Sometimes it is said, "A Syrian is an Arab who lives in a village or city." The Levant, or eastern coast of the Mediterranean, has been an important trading area since the time of the Phoenicians. A traditional route extends from the coast through Antioch, now in Turkey but a former center of ancient Syria, past Aleppo to the Euphrates Valley and along it to Baghdad and the Persian Gulf. There are also several alternate routes leading eastward from Aleppo. Damascus is another great caravan and trade center. Cafés, shops, entertainers, and local handicrafts add variety to the urban scene. The city of white buildings, on an irrigated fruitful plain at the edge of the desert, is an impressive sight. Textiles and Damascus ware of brass and copper are sold throughout the Mediterranean and Near East regions.

**Lebanon.** Formerly a part of Syria, Lebanon has several characteristics that make it a distinct region. The Lebanese are mostly Christians, and the mountainous country has a Mediterranean climate without deserts, steppes, or nomads. Besides its religion, Lebanon has many other cultural ties with Europe and America. Beirut is the center of American and French educational activity in the Near East. Large numbers of Lebanese have emigrated to the cities of Europe and the United States. The literacy rate is higher in Lebanon than in any other Arab country. The population is fairly dense and is distributed more evenly over the state than in other nearby countries. There are many skilled workers in the cities, and the farmers usually work on their own land instead of sharecropping on large estates. Although standards of living are high for the region, they are low by Western standards, and improvement is sought through increased irrigation and expanded industries.

Lebanon was a part of the ancient Phoenician, Assyrian, Persian, Roman, and Byzantine empires. While Syria was becoming a Moslem area, however, the Maronites, a Christian sect, became established in Lebanon. The Arabs conquered both Syria and Lebanon, but the Lebanese Christians maintained their religion. Later, the Lebanese aided Crusaders who reached the area. After the Ottoman Turks conquered the region, there were massacres of Christians, and the European powers forced the sultans to grant some autonomy to Lebanon. Under the French mandate following World War I, Lebanon was officially separated from Syria and became completely independent on January 1, 1944. The Lebanese are racially similar to the Syrians, both being segments of the Arab world. Since the partition of Palestine many Arab refugees have entered Lebanon from Israel, so that the population is now about half Moslem and half Christian. The liberal tradition of the Lebanese Christians, however, is still dominant.

The Lebanon Mountains lie close to the Mediterranean and extend north and south for the length of the country. The Anti-Lebanon range forms the eastern border with Syria. Between the two mountain ranges is a high fertile valley that provides the best agricultural land of the country. The crops include grapes, vegetables, and grains. Mulberry trees furnish leaves for silkworms. The mountains formerly supplied cedar, but the forests have been reduced to small areas. There are many resorts in the mountains where visitors can escape the hot summers of lowland regions. The major industries are cotton and silk weaving, and shoe manufacturing.

The largest city and capital is Beirut, a busy port on the Mediterranean. Its functions are largely administrative and commercial. The famous old coastal towns of Tripoli, Sidon, and Tyre have recently regained some importance. Tripoli and Sidon are the terminals for pipelines from Iraq and Saudi Arabia.

**Iraq.** Iraq, ancient Mesopotamia, rivals Egypt as a seat of early culture, and it is difficult to determine which first reached a high level of civilization. Egypt was protected from invasion, but Mesopotamia has been one of the busiest of routes for both trade and invading armies. Egypt usually dominated the nearby nomads; Mesopotamia experienced many raids and was often subordinate to nomadic conquerors. Between the two regions are barrier areas, the Syrian and Arabian deserts.

The heart of Iraq is formed by the Tigris and Euphrates Rivers which join above Basra to form a single stream, the Shatt-al-Arab, that empties into the Persian Gulf. Only the northeastern part of the country is humid and mountainous, the rest being low-lying and dry. Like Egypt, Iraq is largely a desert dominated by a great oasis belt that is irrigated by river water. The sources of the Tigris and Euphrates lie in the mountains of Turkey.

In recent years, the oil fields of northeastern Iraq have provided the major export and a considerable share of the nation's income. The wells are operated by British, American, French, and Dutch concerns. A new agreement in 1952 provided for a 50–50 division of profits between Iraq and the international group. After the Arab–Jewish War (1948) all the oil was piped to Tripoli and Lebanon, none to Haifa in Israel. Israel and the Arab countries have not been able to come to an agreement, and trade relations remain severed.

Agriculture is the dominant economy of Iraq. Some authorities believe the country is under-populated for its resources. With British aid, new irrigation and flood control projects are under way. Iraq has many miles of date palms on the lower Tigris and Euphrates, and leads the world in date production. Only petroleum and barley exceed the value of date exports. Cereals are the main food of the people both in the rain-fed zone in the north and in the irrigated region. The oasis lands also produce fruits, vegetables, and cotton; herds of sheep and goats in the arid regions provide milk, hides, skins, and wool. Clothing, sugar, tea, and machinery are the chief imports.

Nomadism is steadily decreasing in Iraq, and farming, sedentary pastoralism, and urban occupations are increasing. About 20 per cent of the population form a Kurdish minority in the north, but the southern economic problems of low standards of living, sharecropping, and shortage of technical skill are generally considered to be more pressing. The Kurdish tribes are not unified as a political pressure group; thus raids and revolts are no longer common.

Baghdad, a railway town, tourist center, and major airport, is the capital of Iraq and a focus of trade and communications. In earlier periods it was a great caravan center and one of the cultural capitals of the Arab world. The period of its greatest wealth and fame is immortalized in the tales of *The Arabian Nights*. Since then the city has been destroyed and rebuilt several times. Few if any of the ancient structures remain. Mosul is the chief market for the cereals, fruits, and livestock of the upper valley and is also the center of the oil industry. Basra, the principal port of Iraq, is the commercial hub of the lower valley. Like Baghdad and Mosul, it has a long and colorful history.

## Israel and Jordan

Like Lebanon, Israel is now an island of non-Moslems in the Moslem world. In Biblical times the area was predominantly Jewish, but the people were partially scattered by early invasions and economic problems. The Arab conquests continued the process, and by the thirteenth century the land was almost entirely held by Moslems. For centuries the Jews were exiles without a country. They wandered from place to place. Many were traders, shopkeepers, and moneylenders settling in cities throughout the world. The religion spread to peoples of many races, but they were united by a common faith, so many supported Zionism, the plan for a permanent Jewish nation in Palestine.

At the time of World War I, most of the Near East was under the control of Turkey, which was then allied with Germany. At the close of hostilities, temporary mandates under the League of Nations were established for the parts of the Turkish empire that were occupied by subject (non-Turkish) peoples, with the understanding that they were to be prepared for self-government. The area west of the Jordan River became the mandate of Palestine and the region immediately to the east of the river, Transjordan. Britain was designated as the country to supervise both mandates. Arab and Jewish interests clashed sharply over the Palestine question. From the standpoint of the Jews, Palestine was the former homeland which should be returned to Jewish control; this was in accord with British promises and with the hopes of the Jewish people. But Arabs had predominated in Palestine since the thirteenth century. The country was not capable of supporting both the Arabs and large numbers of Jewish immigrants, and British officials had promised that the Arabs would be left in control of the lands they had occupied for centuries. It was impossible to find a solution that would satisfy both Jews and Arabs. Palestine continued as a troublesome mandate until after World War II.

The Palestine problem then became more acute. Large numbers of displaced Jews from Nazi Germany, Poland, and other areas made necessary the establishment of a Jewish state. Meanwhile, Arab nationalism was growing. In 1945 Egypt, Iraq, Lebanon, Syria, Transjordan, and Saudi Arabia formed the Arab League to deal with common economic and social problems and to oppose the settlement of Jews in Palestine. Both Arabs and Jews, however, moved into Palestine by the thousands.

The United Nations, which has taken over the work of the former League of Nations, ended the British mandate in 1948 and established the Jewish nation of Israel from part of Palestine and designated the rest as Arab territory. The Arab nations opposed the division by force. After some fighting, a series of truces was imposed by the United Nations, but some Arab nations refused to recognize the state of Israel. The reestablishment of economic relations between Israel and the Arab states and agreement on boundaries and a permanent status for the city of Jerusalem are problems that have not yet been settled. The kingdom of Jordan—the name was changed from Transjordan in 1946—is now independent and has taken over the part of Palestine which was not included in Israel.

More than half a million Arabs fled from Israel into the adjoining Arab states when Palestine was divided. About half of these went to Jordan while others migrated to Egypt, Lebanon, and Syria. The great population shift into

countries which had difficulty in maintaining adequate living standards even before the influx is a major problem of the Near East. It is a stumbling block to peaceful relations between Israel and the Arab states.

Israel also had a settlement problem. Thousands of Jewish immigrants entered the country each month. The majority came from Eastern Europe, especially from Poland. Considerable numbers also arrived from North Africa, Iraq, and Yemen. The population of Israel increased from 782,000 in 1948 to 1,555,000 in 1951.

Israel, like Palestine before it, is an agricultural country, but European immigrants have patterned its economic and social life after Western standards rather than those of the Near East. Mechanization of farming is already at a high level and extensive irrigation projects are under way. The major product for export is citrus fruit, which is raised on the Mediterranean coastal plain. The economy of the country has been planned to accommodate the immigrants who arrive each month. The total production of cereals, vegetables, meat, and fruits is only about half the requirement for the population. Thus food must be imported, along

*Figure 11-17  Harrowing irrigated farmland in the arid Negev of southern Israel. The desert background is typical of many parts of the Near East. (Courtesy of Israel Office of Information.)*

*Figure 11-18 Seaside park and new apartment buildings in Tel Aviv, Israel, one of the most rapidly growing cities in the Near East. (Courtesy of Israel Office of Information.)*

with many types of consumer goods, machinery, and feed for poultry and livestock. Plans have been made to use the Jordan River for additional power and irrigation for both Israel and Jordan, but the continued hostility between the two countries has prevented their fulfillment.

To increase exports and decrease imports, light industries were developed and food was rationed. Israel now has a diamond-cutting industry that ranks next to citrus production in value of goods exported. Other industries, all of them small but increasing in importance, include food processing, textile weaving, chemical manufacture, and metalworking. These industries, like agriculture, are as yet unable to supply both the need for exports and the demands of the increasing population. The country is dependent upon loans and gifts from abroad, especially from the United States.

Culturally, Israel may be regarded as an outlying area of European rather than a typical part of the Levant. Physically, it is composed of a strip of fertile lowland along the Mediterranean Sea, the interior rift (depressed block) valley of the Jordan River and the Dead Sea, and the Negev (desert) in the south. In the last few years urban population and urban occupations have greatly increased. Tel Aviv–Jaffa, with a population of more than 300,000, is the chief port and trade center. Haifa is the second

port. Jerusalem is mostly controlled by Israel, but the Arab, or "old" section contains many mosques and is occupied by Jordan.

The kingdom of Jordan lies on the plateau which continues eastward from Israel. The capital, Amman, and the best agricultural land are in the west. There sedentary farmers produce cereals, vegetables, and fruits. The eastern part of the country has a nomadic population, under tribal organization, which supports itself with herds of sheep and goats. Jordan formerly had a surplus of wheat and barley. Since the influx of Arab refugees from Israel, the country has difficulty in supporting its population.

### Arabian Peninsula

The peninsula of Arabia consists of a large, almost rectangular block of desert area. It is tilted so that the southwestern edge, along the Red Sea, lies at an elevation of several hundred feet, but the surface slopes downward to sea level along the northeast coast at the shores of the Persian Gulf. The population and cities are largely concentrated in the highlands near the Red Sea, where rainfall is greater and temperatures are somewhat lower than in the central and eastern deserts. Even in the Arabian highlands, however, the climate is semiarid. Despite the great size of the peninsula the population is about half that of Egypt or Turkey.

The Moslem religion had its origins in the

cities of Mecca and Medina during the early seventh century. The Arabs spread their faith, as well as their language and culture, to adjoining regions. Islam spread even farther: eastward to parts of India, the East Indies, and the Philippines; westward to Morocco; and northwestward to Turkey and Albania. The Ottoman Turks later took over the initiative in spreading Islam through the extension of the Turkish empire over other nations. At the time of World War I Turkey even controlled Arabia.

Following World War I, with Turkey defeated, the new nation of Saudi Arabia gradually conquered most of the peninsula. The areas of Yemen, Aden, Oman, Trucial Oman, Qatar, and Kuwait, however, lie beyond its control.

Saudi Arabia has its agricultural heart in the highlands near the Red Sea, where the major products are wheat, barley, millet, and coffee. The holy city of Mecca attracts Moslem pilgrims from many countries and gives Saudi Arabia added prestige in the Arab world. Medina contains the tomb of Mohammed and is also an important religious center. Jidda is the main port.

The interior of Saudi Arabia is desert country similar to the Sahara. Riyadh, in a centrally located oasis, is a caravan center and capital of the country. In 1951 a railroad was completed from Dhahran on the Persian Gulf to Riyadh,

a distance of 366 miles. The nomadic desert tribes move their camels, sheep, and goats in accord with the seasonal rains and resulting temporary pasturage. In the remote section, tribal life and customs have changed little for centuries. Southeastern Arabia contains a large "empty quarter" of stony and sandy desert that rivals the barrenness of the southern Sahara.

An American oil company operates the oil fields near the Persian Gulf and divides profits equally with the Saudi Arabian government. Oil production rose after World War II until Saudi Arabia rivaled Iran as the leading producer in the Near East. Petroleum is the major source of government income and accounts for 90 per cent of the value of exports. Minor exports of the country are gold, silver, and copper; its chief imports are machinery and other manufactured goods. Saudi Arabia also benefits from American expenditures on the United States air base at Dhahran.

Great Britain controls, in more or less degree, a series of areas along the Persian Gulf. Kuwait and Bahrein Island are important sources of petroleum and like Qatar, Trucial Oman, and Oman, they are under the nominal rule of local sheikhs and sultans. The port of Aden, at the southwestern corner of the Arabian Peninsula, is a British possession that commands the entrance to the Red Sea.

*Figure 11-19   An aerial view of a residential section of Dhahran, Saudi Arabia. The plant in the circular area is central air-cooling equipment which serves this section of town. (Courtesy of Arabian American Oil Company.)*

Yemen is an independent country with landscapes and products similar to the hill and coastal lands of southwestern Saudi Arabia. The country is noted for coffee which is one of its major exports. The capital and largest city is San'a.

## Cyprus

During the latter part of the nineteenth century Cyprus came under British influence, and control by Turkey (the Ottoman Empire) weakened. At the outbreak of World War I, Britain obtained full control, ending Ottoman suzerainty. Cyprus has been known for centuries as an exporter of copper and as a producer of wheat, barley, and wine. It has fertile soils and a Mediterranean climate, and is the most highly cultivated territory of the Near East. Political

factors, however, account for its present prominence. About three-fourths of the inhabitants are of Greek language and culture, and a recent movement for union with Greece has been marked by riots against the British. The island is only 40 miles from the Turkish coast but hundreds of miles from Greece, and Cyprus was long a part of Turkey. Consequently, the Turkish minority on the island and the Turkish government argue that any change in the island's status should put it not into Greek but Turkish control. Meanwhile, Cyprus has replaced Suez as Britain's major military base in the Middle East. It is the last area in the eastern Mediterranean over which Britain has full control, and the movement for the union of Cyprus with Greece has been strongly resisted both by the British and Turks.

## IN PERSPECTIVE

### The World's Largest Dry Area

North Africa and the Near East lie south and east of the Mediterranean Sea and north from the Sahara and the Arabian Sea, with the peninsula of Arabia being bounded by the Red Sea on the west and the Persian Gulf on the east. To the north of Turkey and Iran are the Black and Caspian Seas respectively. The region includes about a score of political entities. Of these, nearly half are independent, the rest are colonies, protectorates, and other varieties of dependency.

The unity of North Africa and the Near East is cultural; its people are predominantly Moslem in religion, farmers, stockmen, and traders by occupation, and mostly Semites in race, with some Turks and other minor ethnic groups. Climatically the region has a water problem with vast deserts and semiarid steppes. Only small areas have enough rainfall for crops, and the sections with such a humid climate are generally highlands where little tillable land is available. Fortunately, nearly all of the region has a long growing season so that, where water and good soil are available, large yields of crops are possible. Irrigation is widely practiced especial-

ly in the floodplains and deltas of the major rivers like the Nile, Tigris, and Euphrates which support large populations.

Strategically located between Europe, the Far East, and Central Africa, the region has been the site for European penetration. The Western powers established major colonies, and their system of economic exploitation often irked the local populations. From this region, Europe draws important quantities of petroleum, metals, cotton, and foodstuffs, and free access to such supplies is essential to the industries of the West. Petroleum is the outstanding mineral resource. The countries that border the Persian Gulf—Saudi Arabia, Bahrein, Kuwait, Iran, and Iraq—produce nearly one-third of the world's output. Exports of petroleum and its products to Western and Southern Europe are large, and the maintenance of a continuous flow via the Suez Canal and overland by pipelines to Mediterranean ports is of great concern to industrialized Western Europe.

Much of North Africa and the Near East has been and still is politically unstable. In 1956, the Barbary states of Morocco, Tunisia, and Libya were nominally independent countries, and Algeria, a province of France, was demanding complete independence. Farther east Egypt, which stands astride the Suez Canal, and the Asiatic Moslem countries of Saudi Arabia, Jordan, Syria, Lebanon, and Iraq have been involved in boundary quarrels with Israel since the end of World War II. Turkey and Iran face the Soviet Union which seemingly hopes that tur-

moil in the Near East will work to its advantage. The general poverty of the people in North Africa, Egypt, and southwest Asia, and the hereditary hatreds they hold toward some of their neighbors increase the difficulties of maintaining peace and order. The policy of the U.S.S.R. also is to promote trouble in the area.

## EXERCISES

*1.* What are the dominant characteristics of this region?

*2.* What countries are located in North Africa and the Near East? Which have gained independence within the last forty years? How does the culture of these countries compare with the culture of Western European countries?

*3.* What are the principal handicaps of the countries of this region? What can man do to change these conditions?

*4.* What are the principal economic activities? In what ways do these show an adjustment to the physical environment? Which is least influenced by the environment?

*5.* What is the dominant religion of the region? Why is the region one of great religious conflict? Where was the focal point for each?

*6.* What are the important rivers of the region? Through which countries do they flow? How do they influence the life of the country? Why are they so important?

*7.* What is the chief mineral product of the Near East? In which countries is it produced? Who controls the production? What changes has it made in the life of these countries?

*8.* Where is the Suez Canal? What bodies of water does it connect? Why is it of special importance to several European countries?

*9.* What are the principal transportation problems of North Africa? Where have railroads been developed? What is the most common mode of transportation through the desert areas? How has the automobile affected this situation?

*10.* Which country in this region do you believe to be the most important? What are its physical and economic advantages? How does its culture differ from that of the other countries?

*11.* Where is Israel? How does the background of its people differ from that of the neighboring nations? Does it have a natural physical advantage over Jordan? Why are both countries interested in the Jordan River?

*12.* What North African products are important in the economy of France? Where are these produced?

*13.* Which area of North Africa and the Near East are important for the production of dates? Oranges? Cotton? Tobacco?

*14.* Why are Istanbul, Alexandria, Baghdad, Jerusalem, Tel Aviv, Mecca, Cairo, Port Said, and Damascus important cities? Where is each located?

## SELECTED REFERENCES

Bowman, Isaiah: "The Mohammedan World," *Geographical Review,* 15:62–74, January, 1924.

Fish, W. B.: "The Lebanon," *Geographical Review,* 34:235–258, April, 1944.

Fisher, W. B.: *The Middle East: A Physical, Social, and Regional Geography,* E. P. Dutton & Co., Inc., New York, 1950.

———: "Problems of Modern Libya," *Geographical Journal,* 119:183–199, June, 1953.

Fitzgerald, Walter: *Africa,* E. P. Dutton & Co., Inc., New York, 6th edition, 1948.

Gautier, E. F.: *Sahara: The Great Desert,* Columbia University Press, New York, 1935.

Mountjoy, Alan B.: "The Development of Industry in Egypt," *Economic Geography,* 28:212–228, July, 1952.

Sanger, Richard H.: *The Arabian Peninsula,* Cornell University Press, Ithaca, N.Y., 1954.

Shaw, Earl B.: "Land Reform in Egypt," *Journal of Geography,* 53:229–237, September, 1954.

Thomas, Benjamin E.: "Modern Trans-Saharan Routes," *Geographical Review,* 42:267–282, April, 1952.

————: "The Railways of French North Africa," *Economic Geography,* 29:95–106, April, 1953.

Twitchell, K. S., and Edward J. Jursi: *Saudi Arabia,* Princeton University Press, Princeton, N.J., 1947.

Van Valkenburg, S.: "The Hashemite Kingdom of the Jordan: A Study in Economic Geography," *Economic Geography,* 30:102–116, April, 1954.

Whittlesey, Derwent: "Lands Athwart the Nile," *World Politics,* 5:214–241, January, 1953.

N.B.: Egypt and Syria announced on February 1, 1958, that the two countries would merge and form a new state to be called the United Arab Republic.

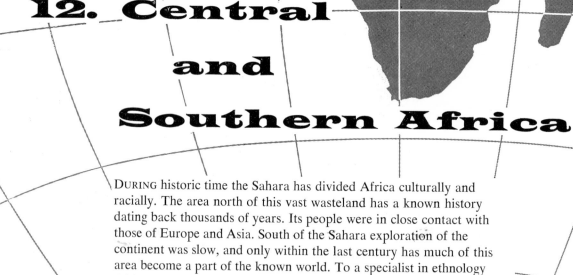

# 12.  Central

# and

# Southern Africa

DURING historic time the Sahara has divided Africa culturally and racially. The area north of this vast wasteland has a known history dating back thousands of years. Its people were in close contact with those of Europe and Asia. South of the Sahara exploration of the continent was slow, and only within the last century has much of this area become a part of the known world. To a specialist in ethnology Africa south of the Sahara presents a complex problem because of the variety of peoples and cultures. There the anthropologist can study primitive societies and tribal life which disappeared ages ago in the more advanced parts of the world. To the explorer and scientist Africa offered opportunities to visit unknown areas and describe their physical features, plant and animal life, minerals, and other resources. To the missionary there was the opportunity of making converts from paganism. Traders came seeking quick wealth from the ivory and slave traffic. Readers interested in adventure enjoy learning about David Livingstone, the missionary-explorer, and how he was found far in the interior of

432

Africa by Henry M. Stanley; how Mungo Park, Speke, Baker, and others helped to unroll the map of the continent; and how Cecil Rhodes made a fortune in gold and diamond mining and added vast territories to the British Empire.

Africa is the second largest and most tropical of the continents. Approximately 9.5 of its 11.6 million square miles lie south of 20° north. Central and Southern Africa extends from the Sahara (20° north latitude) southward for 4,000 miles to Cape Agulhas (34°40′ south latitude). In this part of the continent live approximately 152 million people whose ancestors, unlike those living in the Mediterranean part of the continent, had few contacts with the ancient civilized world. The distribution of population is very uneven, ranging from the fairly densely settled parts of Nigeria and Uganda to almost uninhabited desert and tropical forest areas. During the present century, as their knowledge of the world improved, the natives have struggled toward self-rule and improvement in their standard of living. Since 1930, several countries have become independent or autonomous in local government, and these will be followed by others (Figure 12-1).

The European explorers found most of Central and Southern Africa occupied by peoples too politically weak and culturally backward to resist aggression. Before the close of the nineteenth century all of Central and Southern Africa, except Ethiopia and Liberia, had become colonies of England, France, Germany, Portugal, Belgium, or Spain. This division into colonies was done with small regard for native peoples. To the Western world Central and Southern Africa was a source of minerals and raw materials for manufacture, a place for establishing colonies where a country could monopolize the trade and control the opportunities for settlement and investment. To a great extent Africa has served Europe's economic needs and probably will continue to do so in the immediate future whether many of the colonies become independent or remain subject to foreign rule.

The colonial system, although it did not benefit all native peoples, did much to improve economic conditions. Through the establishment of missions, schools, and medical services the education and health of the Africans has been improved. Railroads, highways, airfields, and port improvements provide better transportation for freight and passengers. New crops which include corn (maize), cacao, rubber, and tea, have been introduced. Plantations have been established and mines developed.

In many parts of Central and Southern Africa the problems of race relations, low living standards, and endemic disease need intensive study. Over some large and populous regions, conditions are slowly changing for the better. Africa is truly a continent whose people are in transition from old ways, occupations, and tribal rule to a higher culture and a place in the modern world. Native Africans want not only improved living conditions and a greater share in the development of their resources but also social equality. The desire for these things accounts for many of the difficulties between governing powers and the natives in such places as the Union of South Africa and Kenya.

The former "dark continent" has now become a great source of mineral, forest, and agricultural wealth. Its gold, diamonds, copper, uranium, tin, chrome, iron, and other minerals are in great demand. Its output of forest products, fibers and vegetable oils, cacao, and various tropical plantation crops contributes increasingly to world markets. Africa has the largest potential water power of any continent. Production of hydroelectricity, however, has lagged because there are few large consumers. As yet only a small portion of Africa's capacity to produce food, fibers, power, and minerals for the ever-increasing demands of the world's market has been used.

Several factors made it difficult for Europeans to explore interior Africa. The coasts were not attractive to settlers; some were deserts, others were swampy, hot, humid, and unhealthful. There were few harbors. Within a few miles of the coast, most rivers became unnavigable because of the many rapids in the lower courses where the rivers descended from the edge of the vast plateau that forms most of Central and

*Figure 12-1  Africa south of the Sahara is a land controlled largely by Europeans. Some few countries have become or will become independent in the near future.*

Southern Africa. Above the rapids some rivers could be navigated. Over large areas, however, human carriers were the only means of transport available. The upper Nile was lost in a vast swamp, called the Sudd, that was for many years an impassable barrier to explorers. Many native tribes were unfriendly and fearful of strangers because of the raids made by slavers. The cattle disease, called nagana, which is transmitted by the tsetse fly, made it impossible to use draught animals in the humid equatorial regions. South Africa, however, had extensive grasslands and savannas, and except in the river valleys, the land was free of tsetse-borne disease. Thus, animal transport could be used; hence, tropical interior Africa was first reached from the south, a longer but easier route than from the east or west coast.

Modern political patterns of Africa reflect four centuries of colonial expansion by European nations. Small areas of coastal regions were first claimed by the Portuguese. Soon thereafter came the Dutch and English, the latter replacing the Dutch in South Africa during the Napoleonic Wars. France and Germany oc-cupied large regions during the nineteenth century. Leopold of Belgium organized the Congo Free State, now the Belgian Congo. Spain secured some small territories. The former German colonies are now governed by England, France, Belgium, and the Union of South Africa. In 1822, Liberia was established as a home for freed slaves from America, descendants of whom now govern the country. In East Africa, Ethiopia has, throughout most of its history, maintained itself as an independent monarchy.

Since World War II, the natives of Central and Southern Africa have made many efforts to win independence. In 1957, Ghana (the Gold Coast) became a self-governing country within the British Commonwealth of Nations. Nigeria will probably assume the same status soon although the inhabitants of the country are still trying to reach an agreement among themselves regarding the form of government. The Union of South Africa is a member of the British Commonwealth but exercises complete autonomy. Somalia is scheduled for independence in 1960.

## PEOPLE

Of the 152 million people of Central and Southern Africa, only about 2 per cent are of European ancestry. The Belgian Congo, for example, has only 90,000 non-natives in a total population of over 12 million. The latter, however, seldom control either political or economic affairs. Over most of Central and Southern Africa the population densities are low, averaging only 16 per square mile (Figure 12-2). Only small areas along the Guinea Coast and in parts of the Union of South Africa have densities exceeding 200 persons per square mile. Large cities are few; only five in the Union of South Africa exceed 100,000 in population. In all the rest of Africa south of the Sahara only 10 cities have populations greater than 100,000. Most of the natives live in small villages.

The native peoples are of varied races and cultures, comprising hundreds of tribes that speak scores of languages and dialects. The most primitive natives are the Pygmies who live in the rain forest of the Congo Basin and the Bushmen who roam the Kalahari Desert in Southwest Africa. Neither group is numerous and both wander over wide areas as they hunt wild animals and gather the roots, seeds, and fruits provided by nature. The African Negroes who live in the Guinea region and French Equatorial Africa gain a livelihood by primitive farming. The Hamites of Ethiopia and eastern Sudan are believed to be a mixture of Negro and Semitic or other Asiatic blood. The husky, dark-skinned Bantus occupy most of the continent south of the equator. They are a pastoral people who practice supplemental farming.

Non-natives living in Central and Southern Africa include thousands of Europeans who live in the government administrative centers, seaports, or other areas of economic development and exploitation. The chief exception to this is

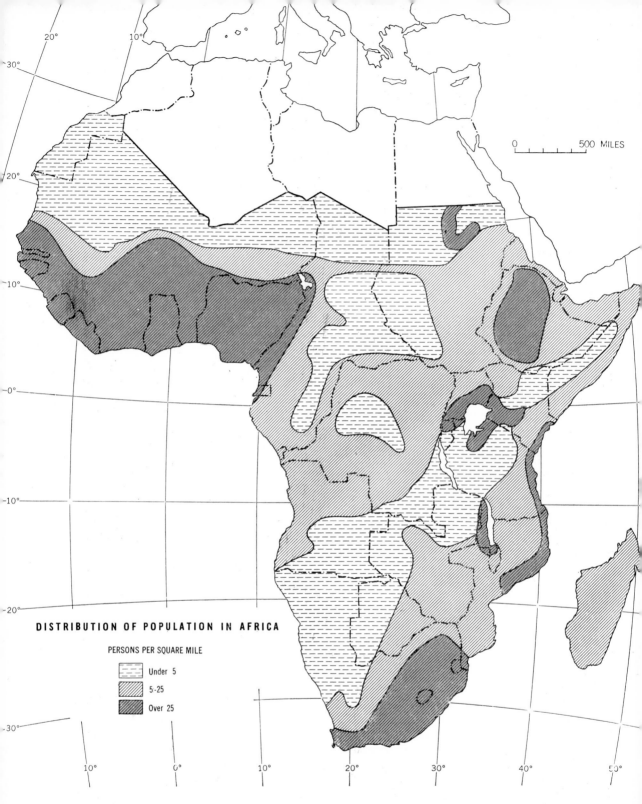

DISTRIBUTION OF POPULATION IN AFRICA

PERSONS PER SQUARE MILE

- Under 5
- 5-25
- Over 25

0      500 MILES

*Figure 12-2   Population in Africa south of the Sahara varies greatly accord-*
*ing to local conditions. In general the regions of greatest population are*
*around the large lakes, in the highlands of Ethiopia, and along various coastal*
*areas.*

the Union of South Africa where half the nearly 3 million people of Dutch and English ancestry are farmers and stockmen. Arabs live along the coast of Kenya, Tanganyika, and Mozambique, and in Natal and British East Africa are many Indians.

Most native Africans retain their pagan religions, which are characterized by fears, fetishes, and witch doctors. Ethiopians are generally Coptic Christians. Islam is influential on some of the East African coast. Moslems are also numerous in parts of West Africa especially along the Saharan margins. Missions of several Christian denominations are scattered throughout Negroid Africa and often serve as cultural and educational centers.

The hundreds of native languages and dialects make communication between neighboring peoples difficult. As a result a conglomeration of tongues, called Swahili, has become the lingua franca in East Africa. In colonies, the official language is that of the governing power. It is spoken by some of the natives, especially the young people who almost everywhere have some use of a European tongue and to a less extent of the written languages.

## PHYSICAL SETTING

### Relief Features

Although most of Central and Southern Africa is a plateau of ancient rocks there are many variations in landforms. Areas of volcanic peaks and lava plateaus are to be found in the east and northeast. In the Congo Basin, parts of South Africa, and the Sudan, are quantities of young sediments. In some places the plateau rises abruptly from the shore line, in others the rise is rather gentle, often forming a series of successive terraces. In a few places like Ethiopia there are escarpments that tower several thousand feet. Most African rivers reach the ocean only after flowing over rapids or waterfalls and through great gorges that are unnavigable. To get into the interior, difficulties must be overcome; for example, the Congo gorge begins quite close to tidewater, and the upper river can be reached only by portaging around the falls and rapids. Some rivers, like the Niger, have deposited silt to form huge deltas. Where coastal lowlands exist, they are frequently difficult to cross because of swamps or deserts. Once the interior is reached the surface is predominantly flat and travel is easier.

The surface is highest in the eastern and southern part of the continent. The East African plateaus, extending from the Zambezi River to the Red Sea, vary from elevations of 3,000 to 6,000 feet in the south to more than 10,000 feet in Ethiopia. Parts of this area have been covered by lava flows. Inland slopes to the Congo Basin are gentle. Toward the Indian Ocean and around the Ethiopian Plateau the slopes, except in parts of Somaliland, are usually steep. The high elevation of the plateaus makes for cooler, more healthful and more invigorating climates than the lowlands. Greater freedom from malaria and other fevers makes the highlands more favorable for settlement by both Africans and Europeans. Here in the moderately cool uplands Europeans find that even under a vertical sun they can live, work, and retain their health and vigor. Also, the highlands are free of the cattle disease transmitted by the tsetse fly so that the grazing of livestock is an important industry.

**Eastern Horn.** Ethiopia and the adjoining coastal areas, because of their projecting position in eastern Africa, form what is known as the Eastern Horn of Africa. The western two-thirds of this region is dominated by a high and deeply eroded plateau which attains elevations of 6,000 to 10,000 feet. Rugged topography continues eastward, bordering the Gulf of Aden. The Somali Plateau, in southeastern Ethiopia and Somaliland, descends to the Indian Ocean by gradually dropping 3,000 feet in a distance of 400 miles. Lake Tana, the source of the Blue Nile and the chief contributor to the Nile floods, is located in the northern part of the Ethiopian Highlands.

## TABLE 12-1. CENTRAL AND SOUTHERN AFRICA

| Country | Approximate population, in thousands | Area, sq miles | Political control |
|---|---|---|---|
| Angola | 4,094 | 481,350 | Portuguese overseas province |
| Basutoland | 574 | 11,716 | British High Commission Territory under Commonwealth Relations Office |
| Bechuanaland | 289 | 275,000 | British High Commission Territory under Commonwealth Relations Office |
| Belgian Congo | 11,789 | 904,750 | Belgian colony |
| British Togoland | 400 | 13,040 | British trusteeship |
| Cameroons (Br.) | 1,000 | 34,080 | British trusteeship |
| Cameroons (Fr.) | 3,065 | 166,500 | French trusteeship |
| Canary Islands | 565 | 2,807 | Spanish province |
| Cape Verde Islands | 147 | 1,577 | Portuguese overseas province |
| Eritrea | 1,100 | 48,000 | Autonomous province with Ethiopia |
| Ethiopia | 18,000 | 350,000 | Independent kingdom |
| Federation of Rhodesia and Nyasaland | | | British Federation |
| *Southern Rhodesia* | 2,398,700 | 150,333 | Self-governing |
| *Northern Rhodesia* | 2,128,300 | 290,323 | British protectorate |
| *Nyasaland* | 2,544,600 | 37,374 | British protectorate |
| French Equatorial Africa | | | Federation of French Overseas Territories |
| *Chad* | 496,000 | 2,242,000 | French territory |
| *Gabun* | 103,000 | 413,000 | French territory |
| *Middle Congo* | 152,000 | 694,000 | French territory |
| *Ubangi-Shari* | 238,000 | 1,071,000 | French territory |
| French Togoland | 982 | 21,000 | French trusteeship |
| French West Africa | | | Federation of French Overseas Territories |
| *Dahomey* | 45,900 | 1,565,000 | Colony |
| *French Sudan* | 450,500 | 3,466,000 | Colony |
| *Guinea* | 105,200 | 2,261,000 | Colony |
| *Ivory Coast* | 123,200 | 2,390,000 | Colony |
| *Mauritania* | 415,400 | 567,000 | Colony |
| *Niger* | 494,500 | 2,180,000 | Colony |
| *Senegal* | 80,600 | 2,108,000 | Colony |
| *Upper Volta* | 105,900 | 3,136,000 | Colony |

| Country | Approximate population, in thousands | Area, sq miles | Political control |
|---|---|---|---|
| Gambia | 273 | 4,100 | British colony and protectorate |
| Ghana (Gold Coast) | 4,500 | 91,500 | Self-governing member of British Commonwealth |
| Kenya | 5,900 | 224,960 | British colony and protectorate |
| Liberia | 1,648 | 43,000 | Independent republic |
| Madagascar | 4,470 | 241,090 | French overseas territory |
| Madeira Islands | 280 | 308 | Part of Portugal |
| Mauritius Islands | 540 | 720 | British colony |
| Mozambique | 5,698 | 297,730 | Portuguese overseas province |
| Nigeria | 31,200 | 373,250 | British colony and protectorate |
| Portuguese Guinea | 544 | 13,948 | Portuguese overseas province |
| Reunion Island | 275 | 969 | French overseas department |
| Rio Muni | 134 | 10,040 | Spanish colony |
| Ruanda-Urundi | 4,000 | 20,900 | Belgian trust territory |
| Saint Helena Island | 5 | 47 | British possession |
| Seychelles Island | 37 | 156 | British possession |
| Sierra Leone | 2,000 | 27,900 | British colony and protectorate |
| Somalia | 1,255 | 194,000 | Italian trusteeship |
| Somaliland (Br.) | 640 | 68,000 | British protectorate |
| Somaliland (Fr.) | 60 | 9,000 | French territory |
| Southwest Africa | 477 | 318,000 | Mandate to Union of South Africa |
| Sudan | 8,350 | 967,500 | Independent republic |
| Swaziland | 197 | 6,700 | Native territory, British High Commissioner under Commonwealth Relations Office |
| Tanganyika | 7,707 | 360,000 | British trust territory |
| Uganda | 5,125 | 93,980 | British protectorate |
| Union of South Africa | 13,900 | 472,700 | Independent member of the British Commonwealth |
| Walvis Bay | | 374 | Administered by Southwest Africa |
| Zanzibar | 247 | 1,020 | British protectorate |

**Rift Valleys.** An extraordinary feature of the East African plateaus are the long, narrow depressions called grabens (rift valleys). The western graben is marked by a chain of lakes which extends south from Lake Albert, through Lake Tanganyika, to Lake Nyasa. One of the most spectacular and best-known peaks along the edge of this rift is Mount Ruwenzori, 16,800 feet. The eastern rift crosses from French Somaliland into Ethiopia then curves to Lake Rudolf and continues southward to Lake Nyasa, curving 150 miles east of Lake Victoria. Both rift valleys are bordered by uplands having elevations of 8,000 to 10,000 feet. Along the eastern rift are such volcanic giants as Mounts Kenya, 17,040 feet, Kilimanjaro, 19,565 feet, and Elgon, 14,000 feet. The rolling surfaces of the Lake Victoria Basin occupy an area between the rift valleys.

**South Africa.** Southern Africa is separated from the rest of the high plateaus by the lower course of the Zambezi River. The region includes a series of uplands which encircle the Kalahari Basin. The basin, with elevations of 3,000 to 5,000 feet, is an area of little relief, with the lower northern parts swamp-filled after rains. Because of the surrounding uplands and outblowing winds most of the Kalahari is desert. Much of the remainder is too dry to support crops unless they are irrigated. To the north and northeast of the basin, the topography is gently rolling, rising to elevations of about 5,000 feet. Except in the vicinity of the Zambezi River, below Victoria Falls, and near the eastern sea coast, the land is relatively level. East of the Kalahari Basin, high rolling plateaus, or grassy velds, attain elevations of 6,000 feet or more. The rugged topography of the Drakensburg and other mountains to the south and west reaches elevations of 7,000 to 10,000 feet. Eastward these mountains descend abruptly over steep escarpments to sea level within a distance of 80 miles. South of the Kalahari Basin rolling tablelands descend in broad, step-like, dry benches, called karroos, from 6,000 feet to sea level. Most of the eastern and southern coast rises to over 6,000 feet within a few miles of the sea. The coastal plain of Mozambique, however, is an exception since it has widths up to 200 miles. On the west coast, the lowlands are 20 to 50 miles wide. Behind them

*Figure 12-3 Waterfalls and tropical vegetation on the Lucala River in Angola. (Courtesy of Portuguese Embassy.)*

the rugged plateau edge rises over escarpments to 7,000 feet before descending to the Kalahari Basin in the interior.

**Congo Basin.** The Congo Basin, an area of nearly 1 million square miles, is roughly circular in shape and lies athwart the equator. It is separated from the Atlantic Ocean by highlands which are slightly over 3,000 feet in elevation. Through these the Congo River has cut a deep gorge. The lower part of the Congo Basin, about half its total area, is quite flat and lies between 1,000 and 1,500 feet above sea level. From this low basin the surface rises abruptly over low escarpments to about 2,000 feet and then continues gently to the surrounding uplands. These attain elevations of 6,000 to 7,000 feet in the south and east, and about 3,000 feet in the north and west.

**Guinea Coast.** Extending westward from the volcanic Cameroon Mountains is the Guinea Coast. In general, the region is a nearly flat upland with elevations that seldom exceed 2,000 feet. A few low hills and some deep valleys are to be found along the northern and southern edges of the region. The Guinea Coast has extensive sandy beaches and coastal swamps with headlands and promontories where the plateau edge reaches the sea.

**Sudan.** The Sudan is the largest populated lowland in the continent. Extending across Africa from the Atlantic Ocean to the upper Nile Valley and Red Sea, it is located south of the Sahara between about 10 to 18° north latitude. The Sudan is a nearly level to gently rolling plain except for a few isolated uplands. The Senegal and Gambia Rivers flow westward into the Atlantic, but most of the Sudan, north of the Guinea Coast, is drained by the Niger River because its course bends widely to the north and east before turning south to the Gulf of Guinea. Shallow basins with "land deltas" occupy three areas, each of considerable size. In them are found swampy flatlands that flood during periods of high water, vegetation-choked streams, and deep deposits of silt and peat. One such basin is southwest of Timbuktu (Tombouctou) along the Niger River, a second is in the Lake Chad Basin and along the Shari (Chari) River, and the third is in the Sudd region of the Nile in the eastern Sudan region and the southern part of the country of Sudan.

## Climate and Vegetation

The climatic zones in Africa change regularly north and south from the equator (Figure 12-4). In the vicinity of the equator, the high sun causes the air to expand and rise during the day. In the process of rising, the air is cooled enough to produce rain. Since this process is repeated day after day throughout the year, there is almost daily rain in the equatorial region. The low-pressure zone which results from the air rising and flowing elsewhere is called the doldrums, and the climatic zone existing in the vicinity of the equator is called the rainy tropical. The seasonal shift in the position of the high sun north of the equator in the northern summer and south of the equator in the northern winter causes the rainy belt to shift north and south also. This shifting results in the heaviest rains falling during the summer seasons of the respective hemispheres. Along the Gulf of Guinea the summer rainfall is especially heavy since very moist air is drawn from over the ocean toward the inland position of the doldrums. When the doldrum belt is south of the equator (southern summer, northern winter), the trade winds blow over the part of the area that is north of the equator; the rains stop, and the weather becomes dry. The seasonal reverse of this is true along the southern edge south of the equator. This tropical region that has both wet and dry seasons is the savanna.

Poleward from the savanna, the rainy season becomes short and the total rainfall is small, which gives a semiarid climate called the semiarid tropical steppe. This is transitional to the tropical deserts over which the dry trade winds blow almost continuously. Still farther poleward on the northwest and south tips of Africa are regions with the Mediterranean climate characterized by dry, hot summers and mild, rainy winters. This results from the shift of the

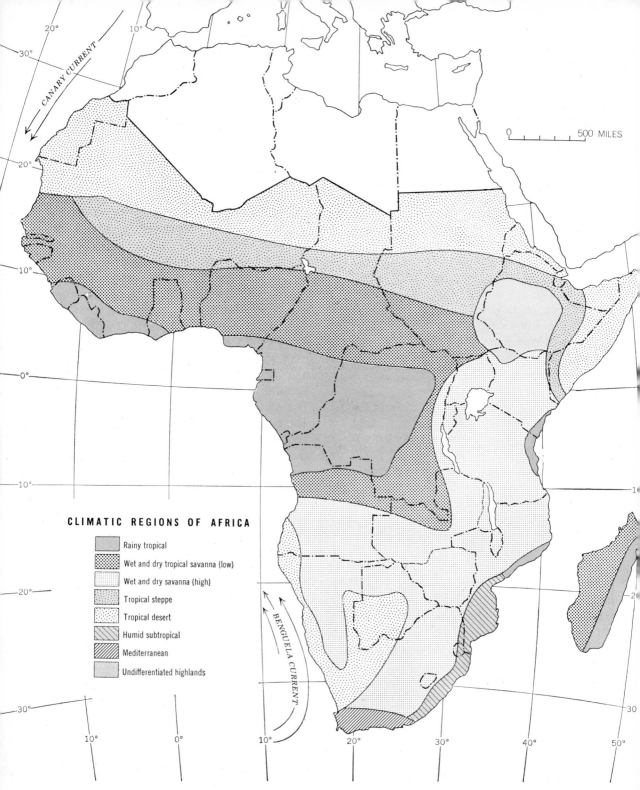

CLIMATIC REGIONS OF AFRICA

- Rainy tropical
- Wet and dry tropical savanna (low)
- Wet and dry savanna (high)
- Tropical steppe
- Tropical desert
- Humid subtropical
- Mediterranean
- Undifferentiated highlands

CANARY CURRENT

BENGUELA CURRENT

0    500 MILES

*Figure 12-4  The climatic regions of Africa south of the rainy tropical re-gion are almost the same as those north of it. Only in the eastern highlands is there great variation. Note the regions through which one passes in travel-ing from the Cape of Good Hope north to the Mediterranean Sea.*

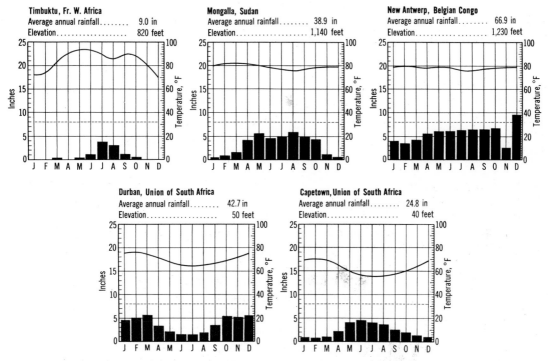

*Figure 12-5   Climate graphs for selected stations.*

dry wind belts away from the equator in summer and toward the equator in winter during which time the stormy westerly winds bring rain. Again summer and winter are in opposite calendar months in northern and southern Africa. A small coastal area in Southeast Africa has a humid subtropical climate, partly because of the southeast trade winds blowing onshore from the Indian Ocean.

In general, rainfall reaches a maximum in the season of high sun. It decreases from the wet equatorial climate through the savannas and steppes to the deserts and then increases again where the Mediterranean climate prevails (Figure 12-5). The mean annual temperature also decreases with the distance from the equator. In sunny regions like deserts, however, maximum daily temperatures often exceed those at the equator, where it is cloudier and the period during which the sun shines daily in summer may be shorter than in a desert. Both rainfall temperatures are affected by mountains. The heaviest rainfall in Africa, about 300 inches annually, is on Cameroon Peak close to the

Gulf of Guinea. Increased elevations of plateaus and mountains may cause the average temperature to drop by 10 to 30°F, as compared with nearby lowlands.

**Rainy Tropical.** Areas with rainy tropical climate occur along both sides of the equator in Central Africa and west along most of the Guinea Coast to Liberia and Gambia. The eastern side of Madagascar and mainland coastal areas in tropical Southeast Africa are included because of the heavy rainfall that results from the moist southeast trade winds rising over the highlands near the Indian Ocean shores. Annual rainfall generally exceeds 60 inches and occasionally rises to 100 inches. The temperature averages about 80°F and varies but slightly from day to night or from season to season. The climate is unpleasant and enervating because humidity and temperature are both high. Almost daily rains, largely from thunderstorms, make the temperature of about 80°F extremely uncomfortable. The moisture and warmth of such a climate supports a lux-

*Figure 12-6 The Congo rain forest includes a profusion of trees, vines, and undergrowth among which palms and tropical hardwoods are of commercial importance. (Courtesy of Belgian Government Information Center.)*

uriant rain forest that has great variety in kinds and species of plants including a profusion of vines and parasitic growths (Figure 12-6).

**Wet-and-Dry Tropical Savanna.** This climate prevails over vast regions north, south, and east of the rainy tropical climates. The savanna occupies the transition zone from wet to semi-arid conditions. The rainy season has 30 to 60 inches of total rainfall, and its period coincides with the high sun when there is a shift poleward of the tropical rainy belt. When the

high sun shifts to the opposite hemisphere, the dry trade winds displace the tropical rains and bring a dry season which varies from two to seven months in length. Although temperatures vary only moderately during the year, the heat maximum is during the dry season and is highest, often above 100°F, just before the rains begin. During most of the rainy season, climatic conditions closely resemble those of the rainy tropical climate. Bright skies, hot and intense sunshine, dry winds, and low relative humidity prevail during the dry season.

Vegetation presents a parklike landscape with trees predominating in the wetter areas and grasses dominating in drier savannas. Grasses are frequently several feet tall, coarse, and canelike. Many of the trees have a gummy sap, are curiously flat-topped, and well supplied with thorns. They lose their leaves or have curled leaves during the dry season. The barrel-trunked baobab tree is characteristic of much of the savanna, but thickets of thorny brush may predominate over wide areas. Vegetation in savanna lands must be capable of enduring several months of drought. Most commonly tropical savannas consist of open woods mixed with grasses and shrubs. Except where they have been reduced in numbers by hunting, wild animals abound. There are many species of antelope along with the elephant, giraffe, zebra, and various kinds and sizes of carnivores. The savannas are the African big-game areas. Insect pests are common, especially during the rainy season.

The high savannas occupy interior areas with elevations above 3,000 feet where temperatures are lower by 10 to 20°F than those in the lowlands. There is usually slightly less precipitation than in the savannas at lower elevations because the moisture has been partly lost before the rain-bringing winds reach the interior. The wet-and-dry season regime prevails, but near the equator in East Africa it varies by having the wettest seasons in April and October when the sun is nearly overhead with periods of less rain and greater temperature intervening. Grasses are shorter on the high savannas than on those of lower elevations and there is considerable thornbush. Wild animals were originally abundant, and in parts of the high savannas herds of big game still live. South of the wet equatorial rain forests the high savanna is called the dry forest. This dry forest area has stunted open woods of drought-resistant trees and shrubs mixed with grass. It covers much of the southern Belgian Congo, northern Rhodesia, and Angola. In the high savannas (velds) of South Africa winter frosts are common during the cooler months.

**Semiarid Tropical Steppes.** The semiarid tropical steppes are largely north of the equator between the savannas and the desert. They stretch across Africa in a zone 3,000 miles long and average about 300 miles in width. Between 12 and 20 inches of rain falls during a three- to four-month season, but the rains are not dependable. As in the savannas the time for the highest temperatures that soar well above 100°F is just before and after the rains. Dry weather is often windy and intensely sunny with relatively cool nights. Short grasses and low, thorny brush comprise the common vegetation.

**Tropical Deserts.** Two of the three African deserts, the Kalahari and the Somali, are in Central and Southern Africa. The Kalahari extends along the southwest coast from about 12 to 28° south latitude. Its lack of rainfall results chiefly from its location in the southeast trade wind belt. There winds lose their moisture while ascending the highlands on the east side of the continent. The presence of the cold Benguela Current along the west coast often causes fogs near the Atlantic shore. Rain seldom falls until the air rises thousands of feet to cross the highlands back of the narrow western coastal lowlands. Except when fogs intervene on the Kalahari coast, temperatures are high during the day but may drop considerably at night.

The Somali Desert, which includes the Danakil and Eritrea lowlands, is on the east side of the continent extending northward from the equator along the coast to about 15° north latitude, or until it joins the Sahara. In this area the monsoon winds blow south, parallel to the coast, in the northern winter and north, parallel to the coast, in the northern summer. Rains are heavy inland in the highlands of Ethiopia, but the coasts have very scanty rainfall.

Rainfall in both the Kalahari and Somali Deserts is not only small but also unreliable, coming usually from local thunderstorms. Hot, dry winds and punishing dust storms and sandstorms occur. The vegetation is always scanty and the plants are of drought-tolerant species.

**Humid Subtropical.** The humid subtropical climate of southeastern Africa extends inland only a short distance, for increasing elevation soon makes cooler temperatures. Rainfall varies from 40 to 60 inches per year. Although some rain falls in each month, the heaviest rainfall is associated with the period of the southeast trade winds, which occur during the warm season from October through March. Fairly heavy rains from May to August result from the winter cyclonic storms that the shift of the wind belts equatorward brings to South Africa. Temperatures are always mild at the lower elevations. The cold months average not less than 50°F, and warm months are seldom above 77°F. Vegetation along the coast is dominated by a forest of palm and other subtropical trees. The higher slopes and benches are covered with a brush and grass vegetation; in the frostless north, even the banana will grow.

**Mediterranean.** On the southern coast of Africa, a limited area approximately 100 miles wide has a Mediterranean climate. The 20- to 25-inch rainfall is concentrated in the winter months. The summer season, December to March, averages less than 1 inch per month. Mild summer (January) temperatures seldom average above 70°F at Capetown. This is colder than is common for Mediterranean summers because of the cooling effect of the Benguela Current which flows along the southwestern coast. Winter temperatures (July) at Capetown average 54°F. The coastal region is without frost, but the higher inner edge of the Med-

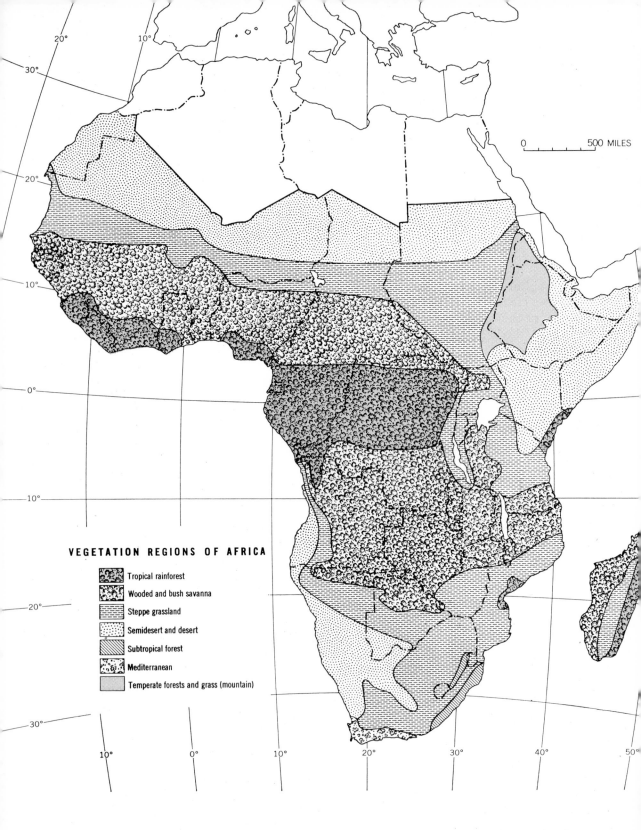

**VEGETATION REGIONS OF AFRICA**

- Tropical rainforest
- Wooded and bush savanna
- Steppe grassland
- Semidesert and desert
- Subtropical forest
- Mediterranean
- Temperate forests and grass (mountain)

0        500 MILES

*Figure 12-7    The vegetation regions are directly related to the climatic regions. Note the similarity of the two maps.*

iterranean region has occasional frosts and cooler winter temperatures than the coast. The rainfall concentration in the cooler season of the year leaves the summer dry, with bright sunlight and clear skies. Natural vegetation is sparse, grasses and bush vegetation being adapted to the hot, dry summer weather.

## Soils

African soils have largely been developed under tropical and subtropical conditions. The residual soils, formed by the weathering of many different kinds of bedrock, are typically rather dense clays of low fertility. Since there is no season during which the ground freezes and weathering stops, the weathering process and the decay of plant and animal matter is continuous. Under tropical conditions the humus, which is valued as a fertilizer and needed to maintain the soil in good physical condition, rapidly disappears. Furthermore, in humid climates the soluble minerals are dissolved by the percolating rain water leaving the soil poor from the loss of much of its fertility by leaching. Many African soils, therefore, are of inferior quality. Some of the best soils are made of the alluvium or silt deposited on river floodplains and deltas.

In tropical Africa the most common soil is laterite and other red to red-brown lateritic types that develop in the rainy tropical and humid subtropical climates. Laterite is a red clay-like material that, when dry, resembles brick. It is usually a residual soil formed by weathering processes under a forest cover in a hot, rainy climate. Laterites occur along the Guinea Coast, on both sides of the equator in the Congo Basin, and in eastern Madagascar. The red and red-brown tropical lateritic soils developed under ample but somewhat less rainfall than the true laterites. Since laterite and lateritic soils are leached of most of the soluble minerals that make soil fertile, both are poor to mediocre soils for farming.

In the dry forest and high savannas, the soils are light-brown in color and are less leached because of the long dry season. In the grassy savannas of the Sudan region, the abundant humus derived from the decay of grass causes the soils to be black and quite fertile. There has been a minimum of leaching because the rainfall is seasonal and totals less than half that which occurs where laterite soil is being formed. These black soils are among the best in Africa for growing grains and cotton. They somewhat resemble the chernozem or black prairie soil of the middle latitudes. On the semiarid tropical steppes, the grass is shorter and so there is less humus contained in the soil than on the savannas. In such places the soil is light-brown or chestnut in color. These soils border the Sahara in the Sudan and the Kalahari Desert in South Africa where the rainfall is low and uncertain. They are fertile soils but so light that dust may be blown during windstorms; hence, they require careful handling to prevent wind and rain erosion. The desert soils are gray in color because the scant vegetation can supply little humus. Desert soils are unleached and may be quite productive if water is available for irrigation, otherwise, there will be only a little fodder for livestock.

## THE GEOGRAPHICAL REGIONS

The geographical regions into which Central and Southern Africa have been divided are Central Africa, Sudan Lands, Guinea Coast, Eastern Horn of Africa, East African Plateaus, and Southern Africa (Figure 12-8). The basis for these divisions is largely locational, but they also usually have characteristic climate, elevations, and landforms that help to differentiate them.

## Central Africa

Central Africa is the heart of the continent and comprises the Cameroons, the southern half of French Equatorial Africa, the Belgian Congo, and most of Angola, an area of nearly 2 million square miles in which live about 20 million people. The region centers around the more level part of the Congo Basin and extends into

*Figure 12-8    The geographic regions are based on both physical and cultural factors. Political boundaries are used in many instances as they facilitate the discussion of the different areas.*

the surrounding plateaus and mountains. The Congo River and its tributaries drain most of the area.

The people are primarily Bantu-speaking tribes, but also included are the primitive Pygmies of the equatorial forests who have no fixed abode. Much of Central Africa is sparsely populated, with large areas of forests and swamps that are practically uninhabited. Elsewhere small tribal villages of thatched huts are built near forest clearings.

Small patches of land, from which food can be harvested each season, are cultivated. Fields are abandoned and villages moved every two or three years, if necessary, when the infertile soil is exhausted and choked by weeds and the ever-encroaching forest. The abandoned fields are soon covered by a second-growth forest, and several years will pass before the ground is again cleared for crops. The term migratory agriculture is applied to this type of farming, which is much used in tropical Africa, including the Guinea Coast.

In the practice of migratory agriculture, the forest is hacked down and burned or the big trees are killed by girdling. Plantings are made by crude implements, and ashes serve for fertilizer. Cassava, yams, beans, and bananas are usually the staple crops. These are often planted together to conserve space so that less land need be cleared. The man who clears and plants a piece of land owns the crops grown there, but the land is owned by the tribe, not by any individual. Generally among the tribes using this form of agriculture there is no strong centralized government because the natives live in small isolated groups. Partly because of the ease with which needs could be satisfied, such groups had a static, primitive culture which remained unchanged for centuries. With the coming of Europeans, palm oil and wild rubber became salable commercial products which the natives could exchange for other goods. The gathering of wild rubber is no longer important, but the production of palm oil from both planted and wild trees is a leading industry.

In the wet equatorial region insect pests, intestinal parasites, and skin infections are constant plagues to man. Mosquitoes, ticks, flies, and especially the dread tsetse fly that transmits sleeping sickness to man and nagana to domestic cattle are an ever-present irritation and threat. Wildlife is largely restricted to apes, monkeys, birds, and reptiles, although the hippopotamus lives in the rivers and marshes. Ground-living forest mammals are scarce and include the rare and shy okapi, not discovered by Europeans until after 1900. The gorilla, largest ape in the world, lives in the Cameroons and the Iturbi Forest in the northeast Belgian Congo. Near Mount Ruwenzori, a national park has been established that will preserve much of the native fauna, including the gorilla that lives in the forest.

The lowlands of the Congo Basin, above Stanley Pool, are one of the striking physical features of Central Africa. For approximately 700 miles east and west, and nearly 400 miles north and south, the land is almost flat. The Congo River and its tributaries resemble narrow lakes, varying from 1 to 6 miles wide, island-filled, and bordered by many miles of swamps. From Stanley Falls to Stanley Pool, a distance of 1,000 miles, the river drops less than 5 inches per mile. A low plateau borders the flat part of the basin on the south and east, rising about 500 feet above it. Eastward, in less than 200 miles, the land ascends from an elevation of 1,400 feet along the Congo River to over 6,000 feet in the mountains bordering the western rift valleys. Southward from Stanley Falls for about 500 miles the surface becomes undulating and rises gradually to more than 5,000 feet on the Congo-Zambezi divide.

A sparsely settled upland separates the Congo Basin from the Atlantic Ocean. The upland has a plateaulike surface, generally 2,000 to 3,000 feet in elevation, yet so flat that streams frequently rise in swamps. Streams descending both into the Congo Basin and to the Atlantic Ocean tumble over rapids and waterfalls, through gorges and narrow valleys, making land transportation difficult. The Congo River flows westward through these uplands in a gorge 220 miles long and 1,600 feet deep, plunging over a succession of falls and rapids which make the river the greatest undeveloped power stream on earth. Above the gorge, the Congo becomes a major artery of commerce and a fleet of river boats handles the imports and products.

Central Africa has two principal climatic types, rainy tropical and savanna. Originally most of the Congo Basin was covered by a tropical rain forest which contained a wealth of hardwoods, dyewoods, palms, and cabinet woods along with a profusion of vines and parasitic plants. Centuries of shifting native agriculture have destroyed much of the virgin forest. The forest grades north and east into savanna as the rainfall decreases and becomes seasonal. The northern savanna is dominantly of the wet type with luxuriant tall grasses and tree-lined streams and valleys, but south of the rain forest it becomes a "dry forest." The forest lands of the northern Congo Basin are sparsely populated and little developed because of isolation and divided political control. In the savanna the Africans keep cattle since there is abundant grass and the tsetse fly is not present.

The political life and economic development of the region is largely controlled by the whites, who number about 125,000, chiefly French, Belgians, and Portuguese. Millions of Africans still live in a tribal society and have little contact with other people. Nevertheless, in places a spirit of nationality is developing. Missionaries have made a small but growing impression against witchcraft and paganism. There are too few doctors and hospitals; thus health conditions are poor. Although highways and railways are few development of mineral, forest, and agricultural resources is expanding.

**Belgian Congo.** The Belgian Congo is a relatively empty land. It is as large as the United States east of the Mississippi River but has only 12 million people, of whom about 90,000 are whites. Mineral wealth is great, especially in the eastern and southern parts. Copper, industrial diamonds, uranium, gold, and radium account for most of the production, but large mineral deposits remain unexploited largely because of poor transportation for bulky commodities. Mail, package freight, and passengers are transported by airplanes, Central Africa having a number of regularly operated routes. The colony is well managed and, except for the mines, the land is mostly owned by the native tribes. Since whites are not encouraged to settle in the colony, the Europeans living in the Belgian Congo are administrators, technicians, businessmen, and professional personnel. The many natives who are being trained as skilled mechanics earn high wages and enjoy good living standards for Africa. Five large corporations, partly state-owned, manage most of the business. Exports total over 1 billion dollars annually, the majority coming from minerals. Cotton and mahogany also are among the important exports. There are a few plantations of oil palms, but the smaller farms of native Africans have for much of the output.

Minerals are especially important in the Katanga district in southeast Belgian Congo. The mines produce annually not less than 7 per cent of the world's copper, 80 per cent of its cobalt, and 5 per cent of its zinc, besides cadmium, gold, and radium. The Chinkolobive mine is the largest source of uranium used for atomic energy in the world, but exact production figures are kept secret. It is estimated that this mine produces 60 per cent of the world's uranium and 90 per cent of its radium. In the Kasai Valley, tributary to the Congo, are im-

*Figure 12-9 Towboats and barges on the quiet waters of the Congo River above Stanley Pool. Their loads will be transshipped at Leopoldville for the coast. (Courtesy of Belgian Government Information Center.)*

portant deposits of diamonds, mostly of the industrial variety. Exports of minerals greatly exceed in value all other products shipped from the Belgian Congo.

Leopoldville, a modern city with one 12-story "skyscraper," has more than 200,000 people, 16,500 of whom are white. It is the capital and chief commercial center, having rail connections with the port of Matadi which is near the mouth of the Congo River. Air routes connect Leopoldville with many other cities. It also has river connections upstream. Elizabethville, a city of almost 60,000, is in the Katanga mining district. It is the second city in size, and its location at an elevation of nearly 5,000 feet makes life there quite pleasant and healthy. Railroads connect the Katanga district with Benguela in Angola, Beira in Mozambique, and with the diamond mines near the Kasai River.

**Ruanda Urundi.** The former German territory of Ruanda Urundi, is now a Belgian trusteeship from the United Nations. This territory of 20,900 square miles contains more than 4 million Africans and a few whites. The area is only 2.3 per cent as large as the Belgian Congo but it has one-third as many people. Many of the men work in the Katanga mines. Subsistence agriculture and livestock grazing are the principal native occupations. The high elevations help to make the climate healthy. The soil is more fertile than in the lowlands.

**French Equatorial Africa.** French Equatorial Africa has an area of 989,000 square miles and a population of 4.5 million persons, but nearly two-thirds of the colony is desert and steppes where few people live. The capital, Brazzaville, is across the Congo River from Leopoldville. This French colony has only 350 miles of railroad, all in the south, and few highways. Economic development is greatly handicapped by the limited transportation.

**Cameroons.** The Cameroons, 166,500 square miles in size, is a former German colony and is governed by France under trust from the United

*Figure 12-10  Tin mines of Manono, Katanga. The open-pit mines of the Katanga region are some of the largest in the world and produce some of the highest-grade ores. (Courtesy of Belgian Government Information Center.)*

Nations. A 23,000 square-mile area of the Cameroons, which borders Nigeria, is a British trusteeship from the United Nations. The chief exports from these territories are cotton, palm oil, cacao, coffee, and mahogany. Minerals are only slightly developed. Native agriculture is of the primitive migratory type in contrast to the generally sedentary farming in the drier Sudan lands to the north.

**Angola.** The Portuguese province of Angola has an area of 481,000 square miles of which about one-third is in the rainy tropics. Of over 4.09 million people, approximately 100,000 are white or mixed. Luanda, the capital, is a large city with a population of 165,000. The natives are extremely backward, approximately 97 per cent being illiterate. Among native agricultural crops are manioc, corn, beans, peanuts, castor seed, and yams. Of the commercial crops, coffee raised in the highlands is worth from 40 to 50 million dollars annually and accounts for 45 per cent of the exports; much of it is shipped to the United States. Cotton, maize, rice, sugar, and cacao are other products exported. The province has several railroads, including the Benguela line from Lobito eastward to the Katanga area. In general, however, transportation is poor. Most of the area in the southern half of the country and along the coast is sparsely settled because of a dry climate, having seasonal and undependable rains of less than 15 inches annually. Mineral deposits are widespread but few mines are in production. Large occurrences of copper have been found in the north, and significant resources of iron and coal are known. Manganese is mined extensively and is exported from Lobito. Diamonds of the in-dustrial sort, manganese, and copper are the chief minerals exported.

## The Sudan Lands

South of the Sahara, the steppes and savannas of the Sudan Lands form a strip about 600 miles wide and over 3,500 miles long, extending east-west across the continent from the Atlantic Ocean to the Red Sea, an area two-thirds as large as the United States. Politically, the area includes most of French West Africa, the semiarid northern parts of Nigeria and French Equatorial Africa, and the independent country of the Sudan, formerly the Anglo-Egyptian Sudan. (The country of Sudan was discussed in connection with Egypt in Chapter 11.) The Sudan has a wet-and-dry tropical climate. Precipitation decreases from about 45 inches, which falls during the five- to six-month summer rainy season, along the southern margin to a nearly rainless desert on the north. The region is flat to slightly rolling with a few uplands in the interior, such as the Darfur in Sudan, exceeding 5,000 feet. The western Sudan is drained by the Senegal and Niger Rivers, the eastern part by the Nile. The Lake Chad Basin and a few other

*Figure 12-11 Leopoldville is the principal city and business center of the Belgian Congo. It is situated on the flat plains of the Congo Basin on the shores of Stanley Pool. (Courtesy of Belgian Government Information Center.)*

broad, shallow depressions have only interior drainage, for the rainfall in these basins is inadequate to support rivers tributary to the ocean. Because of the uncertain supply, water must be carefully used and husbanded during all of the year.

The people are a mixture of races that include Hamites, Semites, and Sudanese. In Senegal alone, the tribes are so numerous that about 120 different dialects are spoken. The Moslem religion predominates, with some pagans and a few Coptic Christians toward the east. There are few Europeans except in some cities. Until overthrown by Europeans, feudal states, sometimes with populations of several million, like those of the Fulani around Kano in northern Nigeria and the Ashanti in the Gold Coast interior, ruled the Sudan. Such nations were frequently at war with each other as well as with the weaker tribes living along the Guinea Coast and in the equatorial forests.

The economic development of the region is generally primitive. Although rail and air transportation is available to coastal ports in Senegal and on the Gulf of Guinea, both are lacking over large parts of the interior. From Dakar and a few other cities, regular flights are made to Europe, and in emergencies, small planes land almost anywhere in the open, flat country. Most of the highways might better be called trails or tracks and are often impassable during the wet season. Where the principal activity is the grazing of livestock, the population is sparse. The strictly pastoral peoples are often

nomads, and may exchange animal products for the grain they need but disdain to grow. Politically, some French territories extend into the Sahara.

**French Africa.** France controls most of the territory in the Sudan region. French West Africa occupies most of the western Sudan and includes the colonies of Senegal, Sudan, Niger, and Upper Volta, besides Mauritania, which is mostly desert. The territory also includes French Guinea, Dahomey, and the Ivory Coast, which will be discussed with the Guinea Coast region. The western Sudan is a land of open woods, tall grass, and shrubs. Its great commercial crop is the peanut, in Africa called the groundnut. Cotton is also grown but export of this staple is far behind that of the country of Sudan. Untroubled by tsetse flies, large herds of cattle and many sheep, goats, and horses are kept. On the steppes along the edge of the Sahara, thousands of camels are raised.

Farming of the migratory subsistence type is the common occupation of the natives. It may be supplemented by grazing livestock. Corn, yams, barley, bananas, rice, and many vegetables are among the foodstuffs grown. Commercial agriculture is important only in sections of French West Africa, usually near railroads and rivers. On the most productive land are found a few concentrations of populations with densities exceeding 50 per square mile. Natives own and cultivate almost all the farmland. Peanuts are the most important mon-

*Figure 12-12 View of Luanda, chief seaport, largest city (165,000 inhabitants), and seat of government in Angola. Note the modern buildings and houses in this city famed for its flowering bougainvillaea vines. (Courtesy of Portuguese Embassy.)*

*Figure 12-13  Coiffure and costume of an African bride in Angola. (Courtesy of Portuguese Embassy.)*

ey crop and the exports of this commodity to Europe annually amount to hundreds of thousands of tons. Hides and skins are also exported.

Dakar, built near the westernmost peninsula of Africa, is a major French seaport and commercial center. During World War II, it was a strategic naval and air base of great importance. By air, Dakar is only 3,300 miles from New York, 3,070 miles from Paris, and 1,600 miles from the nearest point of Brazil. The city has one of the best airports in Africa. From Dakar, a railroad runs inland to Bamako on the Niger River to connect there with river boats. Although most of the Africans live in villages, a few other cities, including St. Louis, a port north of Dakar, and Bamako, are important. Timbuktu, located on the shore of the Niger River where it makes its great bend toward the Sahara, no longer has the importance held when the city was a terminal for ancient caravan routes across the desert to North Africa.

French Equatorial Africa includes the Chad and other parts of the Sudan region which lie to the eastward of northern Nigeria and west of the Sudan. From Senegal to the easternmost border of French territories is a distance of over 2,000 miles with an area in the Sudan region of about a million square miles. The Chad province was named after Lake Chad, a shallow lake that varies greatly in size depending on the rainfall and the volume of water brought in by tributaries like the Shari (Chari) River. In places, the country is so flat that during floods the Shari discharges its flow both to Lake Chad and into the Benue River, a tributary to the Niger. The Chad is isolated; trade is small and about two million people live in its nearly 500,000 square miles. The Africans raise a few subsistence crops and keep sheep, goats, camels, and cattle. Some of the tribes are nomads, but mostly the people live in small villages. The mud and thatched huts are often arranged in a circle within which the herds can be driven for protection during the night. The hunting of wild game furnishes some meat to supplement food derived from domestic livestock and the grains like grain sorghum and barley. Meat is not an export product; only hides and skins are sold.

Life in the isolated Chad is in strong contrast to that in the irrigated middle Niger Valley where cotton and groundnuts are grown for export, and rice and other food crops for local use. The Office du Niger, a nonprofit concern that might be called the African TVA, is in charge of construction for a large irrigation and hydroelectric project in the Niger Basin. The new land being developed is fertile and when under irrigation will greatly increase the output of both food crops and commercial crops like peanuts. Already 30,000 Africans have settled on 95,000 acres of former desert. The Chad could benefit from some similar reclamation project.

**Gambia.** The long, narrow country of Gambia forms an enclave into French West Africa along both sides of the Gambia River. The chief port and capital is Bathurst located at the mouth of the river. Upstream, the alluvial soils are especially suited for the production of groundnuts which form the chief export. The river can be navigated by river boats as far inland as the eastern boundary.

**Portuguese Guinea.** The Portuguese overseas province of Guinea also forms an enclave into French West Africa. Although this area has been under the control of Portugal since 1462 it is one of the least developed parts of the continent. The annual rainfall is about 80 inches and the average yearly temperature over 81°F. Few Portuguese live in the country, most of the trade being controlled by French and Belgian companies.

*Guinea Coast*

The Guinea Coast region extends from the British Cameroons on the Bight of Biafra to Sierra Leone on the Atlantic Ocean. Included are English, French, and Portuguese colonies or other territories and Liberia, an independent republic. The area covers approximately a million square miles and has a population of nearly 50 million persons. Located largely between 5° and 10° north latitude, the Guinea Coast region extends inland about 350 miles. Climatically, it has constantly high daily temperatures and abundant rainfall, especially during the period of high summer sun when the doldrum

*Figure 12-14   Bananas are an important product of French Guinea. This picture was taken on a plantation near Conakry. (Courtesy of French Cultural Services.)*

belt centers over the region. Many stations record rainfall up to 15 inches for the month of July. Originally the region was densely forested but the practice of burning the trees to make farmland has ruined the forest over large areas. Inland the rain forest grades into more open savanna vegetation of tall grass and scattered trees or brush. Cacao trees and oil palms flourish and, with plantation rubber in Liberia, constitute the principal exports.

A coastal plain adjoins the Gulf of Guinea to which the Niger, Volta, and scores of shorter rivers are tributary. Along much of the coastal lowland there are alternate mangrove swamps and sandy beaches against which the breaking surf crashes. Here landing except in rowboats is impossible and only roadsteads are established. Inland from the coastal plains rises an upland of old rocks. Where this approaches closely to the ocean, as in Sierra Leone, the frontal scarp of the upland is quite impressive. The headwaters of the Niger River drain the northern slopes on part of the upland.

The Guinea Coast is one of the areas of earliest European exploitation. Gold, slaves, and ivory were sought by the Portuguese, French, and English. Several railroads now penetrate the interior from the coast but no railway network exists. Mining, a little lumbering, and some commercial agriculture are a part of the growing economic development. Population densities on the Guinea Coast are among the greatest in Africa, often exceeding 100 per square mile.

The Negro of the Guinea Coast dwells in small villages of thatched huts. For many natives, tribal life still continues and ancient pagan rites are often practiced. Frequently, only dim forest trails lead from the villages to the outside world. Thus, communication between them is limited by the difficulty of travel in the tropical rain forest. Small agricultural plots for subsistence crops are maintained for only a few plantings, since frequent moves to new clearings are necessary. Infertile soils, leached and eroded by the torrential rains, and a constant struggle against the encroaching vegetation make the primitive hoe-farming methods extremely difficult. The tsetse fly prevents the keeping of animals, and insect-borne diseases are common among human beings. Small commercial plantings, most of which are operated by Africans, produce such commodities as palm oil and cacao. The suitability of tree crops to humid climates and infertile soils favors this kind of development.

West of the Cameroon Mountains, the wide delta of the Niger River extends inland in a maze of swamps and channels for over 100 miles. West from the Niger Delta, for about 350 miles, the coast is a stretch of swamps, lagoons, and sandy beaches, reaching almost to Accra and extending 20 to 50 miles inland. There is another 200-mile series of swamps and lagoons along the Ivory Coast. Back of the coastal lowlands is the Guinea Coast Upland which ranges from 1,000 to 3,000 feet in elevation. In Liberia, Sierra Leone, and parts of

French Guinea, and at Accra in Ghana the front of the uplands approaches to within a few miles of the sea. Elsewhere the lowland extends 100 to 200 miles inland from the coast before reaching the abrupt margin of the uplands. Lowlands 100 miles wide extend up the Niger and Benue Rivers in Nigeria.

From the coast of Nigeria and that of Ivory Coast–Sierra Leone–Liberia, the tropical rain forest extends inland for distances of 100 to 200 miles. Rainfall on parts of the coast ranges from 80 to over 150 inches per year, with 80 per cent or more falling between May and October. In the Cameroons an annual rainfall of 400 inches has been reported, making this among the wettest places on earth. In contrast, Lagos in southwest Nigeria has a rainfall of only 50 inches a year.

Commercial production on the Guinea Coast is varied. Most of it comes from small plantings under native management. The indigenous oil palm, growing primarily in the rain forest region, yields great quantities of palm oil. Part of the oil is extracted from the pulp by the natives. Small cacao plantings, under native management, are concentrated in the Gold Coast. These plantings produce about 40 per cent of the world's supply, but a disease of the cacao trees now threatens the industry. Smaller quantities of cacao come from the Ivory Coast and other parts of the region. Bananas are produced and exported in large quantities both as fresh fruit and as banana flour. Nigeria exports large numbers of skins and hides taken from the millions of cattle, sheep, and goats raised in the northern part of the country. Ebony and mahogany are cut and exported from the coastal forests. Mine timbers and railroad ties are taken in quantity from the mangrove forests of the coastal swamps. There is some plantation rubber production and a little gathering of wild rubber.

The ancient crystalline rocks of the Guinea Coast Upland are well endowed with minerals. The British colonies or former colonies contain most of the known and developed mineral reserves. Nigeria is one of the important tin producers of the world, usually ranking fourth.

Ghana (Gold Coast) during recent years has ranked second to the U.S.S.R. in manganese production with 14 per cent of the world's total. The Guinea Coast region produces considerable gold, over 20 per cent of the world's industrial diamonds, and significant amounts of high-grade iron ore which is shipped to England and the United States. The only coal in West Africa is mined in Nigeria and supplies fuel for local rail and steamer services. Unexploited iron ore and bauxite wait the necessary capital for development.

**Ghana (Gold Coast).** The English have long followed a policy of educating the inhabitants of their colonies for eventual self-government within the British Commonwealth of Nations. The Gold Coast, in 1954, became a virtually self-governing state of nearly 91,500 square miles with a population of almost 4 million Africans and only 6,700 Europeans. In 1957 the nation became an independent member of the British Commonwealth. Ghana is a rich country and the valuable cacao trade is largely managed by Africans. Hydroelectricity could be generated along the Volta River.

**Nigeria.** The most populous country in Africa, Nigeria has a population of over 31 million Africans and about 12,000 Europeans in an area of 373,250 square miles. The country will have self-rule as soon as the Moslems of the north, with their feudal society, can agree with the people in the southern part of the colony about governmental conditions. Rifts between the people of eastern and western Nigeria have also delayed complete autonomy. Kano in the north, Ibadan in the southwest interior, and Lagos, the capital and seaport, are the chief cities. Kano in northern Nigeria is famed for cotton textiles, pottery, and other manufactures. It is the largest city in the savanna section of Nigeria. Once it was the terminal for camel trails north across the Sahara, but that trade is now a thing of the past. Nigeria has good ports and air connection to the rest of Africa and Europe. Peanuts, cotton, palm oil, cocoa, hides, and tin are the leading exports. Nigerians are

good farmers and produce a variety of subsistence crops. The country is self-governing but its foreign affairs are controlled by the British.

Many of the native Nigerian farmers practice a system of agriculture known as brush fallowing. The farmer owns land, perhaps 20 acres, and plants only about 5 acres to crops for two or three years. After that, decreased yields make it sensible to let the land grow up to brush and weeds. The brush on another piece of land is then cut and burned, the ashes furnishing some fertilizer and the weathering of the soil during the several years of fallowing also adding to the supply. Under these conditions the land will be in crops for two or three years and in fallow to rest and accumulate fertility for six to nine years. This system works well in the tropical savannas. It is widely used all through the Sudan region when people live in permanently located villages in contrast to the shifting farms and villages of the rain forest. The biggest difficulty develops when the population increases. Since there is no increase in the amount of tillable land, farm acreage per family diminishes. Under such conditions, the pressure for food decreases the time in which land is left fallow, but since it is allowed to rest only a half or a third as long, crop yields decline and poverty increases. Part of Nigeria appears to have reached this saturation point. Elsewhere the amount of farmland is still adequate for the population.

**Sierra Leone.** The country of Sierra Leone is self-governing but its foreign affairs are controlled by the British. It is a small and little developed country. The population includes about a thousand Europeans as compared to 2 million Africans. Chrome ore and industrial diamonds, along with palm oil and kola nuts, are exported through Freetown, the capital and a seaport. Iron ore is also exported.

British-owned Gambia, which occupies a narrow strip along the river of the same name, and Portuguese Guinea are small colonies that are bordered on three sides by French West Africa.

**Liberia.** During the administration of President Monroe, Liberia was founded as a country for freed American slaves. It has been an independent republic since 1847. The country is known to many Americans as the site of the Firestone rubber plantation which employs over 25,000 workmen. More than a million tons of iron are shipped from Liberia to the United States each year. Many ships, half of which are tankers, are under Liberian registry although few of these actually operate to and from Liberia. In return for fees paid the Liberian government, shipowners secure freedom of movement and lower taxes. Monrovia is the capital and principal port.

**French West Africa.** The principal French colony in the region is the Ivory Coast. It is a rail outlet for much of French West Africa. An artificial harbor, which can accommodate large ocean-going vessels, has been constructed at Abidjan. The harbor is also used by the many native craft that bring cacao, peanuts, and palm oil which are transferred to larger ships. Manganese and diamonds are mined. Between Ghana and Nigeria are the French colonies of Dahomey and Togoland, the latter a former German colony which is now divided between France and England and governed as trust territories under the United Nations. In 1956, French Togoland voted for union with France.

### Eastern Horn of Africa

The Eastern Horn of Africa, named for the projection of Cape Guardafui, comprises Ethiopia and adjoining coastal territories. It covers an area of about 669,000 square miles and has an estimated population of 21 million people. This region of high plateaus has natural topographic barriers that have served as defense against invaders, but the barriers have also reduced communication and trade. Arab traders, Europeans, and Africans have found this area difficult to enter because of the rough terrain and rocky, desert coastal wastes. Politically the ancient kingdom of Ethiopia, which has maintained its independence for over 2,000 years, dominates the region. The country is

separated from the Red Sea by the autonomous province of Eritrea, which is federated with Ethiopia, and from the Gulf of Aden and the Indian Ocean by French and British Somaliland and Somalia which is held by Italy under trusteeship from the United Nations.

Western Ethiopia, a rugged highland with elevations varying between 8,000 and 15,000 feet, is marked by steep and deeply dissected edges. These uplands, in which the sprawling capital of Addis Ababa is located, are the cultural and political stronghold of the country. The Somali Plateau, in eastern Ethiopia, is mostly rocky, barren desert country, sparsely occupied by nomads who follow their herds. Between the Somali Plateau and the Ethiopian Highlands is a sharply defined rift valley in which volcanoes, lava flows, hot springs, and salt basins are found. The coastal Danakil region is a rough desert about 300 miles wide near the Red Sea and forms one of the most difficult parts of Africa to traverse.

Climatic differences in the Eastern Horn of Africa are due to variations in elevation, direction of prevailing winds, and low latitudes. Temperatures are fairly even throughout the year, the annual range being about 7 to 10°F. At elevations below 6,000 feet, it is always hot. Along the Red Sea and Gulf of Aden is one of the most disagreeable desert and steppe climates in the world. During the cooler season daily temperatures range between 70 and 80°F. In the warmer season the average daily temperature is from 85 to over 90°F. Rainfall is low, varying from 4 to 10 inches yearly. The lower valleys of the Ethiopian highlands have high temperatures and humidities. Higher slopes and rolling uplands, between 6,000 and 9,000 feet, usually have over 40 inches of rainfall, starting in March or April and ending abruptly in September. Over large sections of the western edge of the plateau, precipitation exceeds 75 inches. Within this area is Lake Tana, the source of the Blue Nile. The excessive rains send vast quantities of water down the Blue Nile which, swollen, causes the Nile floods that are so important to the agriculture of Egypt. Cooler temperatures prevail at these higher altitudes, averaging between 60 and 70°F, at 8,000 feet.

In the dry climate, along the Red Sea and Indian Ocean, only drought-resistant shrubs and salt grasses grow. Gum and acacia trees and extensive thorn thickets yield gum arabic and incense products. There is limited browse and coarse grass for grazing animals. Grasslands similar to those found in temperate areas cover the uplands, and dense forests are found on the rainiest part of the plateau. The uplands of central Ethiopia contain extensive growths of wild coffee trees. This area may be the original home of coffee.

**Ethiopia.** The ruling class in Ethiopia are the Amharas, a Semitic people. In addition there are Hamites, Arabs, and Negroes, the latter living chiefly in the lower parts of the western highland section. The Amharas are mostly Coptic Christians, but the Moslem religion is also widespread. The country needs education and help to develop its potential resources, which are believed to include many minerals. Since much of the soil is fertile, agriculture could be greatly expanded if modern methods were used and transportation to market available. Actually many of the people are living much as did their ancestors during Biblical times. Roads are very poor and the one railroad from Addis Ababa, the capital, to Djibouti in French Somaliland operates only in the daytime on a schedule of two trains per week. Three days are needed to make the 486-mile journey. Air travel is increasingly important and airlines are operated by British, French, American, and Ethiopian companies. The United States is helping Ethiopia by furnishing educational and technical specialists needed for the improvement of the country.

The well-watered uplands have only a sparse population of farmers or herders. Rough topography limits transportation of products and continues to isolate the small native villages. Livestock and subsistence crops such as millet, wheat, barley, and beans are the chief foods of the people. Except for native craftsmen, industry is practically nonexistent. Hides and coffee are the most important agricultural exports.

Eritrea separates Ethiopia from the Red Sea. Because of the dry, hot climatic conditions, much of the population is nomadic. A limited grazing industry and the collection of gums and resins are the chief occupations. Agriculture is limited to the better-watered areas in the mountains or where irrigation can be developed. Massaua (Massawa) and Assab are two ports through which Ethiopian trade can pass to the Red Sea. The former is the better developed.

**French Somaliland.** This French territory is located on the Gulf of Aden and the Strait of Bab-el-Mandeb. Its chief city, Djibouti, Ethiopia's principal outlet, is a free port and the terminus of the railroad from Addis Ababa.

**British Somaliland.** Known officially as the Somaliland Protectorate, this British possession stretches along most of the south shore of the Gulf of Aden. A hot, dry land, the grazing of camels, goats, and sheep is the principal occupation.

**Somalia.** At present Somalia is a United Nations trust territory under the guidance of the Italians. It is to become an independent nation in 1960. Like people in the other countries of this area, the Somalians are largely pastoral and supplement their income by collecting gums and resins. Agriculture is limited to the area near streams where irrigation can be practiced. Mogadiscio is the capital and one of the two chief ports. The country has no good natural harbors.

## East African Plateaus

The countries of the East African Plateaus—Kenya, Uganda, and Tanganyika—cover an area of about 679,000 square miles and are occupied by approximately 19 million people. Among these, 110,000 are Europeans; another 125,000 are Indians and Arabs. The regional boundaries extend inland from the Indian Ocean to the line of the westernmost rift valleys. The area is characterized by high plateaus which have broad expanses of level or nearly level surfaces. Elevation gives the plateaus relatively cool temperatures for an equatorial location. The moderate temperatures and healthful conditions have attracted about 30,000 white settlers, most of whom are merchants or operators of stock ranches and plantations. The labor, however, is done largely by Africans. In Kenya, friction has developed between the whites and the native Africans who have no real share in the government. Uganda is a British protectorate in which the Africans are nearly self-governing. Kenya is a British colony; Tanganyika is governed by the British as a United Nations trust territory.

The plateaus rise from the coastal lowlands in great terraces which are 30 to 125 miles in width. The highest elevations are immediately east and west of Lake Victoria and along the Tanganyika-Rhodesian boundary. The rift valleys, 20 to 40 miles wide, descend steeply a thousand feet or more below the plateau surfaces and are occupied by elongated lakes. The western rift contains Lakes Tanganyika, Kivu, Edward, and Albert, and the eastern rift has numerous small lakes between Lake Rudolf in Kenya and Lake Nyasa to the south.

Much of East Africa is sparsely populated, the Africans consisting of Hamites and small isolated groups of quite primitive Negroes. Some of the Africans are milpa farmers, others depend almost wholly on cattle, and some combine livestock with farming. The presence of the tsetse fly in the wet areas prevents such localities from keeping cattle. Often, the uncertainty of rainfall and the overgrazing of grasslands make life precarious for whole villages. Insect pests and wild animals, especially lions and leopards, are a constant menace to native herds. The native kraal, with its thatched huts surrounded by a thorn fence, affords some protection from predators. The demand for laborers by the white operators of coastal plantations, for road and railroad building, and for work in the mines has reduced the number of men of working age in some areas to the danger point for the local economy. Villages sometimes have an insufficient number of young men to care for the livestock and provide food.

Along the coast live the mixed type called Swahili, large numbers of Arabs, and Indians who operate stores, provide skilled labor, and control much of the business. Concentrations of white farmers are found in the high plateaus and on the gentle lower slopes of the volcanic peaks in Kenya.

Several factors limit economic development in the East African Plateaus. Transportation is inadequate. Two railroads from the coast penetrate the interior from seaports, but they are not linked together. One from Mombasa into Uganda has several spur lines serving areas north of Lake Victoria. The other, extending from Dar es Salaam to Lake Tanganyika, has a spur line north to Lake Victoria. Kenya has practically no all-weather roads. Roads are usually deep in mud or dust, depending upon whether the season is wet or dry. The roads in Uganda are somewhat better. Only a few small ships navigate the larger lakes. Labor for the plantations is inadequate and usually must be secured from the more isolated areas. Although Africans can learn to operate machinery fairly well, they are not adept in maintenance. Diamonds and gold have been discovered but much remains to be learned about the region's mineral wealth.

**Uganda.** This plateau country north of Lake Victoria has an elevation of 3,500 to 4,000 feet, with many higher mountains near the eastern and western borders. As the rainfall decreases from Lake Victoria northward, there is a corresponding change in the natural vegetation from rain forest to open savanna. In the 94,000 square miles of Uganda are about 5 million people. There are only 7,600 Europeans, mostly British. Of these 1,200 are missionaries. Many schools and a university have been established.

In Uganda, where most of the land is owned by the Africans, the people are largely sedentary farmers. Such food crops as bananas, millet, corn, and rice are raised. There is some tobacco and sugar cane production but most of the remaining land is in cotton, usually grown on 5-acre plots. A few white planters produce coffee, tea, and rubber. Cotton is the chief export of the country, with coffee second in importance. Marketing of these crops is handled through cooperatives under government auspices.

On the Nile River, north of Lake Victoria, a dam for power development is operated at Owen Falls. This is of interest to Uganda, the Sudan, and Egypt since, by raising the level of the dam, it could provide power for manufacturing and at the same time help control the flow of the Nile. Irrigation in both the Sudan and Egypt would be aided by the storage and more even discharge of Nile waters. There is a public agency, the Uganda Development Corporation, Ltd., which is in charge of much of the planning and economic development. It operates a cement plant, handles the marketing of fish, runs the hotel in Entebbe, one of the dual capitals (the other is Kampala, the site of a university), and is in charge of mining and other projects.

**Kenya.** The interior of this British colony, consists of plateaus, low near the coastal plain but higher inland, where they range in elevation from 1,600 to more than 6,000 feet. Towering above the plateaus in some places are high volcanic peaks. About 60 per cent of the north and northeastern part is dry steppe and savanna. The rainier areas are on the coast near Mombasa, around Lake Victoria, and the mountain peaks in the south and west.

Kenya is more than twice as large as Uganda, but because of its aridity has only a slightly larger population. Most of the people are concentrated near the southern border of the country between Lake Victoria and Mombasa. Of the 5.9 million people, 30,000 are Europeans. The white settlers live mainly in Nairobi and on the nearby high plateaus. People of Arab and Indian descent, numbering nearly 125,000, live in Mombasa and the neighboring coastal region.

Agriculture is the principal wealth of Kenya. European settlers control a little less than one-fourth of the arable land, most of which is on the uplands along the main line of the railroad.

Coffee, sisal, tea, and cereals are the principal commercial crops of the European-owned estates. Native agriculture includes maize, the principal food crop, livestock, vegetables, and potatoes. Commerce and the small amount of manufacturing that is done is generally in the hands of Indians or Arabs.

Nairobi, on the plateau, and the seaport and rail terminal of Mombasa are the principal cities. Nairobi is the capital of Kenya and the headquarters for outfitting big game hunting parties. The city is also a major airport.

**Tanganyika.** The largest country in the East African Plateaus is Tanganyika. It covers almost 50 per cent of the total region, but is the most sparsely settled, having less than one-third of the total population. Much of the country is almost uninhabited. Tanganyika has a narrow, coral-fringed coastal plain from which the surface rises over steep escarpments to the interior high plateaus. This makes highway and railroad construction difficult, only dirt roads being found in the interior. The highest lands and numerous volcanic mountain peaks are in the area north of Lake Nyasa, extending northward along the line of the rifts. Mt. Kilimanjaro, the highest mountain in Africa, is near the Tanganyika-Kenya border.

Many of the physical factors have an adverse effect upon economic development. The humid climates along the tropical coast are enervating, whereas lands having cooler, rainy climates in the highlands are limited. Not much good soil is available, the land frequently being rough and rocky, and often areas of the better soil are hard to reach over poor roads. Rainfall on the plateau, usually not more than 30 inches a year, is very irregular and generally there is a long dry season.

The nonnatives in Tanganyika are comparatively few, 15,000 whites and about 37,000 Arabs in a total population of over 7 million. The largest native populations are in the vicinity of Lake Victoria, along the Kenya border, and along the railway line.

Agriculture is the principal economic activity of the territory although mining developments are outstanding. The most important agricultural enterprise is the production of sisal on lower lands near the coast. This commodity accounts for more than half the value of the country's exports and in recent years has been equal to three-fourths of the value of imports. Coffee and native cotton are of importance on the northern uplands and plateaus. Many Africans are cattle raisers and hides and skins are exported, but the tsetse fly prevents livestock production near wet forests. Native farmers grow sunflowers for seed, peanuts, sugar, and rice. Minerals were unimportant until recent discoveries of gold and diamonds. The diamond mines, located about 100 miles south of Lake Victoria, have had an extremely rapid development, in recent years accounting for 10 per cent of the world's production of these gems. A little copper and lead are mined.

Three rail lines extend inland from the coast but only one, and that of narrow gauge, crosses the country to reach Lake Tanganyika. A branch line extends northward to Lake Victoria. Dar es Salaam is the principal port city and terminus of the main railroad.

**Zanzibar.** This sultanate includes the islands of Zanzibar and Pemba. The population of 247,000 is a racial mixture including Africans, Arabs, Indians, and other Asiatics. The humid, rainy climate is not attractive to Europeans. Cloves, the most valuable crop, account for over two-thirds of the value of exports. Copra and coconut oil make up another 10 per cent.

## Southern Africa

Southern Africa lies to the south of Central Africa and the East African Plateaus. The region has an area of about 1.8 million square miles with a population of about 28 million people. The Union of South Africa, with the territory of Southwest Africa, Mozambique, and the British Federation of Rhodesia and Nyasaland are all included.

Southern Africa consists largely of high plateaus and basins which, along the outer margins, descend abruptly to narrow coastal plains. Cooler climates than in most of the rest of Africa have made the region more suitable for settlement by Europeans. The average population density is 18 persons per square mile as

*Figure 12-15   Types of Moslem merchants from Asia who live in the coastal towns bordering the Indian Ocean. (Courtesy of Portuguese Embassy.)*

compared with 16 for the continent as a whole. On the other hand, over 12 per cent of the population is nonnative, which is several times the proportion for the balance of Africa. The per capita foreign trade of Southern Africa, except for Mozambique, is generally three to ten times that of the rest of the continent. Seventy per cent of the exports are minerals or manufactured metal products; the remaining exports are mostly agricultural and animal products.

Coastal plains and lowlands are narrow or nonexistent except in Mozambique. The land rises in steep, step-like escarpments to elevations of 5,000 to 10,000 feet. The interior plateaus descend more gradually to interior basins which, in northern Bechuanaland, are less than 2,000 feet above sea level creating an area of interior drainage and salt marshes. East from Victoria Falls the gorge of the Zambezi River, bordered by deeply dissected terrain, continues to the coastal plain in Mozambique.

Climates along the east coasts, in Mozambique, are humid with tropical temperatures although there are subtropical temperatures to the south in the province of Natal, Union of South Africa. Cool temperatures generally prevail in the interior except at elevations below 3,000 feet. Warm season monthly averages of 70°F are common on the higher plateaus, but frosts may occur there during the cool season from May to November. Inland, rainfall of 35 to 40 inches annually occurs in the north and east, but deserts and dry steppes with less than 10 inches of rain occupy most of the interior and west coasts. The rainfall of these dry areas is seasonal and very uncertain. The Zambezi is the only large river of Southern Africa that maintains a significant year-round flow. Other streams, of which the Orange River is the largest, become almost completely dry part of the year. A small part of the southern coast, near Capetown, has a climate of the Mediterranean type.

Interior Southern Africa has a rainfall of about 20 inches annually which is sufficient for some grain production. Unfortunately droughts occur and then the yields of grains are halved,

grass for sheep and cattle is scant, springs and water holes go dry, and everyone suffers from the water shortage. An attempt is being made to solve the water problem. Water resources surveys are being made, including a study of the location of sites for dams. Erosion is another problem in South Africa. Much of the rainfall comes in torrential storms and the run-off from row crops carries away soil and seriously gullies the fields. The resulting decline in production causes men to break up more sod and plant corn where often the land is steeper and erodes faster, thus the problem becomes worse. Control of erosion and an adequate supply of water are dual problems for the farmer.

Those parts of the interior and west coast that are arid hold little promise for economic development, except possibly the Okavanga Delta where surveys for reclamation are being made. These hot, arid lands are sparsely occupied by the primitive Bushmen and a few remaining Hottentots. Negro tribes live in some of the less arid parts, but have a precarious existence fighting drought, predatory animals, and insect pests which threaten both the native animals and crops.

Mineral resources—gold, diamonds, and others—as well as agricultural possibilities attract many Europeans to the Union of South Africa and the Rhodesias. The early pioneers settled first along the coast and then moved into the higher and cooler velds, bringing with them European cattle, sheep, and wheat. Along the coast they developed Mediterranean agriculture and started irrigation. Steep approaches to the interior from all coastal points makes railroads and highways difficult and expensive to build and operate. Only the most valuable products from the interior can afford the high cost of transportation.

**Union of South Africa.** Composed of the combined provinces of Natal, Cape of Good Hope, Orange Free State, and Transvaal, the Union of South Africa has nearly 48 per cent of the population, over 25 per cent of the area, and 65 per cent of the foreign trade of Southern Africa. Approximately 24 per cent of the total

*Figure 12-16 Scene in the Drakensberg uplands of South Africa. If conservation practices to control erosion on such rolling lands are needed and are beyond individual resources, the farmers may be aided by expert advice and heavy machinery furnished by the state. (Courtesy of Government Information Office, Union of South Africa.)*

population of nearly 13.9 millions in the Union of South Africa is non-native, including 2.9 million Europeans, mostly of Dutch and British extraction, and 400,000 Asiatics. About 9 per cent of the population is a mixture of native African, European, and Asiatic blood called Cape Colored. Native Africans number about 9.3 million. Native Africans are employed as unskilled workers, and some are farmers or herders on their own. Many still live under tribal organization in reservations. The natives own several millions each of cattle, sheep, and goats. However, the general low social, political, and economic status of the native Africans and colored people is a cause for much unrest and constitutes one of the country's important problems.

The Union of South Africa is a bilingual state. Persons of European descent speak English or Afrikaans, a dialect derived from Dutch and other languages. Those of Dutch origin, formerly the Boers, and now called Afrikaners, are primarily ranchers and farmers. The British are chiefly engaged in commercial activities. The Union of South Africa is the most powerful country in Africa in which people of European descent live permanently as farmers and workmen and control the state politically. The Union is a self-governing member of the British Commonwealth of Nations.

The topography both favors and hinders development. The steep rise of several thousand feet from the coastal ports to the interior plateaus constitutes a serious problem in the development of adequate and efficient transporta-

tion. In the eastern part of the country are the Drakensberg Mountains which extend for 700 miles in a general northeast-southwest direction. A few of the peaks exceed 10,000 feet in elevation. Although temperature conditions generally favor European settlement, rainfall for about half of the country is either too little or very uncertain. Extensive grasslands and the absence of serious tsetse fly infestation favors grazing, but pests, disease, and uncertain rainfall over wide areas make the industry unprofitable in some years. The great annual variation of flow in the plateau streams limits both irrigation and hydroelectric development in the Union. The sudden and violent nature of much of the rainfall results in rapid runoff, serious soil erosion, formation of deep gullies, and sudden floods on the rivers.

The economic development of the country is dominated by the mining, processing, and manufacturing of metals. Gold, uranium, and diamonds are the principal minerals exported, but copper, chrome, manganese, and many others are also mined. Some iron and steel is manufactured in the southern Transvaal and Natal near the chief coal mines. South Africa lacks petroleum but some oil is obtained by the liquefaction of coal.

In the Transvaal is the world's greatest gold mining zone, the Witwatersrand, which is usually referred to as the Rand. Since its discovery in 1886, the Rand has produced over 3 billion pounds sterling in gold and its average annual output is worth about 460 million dollars. Gold accounts for about 60 per cent of the export value of the Union of South Africa. Uranium is now being secured by reworking tailings from the mills after the gold has been extracted. The principal city of the Rand is Johannesburg which, with its suburbs, has a population of almost a million persons. The city is the largest mining center in the world, and resembles a big American city with its tall buildings and dense automobile traffic, but the many hills of debris show the source of its wealth. Coal used in the power plants for generating electricity is brought in from Natal. Although some food is grown in the vicinity, much more must be brought in from other parts of the country or imported from abroad.

Diamonds were first discovered at Kimberley in 1867. Until 1908, when diamonds were found in Southwest Africa, the Union of South Africa had a monopoly. Since that date, these valuable stones have been discovered in many parts of the continent. The famous Kimberley mine, often said to be the largest man-made hole in the earth, was abandoned in 1915. The largest active diamond mine in South Africa at present is the Premier near Pretoria. Diamonds make up about 4 per cent of the total value of goods exported, being exceeded by both wool and gold.

Agriculture is varied, but animal products predominate in the export trade, with wool commonly accounting for nearly a quarter of the total value of exports. The coastal regions of Natal produce subtropical fruits, vegetables, and sugar cane for domestic use and export; near the coast of Cape Province, with its cooler winters, wheat, grapes for wine, and livestock are the chief products. Irrigation in the southern valleys of the Cape Province is aiding the production of fruit and vegetables. Vineyards and citrus groves are of importance. Dairying and pig raising are increasing in both the coastal and interior parts of the Union. Farms in the coastal regions and on adjoining plateau slopes frequently exceed 1,000 acres and are owned by Europeans. Agriculture in the dry interior is dominated by sheep and cattle grazing. Afrikaners prefer ranching to other occupations, and have occupied most of the lands best suited for livestock. They own 6 million cattle, 33 million sheep, 1.8 million goats, and 1.5 million horses. Wool, of which about 300 million pounds are annually exported, is the

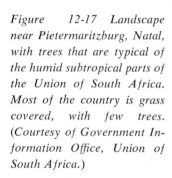

*Figure 12-17 Landscape near Pietermaritzburg, Natal, with trees that are typical of the humid subtropical parts of the Union of South Africa. Most of the country is grass covered, with few trees. (Courtesy of Government Information Office, Union of South Africa.)*

*Figure 12-18 Capetown is situated between the harbor and Table Mountain. Table Mountain has its familiar "tablecloth" indicating a strong southeast wind. (Courtesy Government Information Office, Union of South Africa.)*

most valuable farm product. Their ranches may occupy thousands of acres and employ scores of natives. The high velds, in the eastern part of Orange Free State and Transvaal, have enough moisture for the crops of wheat, corn, and grain sorghum that are grown extensively by both natives and Europeans. Tobacco is a cash crop of local importance. Unfortunately, since little attention has been paid to either soil conservation or the rotation of crops, the soils are badly eroded and depleted.

Manufacturing, although an infant industry in the Union of South Africa, has increased greatly since World War II. Government capital invested in power development, transportation facilities, and selected industries has been augmented by large investments from the United States and Western Europe. Expansion has taken place in almost all lines of manufacturing, but some of the most noteworthy is in iron and steel production, machinery and motor manufacturing assembly, electrical equipment, textiles, clothing, chemicals, and building materials.

In spite of the difficulty of mounting the high steep edges of the plateau, road and rail transportation facilities are better developed in the Union of South Africa than in most of Africa.

Three main railroads reach the coast and link the ports of Capetown, Durban, and Port Elizabeth with important mining and commercial cities of the interior such as Kimberley, Pretoria, Johannesburg, and Bloemfontein. Railroads and highway networks serve the interior and coastal regions and connect with the continental trunk-line railways. Johannesburg and Pretoria are connected by rail to Lourenço Marques, and the rail line inland from Capetown extends northward into Rhodesia.

The larger cities and many of the smaller ones have good airports and are served by regular airlines. The seaports of Capetown, Port Elizabeth, and Durban are also important for food processing and the manufacturing of a variety of products including machinery and clothing. East London is a noted seaside resort and port. Pretoria and Capetown are dual capitals of the Union: Pretoria, the administrative center; Capetown, where parliament sits. Bloemfontein has the supreme court. In the eastern Transvaal, the Kruger National Park has been established for the preservation of the native African animals that were threatened with extinction. Tourism is increasing, although still small by European standards.

The Union of South Africa faces many problems, including soil erosion and efficient development of its resources, but the outstanding one is racial relations. The government has adopted a policy called *Apartheid,* meaning "separateness," which emphasizes race segregation. No native or colored person can vote and there are other restrictions and discriminations favoring the white people. Broad-minded wisdom is needed to reduce the tensions which have developed.

Southwest Africa, a former German colony, was given under mandate by the League of Nations to the Union of South Africa, which has retained control and refuses to accept trusteeship for the territory from the United Nations. The country occupies over 300,000 square miles of arid land. Its narrow coastal lowland is bordered by a highland which rises abruptly several thousand feet before descending eastward toward the Kalahari Basin. There are no permanent surface streams. Away from the coastal deserts, the vegetation is bush or sparse grasses. Population density is about 1.5 persons per square mile. Grazing sheep, goats, and some cattle is the chief occupation. Many minerals are known to exist in quantity but, except for diamonds found in placer deposits and one mine which produces copper, the output is small. Walvis Bay, a small enclave of British territory with an excellent harbor, is bordered on all land fronts by Southwest Africa and is administered by the government of that country.

**High Commission Territories of South Africa.** Bechuanaland, Basutoland, and Swaziland are territories under the direct protection of the British government in London and known as the High Commission Territories. Basutoland, in the southern edge of the Drakensberg Mountains, is completely surrounded by the Union of South Africa. Swaziland is in the southeastern part of the Transvaal but also borders Mozambique. Each of these territories is relatively densely populated being, to some extent, reservations for native Africans. The principal occupation in each is agriculture; maize and kaffir corn are the leading crops. Bechuanaland, a

*Figure 12-19   View of downtown Johannesburg and some of its high buildings taken from Johann Rissik Bridge over the new railway station. (Courtesy of Government Information Office, Union of South Africa.)*

territory larger than the state of Texas, has a population of slightly more than one per square mile. The southern half of the country is the arid Kalahari Basin; in the northern part are salt marshes that occasionally overflow into the Zambezi River. A part of this vast area is used for grazing. In these three countries approximately 99 per cent of the people are natives.

**Federation of Rhodesia and Nyasaland.**
Northern and Southern Rhodesia, together with
Nyasaland Protectorate, constitute the Federation of Rhodesia and Nyasaland. Rolling uplands, mostly between 3,000 and 5,000 feet
above sea level, are the usual surface features.
The Zambezi River separates Northern from
Southern Rhodesia with much of this boundary
being the gorge below Victoria Falls. Although
between 8 and 22° south latitude, the elevation is sufficient to minimize the tropical temperatures in most of the Rhodesias. Rainfall is
seasonal, most of the area receiving less than
5 inches of rain from April to September, but
from 10 to 40 inches during the rainy season,
November to May. Tree and grass savannas are
the common vegetation type.

The population of the Rhodesias exceeds 4
million, only 5 per cent being of European extraction. The average density is about 10 persons per square mile, which is less than that of
Africa as a whole and considerably below that
of the Union of South Africa. The Africans
are principally pastoralist-farmers, but many
work on European-owned farms, or in factories and mines. As in other parts of Southern
Africa, transportation and procurement of native labor constitutes somewhat of a problem
in mining and industrial areas as well as during
crop harvests. Of the 180,000 Europeans, 75
per cent are in Southern Rhodesia, most of
them living in such cities as Salisbury and Bula-
wayo. Livingstone is the largest city in Northern Rhodesia.

Mining provides the most important exports
and the principal commercial development in
Northern Rhodesia. The copper belt in the
north, near the Katanga district of the Belgian
Congo, produces copper along with some zinc,
cobalt, and vanadium. Minerals, mostly copper, account for nearly 95 per cent of the total
exports of Northern Rhodesia. In Southern
Rhodesia mining, chiefly of asbestos and
chrome, supplies about 16 per cent of the exports. Coal and iron deposits are the basis for
a small local iron and steel industry. About 300
miles downstream from Victoria Falls, the high
Kariba Dam and hydroelectric plant is being

constructed. Power from the project will be of
great aid to mining and industrial activities in
the Federation.

Agriculture includes a variety of staple
crops, and livestock is raised for domestic use.
Tobacco is the largest single item in the export
trade of Southern Rhodesia and is the main
cash crop of the European farmers. Cattle hides
are also exported. Manufacturing, which includes food processing, is largely for local use,
only small amounts of manufactures being exported.

Rail transportation, especially for Africa, is
relatively well developed. The Rhodesias have
rail connections to Benguela on the Atlantic
Ocean, Elizabethville in the Belgian Congo,
Beira in Mozambique, and the rail network of
the Union of South Africa. In addition, Southern Rhodesia has several branch lines into the
interior of the country.

Nyasaland occupies high plateaus and mountains, generally above 5,000 feet, along the
western shore of Lake Nyasa. It also borders
the Rift Valley and the low, unhealthy Shire
River valley, south of the lake. Isolation has
limited development, but plantations produce
important amounts of tea, tobacco, and tung
oil which, together, account for 80 per cent of
the exports. A few white settlers own over a
million acres of the best land. Native food
crops include rice, millet, peanuts, and beans.
About 5,000 Europeans, mostly working for
the government or managing plantations, are
lost among the 2.5 million Africans.

**Mozambique.** This Portuguese province on
the east African coast has a lower average elevation than the rest of Southern Africa. Its
nearly 300,000 square miles are bisected by the
Zambezi River, the land to the south of the river seldom being higher than 600 feet. The flat
deltas of the Zambezi, Sabi, and Limpopo Rivers are a part of the low coastal plains. Rolling
hills extend inland to the borders of the Transvaal and Southern Rhodesia. In the north, east
of Lake Nyasa, the broad coastal plain rises to
plateaus and mountains that exceed 6,000 feet.
The rainfall is seasonal but the warm ocean

water helps keep the relative humidity high during all the year. The vegetation is mostly savanna except for mangrove swamps along the coast.

The population density, nearly 20 per square mile, is above the average for Africa, but out of a total population of 5.6 million only 50,000 are Europeans. Native agriculture produces corn as the main food crop, with peanuts, bananas, and fruits supplementing the diet. Commercial production of tea, cotton, sisal, sugar, and cashew nuts accounts for 70 per cent of the export trade. Besides shipping exports originating in Mozambique, the ports of Beira and Lourenço Marques are important outlets for Southern Rhodesia and the Transvaal; 75 per cent of their commerce comes from these areas. This transit business balances the trade of Mozambique and is responsible for the flourishing business in the two principal ports of the country. British interests built the railroad to Beira from the Rhodesias. The British also have sizable business interests in Mozambique. Lourenço Marques is the chief port for Johannesburg and the whole Transvaal whose trade accounts for three-fourths of the shipments to and from the port.

## African Islands

Many small islands, some in groups like the Cape Verde or the Madeira, others isolated like Ascension and St. Helena, have significance. The island of greatest area near Africa is Madagascar, which is the fourth largest island in the world.

**Madagascar.** The largest of the African islands, Madagascar, is approximately 1,000 miles long and has an area of about 241,000 square miles. The island has been part of the French overseas empire for more than half a century. Except for a few African Negroes of mixed blood living along the west coast, the ancestors of Madagascar's 4.4 million people originated in southern and southeastern Asia rather than in Africa. The natives, called Malagasy, are not of Negro stock but are related to the Malays and Polynesians.

Topographically the island is a series of plateaus and mountains that attain elevations of 3,000 to over 6,000 feet. Eastward these highlands descend abruptly to a narrow coastal plain. The eastward-flowing streams are turbulent and occupy steep ravines and gorges. The westward descent is over broad plateaus, descending in step-like formation to the sandy coastal plains. The low altitude location causes tropical temperatures which range between 70 and 80°F along the coast but are 10 to 15° cooler on the interior plateaus. The east coast has an annual rainfall in excess of 60 inches. West of the mountains, rainfall is seasonal and varies between 40 and 60 inches. The southwest lowlands have less than 20 inches of precipitation and are almost desert. Although most of the island was probably once

*Figure 12-20 A broad avenue in Lourenço Marques, the chief seaport of Mozambique. Note the large windows and the porches on the buildings planned for tropical living, the many automobiles, and the modern bus. (Courtesy of Portuguese Embassy.)*

well forested, migratory native agriculture and the burning for pasture have reduced much of the vegetation to a steppe-savanna type.

The island is not industrially developed. Rice is the principal item in the native diet. Corn, cassava, yams, and beans are also produced. Cattle, raised in the savanna lands, are the principal domesticated animal. The ancient rocks of Madagascar, similar to those of the African continent, yield few minerals in commercial quantities. Gold, graphite, mica, and semiprecious stones are the most important. A few minerals, in addition to small amounts of vanilla, rice, and forest products, are exported. Tamatave, the principal seaport, is on the east coast. A 150-mile long railroad connects the port with Tananarive, the capital and the center of an important interior agricultural district.

**Small Islands.** Far out in the Indian Ocean are the Mascarene Islands among which is Mauritius, famous for its production of sugar cane and a colony of Great Britain. Réunion Island is a French possession. The Seychelles, a group of 92 small islands north of Madagas-car, are a British possession.

In the North Atlantic Ocean are the Portuguese-owned Madeira Islands and the Spanish-owned Canary Islands, both famed for wine. The Canary Islands grow and export quantities of bananas. Both island groups are densely populated. Farther south are the Cape Verde Islands which also belong to Portugal. All of these islands are of volcanic origin. In the South Atlantic are the lonely British islands of Ascension and St. Helena. Few people now live on either, but in the days of sailing ships they were ports of call to secure fresh water and vegetables. During World War II, Ascension was a base and refueling station for aircraft flying between Natal in Brazil and Africa.

In the Gulf of Guinea about 125 miles offshore, the Portuguese islands of São Tome and Principi are important for exports of cacao. The islands have about 60,000 inhabitants on their 375 square miles of land and are governed as a province of Portugal. Included as a part of Spanish Guinea is the volcanic island of Fernando Po, another cacao producer near the shore in the Bight of Biafra.

### IN PERSPECTIVE

*Emerging Africa*

During the nineteenth century Central and Southern Africa passed from rule by native tribal governments to rule by the Western powers which established colonies and protectorates. In this process little attention was paid to claims of the tribes and adequate payment was seldom made. As the Africans were farmers, the loss of land was a serious matter to them. Native occupations of subsistence farming and herding were frequently replaced by the development of mines, the exploitation of forest resources, and the starting of plantations. Although sometimes Africans owned and operated farms producing raw materials and foodstuffs for export, generally Westerners managed such operations, paid the natives low wages, and retained most of the profits. In some colonies like Nigeria, Uganda, and the Belgian Congo, settlement and ownership of farmland by Europeans was discouraged; in other cases, as in Kenya, the Rhodesias, and the Union of South Africa, a large share of the best land is occupied by whites, and rapidly increasing populations of Africans are unable to secure farmland sufficient for their needs.

Overturning of their manner of life and slow adjustment to changing conditions are discouraging to millions of natives. Memories of centuries of slave raids, the operation of color line or racial discrimination in some countries, and the usual great disparity between wages paid natives and whites, which result in tremendous differences in living standards, have made Africans restless, resentful of the governing powers, nationalistic, and ready to assert the right of Africans to govern themselves. Ghana and the Sudan have been established as self-governing countries. Nigeria and Somalia are soon to become self-governing. All Portuguese territories have become provinces of Portugal. In the Belgian Congo there is no political participation by anyone, white or Negro. Negroes, however, are not barred from certain government jobs because of color.

More than 90 per cent of the native inhabitants of central and southern Africa are illiterate, and only in selected areas do the Africans appear ready for self-government. Yet many natives believe that the way to learn self-government is to try to practice it. Such political transitions create difficult problems for both Africans and nonnatives as is shown by guerilla raids by the Mau Mau society of natives against the British in Kenya during the early 1950s and the segregation problem in the Union of South Africa.

Europeans have helped raise the status of native Africans by improving health and sanitation, stopping tribal warfare and most ritual killings, usually establishing honest and efficient government, and providing considerable opportunities for improving the standard of living. Millions of Africans have abandoned tribal living and now dwell in cities and other communities that offer employment, but wages are very low, 50 cents or less per day. Naturally, most Africans can buy little from abroad. Teaching is done in the language of the colonial powers, although the Bible or parts of it are published in more than 300 native tongues.

Not only are many Africans illiterate and living under primitive conditions, but the continent as a whole is backward and, in many ways, underdeveloped. South of the Sahara, railroad mileage is only 3 or 4 per cent of the world's total, highways are generally very poor, and over large areas are entirely lacking. Although Central and Southern Africa produce 55 per cent of the world's output of gold, 98 per cent of the gem diamonds, 22 per cent of the copper, 65 per cent of the cacao, and 60 per cent of the world's palm oil, as well as many other items, the region's share of the world's total export of raw materials is under 3 per cent. The great majority of manufactured goods are imported. Imports include machinery, hardware, steel, and other metal goods, cotton textiles, clothing, drugs and chemicals, petroleum products, and much flour and processed foodstuffs.

As a whole, Africans are poorly nourished and their calorie intake is hardly half that of an average American. Improvement in food supplies and standards of living are greatly needed. There is almost no manufacturing although Africa has the largest potential water power resource of any continent. The continent has problems of soil erosion, crop diversification, and control of pests and diseases affecting cultivated crops, domestic animals, and man. Africa is in a process of transition, economically and politically.

## EXERCISES

*1.* What race of people makes up the major part of the population of Central and Southern Africa? In which part of the area are these people most numerous? Why is there such a variety of languages among them?

*2.* In what ways does the climate of Central Africa differ from that of Southern Africa? What are the advantages and disadvantages of each for agriculture and industry?

*3.* Which nations in the area are independent? Which European nations have colonies in this part of Africa? Politically how does the Union of South Africa differ from the other countries?

*4.* What are the principal physical features of the Congo Basin? How does this basin differ from the topography of Ethiopia? In what ways has each influenced the economic activities of the people living in the area?

*5.* What do the terms graben, veld, and land delta mean? Where are examples of each located?

*6.* Why is South Africa more advanced economically than the other countries? Why is there a great cultural contrast between the peoples of this country? In what ways has the economy of the country caused this contrast to become more marked? Does a majority or a minority rule?

7. What are the principal mineral products of Central and Southern Africa? Where are the chief areas of production? Why are the natives an essential factor in the mineral economy?

8. What are the chief agricultural activities of the area? How does cultivation here differ from that in Greece or the United States? What are the handicaps to agricultural production?

9. How do the villages in this area differ from villages in the United States, Libya, and the Soviet Union? What causes these differences?

10. What are five large, modern cities in Central and South Africa? How do they resemble and how do they differ from European and American cities?

11. What are the principal problems facing the people and countries of this region? What attempts are being made to solve some of them? What are the principal handicaps to their solution?

12. What are chief minerals mined in the Union of South Africa? Where are the principal mining districts located?

13. What is especially noteworthy about the development of the people in Uganda, Ghana, and Nigeria?

14. What are the principal problems of the independent nations of Ethiopia and Liberia?

## SELECTED REFERENCES

Brookfield, H. C.: "New Railroad and Port Developments in East and Central Africa," *Economic Geography,* 31:60–70, January, 1955.

Hance, William A., and Irene S. von Dorgen: "Lourenço Marques in Delagoa Bay," *Economic Geography,* 33:229–256, July, 1957.

Howell, P. P.: "The Equatorial Nile Project and Its Effects in the Sudan," *Geographical Journal,* 119:33–48, March, 1953.

Kuo, Leslie T. C.: "Ethiopia," *Focus,* 5(10):1–6, June, 1955.

Light, R. U.: *Focus on Africa,* The American Geographical Society, New York, 1944.

Marshall, Anthony D.: "Somalia: A United Nations Experiment," *Focus,* 6(8):1–6, April, 1956.

Mitchell, N. C.: "Nigeria," *Focus,* 4(7):1–6, March, 1954.

Roucek, Joseph S.: "Liberia," *Journal of Geography,* 54:407–413, November, 1955.

Scott, Peter: "The Witwatersrand Gold Field," *Geographical Review,* 41:561–589, October, 1951.

Stamp, L. Dudley: *Africa, a Study in Tropical Development,* John Wiley & Sons, Inc., New York, 1953.

Thomas, Benjamin E.: "The Legend of Timbuktu," *Journal of Geography,* 55:434–441, December, 1956.

Thorne, Jr., Samuel, and Alice Taylor: "Union of South Africa," *Focus,* 4(2):1–6, October, 1953.

Trewartha, Glen T., and Wilbur Zelinsky: "Population Patterns in Tropical Africa," *Annals of the Association of American Geographers,* 44:135–156, June, 1954.

Wayland, E. J.: "More About the Kalahari," *Geographical Journal,* 119:49–56, March, 1953.

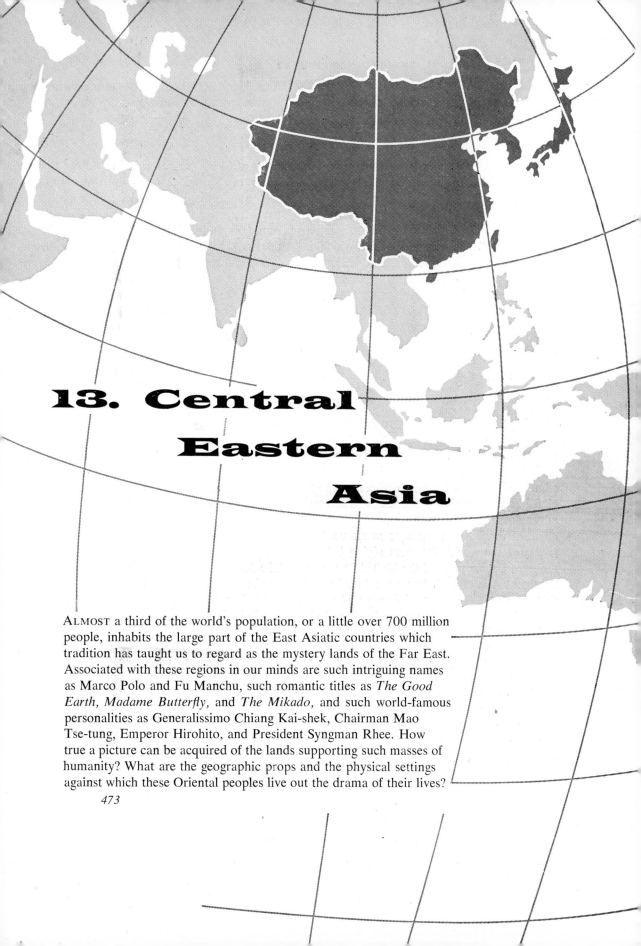

# 13. Central
# Eastern
# Asia

ALMOST a third of the world's population, or a little over 700 million people, inhabits the large part of the East Asiatic countries which tradition has taught us to regard as the mystery lands of the Far East. Associated with these regions in our minds are such intriguing names as Marco Polo and Fu Manchu, such romantic titles as *The Good Earth, Madame Butterfly,* and *The Mikado,* and such world-famous personalities as Generalissimo Chiang Kai-shek, Chairman Mao Tse-tung, Emperor Hirohito, and President Syngman Rhee. How true a picture can be acquired of the lands supporting such masses of humanity? What are the geographic props and the physical settings against which these Oriental peoples live out the drama of their lives?

How, clear of the cobwebs of mystery and romance, can one discern the true culture, livelihood, and activity in which the people of these East Asiatic countries engage?

## REGIONAL CHARACTER

Eastern Asia has three parts which, by their cultural and historical development, form natural groupings. These are Northeastern Asia, which is in the Soviet realm, Southeastern Asia, which comprises the lands south of eastern China, and Central Eastern Asia, which includes China, Japan, Korea, and Mongolia. The term Far East, traditionally applied to Central Eastern Asia, has been an accepted misnomer for the region. This derives from concepts of geography dating to the time before Magellan proved the earth was round by sailing westward to the Far East. It is a term which no longer makes geographical sense.

### Situation

The situation of Central Eastern Asia is that of a continental land mass which merges into Central Asia in its west and which is fringed by great island arcs of the Pacific in its east. The climates vary from boreal to tropical. The region has commercial, economic, and strategic advantages. Commercially, the eastern parts lie adjacent to one of the major maritime trade routes of the world. Steamers plying between the great Pacific ports of the United States and Southeast Asia often follow a great circle route that runs past the coast of Japan and China. Korea does not have the same advantage in location, but it does not suffer the land-locked isolation of Mongolia. Strategically, this region is most significant. Its land surface is one-twelfth that of the entire world, whereas a quarter of the world's population is crowded on its more productive lands. In its north and west, the region is contiguous to the powerful Soviet Union; its eastern island chains and coasts command the west Pacific.

### Factors of Area and Geographic Shape

The four countries of this region differ in many respects, and these differences also apply to size and shape. The more than 3.5 million square miles of China contrast with the 85,000 square miles of Korea. Japan, with over 147,000 square miles, is less than one-fourth the size of the Mongolian People's Republic, which has some 606,000 square miles. Area, however, does not necessarily give any idea of capacity for population support. The significance of great area lies in the greater likelihood of mineral wealth and of greater agricultural variety, although it does not guarantee even this. Strategically, China's great area permits the use of space for defense in depth and for a certain amount of mobility. It has its disadvantages in the difficulties of communications.

In shape, China and the Mongolian People's Republic both are rather chunky blocks with relatively short boundaries in terms of the large area. By contrast, Japan and Korea are elongated countries that lend themselves to segmentation and outflanking movements militarily. They are chiefly maritime in situation, and their coast-line boundaries are long relative to their areas.

### Climate

The 35° latitudinal spread of China brings its northernmost limits to the latitude of southern Labrador; its southernmost territory reaches the latitude of Puerto Rico. Although Japan and Korea do not have such an enormous latitudinal stretch, their generally north-south elongations also bring with them much climatic variety. Certain common climatic influences are distinguishable in the region despite the climatic variety. The huge continental interior of China not only has great continental extremes itself, but also exerts far-reaching climatic effects upon maritime and peninsular neighbors to the east. In this effect, Mongolia shares the position of progenitor with the rest of the Central Asian heartland. It is the existence of this immense land surface, with its great capacities for heat radiation and absorption, that has brought about the influences creating what is known as the monsoon climate of Eastern Asia. It is a monsoon that differs from the Indian monsoon, however, in having dry, cold winter air masses as the dominant element.

## Natural Resources

Compared with North America and Northwestern Europe, Central Eastern Asia is faced with a general inadequacy of known resources for large-scale industrial development. There is limited variety in the more important deposits of mineral resources, but a few minerals are concentrated overwhelmingly in a few districts within the region. Most of this mineral wealth lies in China. In terms of accessible forest resources in this region, only Japan has large stands. China is the only one with large arable land resources, but because of the large population, that country resembles the others in having only small units of cultivable land per capita. China, Korea, and Japan have certain cultural similarities embodied in the written language, in Buddhist religion, in Confucian philosophy, and in the careful and intensive methods used for agriculture.

## CHINA

China, with nearly 600 million people, has approximately the same acreage of land under cultivation as the United States; yet it has a population over three times as great. Both natural and social factors have helped China become the most populous country in the world. Favorable natural factors include the large size of the country, the soil, climate, and native plants. There is a large amount of arable land, including fertile alluvial and loessal soils. Much of China has a long growing season and abundant rainfall, with maximum precipitation in the summer when it aids crops the most. More than 9,000 plant species have been described for China, nearly half of which are peculiar to that country. Many of these plants have been domesticated for food production. Social factors include early marriage and the desire for sons, the substitution of human labor for animal power, and the use of a grain and vegetable diet rather than animal products, so that little land is needed to grow fodder. The animals that supply most of the meat are pigs and poultry that are commonly fed scraps and refuse. On otherwise wasted land, ponds are used to raise bulbs and other water plants, fish, and ducks for food. Chinese are masters of irrigation, and in preserving and fertilizing soils to secure maximum yields, even though the pressure of population and lack of public responsibility have resulted in deforestation and erosion, especially in regions where the soil is a loess which erodes easily. The people are willing to toil long hours to support large families; they remain cheerful and reasonably healthy under crowded and often unsanitary living conditions that would be very depressing to Westerners.

## Relief Features

**Rivers.** China occupies the large eastern segment of the Eurasian land mass and shares in the radial system of river drainages running out from the elevated heart of the continent (Figure 13-1). Flowing northeastward and out of China into the Soviet Union's Pacific maritime province is the great Black Dragon River (Heilung Chiang) called the Amur by the Russians. While economically the main stream of the Heilung is of greater importance to the Russians than to the Chinese, its tributary, the Sungari (Sung-hua) is the most important river of Manchuria, draining the greater part of the Manchurian Plain.

The other great rivers of eastern China run in great bends and loops generally from west to east, emptying into one of the three seas bordering the China coast. The greatest of these rivers is the Yangtze Kiang (Yang-tzu Chiang), over 3,000 miles in length and navigable by steamboats for over half its course. It empties into the East China Sea near Shanghai. Some of

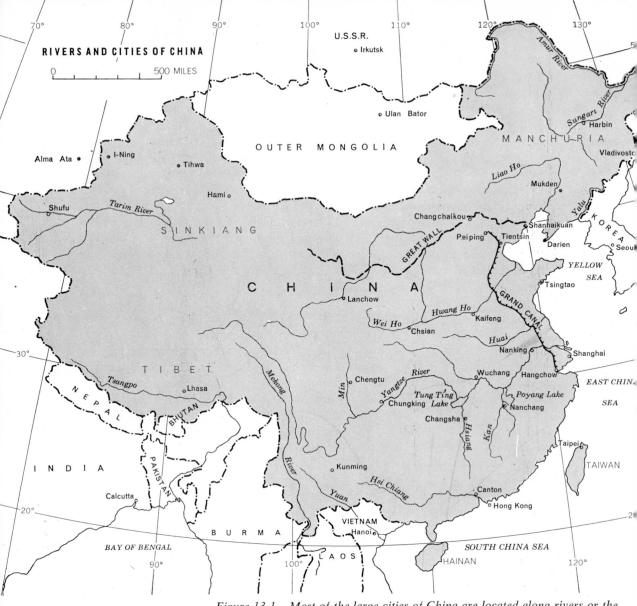

*Figure 13-1   Most of the large cities of China are located along rivers or the seacoast. Rivers form the principal means of transportation for heavy goods. They are also the source of much of the water used for irrigation in the densely settled rice-producing areas.*

its tributaries are 500 to 900 miles long and also rank as great rivers. Many are navigable by small boats for hundreds of miles.

Draining the southernmost provinces is the West River (Hsi Chiang), forming an important navigation net for the mountainous south where topography is difficult for road construction. The Hsi system brings the trade of the south to the commercial gates of Canton (Kuang-chou) and British Hong Kong.

In North China, the Yellow River (Huang Ho) long ages ago laid the silt that filled in the great arm of the sea that now is the Yellow Plain (Figure 13-2). Running out of arid regions and through a dry loessland of fine-particled, easily eroded soils, the Yellow River has created a standing invitation to land-hungry farmers to crowd its plain. At the same time, it has qualified this invitation by the misery it inflicts in frequent rampaging floods. Although a

*Figure 13-2  The geographic regions of China are numerous and have irregular shapes. Their boundaries are largely the result of physical factors.*

mighty river, the Yellow River's shifting channels and sand bars restrict its use as a navigable artery. Between the Yangtze and the Yellow Rivers runs the Hwai River (Huai Ho). The Hwai is significant in three important ways. It is a navigable stream. It coincides with and thus marks the climatic boundary between dry North China and humid South China. It occupies a low-lying trough in the southern part of the Yellow Plain and often receives Yellow River flood waters during major breaks in the south bank dike along Yellow River levees. Along the mountainous southeastern coast, rivers a few hundred miles long form small delta plains of local significance.

**The Great Plains.**  Although rivers form important arteries and bring both blessing and calamity to people in their drainage areas, the valley plains they have carved or deposited are of much greater significance for the livelihood of China's large population. The great plains of China are mainly in the north (Figure 13-2). In northeastern China (Manchuria) the depo-

**TABLE 13-1. CHINESE AND ENGLISH NAMES**

| Chinese | English |
| --- | --- |
| Ch'ang-sha | Changsha |
| Ch'in-ling | Tsinling |
| Ch'ing-tao | Tsingtao |
| Chou-Shan | Chusan |
| Ch'ung-ch'ing | Chungking |
| Hang-chou | Hangchow |
| Hei-lung Chiang | Black Dragon River |
| Hsi Chiang | West River |
| Hsia-men | Amoy |
| Hsin-chiang | Chinese Turkestan |
| Huang Ho | Yellow River |
| Kuang-chou | Canton |
| Kuei-chow | Kweichow |
| Lu-shun | Port Arthur |
| Nan-ching | Nanking |
| Pei-ching | Peking |
| Shang-hai | Shanghai |
| Shen-yang | Mukden |
| Ssu-ch'uan | Szechwan |
| Sung-hua | Sungari |
| Ta-lien | Dairen |
| T'ai-wan | Formosa |
| T'ien-ching | Tientsin |
| Wu-han | Hankow |
| Yang-tzu Chiang | Yangtze Kiang |

sitional Liao Ho plain of the south joins with the erosional plain of the Sungari (Sung-hua) over a hardly noticeable water divide and forms a continuous surface of some 138,000 square miles. The Liao Ho section is relatively level, with the Sungari section somewhat rolling.

Connected to the Liao Ho plain by a narrow corridor, which is crossed by the Great Wall at the seaport of Shanhaikwan (Shan-hai-kuan) the Yellow Plain runs southward without interruption around the Shantung hill country to merge with the Hwai and lower Yangtze River plains. With the Hwai as a southern boundary, this great plain covers an area of about 125,000 square miles, for the most part level and under 100 feet in elevation.

The Yangtze Plain, although of smaller extent, is more fragmented, more irregular in shape, and extends much farther inland. Its ap-

proximately 75,000 square miles of level surface include the central plains of the Tung Ting (T'ung-t'ing) and Poyang (P'o-yang) Lakes as well as the lower Yangtze Plain and the connecting corridors of lowland between them.

**The Mountainous South.**   South of the Yangtze the plain extends in narrow slivers up the river valleys to be closed in soon by hills of increasing elevations and ruggedness. Most of South China is in slope land so that level land for farming is restricted to narrow, scattered valleys and basins which total to a small percentage of the land surface. The largest of these alluvial farmlands occur along the coast.

Separating the Yangtze drainage from that of the Hsi (West River) and the small southeast coastal rivers is the great mountain system of the Nan-ling. Running out of northern Yünnan, it reaches eastward as the Ta-yü Range until about the 116th meridian east where the mountain system makes a northeastward bend and becomes the Wu-i Mountains. The general elevations of this Nan-ling system in the eastern sector is from 3,000 to 5,000 feet. From it the land slopes northward to the Yangtze Plain and southward to the Hsi River Plain. The latter comprises a network of narrow river floodplains until it fans out into its delta south and east of Canton, where the so-called Canton Delta spreads over almost 3,000 square miles, the largest plain south of the Yangtze Plain.

**The Western Plateaus and Basins.**   West of the great plains and the South China hill lands lies the greater part of China's territory. This vast western area generally comprises a number of large plateaus and basin lands of greatly differing characters. Occupying an immense area in the southern part of the far western reaches, the Tibetan High Plateau, averaging over 12,000 feet in elevation, is cold, forbidding, and sparsely populated. North of it the land drops down into the three great desert basins of Tsaidam, Tarim, and Dzungaria. The first is 9,000 feet high; the latter two are from 1,000 to 4,000 feet above sea level. The Tarim and Dzungaria are separated by the 18,000 to

20,000 feet high Tien Shan Range extending a thousand miles eastward into China from the Soviet border. Still farther eastward from the Tien Shan stretch the great desert plains of the Gobi and Inner Mongolia to the Great Wall of China.

South of the Great Wall, east of the Tibetan High Plateau, and west of the great plains and mountainous south, is an intermediate zone formed by four major topographical units. From north to south, these are the Loess Plateau, the Central Mountain Block, the Szechwan (Ssu-ch'uan) Basin, and the Kweichow (Yün-nan Kuei-chow) Plateau. Physically speaking, the last one continues into northeastern Burma and northwestern Vietnam and Laos. Economically, the Szechwan Basin, supporting almost 50 million people, is the most important. In its geographical influence upon the climate of the country as a whole, the Central Mountain Block is of the greatest significance.

**Coast Line and Islands.** China's coast line divides roughly into two differing halves. From Shanghai northward most of the coast is flat and low-lying, often suffering inundations during the onshore summer monsoon winds. The only important exceptions are the coasts of the hilly Shantung Peninsula and its geologically corresponding Liaotung Peninsula jutting south from Manchuria. Ports on the flat coast lands are few and poor. By contrast, such excellent ports as Tsingtao (Ch'ing-tao) in Shantung and Dairen (Ta-lien) in Liaotung are found along the hilly coasts.

South of Shanghai most of the coast is highly irregular, hilly, and with numerous bays, headlands, and good harbors such as Amoy (Hsiamen) and Hong Kong. Off these hilly coasts also are found most of China's numerous small islands, as well as the two great islands of Taiwan (T'ai-wan) and Hainan. Taiwan is separated by about 170 miles from the mainland and forms part of the western Pacific island arcs. Hainan, on the other hand, is only about 25 miles from the Chiao-chou Peninsula and is more closely related to the mainland. About 100 miles southeast of Shanghai is the Chusan (Chou-Shan) archipelago.

## Climate and Regional Differentiation

In a general way, China may be divided climatically into a higher, dry western half and a lower and more humid eastern half (Figure 13-3). Each half in turn divides generally into two halves north and south with differing climatic characteristics. There are thus four climatic quadrants.

The situation of China is such that most of the moisture obtained by the land is borne in by air masses from the Pacific and, to a lesser extent, from the Indian Ocean. Virtually no moisture is brought in from the Arctic Ocean and only a very small amount comes from the distant Atlantic to water the western frontiers of China. Mongolia, Siberia, and Central Asia build up great pressures of cold air masses because of the high heat radiation during the winters, and the outward movement of these masses brings cold, drying winds to much of China. Winter is not only a season of cold, but also of drought in the north and of greatly decreased rainfall in the south.

During the summer, the great heating of the interior of the land mass creates a low atmospheric pressure that draws into the interior warm, humid, maritime and tropical air which furnishes large quantities of rain. Summer in China is the most important wet season. Several obstacles arise, however, to obstruct the penetration of moist air very far inland. The Himalaya Mountains on the southern rim of the Tibetan High Plateau rob the northward moving air of most of its moisture during the Indian summer monsoon. While enough moisture blows in along the Brahmaputra Valley into the Ya-lu Ts'ang-pu to give a rainfall averaging 18 inches yearly at Lhasa, most of Tibet has a low precipitation and is very dry and barren. Evaporation is high because of the large number of clear days and the low humidity. In the western half of Tibet, therefore, streams do not drain out to the sea, but flow into salt lakes.

The high altitude and a southerly location create a climate with great diurnal temperature

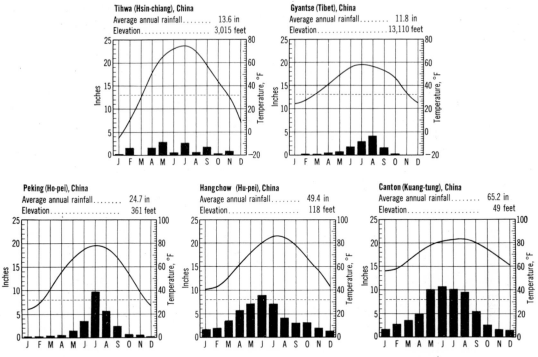

Figure 13-3    Climate graphs of selected stations in China.

differences and cold winters. The sunny side and the shady side of a mountain show great temperature difference. The growing season is limited by the short period between killing frosts.

In the northwestern plains and basins north of the Tibetan High Plateau, precipitation is even more limited and is reduced to 2 to 5 inches annually except in the higher mountain slopes of the Tien Shan and the Altai where it may increase to as much as 30 inches. Desert is the characteristic landscape, except in the line of oases that borders the Tarim and Dzungarian fringes. Evaporation far exceeds precipitation in most of the area, so that rivers generally become of smaller volume the farther they run, to disappear eventually or flow into shallow salt lakes. Desert gives way to steppe in the moister western part of the Dzungarian Basin and on the north slopes of the Tien Shan. Even forest growth occurs on slopes from 5,000 to 9,000 feet, above which meadow grasses again furnish feed for grazing livestock.

In the Tarim the climate is more arid, yet warmer because of the protection from northern winds, and with a longer growing season. Here, about two-thirds of the population of Chinese Turkestan (Hsin-chiang) make their living in oasis agriculture based upon irrigation.

In the eastern section of the Inner Mongolian region, north of the Great Wall, the outer desert gradually changes to steppe as the land comes increasingly within reach of the moist summer monsoon winds from the Pacific. In the vicinity of the Great Wall runs the 14-inch isohyet (line of annual rainfall) that moves in wet periods northward into the pastoral nomad land or retreats during dry years to south of the Great Wall. This forms the pioneer settlement area of a poverty-stricken agricultural population which competes with the herdsmen for the use of the land. Because of exposure to the full force of the Mongolian winter cold waves, extremes of temperatures are great.

In the eastern half of China, moisture decreases generally from the southeast coastal mountain land in a northwesterly direction. It is in this region that the summer monsoon operates. Its dominance brings about uniformly hot temperatures throughout eastern China in summer. Humidity is much lower in the north, however, and northern summers are less oppressive.

In eastern China, too, a topographic barrier effects important climatic changes from south to north. Eastward out of the 20,000-foot high range of the Kunlun (K'un-lun) stretching across northern Tibet runs the lower but still formidable Tsinling (Ch'in-ling) Range. Forming part of the Central Mountain Block, it first separates the Szechwan Basin from the Loess Plateau with 12,000-foot high mountains. Then it jogs in a great southeastward arc toward the lower Yangtze at decreasing elevations to end in low hills north of the city of Nanking (Nanching). The cold, heavy winter air masses of Mongolia cannot surmount the higher portion of this range, so that much of the south is protected during the winter and has mild climates with long growing seasons. This is especially true of the Szechwan Basin where an almost year-round growing season exists. In the lower eastern portions south of the Yellow Plain, cold waves do break through to cool east central China in winter.

In summer, the Tsinling system operates to rob moisture from the north and northwest, so that these areas have a precarious agricultural climate. The cleavage is marked. North of the Tsinling which continues climatically along the line of the Hwai River, there is a steppe climate of the monsoon type where precipitation ranges from about 30 inches in the south to 14 inches in the Great Wall vicinity. Winters are extremely cold, dry, and dusty. Rainfall typically reaches a peak in July, but its occurrence during the growing season often is irregular, so that crops may suffer early drought with disastrous results. Violent downpours come upon the easily eroded soils, creating dangerous floods, especially in the lower Yellow Plain north and south of the Shantung hill lands. The growing season varies from 200 to 240 days.

Although northeastern China (Manchuria) does not come under the climatic control of the Tsinling Mountain barrier, its distance from the source of the summer monsoon air masses and the position of the East Manchurian Mountains create a climate similar to that of North China south of the Great Wall. While rainfall may be as much as 40 inches on the higher parts of these mountains, on the Manchurian Plain it decreases rapidly from 30 inches in the lower Liao Valley to 15 in the northwestern part of the plain. The growing season decreases over the same area from about 220 days in the south to about 150 in the northwest.

The more important soils of the north are the calcareous loess of the Loess Plateau, the loess-derived alluvial silts of the Yellow Plain and the valleys of the Loess Plateau region, and the light-chestnut and black prairie earths of Manchuria. To the north of the Tsinling line, steppe and prairie grasses probably form the most widespread original vegetation, although, in the mountains, forests occur.

South of the Tsinling divide, the earth becomes covered with a year-round green vegetation where it is uncultivated. Rainfall in the Yangtze Valley is over 40 inches and increases toward the South China coast to over 60 inches, with much higher amounts in the mountains. While the monsoon brings in most of this moisture, precipitation is caused not only by orography (mountain barriers) and convection, but

*Figure 13-4   A part of Chungking (Chung-ch'ing) is seen across the Yangtze River at left. The 50-foot-high rock ridge in the foreground is submerged by the annual flood peak which may reach 90 feet above low water. (Courtesy of H. J. Wiens.)*

also by eastern-moving cyclonic storms. The winter season is mild and also has some precipitation, although it is definitely the driest season. April and May have excessive humidity and are known as the mouldy period, especially all along the Yangtze Valley.

South of the Nan-ling there is no cold weather. There is a monsoon type of humid subtropical climate where typical tropical plants grow. On the 6,000-foot high Yünnan Plateau to the west and generally in the same latitudes, the climate is among the most pleasant in China. By contrast, the 2,000-foot lower Kweichow (Kuei-chow) Plateau is often shrouded with fog, and its valley lands are hot and humid in summer. Off the coast, Hainan Island has a maritime tropical climate, whereas Taiwan Island to the north has a maritime subtropical regime.

As a whole, the soils south of the Tsinling divide tend to be badly leached. Most of the southern slope lands have sterile red or yellow earths. The alluvial river plains have relatively fertile soils which have been greatly modified through long cultivation, especially in the water-soaked paddy fields. The Szechwan Basin has an exceptional status because its purplish-red sedimentary earths provide a fertile soil, making possible the most intensive type of slope cultivation.

## Historical Development

China is a land of many cultures and ethnic groups among which, today, the "orthodox" Chinese form the dominant and most widespread group, with over 90 per cent of the population. Some 40 million minority peoples are distributed in the outlying provinces and territories of the south, west, and north. The origin of the Chinese is obscure, but they are believed to have emerged from the northwestern desert oases and to have moved eastward into the region of the lower bend of the Yellow River where its tributary, the Wei Ho, has created an alluvial plain north of the Tsinling Range. The earliest reliable Chinese historical records reveal settlement in this plain before 1400 B.C. From here the people expanded eastward into the Yellow Plain and later into the rest of modern China.

Chinese expansion naturally faced the hostility of the different ethnic groups that already occupied the territory that is now China, in the same manner that European expansion in the Americas faced the hostility of the American Indians. At the same time, the higher civilization and technology developed by the Chinese attracted the admiration of the tribal peoples. The end result was that large masses of these tribal peoples gradually lost their original cultures and became Chinese. Nevertheless, there always were tribes or ruling clans which desired to retain their own cultural dominance. When they found themselves unsuccessful in opposing the Chinese advance, they migrated or fled to mountain fastnesses of areas more distant from Chinese power. Thus, we find that today, the unassimilated T'ai ethnic groups in China made their last stand in the most southwestern and southern frontier regions, while the Miao, Yao, and Lolo exist in the higher, less desirable slope lands of the south and southwest.

Historically, in contrast with the steady Chinese population push against the lesser ethnic groups of the south, the Chinese have been the object of pressure from the northern and northwestern pastoral peoples. This pressure may be attributable to the difference in security of livelihood between the climatically bountiful south and the precarious steppe lands of the north. On many occasions, that insecurity impelled the northern and northwestern nomads to federate themselves and invade the more productive agricultural realm. Thus, during about half of Chinese history, they became the rulers of much or all of China. As a people almost literally born to the saddle, mastery of the strategy of mobility may have helped them achieve success despite great numerical inferiority. Such people were the Mongols and the Manchus. The Manchu conquerors, however, retained empire over the Chinese only at the cost of accepting conquest by Chinese culture.

Tibet, Mongolia, Chinese Turkestan, and Manchuria were united with China under Manchu rule but were not looked on as parts of

China proper. When the Chinese overthrew the Manchu rulers, they also had to take vigorous military steps to keep the outer territories from breaking away, for only in Manchuria did Chinese form the majority of the population in the outer territories. The political disintegration of the Manchu empire gave opportunities for foreign imperial interests to intervene both within China proper and in these outlying territories. At the same time revolutionary ideas from America and Europe were stirring Chinese intellectuals into a ferment. Aside from China proper, where most of the powers wished to bring their influence to bear, Russian interests found outlets in all the outlying territories since they were along her Siberian and Central Asian frontiers. The British who were in occupation of India intervened in Tibet, and Japan competed with Russia to control the political and economic destiny of Manchuria and, to a lesser extent, Mongolia.

Taiwan occupies a somewhat special situation owing to its relatively recent occupation by the Chinese. The original inhabitants were unorganized primitive tribes of Malay people. During the sixteenth century, Japanese pirates had their lairs on its coasts. Portuguese and Dutch explorers made settlements on it only to be driven out by refugee settlers from China fleeing from Manchu rule during the middle of the seventeenth century. The Manchus finally subjugated Taiwan, but no great development occurred until after Japan gained control of the island as a prize of the Sino–Japanese War of 1894–1895. Much economic development took place during the fifty years of Japanese occupation, but the population remains largely Chinese. On this basis Taiwan was returned to Chinese sovereignty after World War II.

Among the 40 million minority peoples of China there are more than 60 distinct ethnic groups with many differing languages. Aside from these, the "orthodox" Chinese are united by a single written language, but divided by seven or eight major spoken languages which are more or less mutually unintelligible to their speakers. Most of these different tongues are in the southeastern coastal hill lands, where isola-

*Figure 13-5   Street scene in Taichung, Taiwan. The bicycles are characteristic. (Courtesy of Chinese Embassy.)*

tion has been an important factor in their development.

### Population and Livelihood

China has had a large population for 2,000 years, for even during the Han Dynasty in the pre-Christian era, official registers claimed a population of 60 million. That the present population is less than ten times that of 2,000 years ago indicates that the land's capacity to support people long ago reached a point of saturation in terms of the prevailing agricultural technology. Traditional tools and implements present definite limitations to the amount of land a farmer can handle, and this forces him to cultivate only the better soils in order to earn a living. The result has been an excessive concentration of population upon the plains and irrigable valleys.

Since about 75 per cent of China's population are farm people, the population distribution corresponds closely to the distribution of cultivated land. Some 150 million people are settled on the great Yellow and Yangtze Plains (Figure 13-2). About 50 million are settled on the Manchurian Plains. In the Szechwan Basin are another 50 million. Other smaller, heavily populated plains include the Canton Delta, the Wei and other plains in the Loess Plateau, and the various coastal delta plains of southeastern China.

Twenty-five per cent of China's population live in towns and cities. About 10 per cent of the population live in large cities. Some of the major metropolitan areas that have developed in China rank with the greatest cities of the world. Nine cities had more than a million inhabitants in 1952. Shanghai led with 5.4 million, followed by Peking (Pei-ching) with over 2 million. The remaining seven are as follows:

| | |
|---|---|
| Tientsin (T'ien-ching) | 1,795,000 |
| Mukden (Shen-yang) | 1,551,000 |
| Canton (Kuang-chou) | 1,500,000 |
| Hankow, Wuchang, Hanyang | |
| (Wu-Han) | 1,200,000 |
| Chungking (Ch'ung-ch'ing) | 1,100,000 |
| Port Arthur (Lu-shun) | 1,054,000 |
| Nanking (Nan-ching) | 1,020,000 |

Intensive use of hand labor is characteristic of all Chinese farming but is especially true of southern paddy agriculture. A smaller unit of arable land can provide a livelihood for a family in the south because of the ample rainfall and the long growing season which permits double- or triple-cropping during one year on the same piece of land. Thus, the greater density of population per unit of arable land in the south does not necessarily indicate greater population pressure there. In the dry and unreliable climate of the north, a lower density per acre may actually coincide with a more marginal standard of living. It may generally be said,

however, that the arable land already is supporting the maximum population that can exist on its present productivity. In the Canton Delta there is only 0.2 of an acre of cultivated land per person. In the Yangtze Valley this rises to about 0.45 acre and in the Yellow Plain to an average of about 0.5 of an acre. In the steppe margins outside the Great Wall, this may rise to 1.5 acres per person, indicating the greater land area needed for subsistence. Only in Manchuria is the density lower in relation to the capacity of the land.

After millenniums of trial-and-error learning, crops in the various agricultural regions have been selected which are adapted to the geographical environment of particular localities. Since cultural preference in food has centered upon rice, this has become the dominant crop wherever water availability, soil type, and growing season have combined to permit it. Nevertheless, because the favorable conditions do not prevail north of the Tsinling Mountains, rice is not an important crop in the north. Here, dry cultivation is the rule and there is more variety in important crops. The dominant food crops are wheat, millet, kaoliang (grain sorghum), and soybeans. Most of these are grown in the south as well, and crops of barley, maize, sweet potatoes, and many varieties of beans and vegetables are also important.

In much of the Manchurian Plain and the northwest parts of the loess land, low precipitation and cool climate favor the dominance of spring wheat, millet, and kaoliang; soybeans are a prominent export of the Manchurian Plain. South of the Great Wall, winter wheat, kaoliang, and millet are most important. Between the Tsinling Mountain–Hwai River climatic divide and the Yangtze is a transitional zone where winter wheat and summer rice crops are most important. In the rest of South China and the Szechwan Basin, where irrigation water can be led to fields, rice is everywhere the summer crop. Rice terraces are common on lower hills, slopes, and mountain ravines. In the winter, wheat, barley, and oilseed plants may be planted on drained rice fields. South of the Nan-ling two crops of rice, sometimes a third, may be grown on a field in one year.

Some regional specialties include the cotton crops in the southeastern part of the Yellow Plain and the northeastern part of the lower Yangtze Plain, the tobacco of Shantung, the sugar cane of Taiwan, Szechwan, and Kwangtung (Kuang-tung), the tung oil of Szechwan and Hunan, the tea of the southeastern coastal provinces, mulberry (for silkworm feeding) in the lower Yangtze Plain and adjacent hills, and the tropical fruits of the southernmost provinces and of the two main islands. In the northwestern desert oases, almost every annual crop in China is represented, and grapes, raisins, tree fruits, and melons are local specialties.

For ages the family has been the cornerstone of Chinese society. Families cared for their unfortunates and members of a family stood together for mutual benefit. Deference was paid to the educated and elderly. Three times as many Chinese were farmers as were engaged in all other occupations combined. On the death of a property owner all the children shared equally in his land. This custom resulted in minute subdivision of land, a man's holdings often being separated into tiny plots, but it helped prevent the development of large estates. The ambition of millions of Chinese has been to own land and operate it as they desired. The Communist system of state-operated and communal farms is contrary to custom and the forced installation of this sort of farming has met with strong opposition from many farmers. Whether the change toward communal farms in China will succeed, or whether the strong desire for independent farm operation will continue, remains to be determined. Most Chinese live in villages, and farmers use much time in going to and from the farmland. Hand methods of culture and the use of simple equipment pulled by an ox or water buffalo are traditional. The maximum yield from land is sought with disregard for the human labor required. Thus transplanting rice from seedbeds shortens the time the crop occupies a field and permits multiple crops. In South China two crops of rice are grown and, between these, quick-maturing

plantings of vegetables are often harvested. In central China two grain crops are also grown, but only one is rice; the other is wheat or another grain. Under the Communists, the typical small farms are being consolidated, and the work on the resulting large farms is being done by communal groups using mechanized equipment when available. One result expected from this is to release labor for factory work, but many Chinese want to retain their land and continue as individual operators in spite of the economic theory favoring communal farming.

Living in small farm villages or working for low wages in cities, scores of millions of Chinese exist at a bare subsistence level. The ruin of a crop, sickness, or injury to a laborer brings tragedy to many. It is no accident that the common greeting in hungry China is "Have you eaten your rice?" rather than "How do you do?" China contains many prosperous people who live in fine, well-furnished homes, who wear good clothes, and eat well, but many millions live in tiny huts with dirt floors and almost no furnishings, and these people may dress in rags and hardly ever get enough to eat.

Confucianism, to which Chinese have traditionally adhered, is not a religion but rather a code of ethics which prescribes rules of conduct for the many relationships to other people and for the varied situations of life. Now that China is a Communist country, will the prescriptions of state socialism replace the teachings of Confucius, Mencius, and other ancient philosophers?

## Resources

Because of the demands of a large population as well as because of destruction for other reasons, most of the forests of China have long since disappeared. As a result, in most of the mountain lands, no seed-bearing trees remain to reforest the slopes, which are mostly grass-covered. Today important forests are found only in remote parts of the southwestern mountains, in the northern and eastern Manchurian mountain lands, and in mountainous parts of the southeastern coastlands. In South China bamboo is very widespread and is a most important plant for house construction and for a wide variety of other uses.

Fishing is an important occupation along most of the coastal waters and on inland streams and lakes. Because of the lack of modern fishing vessels, large-scale commercial and deep-sea fishing is not practiced. South of the lower Yangtze, fish-pond culture is a sideline with many farmers.

On the basis of general geological surveys, it is believed that China's major mineral-producing regions have been established, and no sensational new discoveries are likely to occur. China has a moderate supply of the basic requirements for modern industrialization. China has vast quantities of some materials but is very deficient in others. Thus, China ranks fourth in the world in coal resources, but her known petroleum resources are negligible. Her iron ore reserves are estimated at about 1.3 billion tons or about one-fifth that of the United States, but most of the deposits are small, of low quality, and scattered.

There is a high degree of concentration of the reserves of both coal and iron in single regions. Almost 80 per cent of the coal resources are in the Loess Plateau provinces on both sides of the Yellow River where it runs south from its great northern bend. About 60 per cent of the iron ore is in southern Manchuria. Most of the exploitation of both coal and iron has been in the area with the best transportation facilities, that is, in south Manchuria, near the sea just north of Tientsin (T'ien-ching), and in the Shantung hill land not far from Tsingtao (Ch'ing-tao).

Although China needs most of the minerals it produces, the country has a surplus in certain strategic items such as antimony, tungsten, and tin. In the regional distribution of minerals, the north and northeast have most of the coal and iron, the south and southwest the major part of the ferroalloys and nonferrous metals. Abundant ores for the magnesium and aluminum industries are found both in the north and in the south.

What little petroleum there is appears mainly to be in the northwest desert and semiarid lands and in Szechwan. Oil shale occurs in Manchuria and, together with coal, may furnish synthetic fuels. Water power potential is mainly in the south; the total amounts to about 3.3 per cent of the world potential, but it is largely undeveloped. Several excellent sites exist for large-scale power development, the most noted

*Figure 13-6 Artisans saw and split bamboo for house and furniture construction in this scene in Szechwan province. Bamboo is one of the most versatile and useful plants in Eastern and Southeastern Asia. (Courtesy of H. J. Wiens.)*

being the Yangtze Gorge site with a potential capacity of 10 million kilowatts.

In the mineral realm one may say that China has the basis for a moderate degree of industrialization, although per capita, mineral wealth is not high. Retarded development may be attributed to political instability and internal disunity, the lack of large capital accumulations for investments, communications difficulties, and social factors inherent in traditional Chinese culture.

## Manufacturing

Although modern industries have made some progress in China, it is probably safe to assume that about three-fourths of China's domestic needs for manufactured and processed materials are still supplied by home and traditional industries and handicrafts. The leading industries are those serving basic food and clothing needs. Food processing, such as rice milling and wheat flour milling, is most important. Rice is milled mostly by traditional methods, but wheat flour is manufactured in the great modern flour mills of cities such as Shanghai, Tientsin, and Tsingtao.

China's masses need cheap cotton cloth. Formerly, household looms supplied almost the entire demand, but the introduction of modern machinery led to a decay in this branch of home industry. Subsequently, foreign as well as domestic interests established large cotton mills in such places as Shanghai, Tientsin, and Tsingtao to utilize the cheap labor sources there. Cotton textiles are China's foremost modern industry, and the above three cities, in the order listed, are the leading textile producers.

Modern heavy industries such as those connected with chemicals, iron and steel, and machine manufacture have been developed to the greatest extent in southern Manchuria. These industries owed much of their growth to the efforts of Japan, which seized the area in 1931 and tried to build up a continental base for political and military expansion in Eastern Asia.

South of the Great Wall, the region from Peking eastward through Tientsin to Shanhaikwan (Shan-hai-kuan) (where the Great Wall

*Figure 13-7   River steamers negotiating one of the sharp turns in the scenic Yangtze River Gorge where the current may reach 12 knots and where excellent sites for great hydroelectric developments exist. (Courtesy of H. J. Wiens.)*

comes to the sea) is another important industrial area based upon the coal mines located there. Cement, chemicals, glass, and a variety of light industries are found in the larger cities and the towns of the area, as well as some iron smelting. In 1955 the Chinese Communists were building an important industrial center at Pao-Hou outside the Great Wall in Inner Mongolia.

In central China the Hankow (Wu-Han) metropolitan area is an important center for iron and steelmaking, flour milling, textile manufacturing, vegetable oil pressing, and dried-egg processing. Farther westward in Szechwan, most of the industrial concentration is around Chungking (Ch'ung-ch'ing), with a less important region around and south of the provincial capital at Chengtu (Ch'eng-tu). Antimony refining and light industries are found at Chang-

*Figure 13-8   North China furnishes some of the supreme examples of great Chinese architecture. The tower of the "Summer Palace" of imperial days is seen here rising above the plain near Peking. (Courtesy of H. J. Wiens.)*

sha (Ch'ang-sha) south of Tung Ting (T'ung-t'ing) Lake.

In the triangle formed by Nanking (Kiang-ning), Shanghai, and Hangchow (Hang-chou) on the lower Yangtze Plain, there is an industrial complex specializing in silk and cotton fabrics, and having a great multitude of light industries.

In the south, the Canton area and British Hong Kong form the nuclei for a variety of similar light industries. Sugar refining is important in this area as it is, to an even greater degree, on Taiwan. Under Japanese occupation, Taiwan reached a higher stage of industrial development than the China mainland as a whole. Nevertheless, although only about 56 per cent

of the population was engaged in farming, most Taiwan industries were concerned with food processing. In the 1930s, this island was the third largest world exporter of canned pineapple and also an important exporter of sugar and rice. The hydroelectric power developed on Taiwan is used in refining aluminum ore formerly obtained from the mainland opposite. There also is a petroleum refining plant on Taiwan which utilizes imported crude oil.

These examples of modern manufacturing are listed to show that industrialization is making inroads on Chinese economic life, but the country has only begun on the road to industrialization in the Western sense. In certain key commodities such as cotton textiles, village and home industries have been displaced; in other areas, these still play a most important role in filling domestic needs.

## Communications and Trade

China's communications system has always been inadequate to cope with her geographical immensity and climatic irregularities. Traditional means of communications are slow and expensive.

The value of bulk commodities cannot pay for their own transport beyond a few dozen miles where river or coastal boat transportation is not available. Rutted dirt roads in the north, which become impassable mires in rainy periods, require five times the animal power for pulling carts than would be the case on hard-surfaced roads. In the south, the mountainous character of the land formerly made wheeled vehicles a rarity except in large plain areas. Roads followed the most direct route over mountain ridges and required stone steps. Human carriers and pack animals carried freight and passengers. Fortunately, most of the larger streams of China south of the Tsinling are navigable to flat-bottomed craft over great distances. In the north, winter freezing, low rainfall, high silting, and shifting channels limit the usefulness of rivers. Here, wheeled vehicles have been the traditional form of transport.

Railroad construction in China was begun in the late nineteenth century as a result of pressure by Western and Japanese interests wishing to exploit the new materials and markets of China. Because of the strategic and economic importance of Manchuria, historical events have made the railway net here the best in China, and 43 per cent of the 16,650 miles of railroad in 1952 were located in this northeastern sector of the country. North China had 23 per cent of the mileage, central China 12 per cent, and southeastern mainland China 7 per cent. As a result of Japanese construction, Taiwan today has 12 per cent of China's railways.

Vast areas of China are entirely without railroad facilities, for sections outside those listed have only 500 miles of railroad. Nevertheless, rail transport connects the Vietnam boundary in the south with the Siberian boundary in the north, and there is railroad connection with the Korean and Soviet Russian railroads via Manchuria.

Motor highway construction was launched as a flood relief project in 1920, but the highway net grew rather slowly because of the high cost of vehicles and gasoline, both of which must be imported. However, the Chinese government has recognized the need for highway development, particularly because of strategic and political considerations. Highway construction was pushed throughout the World War II period. This program produced the spectacular Burma Road, about 900 miles from the temporary capital at Chungking to the southwestern border, and in the northwest, the longer trans-Tsinling and desert road running to the Soviet Turk-Sib Railroad. By 1950, 105,200

miles of highway had been constructed. As a result, most of the district towns of China may be reached by motor road, although, except on the main routes, the roads are generally dirt-surfaced and often unusable during rainy periods.

As a result of construction by both Japanese and Chinese military forces during World War II, all major Chinese cities and numerous strategic, though lesser, places have airfields.

China's early trade with the outside world was in high-cost, low-weight, low-bulk commodities such as silk, tea, and opium. Even in the early decades of this century, raw silk was the most consistently important export, with tea ranking next. In 1910 raw silk and tea accounted for more than 28 per cent of the exports. The rise of cheaper, bulkier, raw-material products marked changing export trends in the 1930s. In 1936 silk had dropped by two-thirds because of Japanese competition, and tung oil led all exports, followed by ores and minerals such as tungsten, tin, and antimony. In the 1910 period, cotton goods amounted to nearly a third of China's imports, but they declined as modern textile manufacturing grew in the large coastal cities. By contrast, such items as metals and machinery, chemicals, kerosene, gasoline, and motor vehicles became increasingly important. A variety of factors, economic and political, have made postwar trade small. In 1951, production in many lines had not caught up to prewar volume. Even in the period before World War II, however, the per capita trade of China was the lowest in the world.

Until the ascendancy of Communist control

*Figure 13-9   A highway on the motor route crossing the eroded loess country of southern Kansu province. Wheat is ripening on the river flood-plain. (Courtesy of Robert Hall, Jr.)*

*Figure 13-10    The Gobi dominates the southern part of Mongolia. Note that rivers, cities, and most of the people are in the northern part of the country.*

on the mainland, China's trade had been largely with Japan, the United States, and Great Britain. In 1951 about 70 per cent of Communist China's trade was with the Soviet Union and with the latter's satellites.

First among the historically important ports of China is Shanghai, the outlet for the huge Yangtze drainage area, and handling half the country's trade. Canton has been the major Chinese outlet for southern China, although Hong Kong with greatly superior harbor facilities has been at once a rival and a transshipment port for Canton. Tientsin is the most important gateway for the Yellow Plain, although Tsingtao draws off some of its trade. In southern Manchuria, Dairen (Ta-lien) has been the commercial port par excellence, and Port Arthur has been the naval base.

## THE MONGOLIAN PEOPLE'S REPUBLIC

*Relief Features*

The Mongolian People's Republic is the name given by the Communists to the area traditionally called Outer Mongolia. Its separation from Inner Mongolia has no physical basis either in topography or climate and is justified mainly on the rather flimsy ground of dialects and tribal divisions among the Mongolian peoples concerned (Figure 13-10). In the west, the Altai Mountains constitute a natural boundary separating the Dzungarian Basin and Soviet Kazakhstan from the Kobdo Basin of Outer Mongolia. The country as a whole is part of the great Mongolian Plateau and ranges in altitude from 4,000 to 6,000 feet, although the central Khangai and Tarbagatai Mountains have elevations up to 9,000 feet, while the Altai rise above 10,000. Much of the south and southeast are rather level plains arranged in large shallow basins, or "gobi," often with great patches of barren desert pavement. The western third

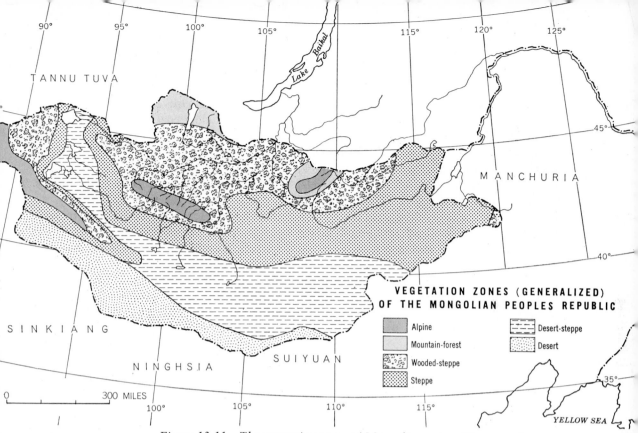

*Figure 13-11   The vegetation zones of Mongolia are transition areas between those of the U.S.S.R. and China. Note that in general they extend in an east-west direction.*

of Outer Mongolia forms a large basin containing many salt lakes, and the northern frontiers of the country have such mountains as the Kentei and Tannu Tuva Ranges.

Since the atmospheric moisture for this area is derived from the scanty evaporation from the Arctic, or from the distant Atlantic Ocean, the precipitation decreases the farther south the land extends. Near the northern frontiers, rainfall averages between 10 and 12 inches. At Ulan Bator (Urga), the capital, it has dropped to about 8 inches. The southern half gets less than 5 inches; the southwestern Gobi and the Kobdo Basin receive about 2 to 3 inches or less.

Only the rivers draining from the northern slopes of the Khangai and northern mountains find their way to the sea after running into Siberian lakes and rivers. The vegetation pattern corresponds closely to the rainfall pattern (Figure 13-11). The southwest Gobi region and much of the Kobdo Basin floor have only xerophytic shrubs and grasses. Toward the east of the Gobi, sparse short grass and bunch grass furnish scanty fodder for grazing animals following the early summer rains. Beginning with central Mongolia and proceeding northward, the land gradually provides a more flourishing steppe grass cover until rather luxuriant grasslands are reached in northern Mongolia. In the higher mountains, even forests thrive where protected from the ax. With the exception of southwestern Mongolia and drier parts of the Kobdo Basin, Outer Mongolia may be described as one vast range land, much of it eminently suitable for grazing livestock, in what is typically continental steppe climate.

### The Pastoral Economy

During the first decades of this century, an estimated 13 million domestic animals grazed the Mongolian plains to furnish a livelihood to about 800,000 Mongols. By 1941, the animal numbers had grown to more than 27 million. More than two-thirds of the livestock were sheep and goats; sheep alone numbered about 16 million. Cattle and horses each numbered between 2.6 and 2.7 million, and there were about 700,000 camels. The sheep has a significant position. The Mongol drinks its milk, eats its meat and the cheese made from its milk, uses its wool for clothing, felt shoes, and tents, and burns its dung for fuel. Because most of Mongolia is climatically unsuitable for agriculture, the Mongol must adapt himself to the needs of his flocks and seek new pastures as old ones become exhausted. Among the characteristic developments of Mongol nomadism is the yurt, a light and collapsible felt tent that furnishes adequate protection from the fierce winter winds and the −43°F temperatures that may occur.

The Mongol meets many problems in his attempt to make a living. He must adapt himself to great continental extremes of heat and cold. Surface water is scarce and must be supplemented by shallow wells, the water of which often may be brackish. Hard-crusted snow and winter blizzards often bring about heavy livestock losses through starvation. Natural enemies such as wolves, animal parasites, and diseases may kill off large percentages of his flocks and herds. Finally, there is a point of saturation in the capacity of the grasslands to support livestock, so that increased human population must find other means of support or starve. Past Chinese and Russian efforts to introduce agriculture have met with little success. A total of about 100,000 acres of land may be in cultivation in the northern humid areas, much of it around Ulan Bator.

Under Soviet Russia's control, continuing attempts are being made to force the nomad to a more sedentary mode of life in which improvements can be carried out more effectively and political control facilitated. Political, agricultural, mining, and other technicians from the Soviet Union direct the present development of the Mongolian People's Republic and the exploitation of Outer Mongolia's resources. Desire for the mineral wealth of the Tannu Tuva sector of Mongolia resulted in its annexation by the Soviet Union in 1946 after more than a decade of occupation. The other parts of northern Mongolia also have significant mineral wealth, including coal mines presently supplying Ulan Bator.

## Historical Development

The Mongols became prominent in history at the beginning of the thirteenth century, when their famous leader Genghis Khan united the divided tribesmen of the steppes through skillful political intrigues and military prowess and launched one of the most amazing empires of all time. The empire proved too large and loosely knit to hold together for long, and Mongol power rapidly declined. In the fourteenth and fifteenth centuries, after the Mongols were driven out of China, the Yellow sect of Lama Buddhism took a firm hold among the Mongols. Church power gained at the expense of the ruling nobles, and the tradition developed that every family should have at least one son in the priesthood. In contrast to the nomadic existence of the Mongols as a whole, the monasteries became the focus of the only large fixed settlements in the country. Some of them had thousands of monks who, for the most part, were a nonproductive, parasitic element burdening the economy. Today, most of the lamaseries have been greatly reduced and the nobles eliminated.

Mongolia became a protectorate of the Manchu rulers in 1691, but when the Chinese revolution of 1911 overthrew the Manchu empire, the Mongol chieftains declared their tie with China dissolved. Although the succeeding Chinese governments refused to recognize this dissolution, Russian and subsequent Soviet intervention, especially since 1931, gradually brought Outer Mongolia into the Soviet orbit during a period of Chinese political and military weakness. Soviet pressure in 1945 forced a reluctant Nationalist Chinese recognition of Outer Mongolian independence from China, but this recognition was repudiated in 1953 by the Nationalists on Taiwan. Communist China, however, continued to recognize the separation of Outer Mongolia from Chinese sovereignty. Because of the region's historical and economic ties to China, rivalry between China and the Soviet Union for control of Mongolia may well continue.

Strategically, Outer Mongolia occupies a dominating position in Central Asia. The northern frontiers are only about 100 miles from the vital trans-Siberian railway. From southwestern Mongolia, it is easy to cut off access to Sinkiang (Hsin-chiang) from China proper via the Kansu (Kan-su) Corridor. In the east, the Great Hsing-an Mountains of Manchuria rise little above the plateau edge and have commanding routes into the Manchurian plains. There is no topographic obstacle to the advance of mechanized forces from the Mongolian plains southward into China. The levelness of much of the country and the hard pavement of the surfaces in many places permit aircraft landings with minimum or no preparation. It is small wonder that Soviet Russia is anxious to control this strategic country.

## THE REPUBLIC OF KOREA

### Relief Features

Topographically, Korea is an elongated block tilted from northeast to southwest. Its greatest length is about 450 miles and its width from 100 to 150 miles. North of the 40th parallel, most of it is a deeply incised plateau and mountain land forming part of the East Manchurian Mountains. In the central part lies the Kaima Plateau at an elevation of some 5,000 to 6,000 feet. A mountain backbone not exceeding this height follows the east coast the length of the peninsula and is known as the Taebaeksaumaek (Tae-baek) Range. The highest elevation is about 9,000 feet on the dead volcanic peak of Baek-tu San, which lies on the Manchurian frontier between the Yalu (Ya-lu) and Tu-men River sources. Cutting across the peninsula from Seoul northward to the east coast port of Wŏnsan (Won-san) (Figure 13-12) is a lowland corridor or depressed valley forming a strategic communications route.

The westward tilt and the situation of the high water divide less than 30 miles from the east coast bring short, steep drops to the streams flowing into the deep Japan Sea, with small alluvial plains near their mouths. Most of the drainage flows westward, except in the southern part and where the river valleys trend southward. The slope of the land is more gradual, and the alluvial plains widen out where the rivers deposit their silt-laden waters into the shallow Yellow Sea (Figure 13-12). The agricultural development, therefore, has largely been in the western and southern parts of the country where level land is more abundant.

Because of the land connection of northern Korea, the continental climatic influence is strongly felt, and the higher elevation of the north also increases the severity of winter extremes there (Figure 13-13). By contrast, the southern maritime parts of Korea have a mild marine climate, owing to the effect of the warm Japan Current bathing its shores. Although southern Korea is almost 300 miles north of Shanghai, its mild climate resembles that of the lower Yangtze Plain. Climatic contrasts between north and south is analogous to those between North China and the Yangtze Plain. Along the northeastern coastlands, the cold currents moving southwestward from the Tatar Strait chill the atmosphere and produce damp, gloomy, and often foggy weather that restricts some forms of agriculture. There also is a striking contrast between the tidal rise of 2 or 3 feet along the eastern coast and the difference of over 20 feet between low and high tide along the western coast where the inrolling tide piles up the water in the shallow Yellow Sea. This creates difficulties for shipping in the western ports.

### Agriculture

Since here, as in China and Japan, rice is the cultural preference in the staple diet, it is raised wherever possible. The rainfall ranges from less than 20 inches in the northeast to over 60 in the southern mountain slopes. Paddy

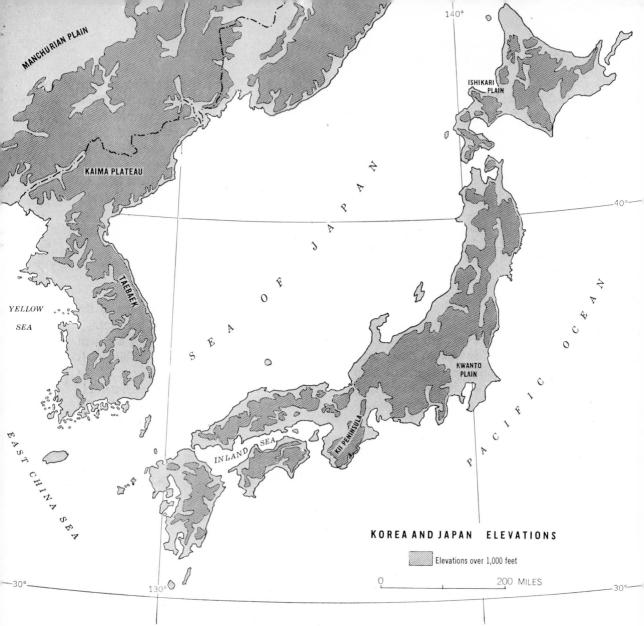

Figure 13-12   *The interior of each of the principal islands of Japan has elevations greater than 1,000 feet. In Korea the highest land is in the north and along the east side of the peninsula. In both countries the highlands cause transportation problems.*

rice, therefore, is chiefly a southern crop, although it is found in limited areas of the northwest, including the Yalu Valley. Millet and winter wheat are most important in northern Korea; soybeans are grown everywhere. Barley, which takes up about three-fifths as much land as paddy rice, is the second most important crop. The bulk of this, too, is concentrated in

the southwest part of the peninsula. The sweet potato also is an important crop in the south. Wheat is most important in the great peninsula jutting westward between the North Korean city of Pyong-yang and the capital at Seoul. From Seoul southward, cotton and tobacco become increasingly significant industrial crops; mulberry and silkworm cultivation is prevalent

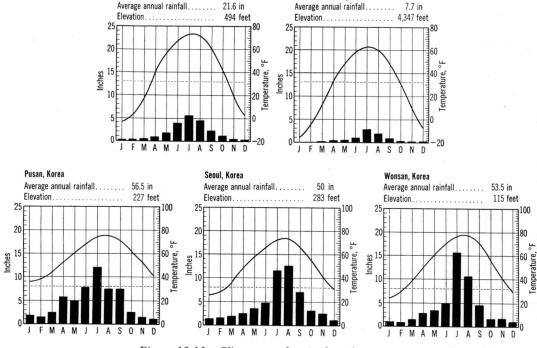

Figure 13-13    *Climate graphs of selected stations in Mongolia and Korea.*

in the southwest and south central provinces of the country. The north, with its short growing season, has only one crop per year, but the south grows two on the same land.

Although intensive hand tillage is carried on here as in China and Japan, there are differences in agricultural practices. The use of night soil as fertilizer is less important, especially in the north, and the use of green fertilizers is widespread. The latter has resulted in the denudation of much mountain vegetation, the destruction of which has been hastened by needs for fuel and by the 250,000 farm households mostly located in North Korea that are engaged in shifting slope cultivation.

Under Japanese occupation, Korea was an important rice exporter to Japan. This export meant that Koreans had to be content with less desirable foods; much millet and kaoliang was imported from Manchuria to fill the deficit left by the rice export. Although Korean population density per square mile of cultivated land was less than half that of Japan, agricultural yields per unit of land also were only about half

that of Japan. Moreover, farm income of Koreans under Japanese occupation before 1945 was only about one-third that of Japanese farmers. This indicates only one aspect of the impoverishment of Korea under Japanese exploitation. Until United Nations forces drove out the Japanese in World War II, one-third of all cultivated land in Korea was held by absentee Japanese landlords, often by corporations.

## Fisheries

Agriculture and some fishing employed 77 per cent of the population in 1938, roughly comparable to the degree of agrarian emphasis in livelihood found in China. Off the Korean coasts are important fishing waters which were largely exploited for Japanese benefit before World War II. The mixing of cold and warm ocean currents in the Sea of Japan has led to exceptionally productive fisheries. Korea, however, had no registered shipping while it was part of the Japanese empire, since all ships were of Japanese registry. Most of the motorized ships were sunk during World War II or withdrawn to Japan, and Korean fishing development has had to start with serious disadvantages. Moreover, fishing rivalry among Japan, the Soviet Union, and Korea makes for added conflicts in the Sea of Japan, especially since Korea insists that her sovereignty extends to 60 miles from her coasts.

### Historical Development

Korea has served as a cultural link between China and Japan for over 1,500 years. For about 1,000 years of Korea's history, much of Korea formed parts of the Chinese Empire. During much of its history it was divided into several kingdoms. Unification of the country under a separate rule occurred during the tenth century, but, like other countries peripheral to China, Korea sent periodic tribute to the Chinese Emperor until the nineteenth century. Korean history records many attempts by its neighbors to dominate its affairs, including several invasions by Japanese armies. Before the nineteenth century this had resulted in a tendency toward extreme isolationism and seclusion, fortified by savage resentment of even accidental intrusions by early trading ships.

The struggle between China and Japan for domination of Korea became acute after Japan emerged from its own period of isolation in 1852 and began to emulate its Occidental teachers in the art of empire-building. The defeat of China in the Sino-Japanese War of 1894–1895 eliminated China's influence in Korea for 55 years. The struggle shifted to a competition between Japan and Russia. As a relative newcomer on the scene, Russia brought her East Asian frontiers down to North Korea in 1858. Japan's victory in the Russo-Japanese War of 1904–1905 gave her a free hand over a Korea ruled by a corrupt, inept, and backward court. Japan annexed Korea in 1910 and for the next 35 years tried, by police-state methods, to stamp out Korean culture and national consciousness. She succeeded only in instilling the deep-seated resentment that resulted in the ousting of the Japanese after Japan's defeat in 1945.

The unfortunate Yalta agreement, bringing the Soviet Union into the war against Japan two weeks before the latter collapsed, permitted Soviet forces to occupy North Korea and led to the splitting of the country into two contending halves. This was demarcated by a boundary, the 38th parallel, meant only for temporary expediency. The determination of the United Nations to form a united independent Korea met with the equally determined Soviet ambition to control all of the country. The clash that came in 1950 was inevitable, and the burden of war was first handled by the Soviet Union's indoctrinated North Korean armies. The failure of these armies caused strategical

Figure 13-14 Korean farmers weeding rice seedling beds. Seedlings are transplanted after a few weeks in dispersed rows in larger fields. This technique has spread from China to both Korea and Japan. It makes possible the longer utilization of drained rice fields for secondary crops. (Courtesy of United States Army.)

difficulties for the Soviet Union which could be solved only by bringing in the forces of its much more powerful satellite, Communist China. Thus, China again was restored to its historical position in the struggle for control over Korea.

## Resources and Industry

Korean resources are so modest that there is little hope for a high degree of industrialization. Coal reserves per capita amount to only 34 tons, about one-seventh that of Japan and a small fraction of that for China. Quality is poor, moreover, and much of the coal must be mixed with imported coal to be satisfactory for industry. Production in 1937 was about one-fifth that of Japan. In iron ore, however, Korea is more fortunate, and production in the same year was three times that of Japan. Other important minerals include gold, tungsten, and graphite. The country has significant water power potential.

In regional distribution of resources there is great disparity between north and south. Korea north of the 38th parallel has 70 per cent of the existing forests, 67 per cent of the coal reserves, 80 per cent of the iron ore, 63 per cent of the gold, and most of the hydroelectric power as well as the better fishing waters. It is not surprising, therefore, to find that the south, with three-fourths of the 32 million population in 1953, is mainly agricultural, whereas the north, with the bulk of the industrial potential, has the greater industrial development.

During the first two decades of the Japanese occupation, Japan's chief interest was in extracting food and raw materials from Korea, and she made little attempt to develop industry there. After 1935, a change in policy toward industrialization resulted from Japan's strategic plans. Nevertheless, in 1938 Korean industry employed only about 200,000 Koreans (including miners but excluding traditional handicraft workers) or about 3.8 per cent of the gainfully employed population. The main emphases are revealed by the gross value of production in different categories. Thus, 31 per cent of the production was in the chemical field, much of it based upon the developed hydroelectric power which, by 1944, amounted to 2 million kilowatt capacity. Twenty-four per cent of the manufacturing was in food prod-

*Figure 13-15 Korean women grind flour with this primitive animal-powered stone mill in front of their mud-walled, straw-roofed house. (Courtesy of United States Army.)*

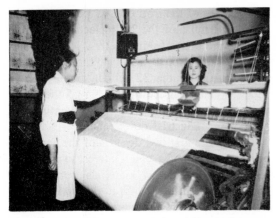

*Figure 13-16    Textiles are the chief products of Korea's relatively undeveloped modern industries. This interior view of a factory in Pusan, South Korea, is duplicated in Seoul, Pyŏngyang, and Kunsan which are textile centers that use domestic cotton. (Courtesy of United States Army.)*

ucts, 14 per cent in textiles, and 8 per cent in metals. Most of this value went to Japan.

Without war or government stimulation and without protective tariffs, industries developed by the Japanese, such as shipbuilding, coal liquefaction, dynamite, steel, motors, and engine manufacture, are likely to decline rapidly. Such present industries as textiles, rubber shoes, marine products, lumber and paper products, cement, synthetic fertilizers, crude drugs, leather products, and beverages are more certain of home and export markets. In spite of considerable promise in such light industries, no rapid change from a predominantly

agrarian economy is likely. Yet Korean production of about 2 million metric tons of rice in 1953 was still inadequate to the food needs of the population.

Some 3,250 miles of railroads existed in 1937, providing a fairly adequate network for the economic and strategical needs of the country. Double-tracked lines run the length of the country from the southeastern port of Pusan (Pu-san) to the Yalu railroad bridge into China at Sinŭiju (Sinui-ju). The most strategic transpeninsular line follows the Seoul to Wŏnsan corridor. Korea has some 14,000 miles of motor highways, but most of them are dirt-surfaced and difficult or impassable in the wet summer monsoon season. Rail connections with China, both north and south of the frontier, provide through routes of trade and transportation. During Japanese occupation, Pusan was an export port for transit freight from Manchuria, and it still is the leading port, whereas Najin (Na-jin) and Chŏngjin (Chong-jin) near the Soviet frontier served as outlets for northern Manchuria. The better natural ports are on the east coast, such as the important port of Wŏnsan. The western and southern ports have the more significant economic hinterlands. Chinnampo (Chin-nam-po) is the port for the North Korean captal of Pyŏng-yang (Pyong-yang). Inchon (In-chon) is the port for Seoul, and Kunsan (Kun-san) and Mokpo (Mok-po) form industrial centers and ports for the southwest. Division into North and South Korea hurts trade badly.

## JAPAN

### Relief Features

Japan differs from the other countries of Central Eastern Asia in being entirely insular and part of the volcanic island chains that form scalloped arcs off the mainland of Eastern Asia. Though hundreds of islands are included in Japan, all except four are of very small size. Among the four, Honshu with 88,031 square miles is by far the greatest and is known as the "mainland" of Japan (Figure 13-12). Hok-

kaido, somewhat detached and northernmost, is second in size, with 30,077 square miles or slightly smaller than Maine in the United States. The southern, smaller two islands, Kyushu and Shikoku, together with the southwestern arm of Honshu, form the bounds of Japan's Inland Sea. Kyushu, southernmost, has 13,768 square miles and is about the size of Massachusetts and Connecticut combined. Shikoku, with 6,857 square miles, is larger than Connecticut but smaller than Massachusetts.

Their recent geologic origin has had marked effects on the Japanese islands. They are composed mainly of high and rugged mountains, parts of a gigantic and partly submerged range rising from the sea bed. From the elevated parts of the range forming Japan, several island arcs extend revealing the existence of further submarine ranges. From northeastern Hokkaido the Kuril (Chishima) Chain stretches toward the Kamchatka Peninsula. Southward from Tokyo Bay runs the Bonin Chain. Southwestward from Kyushu, the Ryukyu (Liu-ch'iu) Chain reaches Taiwan. Okinawa is an important island in the Ryukyu Chain that has been developed as an American military air base since World War II. The Korean Mountains extend in a submerged arc toward southwestern Honshu, while the Sakhalin Mountains dip under Soya Strait to emerge again in Hokkaido.

Where these mountain chains meet in Hokkaido, in central Honshu west of Tokyo, and in Kyushu, high, complex mountain knots, with clusters of volcanoes, occur. The highest mountains are found in central Honshu, with Mt. Fujiyama rising over 12,000 feet. In submarine topography, the 30,000-foot depth of the Tuscarora Deep southeast of Japan contrasts with the shallow Yellow Sea or even the 12,000-foot-deep basin of the Japan Sea. A great part of Japan's coasts is bordered by promontories and indentations, giving the country a coast line of 16,000 miles, or four times that of the much larger country of China. Characteristically, Japan's topography comprises a mountainous center enclosing small interior basins and narrow valleys and surrounded by coastal alluvial plains. These plains are surmounted near the mountains by former lowland plains which have been raised by earth movements to make high, level terraces. Rivers are short, with steep profiles making most of them unnavigable, and with limited backup reservoir capacities. The plains and terraces on which the majority of the population live bring the people into close contact with the sea. These lowlands are generally small and scattered, with the Kwanto Plain, some 5,000 square miles dominated by Tokyo, by far the largest. Following this in size are the plains of Hokkaido, the most important, the west central Ishikari Plain, having only 800 square miles. The coastal plains most often are bordered near the sea by dune ridges which create drainage difficulties but which also serve as settlement sites. Favorable factors affecting occupancy of the coastal lowlands include a long growing season, abundant rainfall, and opportunities for fishing.

*Figure 13-17 Mt. Fuji in winter. (Courtesy of Siegel.)*

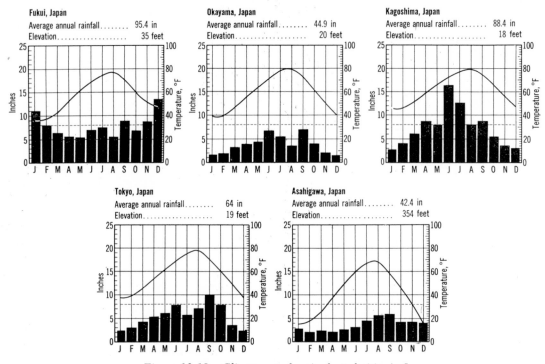

*Figure 13-18    Climate graphs of selected cities in Japan.*

## Climate

Adjacency to the east coast of the Asiatic land mass brings Japan into the monsoon climatic regime, but a regime greatly modified by maritime influences (Figure 13-18). The northward-moving warm Japan Current divides around Kyushu, flows up the northwest coasts of Japan to Hokkaido, and washes the southeast coast as far as Tokyo Bay. To the north of this latitude and around Hokkaido, southward-moving cold currents chill the northern coasts.

The southeastern half of Japan has the familiar midsummer monsoon rainfall peak, with an added peak during the typhoon period in late summer and early fall. Cyclonic storms moving up from the Yangtze Valley also produce the moldy period of the "plum rains" with oppressive heat and humidity. Winter continental winds bring cool, drier weather to the southeast but heavy precipitation to northwest coastal regions. Much of that precipitation is in the form of deep snow which thaws rapidly in

spring and causes serious floods. Although no part of Japan suffers drought as it is understood on the continent, northern Hokkaido and the Inland Sea in the south have only about 40 inches of precipitation in contrast to 57 inches at Tokyo and 84 inches at Kagoshima in southern Kyushu. Moreover, the mountain-ringed Inland Sea region has mild, pleasant winters. Summers in the southern half of Japan are hot and oppressive. In northern Honshu and Hokkaido summer fogs are frequent.

The long latitudinal stretch of over 1,000 miles between northern Hokkaido and southern Kyushu leads to considerable climatic differences. Hokkaido has climatic similarities to Maine; Kyushu resembles Florida. In the south especially, altitudinal zonation brings a range of vegetation that equals the change produced by latitudinal differences at low altitudes. Vegetation varies from subtropical forests in southern Kyushu, southern Shikoku, and the Kii Peninsula of southeastern Honshu to subboreal coniferous forests in the heart of Hokkaido.

## Historical Development

The earliest known inhabitants of Japan were the Caucasoid Ainu, a short, stockily built race with the hairiness characteristic of Europeans. The Mongoloid Yamato race entered Japan via the southern island of Kyushu. Gradually, with the aid of improved weapons and armor, they drove back the fiercely resisting Ainu until they were pushed far into northern Honshu and Hokkaido. Today, only a few thousand pure-blooded Ainu are found on Hokkaido and on Sakhalin Island.

Archaeological finds that include Chinese bronze artifacts dating back to about the beginning of the Christian era indicate some Japanese cultural contact with the mainland as early as that period. However, most of the advances of early Japanese civilization were based upon cultural importations from China subsequent to the Christian era. Korea formed the bridge over which these flowed. Conflicts with the continental areas came through Japanese raiding expeditions against parts of southern Korea, in Japanese pirate raids along the China coast, and in two unsuccessful attempts by Kublai Khan to invade Japan with huge naval fleets. Contact with the West began with the arrival of Portuguese Jesuits in the middle of the sixteenth century. Their numerous converts became embroiled as a group in the political rivalries of the time. Fear of foreign aid to enemies of the reigning Shogun caused the latter to banish the missionaries and suppress Christianity. For two centuries Japan withdrew into cultural and commercial seclusion. Serious internal economic, social, and political unrest developed in Japan in the early nineteenth century. It came to a head at a time when China's weakness before the aggression of well-organized European naval powers was becoming apparent. Fear of falling into the same situation decided Japan to come out of seclusion when Commodore Perry, in 1853, made a show of arms in Tokyo Bay in a move for opening the country to foreign trade and intercourse.

Japan now exerted itself to develop those aspects of technology that appeared to have made the Western powers strong. Foreign experts were invited to help in guiding the development of a modern army and navy, in education, science and industry, and in agriculture. Trade restrictions and the need for dependable markets and sources of raw materials eventually provoked the Japanese to seek them by force of arms. Through skillful political maneuvering and military pressure timed to exploit the struggle for power among the Western nations, Japan by 1937 had built up an empire of great magnitude. Between 1876 and 1879, Japan occupied the Ryukyu Islands vaguely claimed by China. Taiwan was acquired by the Japanese victors in the Sino-Japanese War of 1894–1895. Korea was annexed in 1910 after a military intervention and threatened war with China. Russia ceded the Kuril Islands in 1875 in exchange for the southern half of Sakhalin Island. When Japan defeated Russia in the war of 1904–1905, she took back southern Sakhalin, which she called Karafuto. In return for entry into World War I on the Allied side, Japan was permitted to oust the Germans from their Pacific Islands in 1916 and to occupy what became the mandated Pacific Islands under the League of Nations (the present United States trust territory of the Marshall, Caroline, and Mariana Islands). She was already entertaining ambitious dreams of a continental empire which began to take form with the occupation of Manchuria in 1931 when China was too disorganized and weak to resist. These and Japan's subsequent moves in China and Indochina threatened the power balance in the Pacific, and the interests of the United States and its Allies. Because the United States finally took resolute measures to oppose these advances, Japan made the attack on Pearl Harbor that led to open warfare in the Pacific. Insatiably ambitious, Japan overestimated the geographical foundations of its power, and, at the end of World War II, was stripped of its empire and reduced to the home islands.

## Population and Livelihood

Part of the urge for expansion resulted from the rapid population increase that began after

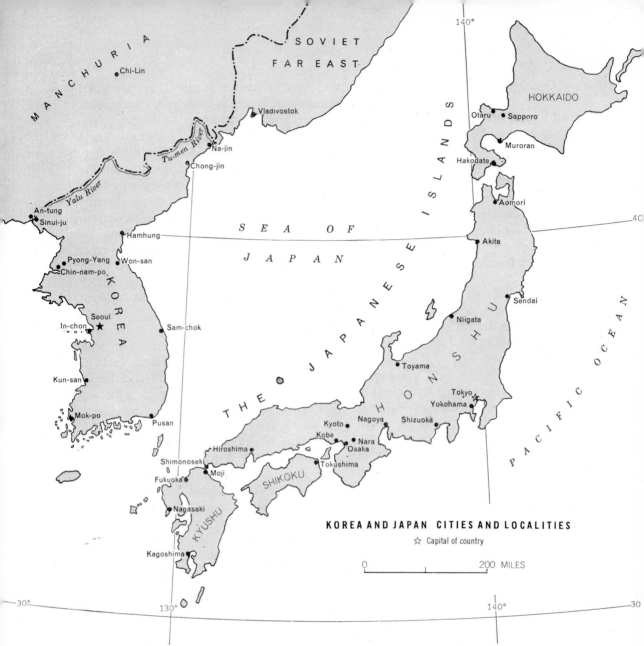

*Figure 13-19   The principal cities of both Japan and Korea are on the plains of each country. Compare this map with Map 13-12. Note the number of large cities in Japan.*

1850. Practices associated with the feudal system, economic poverty, and disease had kept Japan's population fluctuating around 30 millions for two centuries. Between 1850 and 1941, this rose to a level two and a half times as high; in 1955, Japan had more than 88 million people, and population is rising at the rate of 1 to 2 per cent annually. In the century from 1860–1960, Japan's population will have tripled. Land under cultivation, however, will have increased by only a third. Japan in 1950 had only about 14.8 million acres of cultivated land, compared with 344.4 million acres of harvested land in the United States, or a ratio of 1 to 23. Japan's 88 million people in 1955 compared with 165 million for the United

States, or a ratio of about 1 to 2. The Japanese thus had only one-twelfth the cultivated land resources per capita of the United States. In 1955, required food imports amounted to 2.9 million tons. Intensive land use and intense exploitation of fisheries, therefore, have been necessary to cope with the food needs. Moreover, like the British, the Japanese also must manufacture and export to live.

## Agriculture

Though the percentage of Japanese population employed in agriculture has dropped from 80 to 45 during the past century, the total number has increased somewhat; in 1950, there were 6,176,422 farm households with 37.8 million people. In the same year, the United States with a much greater population had only 23 million people on farms. Thus, agriculture still is the leading occupation of the Japanese, and its relative decline in large part has been because virtually no good agricultural land remains to be utilized.

Even more than in China and Korea, rice is the cultural preference of the people, so that even in such subboreal climates as those of Hokkaido, rice growing is pushed wherever water, soils, and growing season permit. More than 55 per cent of the cultivated land is in rice crops. Nevertheless, the area of cultivated land in dry crops far exceeds that used for paddy. This seeming paradox is explained by the fact that winter dry crops are grown on the paddy fields whereas rice cannot be grown on most of the land permanently used for dry crops. The long growing season from the Kwanto Plain southward permits such double cropping, so that the equivalent of 4.48 million acres of crop area is added to the actual cultivated land surface.

Climate is one of the less significant factors limiting agricultural production in Japan, although it becomes important in northern Honshu and Hokkaido (Figure 13-20). Sixty-five per cent of the land is over 15 degrees in slope, and poor drainage and other factors further reduce the land fit for use. With soils generally well-leached owing to the high rainfall, produc-

tivity depends heavily on fertilization. Though maximum use is made of organic fertilizers such as night soil and farm manures, there is heavy dependence upon chemical fertilizers, much of which must be imported.

Pressure of population upon the land is shown by the small amount of land in industrial crops, by the high yields that indicate the most intensive cultivation, and by the high percentage of cereal and starchy tuber crops which yield most calories per unit of land. Eighty-one per cent of the calories consumed are from grains, 95 per cent from grains and tubers, 68 per cent from rice alone. Japanese leaders realize the need to diversify their diet, however, and attempts are being made to popularize bread and other wheat products in order to raise the nutritional level. In the south, fall-sown wheat and winter barley are associated with summer rice together with soybeans on field borders and dikes. A great variety of crop associations occurs on the dry fields. Oats are important in Hokkaido, and barley, naked barley, wheat, millet, and buckwheat are widespread. Sweet potatoes are conspicuous in the southern islands and white potatoes on Hokkaido. Large quantities of vegetables are grown on the diluvial, upland dry fields.

Some regional specialties include tobacco and hemp on the north Kwanto Plain, tatami reeds in the Okayama and Hiroshima sea fringes, green tea and tangerines in the Shizuoka vicinity, flax, pyrethrum, peppermint, and sugar beets in Hokkaido, rapeseed and sesame seed in Kyushu and between Lake Biwa and Ise Bay, and mulberry, especially in the west Kwanto upland plain. A limited amount of dairying is carried on, mostly in Hokkaido.

## Fisheries

For about the last forty years Japan has been the foremost fishing nation of the world, an aspect of livelihood partly attributable to its insular advantages, partly to population pressure upon limited farmland, and in great measure to the natural productiveness of the sea waters. In 1940, one-fourth of the world's fish catch was made by Japan. Fish and other marine products follow rice in importance in the diet of the average Japanese. Because most of the farming areas are on coastal plains, almost half the 1.5 million persons engaged in fishing in 1940 had other occupations, such as farming.

Herring and sardines together constitute one-third to one-half of the total catch. Coastal and offshore waters of the home islands account for about 80 per cent of the catch, two-thirds coming from within 20 miles of shore. Of the total catch in 1940, 3.3 million tons, about one-half came from the former empire areas, thus the loss of these waters has been a serious blow. Because Korea has insisted that her territorial waters extend as far as 60 miles from the Korean coast, the lack of access to other old fishing areas was estimated to cost Japan about 2.8 billion dollars in revenue losses in 1955. As early as 1951, however, the fishing fleet was 1.2 million gross tons or double the prewar fleet and still growing. The annual catch reached 4.3 million tons.

## Industry

Japan cannot live without importing approximately one-fifth of its food needs, and it can pay for this food only through exports. With only limited amounts of raw materials for export, Japan must export labor in the form of manufactures and processed goods. Furthermore, the country is poor in the minerals required for modern industry and must import both fuel and raw materials to supplement meager home supplies. Strategically, therefore, Japan is very vulnerable. Virtually all its raw cotton, wool, phosphate rock, crude rubber, nickel, bauxite, magnesite, and tin has to be imported. The import requirement for iron ore is about 82 per cent, for heavy coking coal 70 per cent, for crude oil 88 per cent, and for salt 80 per cent.

Of the important metals, only zinc is adequate. Except for moderate supplies of chromite, ferralloys essential for high-grade steels are seriously deficient. Fortunately, sulfuric acid, one of the most important of the heavy chemicals, can be adequately supplied from pyrite and as a by-product in the smelting of copper, zinc, and lead. Much of Japan's needs in copper can be met from domestic mines.

In coal, the production of which exceeds in value that of all other minerals combined, Japan has an adequate supply. At the annual rate

of mining about 50 million tons, there is sufficient coal to last two hundred years, but industry needs to import much coking coal. Although Japan has much smaller reserves than China, it long has been the largest producer in Asia. (Unconfirmed reports indicate, however, that Communist China now may surpass Japan in coal output.) Nearly half the coal reserves are in Kyushu. About 40 per cent is found in the northern island of Hokkaido; the remainder is scattered throughout Honshu. Fifty-five per cent of all coal mined comes from Kyushu, mostly from the Chikuho field in the north. About 25 per cent comes from Hokkaido, mostly from the Ishikari field. Supplies for the Tokyo industrial area come from the Joban field just north of the Kwanto Plain.

A combination of unfavorable factors in recent years has seriously depressed the Japanese coal industry. Conversion to oil in many plants has led to the closing of many mines. The most important factor appears to be the crushing expense of getting coal out of the thin, broken seams characteristic of many Japanese deposits. Mechanization in the American pattern often will not work. Japanese coal is high in waste content when compared with American

coal. These and other factors in 1955 made coal imported from the United States five dollars per ton cheaper in Japan than domestic coal.

Petroleum reserves are meager, and its production supplies only 10 to 12 per cent of the needs. Annual production is less than the United States daily production. Most of the reserves are found near the northwest coast of Honshu and in the Ishikari region of Hokkaido.

Japan's hydroelectric power potential is about equal to that of Italy and one-fourth that of China. Before World War II, however, Japan held third rank in the world in developed hydroelectric power. About 60 per cent of the potential is now being utilized. The development of hydroelectric power suffers the seasonal limitation of the monsoon system and is based on a stream flow of an average of about six months per year. Ninety-two per cent of the hydroelectric facilities are run-of-the-river type which produces erratic quantities of electricity and hence requires standby steam plants. Unfortunately, the damming of the few large reservoir sites available would submerge needed agricultural lands. Most of the present develop-

*Figure 13-20   Lake Toya on Hokkaido Island. (Courtesy of Japan Travel Information Office.)*

ment is along the rivers in the central mountain knot of Honshu. In general, high-cost coal, petroleum, and hydroelectric power constitute an unfavorable factor in Japanese industrial development.

Iron ore is largely imported from such suppliers as Malaya, the Philippines, India, and before 1945, China and Korea. Ninety per cent of the small home production comes from two districts, 60 per cent from the Kamashii and Senin mines in northeastern Honshu north of Sendai, and 30 per cent from the Kuchan mines in southern Hokkaido. The ore goes to the coal regions for smelting, so that 70 per cent of the pig iron is produced in northern Kyushu, the center for heavy industry, where about half the country's steel is produced.

Manufacturing in Japan is concentrated in the belt running along the southern side of Honshu and along both shores of the Inland Sea, from the Kwanto Plain to and including northern Kyushu, in which 75 to 80 per cent of the industrial activity is located. Nearly 85 per cent of the value of industrial goods comes from this area. The reasons for such a concentration are to be found in the abundant labor, excellent water and land communications, fine harbors, and the historical focus of the region, as well as in the agricultural and mineral resources immediately adjacent. Sixty per cent of the industrial activity is divided about equally between the Osaka region and the Tokyo region, 10 per cent is found in north Kyushu and 10 per cent around Nagoya. Al-

Figure 13-21  *Many different industries, in various stages of mechanization, exist in Japan. (Courtesy of Robert Hall, Jr.)*

a. *A coal mining town in northern Kyushu.*
b. *Raw materials and mechanized ore-handling equipment of a steel plant in northern Kyushu.*
c. *Heavy industry plants in a north Kyushu coastal city.*
d. *Villagers in the central part of Japan inspecting new farm machines.*

though heavy industry is the principal activity in north Kyushu, the other areas are noted for their great variety of industries. Nagoya specializes mainly in light industries. Metalworking, the making of machines, motors, chemicals, textiles, and food processing are of major importance in the eastern three centers. A limited amount of heavy industry occurs in Southern Hokkaido. Earlier industrial development was centered mainly on cotton and silk textiles, but the war build-up of the late 1930s brought increasing attention to heavy industry and machine making.

In the postwar period Japan's industries underwent considerable changes. War damage amounted to a 25 per cent loss of the national wealth, and world trade restrictions were numerous in the immediate postwar period. Textile production, still the largest industry, in 1952 was the most depressed with only half the prewar cotton spindle capacity, although Japan had regained leadership in world export. Moreover, Japan's raw silk output in 1951 was only 181,620 bales compared with over 650,000 bales yearly in the 1934–1939 period.

Many items show considerable absolute increase in output in the later period, but in terms of an index of 100 for the 1935–1938 period, the index of real industrial production deflated for population increase in 1951 was only 85.9. Nevertheless, Japan's industrial output has been growing faster than that of any other country in the world and has made an amazing comeback. Its cement industry in 1954 ranked fifth in the world, with an output of 10.6 million tons. Southeast Asia formed the largest market for Japan's cement export. Japan's shipbuilding capacity in 1955 was estimated to rank third, following the United States and Great Britain. Ships topped the list of Japan's dollar-earning exports in 1954. The largest tankers and ore-carrying ships in the world have been built by Japanese yards during the postwar period.

Although these heavy industries are the most spectacular, the role of small enterprises is far more important to the nation's economy. Enterprises each with less than 200 employees accounted for over 96 per cent of the nation's half a million workshops, and these employed 68 per cent of the total number of workers. The importance of small enterprises in obtaining foreign exchange is shown by the fact that, in 1955, they accounted for 60 per cent of the articles exported. The bulk of the daily necessities demanded by the Japanese people is produced by these small- and medium-sized enterprises, and they also complement large-scale enterprises by participating in various phases of the production schedule. These phases often comprise the production of parts carried on in the workers' homes.

## Communications and Commerce

As a rugged mountain land with most of its productive areas fringing the sea and with good harbors in abundance, it is natural that Japan should be a seafaring nation. Dependence upon commerce for a livelihood spurred the creation of a large merchant marine, and its strategic ambitions led Japan to build up one of the most powerful naval fleets in the world. The merchant fleet reached a peak of 6 million tons in 1941, but was reduced to 1.34 million tons in World War II, which also resulted in the sinking of virtually the entire navy. Japan has now rebuilt her merchant marine to about 4 million tons and is continuing to increase this rapidly. This is stimulated by the need to eliminate dependence upon high-cost foreign shipping.

Coastal trade between the home islands and ports has always required about a million tons of shipping, for land communications are difficult and costly owing to the rugged terrain. Nevertheless, before World War II 15,000 miles of well-equipped railroads served the different islands. However, railroads are more important for passenger than for freight haul, and passenger transport brings greater gross receipts, a very unusual situation in railroading. The most important line is the Tokaido, following an ancient and famous highway route connecting Tokyo with Kyoto and Osaka. Motor car travel and transport are not so important in Japan. Owing to the low income of most of the populace, less than one person in four hundred owns a motorized vehicle of any kind. Trucks, buses, taxis, and motorcycles constitute most of the motorized traffic. Most country roads are narrow and poor. Military considerations led to the construction of the undersea railway tunnel connecting Honshu and Kyushu between Shimonoseki and Moji. This was completed in 1944. A parallel undersea highway tunnel, second longest in the world, was reported scheduled for completion in 1958.

The chief ports for foreign trade are Yokohama-Tokyo with a combined population of over 6 million, Osaka-Kobe nearly 3 million, Moji at the Shimonoseki Straits, and Nagoya in Ise Bay over 1 million. In the period before World War II, ores and metals, raw cotton, mineral oils, machinery, and machine parts constituted the most important imports. Raw silk, cotton goods, machines, clothing, and metal manufactures were the most important exports. During the 1936–1939 period the major countries trading with Japan, in order of importance to Japan, were China, the United States, Germany, and Great Britain. There has been a considerable reorientation in trade, with China occupying a relatively unimportant position, but with Southeastern and Southern Asia taking half Japan's exports and providing about a third of her imports. There has been a heavy imbalance of imports over exports in her trade with the United States. Unfortunately for Japan, expansion of exports is meeting opposition from competitive producers both in the United States and Europe. The United States is Japan's best customer, followed by Indonesia. Japan replaced Great Britain as chief supplier to Pakistan, and India took China's place as chief coal supplier to Japan. India and Pakistan buy approximately 24 per cent of Japan's textiles; Australia takes about 20 per cent. In order to exist Japan must import food and raw materials and export manufactures.

## IN PERSPECTIVE

### Problems of Central Eastern Asia

Central Eastern Asia's problems are numerous and differ according to the geographical environment and technological development. Generalizations often require exceptions, but it may be fairly said that population increases faster than food production, so that there is general nutritional deficiency, both as to calories and to proteins and vitamins. Whereas average daily caloric intake per person in the United Kingdom and the United States was over 3,000 both in 1938 and in 1951, in Japan the 1938 caloric intake of 2,180 had dropped to 2,142 in 1951.

*Figure 13-22 Tokyo, the capital of Japan, is one of the largest cities in the world. This view of the principal business district shows large, modern office buildings as well as several means of communication. (Courtesy of Japan Travel Information Office.)*

During the same period, protein intake had dropped from 64 to 54 grams, in contrast to a rise to above 90 grams in 1951 for both the United Kingdom and for the United States. Japan still was better off than India and Pakistan, however.

Health and sanitation in most of Central Eastern Asia have not yet come up to desirable standards, and life expectancy is low. As a result of measures introduced into Japan during the Occupation following World War II, the death rate was reduced to 9 per thousand in 1953, and the birth rate dropped from the postwar 34 per thousand to 21 per thousand in 1953 largely as a result of birth control practices and legislation legalizing abortion. Nevertheless, there is still an increase of 12 per thousand per year or an annual addition of over a million people to Japan. In other parts of Central Eastern Asia both birth and death rates are considerably higher.

Poverty and low purchasing power are associated with small savings and surpluses for capital accumulation. Except in Japan where literacy is high, poverty also is associated with low literacy rates. Children must start earning part of their living at an early age, bringing their cheaper, less efficient labor into competition with that of adult workers. Labor generally is unskilled and untrained, cheap in terms of individual wages, but inefficient and costly in terms of productivity.

Economically, natural resources are modest both in variety and in quantity per capita, although in individual items, such as coal in China, there may be great surplus reserves. Production is not at a high level, however. Agriculturally, there is overemphasis on individual crops such as rice, and there is a relatively low state of development in pastoral industries except in Mongolia and in the west and northwest periphery of China. This is particularly true of dairying, a situation partly attributable to cultural distaste for dairy products. Meat-producing animals are raised in great aggregate numbers but are few per capita. Raising animals for food is mainly concentrated on the scavenger type such as hogs and fowls that compete little with man for the food-growing land. In Japan and Mongolia, however, the pig is not important.

Progress is being made in industrialization and technical modernization, but the rate has been rapid only in Japan. Many aspects of society, however, still follow old traditions. Where the forms of tradition have been overthrown, as in Communist China, the earlier pattern of autocracy and rule-from-the-top persists as strongly as ever. This may well lead to more rapid technological progress under the ruthless drive of Communist dictatorship, but such a process also involves a sacrifice of the finer values of civilization, and appears to be unpopular to great masses of the Chinese.

## EXERCISES

*1.* What is the total population of the countries of Central Eastern Asia? What percentage of the world population is this? Why does population density per square mile for each country not present the true population problem?

*2.* Where are mountains, plateaus, and plains located in China? What climatic changes are caused by these landforms? How does the topography of China compare with that of the European part of the U.S.S.R.?

*3.* How does agriculture in South China differ from that in North China? Why? What are the chief food crops grown in northern and southern China? Which of these are exported?

*4.* What are the principal occupations of Tibet and Mongolia? In what ways do these two areas differ? How does the population density of these two areas differ from that of China proper?

*5.* What minerals exist in China in large quantities? Where are they mined? Why have the mineral resources of China been so poorly developed?

*6.* What are the principal rivers of China? In which part of the country is each located? What large cities are along or near each river? Why are the rivers of China of such importance to the country?

*7.* What has been the influence of history upon China? What governmental changes have taken place in China since 1945? In what ways has this political change affected the work of the people?

8. At which parallel of latitude is Korea divided? Why was it divided? How does North Korea differ from South Korea in economic and cultural development? What are the principal occupations in each area? What do you think must be done to improve the Korean situation? Why?

9. What is the area and population of Japan? With which of the United States does it compare in size? How does the density of population in Japan compare with the density of population in that state? Which Japanese cities have populations of over one million?

10. What are the four principal Japanese islands? What kind of landforms dominate each? Why is Hokkaido not as densely populated as the others?

11. What are the handicaps and advantages of the topography of Japan? What are the locational advantages and handicaps? What are the principal problems of land utilization in Japan?

12. What are the common problems of Japan, Korea, and China? How is each attempting to solve its problems? Which do you think will succeed? Why?

13. What is the political status of Taiwan (Formosa)? Do you expect this situation to last? Why?

## SELECTED REFERENCES

Borton, Hugh (ed.): *Japan,* Cornell University Press, Ithaca, 1951.

Chang, Chi-yun: "Climate and Man in China," *Annals of the Association of American Geographers,* 36:44–76, March, 1946.

Cressey, George B.: *The Land of 500 Million,* McGraw-Hill Book Company, Inc., New York, 1955.

————: "Changing the Map of China," *Economic Geography,* 31:1–16, January, 1955.

Friters, Gerard M.: *Outer Mongolia and Its International Position,* The Johns Hopkins Press, Baltimore, 1949.

Ginsburg, Norton S. (ed.): *The Pattern of Asia,* Prentice-Hall, Inc., Englewood Cliffs, N.J., 1958.

Heinrich, Harrer: "My Seven Years in Tibet," *Geographical Journal,* 120:146–155, June, 1954.

McCune, Shannon: *Research Monographs on Korea, Climatic Regions,* Korean Research Associates, 1945.

Osgood, C. B.: *Koreans and Their Culture,* The Ronald Press Company, New York, 1951.

Trewartha, Glenn: *Japan, A Physical, Cultural and Regional Geography,* University of Wisconsin Press, Madison, 1945.

————: "Chinese Cities: Origins and Functions," *Annals of the Association of American Geographers,* 42:69–93, March, 1952.

Trewartha, Glenn T., and Wilbur Zelinsky: "Population Distribution and Change in Korea, 1925–1949," *Geographical Review,* 45:1–26, January, 1955.

Wiens, Herold J.: "Geographical Limitations to Food Production in the Mongolian Peoples Republic," *Annals of the Association of American Geographers,* 41:348–369, December, 1951.

————: "Riverine and Coastal Junks in China's Commerce," *Economic Geography,* 31:248–264, July, 1955.

Winfield, Gerald: *China, the Land and the People,* William Sloane Associates, New York, 1948.

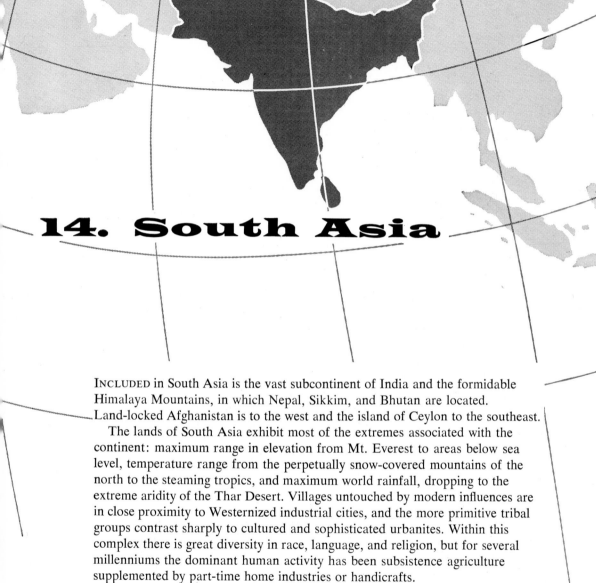

# 14. South Asia

INCLUDED in South Asia is the vast subcontinent of India and the formidable Himalaya Mountains, in which Nepal, Sikkim, and Bhutan are located. Land-locked Afghanistan is to the west and the island of Ceylon to the southeast.

The lands of South Asia exhibit most of the extremes associated with the continent: maximum range in elevation from Mt. Everest to areas below sea level, temperature range from the perpetually snow-covered mountains of the north to the steaming tropics, and maximum world rainfall, dropping to the extreme aridity of the Thar Desert. Villages untouched by modern influences are in close proximity to Westernized industrial cities, and the more primitive tribal groups contrast sharply to cultured and sophisticated urbanites. Within this complex there is great diversity in race, language, and religion, but for several millenniums the dominant human activity has been subsistence agriculture supplemented by part-time home industries or handicrafts.

Dispensing Western ideas along with material goods, the European colonial system reached its zenith in the nineteenth century, but rapidly disintegrated after World War II. Under the impact of Western material culture ancient customs and practices are changing. Both the old and the new countries of South Asia are employing Western science and technology to increase their productive capacity in order to provide a better living for their 490 million people. South Asia has some of the oldest independent nations in the world—Afghanistan, Nepal, and Bhutan—and some of the newest—India, Pakistan, and Ceylon (1947).

*511*

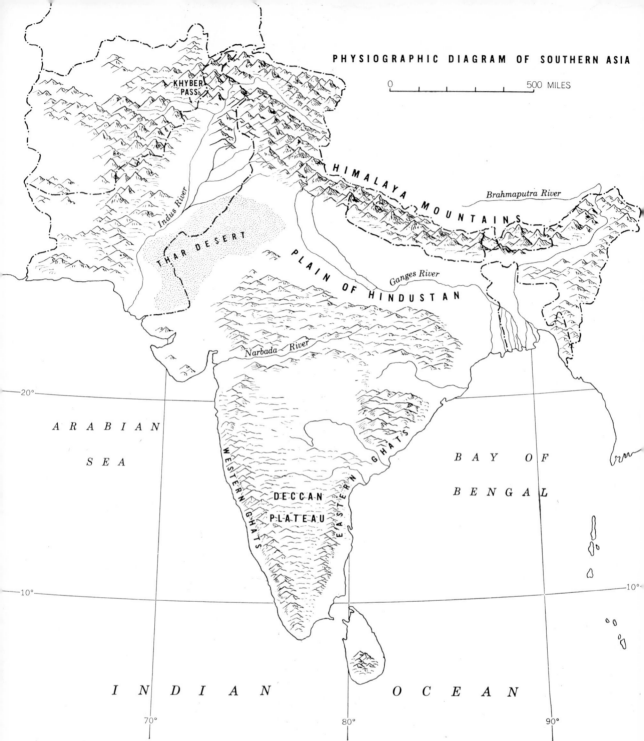

PHYSIOGRAPHIC DIAGRAM OF SOUTHERN ASIA

0                              500 MILES

KHYBER PASS

Indus River

HIMALAYA MOUNTAINS

Brahmaputra River

THAR DESERT

PLAIN OF HINDUSTAN

Ganges River

Narbada River

20°

ARABIAN SEA

WESTERN GHATS

EASTERN GHATS

DECCAN PLATEAU

BAY OF BENGAL

10°                                                                    10°

INDIAN          OCEAN

70°                    80°                    90°

Figure 14-1  Southern Asia is a region of contrasting landforms. Along its
northern edge are the Himalaya Mountains with Mt. Everest located in Nepal.
Between the mountains and the Deccan Plateau are fertile river valleys and
the Thar Desert.

## THE SUBCONTINENT OF INDIA

*Physical Setting*

Physically isolated from the great land mass of Asia by mountain barriers, the subcontinent of India may be divided into three major natural regions: the mountain wall separating it from the Asian land mass; the plain of the Indus, Ganges, and Brahmaputra Rivers; and the compact triangular peninsula thrust into the Indian Ocean (Figure 14-1).

**Relief Features.**   The mountain wall to the north is symmetrically arranged with the massive Himalayas in the center and the Baluchistan and Burmese Ranges on the west and east. From the gorge of the Indus to the gorge of the Brahmaputra, the Himalaya Mountains extend eastward in an arc for about 1,500 miles. With an average crest line of 20,000 feet, several of the world's highest peaks are found here—Nanga Parbat in Kashmir, Mt. Everest in Nepal, and Mt. Kinchinjunga farther east rise to almost 30,000 feet. For more than a thousand miles there are only two commonly used routes through this lofty barrier. The western follows the Jhelum River to the Vale of Kashmir thence via the upper Indus Valley; the eastern route is via Darjeeling and Sikkim, thence through the Chumbi Valley to Tibet.

On the west the less formidable Sulaiman and Kirthar Ranges extend southward to the delta of the Indus. There are two major passes in this mountain wall, the most famous being the strategically important Khyber Pass which for centuries provided major access to the plains of northern India. Farther south where these ranges converge is the Bolan Gate, the best natural route from Southwestern Asia.

To the east the gorge of the Brahmaputra is difficult and the Burmese Ranges are a practical barrier. Passes are high in these folded mountains and they have been little used. During World War II a military highway, the Ledo Road, was constructed to railhead in Burma. It was officially abandoned in 1945.

The Plain of Hindustan is one of the largest and most important in the world; historically and culturally it is the heart of India. More than 2,000 miles long and from 150 to 200 miles wide, the plain is remarkably level throughout, the slope gentle, and the alluvium fine in texture (Figure 14-2). It is drained by three major rivers, the Indus, Ganges, and Brahmaputra, and their tributaries. All three rivers are fed by melting snows of the Himalayas and by summer monsoon rains, and though volume varies with the seasons, they provide considerable water to irrigate the intensively cultivated plain which supports a dense population.

Peninsular India, lying south of the Hindustan Plain, is a dissected plateau with great physiographic diversity. The western escarpment, known as the Western Ghats Mountains, rises to elevations of 3,000 to 5,000 feet; the eastern escarpment is a discontinuous chain of lower hills called the Eastern Ghats. The western coastal plain is narrow, gradually widening toward the south into the fertile Malabar Coast. On the east the Coromandel Coast, with alternating plains and deltas interrupted by many small hills, extends more than 1,000 miles.

Major rivers of the plateau rise on the slopes of the Western Ghats and flow eastward to the Bay of Bengal. Fed by the monsoon rains, these rivers vary greatly in volume and in the dry season are of scant value for either navigation or irrigation.

**Climate.**   Excluding climatic extremes associated with mountain barriers, the tropical monsoon is dominant throughout the habitable portions of the subcontinent (Figure 14-3). Annual range in temperature is often 20 to 40 degrees, but seasonal rhythm in rainfall is more significant. The year is sharply divided into wet and dry seasons, the area receiving 75 per cent to 97 per cent of the annual rainfall during the summer (Table 14-1).

Rainfall variability, increasing from east to west, is a serious problem. For example, a sta-

POLITICAL DIVISIONS AND CHIEF CITIES
OF SOUTHERN ASIA

Land areas less than 1000 feet in elevation

Land areas more than 1000 feet in elevation

0                                          500 MILES

U. S. S. R.

Herat
Kabul
AFGHANISTAN
Helmand River
Kandahar
Quetta
IRAN

KASHMIR

PAKISTAN
Lahore
PUNJAB
Indus River

THAR DESERT
Delhi

TIBET

Brahmaputra River

NEPAL
SIKKIM
BHUTAN
Darjeeling
ASSAM

Gwadar (Oman)
Karachi

I N D I A

Ganges River
Benares

EAST
PAKISTAN
Dacca

Jamshedpur
Calcutta
Chittagong
BURMA

20°

ARABIAN

SEA

Diu Daman
(Port.)

Bombay
Poona

Hyderabad

BAY OF

BENGAL

Goa (Port.)

MALABAR

COAST

Madras

10°                                                                                                10°

Calicut

CEYLON
Colombo

I N D I A N        O C E A N

70°                                  80°                                  90°

Figure 14-2   India, Pakistan, and Ceylon have all become independent nations since World War II. Note that the Deccan Plateau is cut off from the
highland to the north by the Indus and Ganges Rivers. Most of the cities are
in areas having elevations of less than 1,000 feet.

**TABLE 14-1. WET AND DRY SEASONS** (*Precipitation in inches*)

| Station | Altitude, ft | Annual precipitation | Rainy season, June—Oct. | Dry season, Nov.—May | Months with less than 1 in |
|---|---|---|---|---|---|
| **Peninsula** | | | | | |
| Bombay | 37 | 74.0 | 72.8 | 1.2 | 7 |
| Calicut | 27 | 116.2 | 97.3 | 18.9 | 3 |
| Bangalore | 3,021 | 36.8 | 27.0 | 9.8 | 4 |
| Madras * | 22 | 48.9 | 39.0 | 9.9 | 4 |
| **Ganges Valley** | | | | | |
| Calcutta | 21 | 60.8 | 50.3 | 10.5 | 3 |
| Patna | 183 | 44.5 | 40.6 | 3.9 | 6 |
| Benares | 267 | 40.6 | 37.9 | 2.7 | 7 |
| Delhi | 718 | 27.7 | 23.8 | 3.9 | 7 |
| **Hill Stations** | | | | | |
| Darjeeling | 7,376 | 121.8 | 105.5 | 16.3 | 3 |
| Simla | 7,232 | 68.0 | 51.5 | 16.5 | 1 |
| **Indus Valley** | | | | | |
| Multan | 420 | 7.1 | 5.0 | 2.1 | 10 |
| Jacobabad | 186 | 4.1 | 2.7 | 1.4 | 10 |
| Karachi | 13 | 7.7 | 6.1 | 1.6 | 10 |

* August to December and January to July.

tion with a 6-inch average has recorded 20 inches of rain in 24 hours; heavy downpours of this type cause flooding and erosion. Sometimes the rains are late, the season short, and total precipitation less than normal. Population pressure is so great that one or two seasons of rainfall shortage or maldistribution may cause crop shortages and famine.

The success of agriculture is, therefore, largely dependent upon the summer monsoon. President Sam Higginbottom, Allahabad Christian College, said that in northern India "if the rains fail, there is no work for the farmer or for the very large number of casual landless laborers. Without the rain the fodder crops cannot be grown, neither can the fields be prepared for the grain crops which are grown in the cold season. There the failure of the rains means the absence of work for twelve months or until the next rains, and the absence of work means absence of wages and the absence of wages means absence of food, therefore starvation." Irrigation engineers classify areas with 10 to 50 inches of rainfall as precarious for agriculture. Although the variation in annual rainfall seldom exceeds 15 per cent, that variation is crucial in a land where more than two-thirds of the people are primarily dependent upon agriculture. These so-called precarious areas have been cultivated from time immemorial, but with population pressure and mounting food demands, rainfall shortages must be made up by irrigation if crops are to be harvested and famine averted.

Hill stations are used by persons wishing to escape the summer heat of the lowlands. Simla, the former official summer capital north of Delhi, and Darjeeling in the famous tea district north of Calcutta, are over 7,000 feet in elevation. Their average temperatures in June and July are 66 and 61°F, but this is also the rainy season and skies may be overcast for many consecutive days. Octacamund, luxurious resort in the Nilgris Hills southwest of Madras, is noted for its scenery and gardens.

*Cultural Factors*

**Population.** Predominantly rural, population is widely dispersed in thousands of villages averaging about one hundred houses. The dot map of population distribution (Figure 14-5)

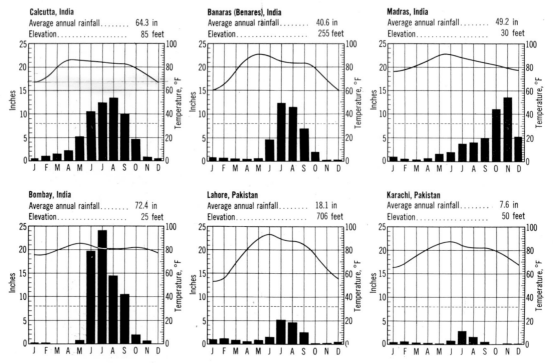

*Figure 14-3   Climate graphs of selected cities.*

shows a marked concentration in the well-watered and intensively cultivated delta and Ganges Valley where certain districts have 800 persons per square mile. A second area of concentration is in the southern tip of the peninsula, especially along the Malabar Coast where coconuts and two crops of rice a year are the main support of more than 1,400 people to the square mile in Cochin. Inland, population is clustered around the Kolar gold fields of Mysore. Settlement in the Indus Valley has grown with the development of its water resources, and the present population pattern correlates closely with irrigated lands. Another lesser grouping is in the northern Deccan, noted for its cotton. In marked contrast are the sparsely populated mountains and the arid lands of Baluchistan and Rajputana.

Since the first census of India in 1872, the growth curve has been consistently upward. In the first half of the twentieth century, population increased from 283 to 432 million, and in the decade 1941–1951, the net increase was 43.6 million or more than 4 million a year.

While the population has always been predominantly rural, a trend toward urbanization is apparent, the 1951 census reporting 13 per cent urban. The most striking feature is the increase in the larger cities, there now being six cities with more than one million each and a number with over one-half million. This urban growth may be attributed to war stimulus, resettlement of population following Partition (as the separation of India and Pakistan is called), and to increasing industrialization.

**Languages.** Successive invasions and conquests of past centuries have left their imprint, and in its complicated ethnic history, the subcontinent has received both cultural and material gifts from each of the invaders. Linguistically this area is highly complex, four main stocks are broken down into 179 languages and several hundred additional dialects. Except in isolated districts, most people are bilingual or even multilingual. Multiplicity of languages reduces intellectual contacts and creates educational problems; in Madras, for example, instruction is given in four indigenous languages. Throughout the country, during the time it was under British control, elementary instruction was in the vernacular, with English taught in the high schools. Most university instruction was in English; already the language of government and business, it also became the language of the intelligentsia.

Although it recognizes fourteen languages and has officially adopted Hindi, the Republic of India will continue to use English for fifteen years. Pakistan has officially adopted Urdu and Bengali but, in practice, continues to use English.

**Religion.** Religion plays a dominant role. Since it regulates customs, diet, occupations, and other aspects of life, Indian religion actually is a way of life. Hindus accounted for 251 million or 66 per cent of the total population in 1941; second was the large Moslem minority, with 92 million or about 24 per cent.

Six other religions were represented in the remaining 10 per cent, Buddhists, Sikhs, Jains, Parsees, Jews, and Christians. Several of these minor religions have millions of adherents; for example, over 6 million Sikhs are concentrated in the Punjab and more than 6 million Christians in the southern part of the peninsula. The small community of Parsees, mainly in the Bombay area, is highly influential in economic and political affairs.

Hindus recognize four main castes and there are some 3,000 subcastes. Traditionally a person born into a particular caste engages in the occupation and observes the social and religious customs of his particular stratum. The system carries stratification to an extreme degree by enforcing rigid marriage rules, regulating contacts between different castes, and making occupations hereditary. While it has provided an element of stability, the rigidity of the caste system has undoubtedly contributed to widespread poverty.

**Separatism and Partition.** As an outgrowth of religious and linguistic complexity, separatist movements developed. In the early 1930s

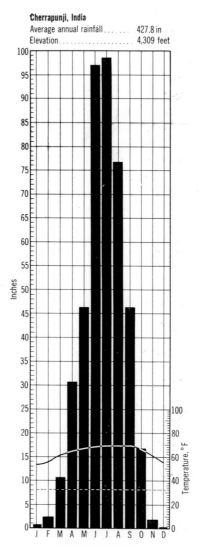

*Figure 14-4   Climate graph for Cherrapunji, India. This station has a total yearly rainfall of 427.8 inches, with almost 100 inches falling during July.*

the name "Pakistan" identified the movement for a separate Moslem state. Indian Nationalist sentiment also grew steadily and, in the long struggle for freedom, the various groups worked together. When the British withdrew, however, internal differences and antagonisms came to the surface. After a year of bitter fighting the country was partitioned along religious lines, with both India and Pakistan becoming dominions within the British Commonwealth

(1947). In 1950 India became a republic and in 1956 Pakistan became the Islamic Republic of Pakistan. Both countries voluntarily retained their association with the Commonwealth.

Partition left the problem of minorities unsolved. India still has a minority of 30 to 40 million Moslems, and Hindus account for about 13 per cent of Pakistan's population.

One-third of India was formerly made up of Native States under their own hereditary rulers, the largest and most important being Hyderabad. With independence, and the establishment of national governments, the Native States have acceded to either India or Pakistan; the status of Kashmir is still unsettled.

**Transportation.** Historically, the great centers of Indian civilization were in river valleys, with streams serving as major arteries of transportation and overland movement largely by bullock cart or pack animals. The railway era began in 1853, and by 1900 the main pattern was almost complete. Originally designed for political and economic control, the railroads moved food in time of famine and also contributed to the growth of Indian trade and industry.

The present railway pattern indicates European interest in commerce, for most lines focus on the major ports of Karachi, Bombay, Madras, and Calcutta. The densely populated plain, extending from the Punjab to the Ganges

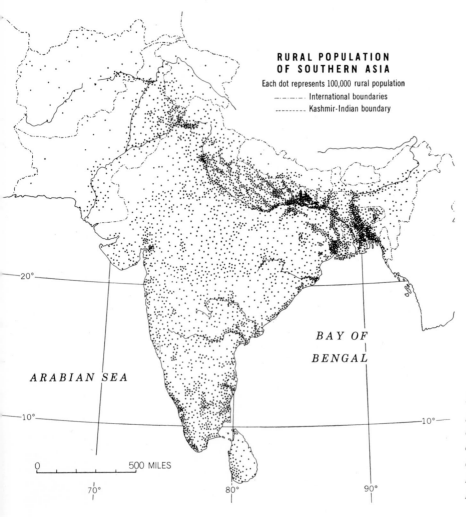

RURAL POPULATION
OF SOUTHERN ASIA

Each dot represents 100,000 rural population
— · — · — International boundaries
— — — — Kashmir-Indian boundary

*ARABIAN SEA*

*BAY OF*

*BENGAL*

0      500 MILES

*Figure 14-5 Note that rural population is concentrated largely in river valleys and along the coast. Contrast the density of population in East Pakistan with that in West Pakistan.*

Delta, is served by the most extensive rail net in Asia.

Under Partition, transportation facilities developed to serve a single country were divided into three parts. India received 34,000 route miles of railways, and Pakistan 7,000 route miles, about three-fourths of which are in West Pakistan, and one-fourth in East Pakistan. The three major ports of Calcutta, Bombay, and Madras are in India; Karachi and Chittagong serve Pakistan.

In contrast to railroads, highway building has lagged. There are only 90,000 miles of all-weather roads in the entire subcontinent, and at least 20 times as many bullock carts as motor vehicles. Waterways are of great significance in Bengal where a network of canals and channels provides access to many areas not served by land transport. In East Pakistan, a large portion of the jute, tea, and paddy crops are moved via waterways which ramify over most of the Delta.

## THE REPUBLIC OF INDIA

The Republic of India supports a human population of 356 million and an animal population of 270 million. Predominantly rural, 88 per cent, in 1950 more than two-thirds of the people gained their livelihood from agriculture. In few countries is the pressure upon the land so

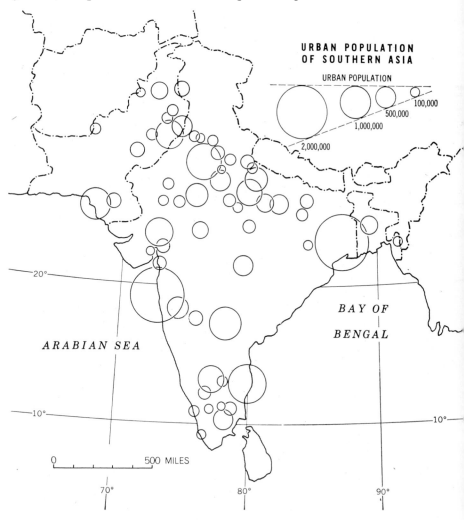

*Figure 14-6　India is a country of town, city, and village dwellers. Note the large number of cities in India as compared with Pakistan and Afghanistan. Compare this map with 14-1.*

great. As population increased through the centuries farms decreased in size, the per capita land resource gradually declining to less than one acre. Under Hindu and Moslem inheritance laws, a small farm may be divided into several smaller parcels to ensure all heirs a fair share in each type of land, such as wasteland, upland, or floodplain. Repetition of these divisions generation after generation has resulted in excessive fragmentation, thus agriculture is often inefficient and uneconomic.

The first concern of farmers is to satisfy their daily food requirements. Major edible crops fall into three groups, cereals, pulses, and oilseeds. About 75 per cent of the cultivated area is devoted to grains, including rice, wheat, sorghums, millet, maize and barley; rice alone occupies one-third of all the cultivated land. Pulses, an important source of protein, rank second in acreage, followed by the oilseeds: peanuts, rape and mustard, linseed, and sesame.

Of the fifteen crops occupying more than one million acres each, all are edible except cotton and jute.

In addition to being one of the most populous countries, India ranks first in the number of cattle, with approximately 140 million. Oxen are used for working the fields as well as for transport. The sacred cows are not worked, but their milk is a valuable addition to the diet. The 40 million water buffaloes are valued as work animals; their milk is larger in quantity and higher in butter-fat content than that of Indian cows.

Crop yields per acre are lower than in many other Asian countries. Contributory causes include unreliable precipitation, erosion, soil depletion, and poor seed, as well as inadequate fertilizer. Since dung is in great demand for fuel, probably less than half the animal manures are applied to the fields, and India makes no systematic use of night soil, a common practice

*Figure 14-7   Threshing rice in a south Indian village by driving oxen around and around over grain spread on the threshing floor. (Courtesy of Government of India.)*

in both Japan and China. Land is too scarce to be planted to soil-building cover crops, and chemical fertilizers are too expensive.

The drier lands carry some 60 million sheep and goats and half a million camels. Horses, ponies, and donkeys are used mainly for transportation in towns and cities. Animal husbandry has received scant attention, but India collects and exports annually some 65 million dollars' worth of wool, hides and skins, bristles, and bones.

There is considerable intensive gardening in areas accessible to urban markets as well as on estates for the large-scale cultivation of export commodities, such as tea and coffee. Although estates employ large numbers of laborers and provide valuable exports, peasant agriculture, with its great emphasis upon food, is infinitely more significant.

## Agriculture

**Food Crops.** One of the world's major cereals, rice, is preferred by that half of the human race living in Southern and Eastern Asia. Rice is accorded highest prestige value and dominates the local economy to such an extent that, in many areas, social customs and religious celebrations are closely related to its growth cycle.

With approximately one-third of the world's rice acreage, India ranks first in land planted but second to China in total harvest. Paddy (rough rice) is a summer crop of the wet lowlands, thriving under temperatures of 75°F and 50 to 80 inches of precipitation. With less than 40 inches, however, irrigation is necessary. Production is heaviest in the well-watered coastal plains and windward slopes of the Western Ghats. One crop a year is usual but a few well-watered areas are double cropped. In villages, husking and polishing are done by hand, but in the larger centers, milling is mechanized. Paddy is generally consumed in the locality where grown, but any small surplus is moved to nearby markets by bullock carts or small boats.

Wheat, the most important commercial grain, is grown principally as a winter crop on the alluviums of the Ganges Valley west of Benares, and on deep, black soils of the peninsula which retain sufficient moisture to carry it to maturity. Yields vary considerably, the national average being 12 bushels per acre. With 24 million acres in wheat, India ranks third in the world. The entire crop is consumed locally and additional wheat and flour imported. Rice and wheat are expensive cereals eaten by the upper-income groups, whereas the cheaper but highly nutritious millets constitute the major food supply of middle- and lower-income groups.

Many varieties of millet are grown throughout India but production is most heavily concentrated in the peninsula. It is generally a winter or dry-season crop grown in rotation with cotton, although in a few places it is planted at the beginning of the rainy season. Millets occupy 67 million acres, ranking after rice (75 million) but ahead of wheat (24 million). Millet will produce 500 to 1,000 pounds of grain per acre, and it is customary to interplant pulses. Millet is primarily for human consumption, but the poorer grain and the stalks are used for animal feed.

Corn and barley are grown extensively in the Ganges Valley and in Kashmir, mainly for human consumption. More than 7 million acres are planted to each. Corn, the chief food grain among certain hill tribes, gives way to barley at higher elevations.

Pulses include a variety of peas and beans, an indispensable source of protein in the predominantly vegetable diet. Most important of the pulses is gram, or chickpea, which is scattered throughout India—20 million acres—but with a major concentration in Uttar Pradesh. Barley and gram are cheap, staple foods in north India.

Although sugar cane is widely grown, it is concentrated on the Gangetic alluviums. Because it competes with food grains for land, it tends to be a minor crop—4 million acres. Two-thirds of the cane is crushed in small local mills worked by animal power and the juice boiled down to make gur (unrefined sugar); one-third of the cane goes to mills using the centrifugal process. The entire output is absorbed by the domestic market and supplemented by imports. Sugar is also obtained from several varieties of palms.

India leads the world in the production of peanuts, the major area being Bombay, Madras, and Hyderabad. Domestic markets absorb the larger share of the crop. High in fat and protein content, peanuts are crushed in local power mills and the oil made into ghee. Other edible oilseeds are cotton, sesame, rape, and mustard. Nonedible linseed and castor oil are used in industry.

Although commercial production is limited, fruits are grown in thousands of individual gardens. Bananas and papayas are basic foodstuffs, but the mango, mangosteen, and durian are more highly esteemed. Oranges are widely distributed, and apples, pears, and grapes are grown in the cooler areas. The coconut has a multiplicity of uses, yielding edible oil and many by-products.

Spices, which attracted early traders, are still grown along the Malabar Coast, especially nutmeg, cloves, and pepper. Chili, ginger, and mustard come from other areas. Indian curry powder is compounded of many pungent spices.

**Nonedible Crops.** The tobacco crop of 550 million pounds annually is second in size only to that of the United States, the Indian leaf coming from the fields and garden patches of small farmers. Coir, made from the fibrous husk of the coconut, is the basis of a profitable cottage industry in south India. Coir yarn as well as mats and matting are exported. Dozens of other crops are locally significant and are traded in the village market.

Most of the Indian cotton, which is high in quantity but low in quality, is grown under the natural rainfall of the summer monsoon rather than by irrigation. It is cultivated in the middle Ganges and in the peninsula but the leading region is the Deccan Plateau inland from Bombay. Here the fertile black soils have been formed by the weathering of old lavas, and although the rainfall is 20 to 35 inches, the soil is sufficiently tenacious to retain moisture until the crop matures. Grown in a region where rainfall is precarious, the Deccan cotton crop fluctuates from year to year and the average yield is low, about 100 pounds per acre.

Until the end of the eighteenth century India was one of Great Britain's major sources of raw cotton, but with advances in the textile industry calling for a longer staple and finer fibers for higher-quality cloth, India lost most of the Lancashire market. Large quantities of short-staple cotton are sold to Japan and other industrial countries which manufacture cotton textiles for markets with low purchasing power. Part of the 3-million bale crop is used locally by the handloom industry as well as by many large mechanized mills.

India was exporting cloth hand-woven from jute in the eighteenth century, but large-scale

*Figure 14-8  Hauling cotton to market by oxcart in southern India. (Courtesy of Government of India.)*

use of the fiber did not begin until about 1840. New machinery and methods pioneered by Scottish weavers in Dundee opened wider markets for this cheap but strong fiber, India securing a virtual world monopoly in raw jute. Optimum growing conditions are found in the lower Ganges-Brahmaputra Basin where favorable climate and alluvial soil, enriched by annual inundation, insure high yields.

Before 1950 all jute mills were in or near Calcutta, although more than two-thirds of the fiber was grown in Pakistan. To supply its mills on the Hooghly, India has recently doubled jute acreage.

**Estate Agriculture.** In the Indian economy, estate agriculture is completely overshadowed by small-scale cultivation. The total acreage in tea, coffee, rubber, and cinchona is minimal compared to that of the major food crops. The million wage laborers on plantations are insignificant in comparison with 240 million peasant farmers and their families.

Tea is India's leading plantation crop. The type grown is of indigenous origin and differs in quality from that domesticated elsewhere in Asia. Large-scale planting began in the late nineteenth century. Tea can be grown in the lowlands, but it thrives best on well-drained slopes between 1,000 and 4,000 feet in elevation. About one-half of the total acreage is now in Assam, with a smaller region in the vicinity of Darjeeling; 60 per cent of the Indian tea industry is owned by long-established British firms which employ many Nepalese laborers.

In the Madras and Travancore highlands, the gardens are about 4,000 feet in elevation. Labor is recruited from the more densely settled parts of India. Distinctive quality and flavor are associated with different districts, Darjeeling tea having a preferential rating in the United States. In addition to the large home market, India exports 445 million pounds of tea, or about half the total entering world trade.

Slope land with good drainage, temperatures averaging 80°F, and afternoon rains provide a suitable habitat for rubber. British estates are localized along the Malabar Coast, but most Indian-owned estates have been established at higher elevations of 1,000 to 2,000 feet. About 100,000 acres of trees are being tapped, with the annual harvest processed mainly by Indian mills.

### Cottage Industries

For centuries small-scale and cottage industries were an integral part of the self-sufficient village economy of India. Utilitarian articles were produced everywhere; in certain areas specialized skills were highly developed, and artistic products were frequently carried long distances by sailing ship or caravan. India claims to have been the original home of cotton weaving and for several thousand years exported fine cloth.

From the sixteenth into the nineteenth century varied textiles including muslins, chintzes, and calicoes were exported, as were embroidered shawls, silks, and carpets. Apprentices under master craftsmen attained skill in metalwork, brass, copper, bronze, and silver; most of these artisans worked at home with simple tools. Integrated into the local economy, such handicrafts enabled India to sell competitively both at home and abroad.

The Industrial Revolution with its outpouring of machine-made goods had the effect of depressing craft manufacture in India, many small industries gradually disappearing. After a long period of stagnation in cottage industries, the national government is officially encouraging their revival as a means of reducing unemployment as well as of increasing production for both local and foreign markets. The handloom industry now produces about 20 per cent of the nation's cloth and employs 14 million workers, five times as many as all factories combined. Weaving silk, wool, and rugs by hand supports additional tens of thousands. Inlaid metals, filigree, lacquer and horn articles, brassware, and ivory are made for world markets.

### Large-scale Industry

India possesses most of the requisites for modern large-scale industry. Coal reserves are large,

*Figure 14-9   Carpet weaver in an Amritsar factory. The two strips of paper on the loom contain design and color instructions to the weaver. (Courtesy of Government of India.)*

India ranking seventh in world production; 90 per cent of the present output comes from the Damodar Valley. Railroads consume about one-third of the coal, and lesser amounts are used by the steel and textile industries, for thermal electricity, and for export.

The most highly mineralized area extends from the coal fields of the Damodar Valley to the gold fields of Mysore. Actively worked minerals include high-grade iron ore, the ferro-alloys manganese and chromite, bauxite, and mica. Agricultural materials most available to industry include cotton, jute, wool, oilseeds, hides, and skins. Although half of the developed hydroelectric power is in the vicinity of Bombay, the greatest potential is along the Himalayas, in the Western Ghats, and in the southern hills.

**Textile Industries.**   It was not until 1856 that the first cotton mill began operation in Bombay where there were many natural advantages; three years later a second was established at Ahmedabad. Coincident with railway building, the industry spread inland to Nagpur,

thence southward through the cotton-growing districts of the peninsula. In the Ganges Valley the first mills were in Cawnpore and Delhi, later in Bengal.

The cotton textile industry, employing some 600,000 persons, is widely dispersed, but over one-half of all the mills are concentrated in Bombay and the Ahmedabad district. For many years India exported raw fiber and imported machine-made cloth, but with the development of the domestic industry that situation has been reversed. India still exports short-staple fiber but imports the long-staple cotton required for higher-grade textiles. The country has become the world's leading exporter of cotton cloth.

Jute manufacturing, concentrated along the Hooghly River, developed after the Bengal coal fields were opened in connection with railway construction. Bengal jute and available coal for power provided the impetus for large-scale mechanization. Jute manufactures fall into the four main classes of gunny bags for rice and wheat; burlap for baling cotton or wool; coarse rugs and carpets; cordage, and yarn.

Jute manufactures add 240 million dollars annually to Indian exports.

Indian silks have long been famous for their fine color and distinctive patterns, but local sericulture declined and India became an importer of silk yarn to supply both the cottage industries and the mills. Certain kinds of high-quality hand-woven materials are in demand at home and abroad, Benares being noted for its silks interspersed with metallic threads. Machine manufacture has developed slowly, the mills being concentrated in the Ganges Valley.

Wool is the smallest of the mechanized textile industries. Because of the warm weather over much of India, there is little need for woolen clothing but in the north there is some demand for handmade cloth and blankets. Punjab mills manufacture short fibers local wool into blankets, carpets, and felts. The better-quality woolens and worsteds are made of long-fiber wool imported from Afghanistan, Iran, and Australia. In several localities carpets and rugs are woven for Western markets.

**Iron and Steel.** The area southwest of Calcutta has varied resources for heavy industry, all conveniently grouped within a relatively small radius. Coking coal from the Damodar Valley, high-grade iron ore from Orissa, and a range of ferroalloys, including manganese and chrome, can be brought together at moderate transport cost.

The Jamshedpur mill, 150 miles west of Calcutta, began pouring iron in 1911 and has expanded into the largest steelmaker in India, the Tata works turning out a million tons of steel annually. An exporter of both pig iron and steel, Jamshedpur is also a fabricator making tin plate, wire and nails, plates, and structural steel. Jamshedpur has become a little Pittsburgh, attracting numerous subsidiary industries.

Large reserves of bauxite are available in the same general area, but aluminum fabrication has barely begun.

*Cities*

Delhi is situated near the low divide between the Indus and Ganges Valleys with the ruins of many previous capitals nearby. Made prosperous by trade, old Delhi expanded under the impetus of irrigation agriculture. When caravan routes in the area were succeeded by railroads, the city became the hub of the Indian rail net and increased in population to over 900,000. A walled city with mosques, palaces, and narrow congested streets, Delhi is famous for its beautiful handicrafts. Local cotton is spun and woven in large mills, and there is considerable handloom weaving and other cottage industries; the finer manufactures include jewelry, carved ivory, and embroidery in gold or silver thread.

Five miles south a new capital was dedicated in 1931, its broad boulevards flanked by government buildings, fine residences, and foreign

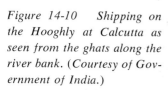

*Figure 14-10 Shipping on the Hooghly at Calcutta as seen from the ghats along the river bank. (Courtesy of Government of India.)*

embassies. The hotels, apartment houses, and colonnaded luxury shops along Kingsway cater to officialdom and the well-to-do. The two Delhis with a combined population of 1.2 million are complementary in function.

Calcutta was established in 1690 as fort and factory of the East India Company. On the Hooghly River, Calcutta is well located. Westernmost of the Ganges Delta channels, the Hooghly is navigable far inland. Calcutta soon became the commercial entrepôt for all of eastern India. One-quarter of the country's factory production is now on Hooghly side where a 60-mile stretch of river has become a great industrial conurbation with Calcutta as its node. Factories line both banks, the heavier industries directly at waterfront where handling costs for raw materials are minimal. This is the world center for jute spinning. Consumer goods manufactured include soap, tobacco, paper, and cotton textiles, and also wares made of iron, brass, and copper. Calcutta has 2.5 million population with another million in the metropolitan area.

Bombay, situated on an island off the west coast of India, resembles Calcutta in commerce, but is less diversified in industry. Based on raw material from the Deccan, cotton spinning is the leading industry. Bombay has one-quarter of all Indian cotton mills, and other manufacturing including rubber, chemicals, machinery, and automobile assembly. The Cotton Depot has warehousing for one million bales, and the Grain Depot provides ample storage for wheat and oilseeds.

Madras, the third largest city, is the major industrial and commercial center of south India. Early English enterprisers who traded in hand-woven cloth and cotton textiles are still dominant. The big mills do more spinning than weaving, the thread being purchased by local handloom operators. Leather is tanned in many large and small factories. Located on a broad coastal plain, Madras is less congested than most Indian cities.

Hyderabad, not to be confused with Hyderabad, Pakistan, is a city of one million and the long-time capital of the feudal state of the same name. Its princely Moslem rulers drew part of their wealth from diamond mines, one of which produced the famous Koh-i-Noor, but cotton, cattle, and food crops raised by tank irrigation are the main sources of income. Modern industry includes locomotive and railway car building but skilled Oriental crafts are the predominant occupation in old Hyderabad, which is less Westernized than the other large Indian cities.

## THE ISLAMIC REPUBLIC OF PAKISTAN

The Islamic Republic of Pakistan is divided into two parts separated by 1,000 air miles, about 1,200 surface transport miles, and more than 3,000 miles by sea. Both the land and the population are unequally divided. West Pakistan with 311,406 square miles of area has 34 million inhabitants, or 109 per square mile; East Pakistan supports 42 million people on 54,501 square miles, or 770 per square mile. West Pakistan is hot, arid, and barren, the struggle for water transcending all else; East Pakistan, hot and humid but well watered by the summer monsoon, is green with luxuriant vegetative cover, a land where floods and drainage pose serious problems. The Republic as a whole is predominantly rural, but in West Pakistan settlements are clustered along rivers and canals whereas in East Pakistan they are dispersed. Mainly agricultural, West Pakistan produces wheat, cotton, millet, hides and skins; East Pakistan is noted for its rice, jute, and tea. Moslems account for 86 per cent of the 76 million people, the Hindu minority, 13 per cent.

### WEST PAKISTAN

West Pakistan is a rectilinear area extending from the Himalayas some 800 miles to the Arabian Sea, and from Afghanistan-Iran on the west to the Thar Desert on the east, with the valleys of the Indus and its affluents as the productive heart of the area.

*Physical Setting*

**The Indus System.**　Rising in Tibet, the Indus cuts through the Himalayas and then flows the full length of West Pakistan to the Arabian Sea. On the west it is joined by the Kabul River from the highlands of Afghanistan but the more significant tributaries are to the east: the Jhelum, Chenab, Ravi, Beas, and Sutlej. All have their headwaters in India. The larger and best-developed part of the Punjab consists of the combined valleys of these eastern affluents which rise in the Himalayas and, fed by melting snows and monsoon rain, become rushing torrents laden with debris and silt. The fan-shaped plain of the Five Rivers is floored with alluviums of great depth. Extending for several hundred miles along the mountain front, the plain in the south is pinched to a narrow gap between the Sulaiman Mountains and the Thar Desert. The Five Rivers, merging into a single stream, enter the Indus halfway to the Arabian Sea.

**Climate.**　Climatically both the Punjab and the Sind (lower Indus Valley) are deserts. Punjab summers are hot, averaging 90 to 95°, although daily maxima may reach 110 to 120°F; winters are cool, 50 to 55°F. Rainfall is scant in total amount ranging from 7 to 20 inches with marked concentration in July and August (Table 14-1). Light winter rains are invaluable. Except for the northern foothills, the area is too dry for agriculture and nearly all crops must be irrigated.

The Sind is a true desert with high average temperatures (Jacobabad: June, 97°F, January, 57°F), clear skies, and low relative humidity except along the coast. Precipitation is both scant and erratic. Hyderabad, which averages 8 inches annually, has recorded a 10-inch downpour in one day.

**Water.**　Crossed by successive waves of conquerors, ancient Pakistan was a transit land with occasional settlements along the rivers or close to the northern mountains. More than two thousand years ago lands in the Indus Valley were being irrigated. The lowlands could be inundated by simple stream diversion, but to raise water to higher levels various devices were used including the scoop, shadoof, and Persian water wheel. Underground sources were tapped by wells, and the water lifted by animals or manpower.

In 1849, soon after the province was annexed, the British began rehabilitating old ca-

*Figure 14-11　The Badshahi Mosque, Lahore, Pakistan, as seen from the southeast showing façade of Prayer Hall. (Courtesy of Embassy of Pakistan.)*

nals which had fallen into disuse. Many of these were on the lower Indus, Jhelum, and Sutlej Rivers. It was the Lower Chenab Canal, however, which first called attention to the high productivity of the soil when irrigated, and to the effectiveness of canal colonies in the settlement of arid but fertile lands. By 1920, the irrigated area had increased to 1.5 million acres, and thousands of miles of canals and distributaries carried the waters of the Five Rivers to the undulating plains of eastern Punjab whose deep alluviums now support over 90 per cent of its people. Since the water of the Five Rivers flows through India, where it is diminished by irrigation removals before entering Pakistan, control of the sources of these rivers might constitute a threat to the agriculture of the Indus Valley. Completion of projects on the Indus and reclamation of land in Western Punjab will lessen the risk. The great Sukkur Barrage, in northern Sind, was built across the Indus in 1932. Nearly a mile long, it supplies one of the world's largest irrigation districts, covering about 5 million acres. The Kotri Barrage on the lower Indus near Hyderabad, begun in 1950, will provide an assured water supply for an additional 3 million acres.

Major irrigation systems have thus far been confined to the lands lying east of the Jhelum, but the new multipurpose Thal Project with its Jinnah Barrage, now under construction on the Indus, will add two hydroelectric plants and 1.5 million crop acres to the Western Punjab. The Warsak Project on the Kabul River near Peshawar will also irrigate 100,000 acres, but its main purpose is to supply power for industries in the local area and to the Punjab power grid.

Throughout West Pakistan irrigation projects have given greater stability to agriculture and a better living to small-holders. The main problem is alkalinity as an aftermath of irrigation.

## Agriculture

**Crops.** In West Pakistan food crops occupy three-quarters of the cultivated area, with wheat in first position—10 million acres. It is sown as a winter crop in the Sind and the Punjab, the latter being the major wheat-growing province. Formerly a surplus producer, the country now imports wheat. The Sind plants nearly as much rice as wheat, part of the surplus going to rice-hungry East Bengal. Corn is grown in various districts. The millets, low water users, are especially suitable for many acres and supply an inexpensive breadstuff at all seasons. Oilseeds—linseed, sesame, and rape—occupy a much smaller acreage than grains but are expanding, and sugar cane is cultivated in many irrigated areas.

In contrast to India where the Deccan cotton crop is dependent on natural rainfall, Pakistan cotton is entirely under irrigation. The fiber is indigenous to the Indus Valley, but higher-yielding American upland varieties have been introduced and constitute 90 per cent of the Pakistan crop. The staple now ginned is nearly an inch in length, grading higher than most Indian fiber; some long-staple Egyptian cotton is also grown.

With each new irrigation project the area in cotton has expanded. Led by the Punjab and Sind the total crop is 1.2 million bales per year, of which about 900,000 are exported, local mills buying less than one-third of a million bales.

**Domestic Animals.**   In the Punjab plains, bullocks and buffaloes are used to plow the fields, cow buffaloes for milk, and camels for riding and plowing. In the Sind, cattle are raised in irrigated areas. Beasts of burden include horses, donkeys, and camels; the last are the most valuable for transport, and there is a network of camel paths in the Sind Desert. In the mountainous Frontier provinces and in Baluchistan to the west, the people are pastoral nomads, keeping sheep, goats, donkeys, and camels and migrating seasonally from lower to higher elevations.

The wool, hides, and skins from millions of animals provide the basis for many home industries, such as weaving, leatherworking, and shoemaking. Local tanning and wool weaving are increasing, but Pakistan annually exports over $35 million worth of hides and wool.

## Industry and Cities

Before Partition, West Pakistan produced one-third of the Indian cotton crop but had few mills; it provided most of the skins, hides, and wool processed in India. Cottage industries included the making of lacquer, pottery, embroidery, and carpets, and the spinning and handloom weaving of local cotton and wool. Large-scale industries were limited to several cement and flour mills and two petroleum refineries. The government has inaugurated a program of economic development, giving priority to irrigation, electrification, and manufacturing. Power fuels are in short supply; developed water power is inadequate and must be supplemented from India over the Punjab grid. An extensive natural gas field, discovered in north Baluchistan in 1953, has added to the industrial potential. Estimated reserves are sufficient to justify building a 350-mile pipeline to Karachi. Mineral resources are limited, although Baluchistan has chromite and sulfur.

Factories using power-driven machinery are now manufacturing cotton yarn and cloth, cement, steel ingots, rubber tires, sugar, and vegetable oils. Industries tend to be concentrated in the northern Punjab between Peshawar and Lahore, but lower Sind has cotton ginning, tanneries, salt, and cement.

Both the agricultural and the industrial future of West Pakistan depend upon the development and wise use of water resources for irrigation and for power.

A small fishing village when acquired by the British in 1843, Karachi had a deep natural harbor but a desert hinterland of scant value. A railway up the Indus Valley made it the recognized outlet for the wheat and cotton lands of the Punjab. With the opening of the Suez Canal, Karachi became a major stop on the trading route from Europe to all Asiatic and Australian ports. It serves as outport for the Afghan trade and is the beneficiary of all irrigation expansion in the Punjab and Sind. Its world significance is enhanced by its strategic location on international air routes. In 1947, Karachi was designated as the new capital of Pakistan and its area enlarged from 30 to 566 square miles. The population has increased to 1,100,000 in the five years following Partition.

Lahore, second city of Pakistan and capital of Punjab province, developed at a crossing of routes between the Ganges and Indus Valleys and the mountain passes to the northwest. Long established as a Moslem culture center, Lahore has expanded as a result of irrigation developments. Produce-marketing, flour, cotton and woolen mills, and modern railway car shops help support a population of about one million.

Hyderabad, a railway junction and market center, is the capital of Sind province. This ancient caravan station of Peshawar is a frontier railhead, much of the Afghan trade with India and Pakistan passing through it. Sialkot and Rawalpindi serve as market centers for mountain flank regions, the latter being the ingress for Kashmir.

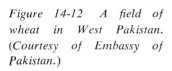

*Figure 14-12 A field of wheat in West Pakistan. (Courtesy of Embassy of Pakistan.)*

## EAST PAKISTAN

East Pakistan consists of the eastern three-fourths of former Indian Bengal which was divided to make two new provinces, West Bengal remaining with India and East Bengal forming the larger part of East Pakistan. A portion of the highland of Assam was also transferred to the new eastern province.

### The Bengal Flood Plain

East Bengal occupies the larger portion of the great plain formed by the joint floodwaters of the Ganges, the Bramaputra, and numerous lesser rivers from the peripheral hills and mountains. In their lower reaches, the two larger streams are joined by the shorter Surma-Meghna system which rises in the Assam Hills. Fed by monsoon rains, these streams annually

*Figure 14-13　Street scene in Dacca, East Pakistan. Note the different styles of clothing. (Courtesy of Embassy of Pakistan.)*

inundate much of the lowland, their waters reaching the Bay of Bengal by a series of interlaced and constantly shifting delta mouths.

The multiple deltas are active areas of land-building, loads of stream-borne silt extending the coast line seaward. The newer delta lands are not immediately available for agriculture. An immense area along the south coast is occupied by the Sunderbans, a wilderness of mangrove swamp and forested jungle cut by numerous creeks and tidal channels. The more active mouths of the larger distributaries are in East Bengal, sometimes called the new delta. In contrast to West Bengal, where old channels are silting and only the Hooghly carries much water, East Bengal has 2,600 miles of navigable waterways.

### Land Use

With its high temperatures and 60 to 80 inches of annual precipitation East Pakistan is a green land where vegetation is luxuriant and most wet crops flourish. Great expanses of flooded paddy and jute fields are interspersed with smaller patches of sugar cane, oilseeds, peas, and beans, coconuts in the south, and tea in the eastern hills—all indicative of an abundant tropical rainfall. Eighty per cent of the total area is under cultivation, mainly by small farmers owning a few acres, or by tenants of the large landowners.

There are few cities and not many market towns, for East Bengal is predominantly rural. Dispersed habitation is more common than settlement in villages. Individual farmsteads, thickly scattered across the low plains, are placed on artificial mounds of earth which serve as safety islands during the flood season. Even these raised bits of land are not idle; patches of tobacco, vegetable gardens, various tree fruits, and coconuts or bamboo surround the thatched houses. Population density in East Pakistan is over 770 persons per square mile.

### Agriculture

**Jute.** The broad floodplains of Bengal have long been the center for the cultivation of jute, one of the world's cheapest but most valuable fibers. Known as early as 800 B.C., the plant leaves were used for food, the fibers extracted and twisted into cordage or woven into coarse cloth. In 1750, sackcloth made on handlooms was a common item of Bengal commerce, the East India Company trading in gunny bags and shipping raw jute to England for the manufacture of rope and twine.

In 1822, a consignment of jute reached Dundee, Scotland, famous flax-weaving center. In addition to working out better methods for spinning and weaving jute the mills developed hessian cloth, a tightly woven and durable fabric suitable for grain sacks. They bleached the fiber, made waterproof canvas and tarpaulins, and mixed jute with cotton and wool to make carpets, curtains, and upholstery fabrics. First developed in Dundee, modern jute milling spread to the Hooghly district of India, the rising world demand for cheaper textiles creating a ready market for the fiber.

Optimum conditions for jute cultivation in the Ganges-Brahmaputra lowlands include the 60-to-80 inch rainfall, high humidity during the growing season, a well-saturated soil, and ample water for retting. Flooded fields with a new layer of alluvium annually can be cropped year after year with high yields, but lands above flood level need fertilizers or crop rotation.

Sown in a well-prepared seedbed, then weeded and gradually thinned, Bengal jute develops a cane-like stalk which reaches a height of 8 to 10 feet in a 5-month growing season. Cut by hand with a sickle, the stalks are tied in bundles and soaked in streams or ponds for ten to twenty days. During this process, known as retting, the pith ferments and disintegrates so that the fibers can be stripped loose. After washing and drying, the soft yellowish fiber is ready for market. Few major crops require more man-hours of tedious labor.

Middlemen travel through the Bengal countryside buying dry jute which is transported to collecting centers by bullock cart, or by cargo boats and small steamers on the delta channels. At the warehouse the loose bundles of fiber are sorted and graded, then compressed into standard 400-pound bales for export.

*Figure 14-14    After retting and washing, Bengal jute is hung on bamboo racks to dry in the sun. (Courtesy of Government of Pakistan.)*

The great Bengal plain produces 98 per cent of the world's jute, two-thirds of it in East Pakistan where it is the most valuable cash and export crop, exceeding 6 million bales per year. Before Partition all the jute mills were in West Bengal along the Hooghly, most of the crop being shipped westward via the long Calcutta and Eastern Canal which bisects the delta. Smaller exports were made through Chittagong.

The newly created East Pakistan of 1947 had few baling stations or warehouses and no jute mills. India is now planting more jute in West Bengal, and East Pakistan is building mills as rapidly as possible. Large mills near Dacca, at Khulna, and at Chittagong, are now weaving burlap for the foreign market, several more are under construction, and Pakistan hopes to export less raw fiber and more manufactured jute. Part of the crop is still exported in bond through Calcutta, and Hooghly mills buy East Bengal jute for processing, the United Kingdom being the next best customer.

**Tea.** The eastern borderlands of Bengal extend into the Assam Plateau. On these hill slopes, particularly in the upper Surma Valley tributary to Sylhet, there are 82,000 acres of tea plantations. Sylhet has a rainfall of more than 150 inches annually, the other natural conditions being similar to the larger Assam tea region across the Indian border. Some 10 to 12 pickings are made annually, the East Pakistan tea crop averaging 50 million pounds. Tea chests move by rail to dockside at Chittagong and are shipped to the domestic market in West Pakistan or overseas to the London tea auctions. In the export trade of East Pakistan, tea is second only to jute.

**Rice.** Although jute is the great cash and export crop, the East Bengal farmer depends on rice; in contrast to 8 or 10 per cent in jute, paddy is grown on three-quarters of the cultivated land. Rainfall is ample, two-thirds of the 60 or more inches coming during the four hottest summer months, with the annual inundation enriching many soils with a thin coating of new alluvium, although excessive flooding is often a serious problem. Where moisture is sufficient, a second crop of rice is planted in the same year. Many different varieties are grown, floating rice, whose stalk lengthens as waters rise, being a specialty in East Bengal floodlands.

The Pakistan paddy crop averages 27 billion pounds annually, one-third that of India, but East Bengal is a deficit area, obtaining additional rice or substitutes from West Pakistan. Land under paddy has been increasing at the rate of 150,000 acres yearly, mainly at the expense of jute. More acreage might be added by the drainage and reclamation of the Sunderbans, the unused jungle of the lower deltas.

## Cities

Dacca, the new capital of East Pakistan, was the capital of Bengal three centuries ago. In the days of cottage industry exports, the city was a famous center for fine muslins. Surrounded by the richest rice and jute lands in Bengal,

*Figure 14-15  Threshing paddy by hand in East Pakistan. (Courtesy of Government of Pakistan.)*

Dacca has grown rapidly since its recent selection as capital of East Pakistan, the population, including its port, Narayanganj, now exceeding 400,000. New industries include cotton and jute weaving.

East of the Ganges-Bramaputra Delta, the small coastal city of Chittagong has become the major port of East Pakistan. Situated some 10 miles upriver from the Bay of Bengal, it was used as a trading post by the Portuguese in the sixteenth century, but was not as well located for Bengal commerce as Calcutta on the Hooghly. At the height of each shipping season, considerable jute moved across Chittagong wharves, and the building of the Assam-Bengal Railway made it a shipping and supply port for the upcountry tea planters of the Assam Plateau.

After 1947, jute poured in faster than dock facilities could handle it; the port was expanded, cargo handled rising from 4 to 16 million tons in the first five years after Partition. Pakistan has given high priority to harbor expansion, dredging, new factories, and a water power project in the Chittagong Hills. In addition to jute mills, a paper factory uses quick-growing bamboo from the local area which was formerly shipped to Calcutta paper mills. Many imports as well as exports are now channeled through Chittagong instead of Calcutta, and there is regular passenger freighter service to Karachi.

## INDIAN BORDERLANDS

On India's northern border in the central and eastern Himalayas are the landlocked independent kingdom, Nepal, and the Indian protectorates of Sikkim and Bhutan.

### Nepal

Nepal, comparable in size to Wisconsin, supports 7 million people mainly by agriculture and cottage industries, but population pressure upon the limited arable land causes steady emigration, especially to Sikkim and Darjeeling. Because of rugged topography, transportation is heavily dependent upon porters. The capital city of Katmandu, which dominates the largest valley, is extremely isolated by land but easily accessible by air.

### Sikkim

Sikkim, tiny enclave between Nepal and Bhutan, commands the main trade route between India and Tibet via the famed Chumbi Valley. Pack animals cross the 12,000-foot pass bringing Tibetan wool to India and carrying in exchange cottons, silks, and other manufactures. Cultivation and dispersed settlements are usually above 3,000 feet, and there is a well-developed system of transhumance. Except for Gangtok, capital and chief market place, villages tend to develop around monasteries or to serve as staging points on the Tibetan trade route.

### Bhutan

Bhutan, like Sikkim, is a Buddhist country with many monasteries. Located in the eastern Himalayas, and cut by high ridges and deep valleys, many of its settlements are concentrated along the track connecting with the Chumbi Valley route. Subtropical crops are grown in the southern lowlands but upland cultivation is of the shifting type with maize and millet. Bhutanese are skilled in working wood and are also noted for their metalware and handicrafts.

Oriented toward the south, Nepal's contacts are mainly with India; Bhutan is physically and culturally oriented toward Tibet. The 70-mile Sikkim corridor functions as a strategic route between the Indian lowlands and the vast Tibetan plateau.

## KINGDOM OF AFGHANISTAN

A diverse and massive highland covers three-fourths of Afghanistan. Extending westward from the central mountain core of Asia, the Hindu Kush varies in height from 15,000 to 20.000 feet; including the lower ranges attached to it on the west and south, this mountain complex is continuous for 600 miles. The broad valley basin surrounding the capital, Kabul, has an elevation of 6,000 feet. On the north, the Hindu Kush slopes gradually to a 2,000-foot plain where the Amu Darya marks the Soviet border. On the south, a flatter tableland of 2,500 to 3,000 feet is rimmed by the border mountains of Pakistan.

Much of Afghanistan's 250,000 square miles is semiarid, precipitation varying from 11 to 15 inches, but vast areas are drier, the Seistan Desert receiving only 2 to 3 inches annually. Although rainfall is both low and irregular, snowfall in the higher mountains is usually dependable. Highland temperatures drop below zero in winter, and there is also below-freezing weather in the southern deserts. Summer heat is everywhere extreme, with high temperatures, strong winds, and blinding dust storms.

Most of the rivers drain to the landlocked Aral Sea or evaporate in various deserts. The waters of the Kabul River, however, reach the ocean by way of the Indus.

## Land Utilization

**Grazing.** In areas of scant rainfall and extensive mountain slopes, grass is the most valuable resource; an estimated 2 million of the 12 million inhabitants are pastoral nomads. Grazing is widespread and transhumance is common, the herdsman with his camels and black tents driving his animals to the mountains in spring, then returning to lower pastures in autumn. Cattle, camels, and goats are grazed, but sheep, a source of milk, meat, wool, and skins, are most numerous. Wool is exported or made into rugs, blankets, and coarse cloth. The north flank of the Hindu Kush sloping to the rich grasslands of the Oxus plain is the recognized center for the 4 million black sheep whose lambs provide the curly karakul (Persian lamb) sold in world fur markets.

**Agriculture.** Agriculture is dependent on mountain snows which feed the many streams. Meltwater in spring swells the Amu Darya, the Kabul, and the extensive Argandab-Helmand

system of the south. Where fertile soil can be reached by small diversion canals, ribbons of cultivation follow the rivers and spread out into the plains. Thousands of tiny streams become miniature oases where husbandmen build their mud huts and till subsistence plots of wheat or barley, rice, vegetables, and fruits. Corn, millet, and alfalfa are grown for feed. Intensive patch farming is practiced in remote mountain valleys, often at high altitudes and by means of terraces.

The hot summer sun speeds the ripening of fruits, and markets in season are piled high with grapes, apples, figs, apricots, peaches, and many varieties of melons. Fruits are preserved or sun-dried for winter use, raisins, dried apricots, and figs reaching the export market in quantity. Certain valleys are famous for their almonds, walnuts, and pistachios.

## Problems of Modernization

Afghanistan's independence was achieved after a long history of invasion, conquest, and pressure politics; during the past century, it has been a buffer nation between an expanding Russia on the north and the British in India. Railways reach the borders in several places, but Afghanistan has not embarked upon railway building. The ancient caravan routes have become the present-day road pattern, including a line of highways connecting Kabul with the various provincial capitals. Mineral surveys have been made, the larger cities electrified, and a few government factories established to supplement local cottage industry.

The greatest potential resource in Afghanistan is mountain meltwater which floods the rivers in early spring and summer, much of it going to waste in the great deserts. Several new reclamation projects are now under construction, including two large dams above Kandahar which will store sufficient water to irrigate half a million acres of arable land. In addition to subsistence crops, commercial agriculture, including long-staple cotton, sugar beets, and tobacco, will be expanded and electricity provided for local industry.

Technical assistance from outside countries

is being employed, but the government is reluctant to grant concessions to foreigners. The age-old problem of Afghanistan has been how to develop the country and expand the economy without losing its cherished independence.

## THE DOMINION OF CEYLON

Situated near the south tip of India, Ceylon is connected to the mainland by a 22-mile ferry across Palk Strait. Sixty per cent of its area, the northeast, is a flat, dry plain, but southwest Ceylon is dominated by a mountain mass some 50 miles in diameter, with upland plateaus and valleys between high ranges. In contrast to the plain, this southwestern highland is verdant throughout the year, with numerous small rivers radiating from it. Many shallow salt-water lagoons fringe the island coasts.

### The Two-season Monsoon

Ceylon has two well-defined rainy seasons, May to August and November to January. The summer monsoon strikes the southwest coast and the central mountains with full force, while the lowlands of eastern and northern Ceylon are left almost rainless. The northeast monsoon gives the plains an average precipitation of 40 to 60 inches, and provides additional rainfall in the mountains. The southwestern third of Ceylon, with a well-distributed rainfall of 70 to 150 inches, is known as the wet zone, the extensive northern and eastern plains as the dry zone. Both the agricultural economy and the population pattern are closely related to these regions of adequate and inadequate precipitation.

Population is concentrated in the wet zone; the fertile coastal area and the intensively tilled upland valleys have a density of 500 to 1,000 per square mile. Here the Sinhalese comprise two-thirds of Ceylon's 8 million inhabitants. One and a half million Tamils, recent Hindu migrants from India, predominate in the dry zone, which averages less than 100 per square mile. Wide expanses of scrubland and jungle are almost uninhabited.

### People of Ceylon

Migrating from the Ganges Valley some twenty-four centuries ago, the early Sinhalese first settled in the dry north where dense forests were lacking; they used the intermittent rivers to develop a civilization based on water storage and irrigation. The ancient Sinhalese kings built great tanks, or reservoirs, 10, 20, or 30 miles in circumference, and developed irrigation agriculture. With the decline of their civilization, partly as a result of wars, the tanks and irrigation canals reverted to scrub and jungle. Most of the people moved to the better-watered and less disturbed southwest, where the difficulty of clearing the rain forests had repelled the first settlers.

Early Arab navigators skirting the south Asia coast made Ceylon a base for spice and silk operations. The Portuguese settled at Colombo in 1505, the Dutch on the east coast in 1640; both developed shore stations to exploit the wild cinnamon. Arriving at Trincomalee in 1782, the English soon expelled the Dutch, conquered the kingdom of Kandy, and made the island a British colony. In 1948, it became a self-governing member of the Commonwealth.

Ever since the days of the early spice traders and sea rovers, Ceylon's location near the tip of India has made it a natural port of call. Modern steamship lines converge at Colombo to the virtual exclusion of the smaller ports. Colombo had no natural harbor but has built several breakwaters which provide ample anchorage. The immediate hinterland includes the densely populated southwest plain and the prosperous upcountry estates with their tea and rubber. Kandy, a former capital and famed for its Buddhist temples, is located in the mountainous part of the island.

### Agriculture

Early experimental plantings included sugar, coconuts, and indigo, but coffee soon became the standard crop on hundreds of British estates around Kandy. When a leaf blight swept the coffee lands in the 1880's most planters turned to tea.

Ascending from sea level to 1,600 feet, the railway from Colombo to the Kandy Plateau traverses one of the best-cultivated sections of the wet zone. Here three export crops meet although each has a well-defined region of concentration: coconuts on the coastal plain within a 60-mile radius of Colombo, rubber at higher elevations, and tea in the mountains.

Most of the large tea estates are at altitudes of 2,000 to 6,000 feet where there is an annual rainfall of 80 to 200 inches. Tamils from south India clear the land, then plant, mulch, and prune the trees. The estates, which average about 300 acres, are mainly British, but Sinhalese planters are increasing. The tea leaves are hand-plucked, wilted, fermented, roiled, fired, sifted, and packed. Sold at the weekly auctions in Colombo, tea comprises one-half of the export trade, Ceylon ranking second only to India.

Rubber is well suited to the almost continuous rainfall of the double monsoon. Some rubber is tapped by small cultivators, but most of it is from large estates owned by British or Sinhalese, employing many workers and processing the latex mechanically. Among Ceylon's exports, raw rubber is second only to tea.

Coconuts, third largest export, are mainly tributary to the port of Colombo. As the special prerogative of the small Sinhalese grower, coconuts are part of a diversified system which includes rice, fruits, and vegetables. Home-dried copra is a ready source of cash, and the wood, husks, and fiber have innumerable household uses. Most copra is processed in Ceylon, coconut oil and desiccated coconut now outranking copra and coir products in the export trade.

Cacao in Ceylon thrives in hot and humid uplands with rainfall of 60 to 80 inches; the leading centers are at 500 to 2,000 feet in valleys well sheltered from winds. Many estates interplant cacao between rubber trees, and it is found at considerable altitudes in the tea region. Numerous shut-in valleys in the Kandy district market cacao of high quality. Cinnamon, first exploited as a wild tree native to the wet lowlands, is now cultivated in gardens. The bark is peeled, fermented, dried, and made into quills, chips, or cinnamon oil for export.

Rice is the main foodstuff and has the widest distribution of any crop. Two-thirds of the paddies are in the wet zone, interspersed with coconut and rubber holdings, and extending into the tea-growing region where terraces line many mountainsides. Paddies fringe the lagoons in the semiempty dry zone of the northern plain. The 900,000 acres of paddy are insufficient for home needs, Ceylon importing a billion pounds of rice annually. In an attempt to remedy this deficiency, many of the ancient tanks are being rehabilitated, and new storage projects such as the Gal Oya irrigation dam are opening up paddy lands in the dry zone.

## IN PERSPECTIVE

### South Asia

Extending from the snow-covered Himalayas to the Indian Ocean and from Iran to Burma, South Asia is dominated both economically and politically by the large and populous Republic of India. Neighboring countries are Pakistan with its arid West and humid East, the tropical island of Ceylon, the small mountain states of Nepal, Sikkim, and Bhutan, and landlocked Afghanistan to the northwest.

Throughout South Asia, the economy is predominantly agricultural and dependent upon the monsoon rainfall. Where double cropping is practiced, irrigation is generally necessary. Agricultural expansion in arid West Pakistan and Afghanistan awaits large-scale reclamation and irrigation. Approaching 500 million, the population of South Asia is heavily concentrated in the fertile floodplains and deltas as well as in certain favorable coastal areas. Population pressure is great but there is scant hope of relief until agricultural practices are improved and water resources more efficiently utilized.

Except in Ceylon, with its heavy emphasis on export crops such as rubber and tea, small-scale subsistence agriculture is widespread; it is supplemented by handicrafts or cottage industries which provide part- or full-time work for millions. The competition of foreign machine-made goods and the growth of large Indian mills formerly caused a general decline in cottage industries; now, however, governments are encouraging their expansion for increased employment as well as goods for export.

Large-scale manufacturing is best developed in India, especially cotton, silk and wool textiles, iron, steel, and subsidiary industries. Most of South Asia has foreign technological assistance in agriculture, mining, and hydroelectric development. Despite the attention focused upon multiple-purpose projects and expanded mechanization, greater production of foods and handicrafts is basic everywhere. Population growth is rapid and improvements in nutrition, health, and living standards are contingent upon a comparable increase in production.

## EXERCISES

*1.* What countries are considered as South Central Asia? How do they compare with each other in area, population, and population density? How does India compare with the other major countries of the world in total population?

*2.* What is the monsoon? What are its characteristics? What is its relationship to agricultural activities in the various countries? Where is the region of greatest rainfall?

*3.* What mountains border northern India? What is the highest peak? In which country is it located? In what ways have these mountains aided and hindered the development of India?

*4.* What are the two principal rivers of the Indian subcontinent? Where does each have its headwaters? How is each used in the area through which it flows? Why is the population density so much greater on one than the other?

*5.* What are the principal agricultural products of South Central Asia? In which part is each grown? How do you account for the variety? Does the total production meet the demands?

*6.* Why was Pakistan divided? In what ways do its two divisions contrast with each other? What are the chief economic and cultural problems of Pakistan?

*7.* Why is India especially interested in the political attitude of the three smaller nations? Are these small nations economically independent? Why?

*8.* What are the chief economic problems facing Afghanistan? In what ways does its physical environment handicap the country? What cultural differences exist between India and Afghanistan?

*9.* What are the principal economic activities of Ceylon? In what ways does the cultural background of Ceylon differ from that of India? Should Ceylon be an independent nation? Why?

*10.* What is the chief problem facing India, Ceylon, and Pakistan? How does this problem influence all other activities in these nations?

*11.* What and where is the Punjab, Deccan, Thar, Sind, Malabar, Bengal, and Kashmir?

*12.* Why are Colombo, Delhi, Benares, Bombay, Calcutta, Madras, Hyderabad, and Lucknow important cities? Where is each located?

*13.* What contributions have the people of India made to the culture of the world?

## SELECTED REFERENCES

Ahmad, Enayat: "Rural Settlement Types in the Uttar Pradesh (United Provinces of Agra and Oudh)," *Annals of the Association of American Geographers,* 42:223–246, September, 1952.

Amhad, Nafis: "Industrial Development in East Bengal (East Pakistan)," *Economic Geography,* 26:183–195, July, 1950.

Anstey, Vera: *Economic Development of India,* Longmans, Green & Co., New York, 1952.

Bennett, M. K.: *The World's Foods,* Harper & Brothers, New York, 1954.

Davis, K.: *The People of India and Pakistan,* Princeton University Press, Princeton, 1951.

East, W. G., and O. H. K. Spate: *The Changing Map of Asia,* E. P. Dutton & Co., Inc., New York, 1950.

Fowler, F. J.: "Some Problems of Water Distribution Between East and West Punjab," *Geographical Review,* 40:583–589, October, 1950.

Fraser-Tytler, W. K.: *Afghanistan,* Oxford University Press, New York, 1950.

Ginsburg, Norton S. (ed): *The Pattern of Asia,* Prentice-Hall Inc., Englewood Cliffs, N.J., 1958.

Kirk, William: "The Cotton and Jute Industries of India," *Scottish Geographical Magazine,* 72:38–52, April, 1956.

MacFadden, Clifford H.: "The Gal Oya Valley: Ceylon's Little TVA, *Geographical Review,* 44:271–281, April, 1954.

Spate, O. H. K.: *India and Pakistan, A General and Regional Geography,* E. P. Dutton & Co., New York, 1954.

————: "The Partition of India and the Prospects of Pakistan," *Geographical Review,* 38:5–29, January, 1948.

Trewartha, Glenn T., and James L. Verber: "Regionalism in Factory Industry in India-Pakistan," *Economic Geography,* 27:283–286, October, 1951.

Vakil, C. N.: *Economic Consequences of Divided India,* Vora and Company, Bombay, 1956.

# 15. Southeast Asia

SOUTHEAST ASIA, the land east of India and south of China, includes the Malay Peninsula, the Philippines, the East Indies, and the independent mainland countries of Burma, Thailand, and the Indochinese states of North and South Vietnam, Laos, and Cambodia (Figure 15-1). Most of these countries gained independence after World War II. Thailand is the only one in the region that had complete independence before 1940, the country never

539

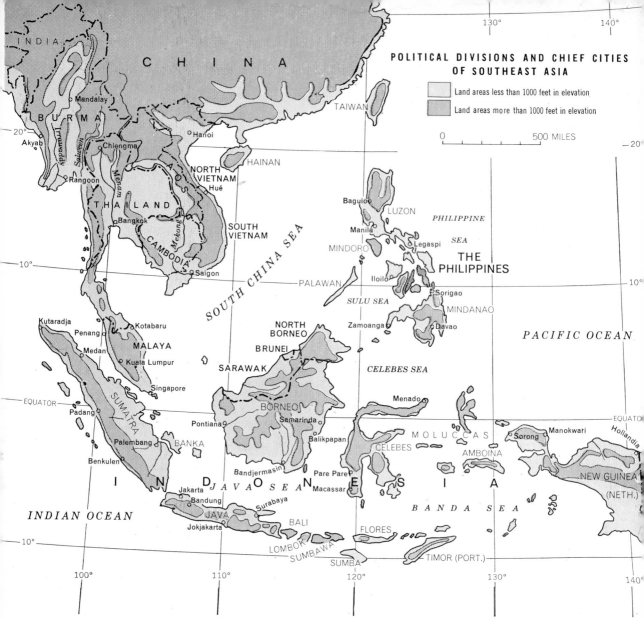

*Figure 15-1   Southeast Asia is an area of new independent nations. The latest to join this group is Malaya which became independent in August, 1957. The Philippines and the Republic of Indonesia are both island nations.*

having been a European colony. In 1957 Malaya was established as an independent country and became a member of the British Commonwealth of Nations, but Singapore remains a colony of the United Kingdom. Offshore, the Philippines and Indonesia are independent republics. In Borneo are the British colonies of Sarawak and British North Borneo, and the protectorate of Brunei.

During the Pacific phase of World War II,

1942–1945, and the Japanese occupation of Southeast Asia, the machinery of production came to a standstill. In the oil fields much valuable equipment was destroyed. Estate agriculture was badly damaged, buildings burned, labor forces dispersed, and management disrupted. Even the economy of the small farms was seriously disturbed. Returning colonial governments were met with demands for immediate independence, and in the following decade most

Figure 15-2   *Southeast Asia is a region of mountainous peninsulas and islands.*

former colonies attained some degree of sovereignty. The new countries are faced with shortages of material and personnel. For pre-industrial, impoverished, and illiterate peoples, the problems of independence are as difficult as those of colonialism.

## PHYSICAL SETTING

Rugged physical features with deep valleys and high peaks are characteristic of the area. The mountainous peninsula of Southeast Asia, including Burma, Thailand, former Indochina, and Malaya, extends from eastern Tibet southward into the tropics until it terminates in the long, narrow Malay Peninsula. Approximately three-fourths of it is above 3,000 feet in elevation, and in the north, mountain ranges rise to 19,000 feet (Figure 15-2). The lofty northern border is characterized by many sharp ridges and deep gorges which spread out fanwise toward the south. Several ranges extend through Burma to the Bay of Bengal; another range forms the backbone of the Malay Peninsula. The broader Annam Mountains lie near and follow the coast of Vietnam. Much of this mountainous interior is inaccessible, almost uninhabited, and of little economic significance.

The great Salween and Mekong Rivers, rising in eastern Tibet, together with the shorter Irrawaddy, Menam Chao Phraya, and Red River (Song Hoi), dominate the economic life of Southeast Asia. Rivers serve as natural arteries of transportation, small craft being aided upstream by the onshore monsoon winds and downstream by the river current. In their upper reaches all the rivers have cut deep gorges with steep, precipitous banks, but as they approach the coast they become sluggish, broaden, and build floodplains and deltas. Most extensive in the valleys of the Irrawaddy, Menam Chao Phraya and Mekong, these alluvial lands provide the only sizable areas of good soil;

hence each of the three river basins has become the site of a culture and a political unit.

Most of Southeast Asia experiences hot, humid summers and mild winter climates (Figure 15-3). Over the region as a whole, annual temperatures average 75 to 80°F. Singapore has a mean annual temperature of 81°F, with less than 5°F contrast between the warmest and coolest months. The annual precipitation of 95 inches at Singapore varies from 4 to 16 inches per month, the only seasonal contrast being from rainy to less rainy.

Farther north, average temperatures become lower and seasonal contrast greater. Burma, Thailand, and Indochina lie in the path of both summer and winter monsoons. The Annamitic Cordillera separates the lands to the west, with their summer rainfall, from the Annam coast to the east, which is watered by the winter monsoon. Rangoon, with an annual rainfall of 99 inches, receives 94 inches during the wet sea-

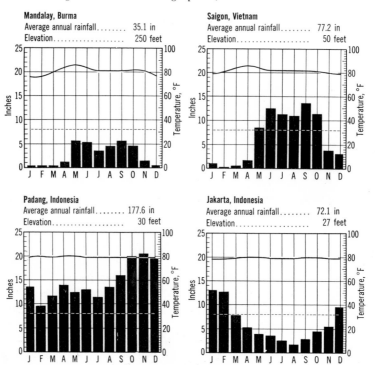

*Figure 15-3   Climate graphs of selected cities in Southeast Asia.*

son from May to October and only 5 inches during the dry season. Northward along the Burma coast, the yearly rainfall is 203 inches at Akyab but only 35 inches at Mandalay in the mountain trough. Maximum summer precipitation often causes serious floods in the lowlands. Burma, Thailand, and most of Indochina are in the rain shadow during the winter months, while the Vietnam coast is in the direct path of the northeast monsoon. Hué gets two-thirds of its 102 inches of rain from September to December.

The tropical monsoon dominates the climate of the East Indies and the Philippines, which receive precipitation from both the summer and winter monsoons, a real distribution being influenced by trend and height of the mountains. However, the northwestern coast of Luzon, the southern half of Celebes, the eastern fourth of Java, and several smaller islands in the vicinity of Java and Celebes may experience long and severe droughts. Temperatures in the mountains are uniformly high with little seasonal contrast, except where modified by high elevations, which may give so-called temperate zone conditions in the tropical highlands.

## CULTURAL SIMILARITIES

High elevation and rugged topography predominate, with a maximum of land area in mountains and plateaus and a minimum of lowland. Except for a few isolated areas, the lowlands are intensively cultivated and densely populated. A large percentage of the 160 million people in the area is concentrated in these lowlands, chiefly on floodplains and deltas where agriculture is most remunerative (Figure 15-4). The majority of the people depend upon small-scale subsistence farming, with the rice economy dominant.

An advance guard of Western enterprisers reached Southeast Asia about 1600, inaugurating a new commercial era. Europeans constituted only a fraction of the total population but possessed superior commercial training, industrial techniques, and organizing ability. They gradually established the colonial mercantile system. Cultivation was organized along plantation lines, with an array of tropical products grown for export. The new estates were widely distributed but were most numerous in the East Indies and Malaya, largely because of favorable soil and climate, abundant labor, and European control.

Since climate varies with elevation, altitudinal zonation of crops is common both on the mainland and in the islands. Coconuts and sugar cane are usually found in lowlands, with rubber at moderate elevations or in rolling hill country, coffee and tea on hillsides and mountains up to 5,000 feet, cinchona at still higher altitudes. At its best, the system organized agricultural production, developed latent natural resources, and improved communications. It provided new sources of employment for native peoples, improved their living conditions, and brought them a certain amount of Western-style prosperity. At its worst, it meant economic or even personal vassalage. It inevitably entailed political dominance and a denial of local self-determination.

The normal emphasis in Southeast Asia is upon food crops with a complementary development of home industries. Throughout the centuries highly skilled arts and crafts had tended to develop, certain cities and regions becoming famous for their designs and fine workmanship in metal, lacquer, woods, and textiles. When superimposed upon this foodstuff and handicraft economy, European commercialization broke the old social and economic organization, frequently destroying even the skilled handicrafts. Emphasis on tropical raw materials for world markets exposed these preindustrial peoples to external economic forces over which they had no control. Consequently, over much of Southeast Asia employment has been irregular, with frequent loss of wage income and a fluctuating food supply which has not always kept pace with the rapidly increasing population. The resulting hunger leads to poor economic and political conditions.

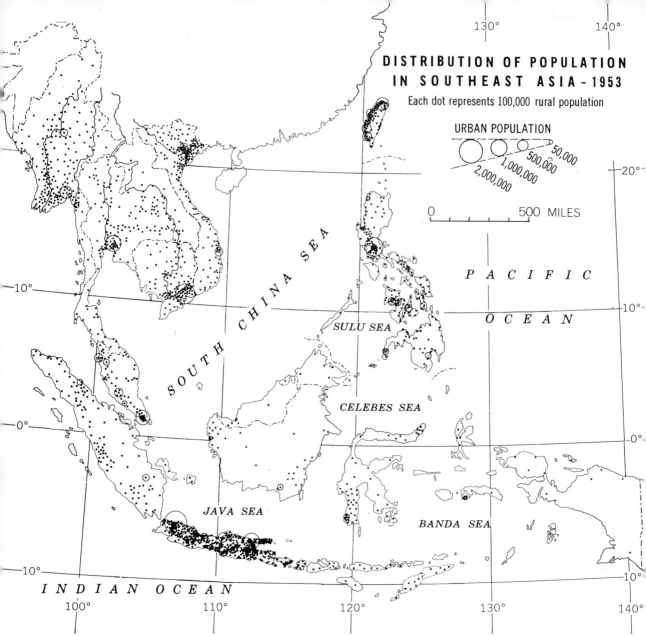

DISTRIBUTION OF POPULATION
IN SOUTHEAST ASIA - 1953

Each dot represents 100,000 rural population

URBAN POPULATION

50,000
500,000
1,000,000
2,000,000

0          500 MILES

*Figure 15-4 Many parts of Southeast Asia are densely populated. Java is said to be the most densely populated island in the world. Note the size of the capital of each country in relation to the other cities within the country.*

## BURMA

After unification under the powerful Mongols and various invasions by border rulers, Burma was annexed piecemeal by the British, beginning in 1826. Long a province of India, it was occupied by the Japanese in 1942, then attained complete independence in 1948.

### Physical Setting

**Relief Features.** A high mountain rim surrounds the country on three sides, walling it off from its neighbors. On the east, this rim becomes a broad plateau, the Shan Highlands, from which a longer mountain range extends southward to form the Malay Peninsula. Within the U-shaped enclosure, the Salween River from the high Himalayas flows southward through the Shan Plateau, cutting a deep and narrow trench. In contrast, the Irrawaddy and its major affluent, the Chindwin, rise on the Chinese-Tibetan border and tranverse two broad valleys separated by a narrow mountain range. The Irrawaddy and other rivers end in deltas on the southern coast combining to form a broad coastal lowland interlaced by many channeled waterways.

The Irrawaddy system provides the major base for the economy of Burma, for its fertile valleys and deltas contain most of the arable land and support the larger part of the 19 million people (Figure 15-4). Forest and mineral wealth is tributary to the river; cities and commerce depend on it. The Irrawaddy has long been the transportation lifeline of the country. Craft of all types—rice boats, sampans, timber rafts, petroleum barges—ply the river, and government-owned steamers ascend to Bhamo, 872 miles from Rangoon. Within the delta there are over 2,000 miles of navigable waterways.

**Climate.** All of coastal Burma, high or low, is well watered. The high mountain ranges of Lower Burma, in the direct path of the southwest monsoon are drenched by a rainfall of 150 to 170 inches annually; the exposed coastal lowland has over 100. Rainfall diminishes inland; halfway to Mandalay it drops to 40 to 50 inches annually, this section of Upper Burma being known as the dry zone. The Shan Highland to the east receives 60 to 80 inches and the high mountains of the northern border 120 inches or more. During the rainy season, Burmese rivers rise to flood proportions, spreading sheets of muddy water over the lower valleys. Great loads of alluvium are deposited in the deltas, which are still extending seaward.

## Land Utilization

Lower Burma, with its heavy rainfall from May to September, is the region of maximum rice cultivation. The narrow coastal plain of the Arakan and Tenasserim Mountains have a similar agriculture on a small scale. Upper Burma, with its broad interior valleys centered around Mandalay, its lower rainfall, and higher summer temperatures, is better suited to mixed farming.

**Forests.** The surrounding mountains and plateaus are largely forested or grass-covered. Small mountain valleys are often intensively tilled and even terraced. With limited areas of good soil, patch agriculture of a subsistence type is common among hill tribes, such as the Shans, Kachins, and Karens.

The nonagricultural lands include thousands of square miles of forests, some worthless, others suitable for exploitation. The most valuable wood is teak, in which the country has long held first rank in the world. The most extensive teak forests are tributary to the upper reaches of the Irrawaddy. Trees ready for market are designated by a government official, killed by girdling, then allowed to stand for two or three years. When dry enough to float they are cut, dragged by elephants to watercourses, and floated to receiving stations on the larger rivers. Here they are made into rafts for the long trip down the Irrawaddy to mills on the Rangoon waterfront. Five to ten years may elapse between girdling a tree on the upper Chindwin and the arrival of the log at the mill. Teak from state forests is a source of revenue for the government. Ironwood and other less valuable species now exceed teak in annual cut, but the latter still leads in the export trade.

**Minerals.** Several oil fields on the Irrawaddy and lower Chindwin Rivers have made Burma a leading petroleum producer. Oil reaches the refineries near Rangoon by river barge or by a 320-mile pipeline. In recent years, however, war and internal disturbances have disrupted the industry.

The leading metal mines are in two districts. Rich lead-zinc-silver ores are mined in the Tenasserim area of the Malay Peninsula, and Burma ranks high in world tungsten production.

**Agriculture.** Two-thirds of the cultivated area in Burma is in paddies, in the adjoining deltas of the Irrawaddy and the Sittang. The apex of this great alluvial lowland is 180 miles inland; its base stretches for 150 miles along the coast. The rainfall of over 100 inches yearly is sufficient to mature a crop without additional irrigation. With the opening of new markets abroad in the 1870s, upland farmers from the dry zone migrated to the delta to clear, dike, and drain the swamp jungle, the movement reaching its height between 1880 and 1910. Ten million acres in Lower Burma were reclaimed.

Rice seedlings are transplanted during the warm rains of midsummer; harvest begins in November, with hand-cutting, drying, threshing, and sacking. Seasonal laborers from India seek employment in Burma during the annual rice harvest. Intersecting the delta in all directions, tidal creeks provide ready access by boat. Some 600 rice mills throughout Lower Burma receive the rough paddy by water, then husk and prepare it for overseas shipment. Rangoon is the recognized marketing and shipping center for the overseas rice trade, the country's most profitable business.

Upper Burma, the extensive central basin around Mandalay, is the second most productive region. Here many valleys converge, and at this focus of routes Mandalay has long been the historic regional capital.

Although called the dry zone, this district of lower rainfall and higher summer temperatures is suitable for a multicropping rather than a one-crop system. There is self-sufficiency in rice but little for export. Because of its low water requirement and drought tolerance, millet is a favorite grain. Peas and beans are cultivated for protein, sesame and peanuts for cooking oils. In the area south of Mandalay, low-grade cotton provides a ready cash crop. Work bullocks and water buffalo are raised for sale to the great commercial paddy lands of Lower Burma. Unlike the paddy workers of the delta, the small farmers of Upper Burma are largely independent, owning their own land, practicing diversification, and using crop rotations.

## Industries and Cities

Rangoon, situated on a deep channel of the delta 21 miles from the Indian Ocean, is the capital, the metropolis, and the dominant port. Canals connecting with the Irrawaddy and Sittang Rivers make it the focus of the interior river trade as well as the delta traffic. It is the assembly point for rice, upriver teak, and petroleum; its major industries are the milling and refining of such export commodities. More than 80 per cent of Burma's foreign trade passes through Rangoon.

Mandalay is the principal city of Upper Burma. It has both rail and water connections with Rangoon. A variety of industries has been developed, among them jade cutting and silk weaving. The city is noted for its numerous temples and monasteries.

## THAILAND

Originally migrants from southwest China, the Thai have had a long record of successful resistance to encroachment, first by powerful rulers in Burma and Cambodia, later by the rival colonial empires of France and Britain. Sovereignty was preserved during a period when independence was rare in South Asia. Long known as Siam, the name was changed in 1939 to Thailand—Land of the Free.

Thailanders in general are water-conditioned. Within its 196,816 square miles, the population is concentrated mainly in the central flood-lands and the long, wet coastlands, the inhabitants being habituated to salt or fresh-water living. Throughout the central plains, rivers and connecting canals are navigable even in the dry season. They serve as main highways, thronged with rice boats, passenger launches, floating bazaars, and sampans for transport or habitation.

Bangkok, capital of the kingdom since 1782, is the hub of rail and water transport and handles 85 per cent of the country's foreign trade. Below the city, on the 15-mile channel of the lower Menam Chao Phraya which leads to the Gulf of Siam, are situated the rice and teak mills as well as most of the port facilities. Chinese merchants and entrepreneurs buy rice, deal in teak, build boats, monopolize money-lending and banking, and control 80 per cent of the trade.

Thailand's positional arrangement in Southeast Asia, with a rim of varied highlands surrounding a central lowland, is similar to that of Burma. The Menam Chao Phraya and numerous smaller rivers rise on the borders, their silt-laden waters flowing into a broad interior plain thence south to the Gulf of Siam. Lower central Thailand, some 60 miles wide, is a maze of interlaced channels built up by continuous sedimentation; the coast is still extending southward.

Although much shorter than the rivers of Burma, the streams are sluggish and subject to annual floods. During the monsoon rains, the Menam Chao Phraya and its affluents regularly inundate some 5,000 square miles of central plain. During this hot, wet season the paddy farmer of lower Thailand has ample need for his house on stilts and his sampan. The Salween on the west and the Mekong on the east are border streams of minor significance.

Shared with Burma as a common boundary, the high range on the west is continuous for a thousand miles. Longer than all the rest of the country, the Kra Peninsula is locally called Siamese Malaya. On the east, the broad Korat Plateau, 1,500 feet high on its western edge, slopes toward the Laos border.

From May through October, the summer monsoon operates with full force. The higher mountain ranges, including the Kra Peninsula, receive 100 to 125 inches of rain annually, but the central plain and the Korat Plateau, partly in the rain shadow, get a maximum of 60, decreasing to 35 inches.

North Thailand is similar to the mountainous Shan Plateau on its western border. Here forest lands are the chief resource and teak the most valuable tree. State forests cover 41,000 square miles, with 10,000 in teak, a much smaller area than in Burma. Chiangmai, the northern railhead, is a primary assembly station but logs from many tributaries are rafted down the Menam Chao Phraya to the Bangkok mills. Some logs are taken out by way of the border rivers, Salween and Mekong. Formerly exploited at the rate of 1 million logs annually, teak production has declined, but the wood is still a leading Thai export and a substantial national resource.

The commercial minerals are tin and a much

*Figure 15-5 The Marble Temple, Bangkok, Thailand. (Courtesy of Royal Thai Embassy.)*

smaller output of tungsten, both from the Kra Peninsula. The mines are foreign-owned and worked by Chinese labor. Tin ores, third largest Thai export, are shipped to Malaya for smelting.

The economic life of Thailand is closely interwoven with rice which is grown on 95 per cent of the cultivated area, most of it in the flat central plain. Much of this great lowland has a rainfall of only 40 to 50 inches yearly but receives an ample water supply from the Menam Chao Phraya. This complex river system is fed by many affluents from the circle of northern highlands. When its major channel is bank-full it disgorges a mass of surplus water into various effluents—distributaries which branch off from the lower Menam Chao Phraya sometimes rejoining it lower down. Smaller parallel rivers contribute their volume of water, and during the monsoon season much of the plain becomes a vast shallow lake.

Flood time is rice planting time for the small cultivator. The heavy and impervious soils of the central plain are highly productive. Since single cropping is usual, however, the average yield of 30 bushels per acre is low in comparison with countries growing two crops annually. One quarter of the paddy area is in floating, or deep-water, rice, which grows in 6 to 7 feet of water. For the past half-century, paddy acreage has been expanding at the rate of 40,000 acres per year. New reclamation projects are under construction to provide additional irrigation, better flood control, and greater rice production.

The yearly rice consumption in Thailand, 450 pounds per person, leaves a large surplus for sale. Assembled at Bangkok, the rice is milled and shipped to deficit countries. High on the list of buyers are Hong Kong and Singa-

*Figure 15-6 The floating market in Bangkok is an assembly and shopping center for all types of goods and produce. (Courtesy of Government of Thailand.)*

*Figure 15-7   Teak from the hills of northern Thailand is worked by elephants. (Courtesy of Government of Thailand.)*

pore, the latter as middleman for Malaya. Rice accounts for two-thirds of Thailand's export trade.

Above the flooded rice lands are scattered zones of upland diversified farming where soy-beans, corn, sorghum, sesame, peanuts, tobacco, and cotton are cultivated. These crops are sometimes intertilled between rows of rice, maturing after the latter has been cut. The largest mixed farming area is in the upper Menam Chao Phraya Basin, extending to Chiangmai. The small upland cultivator relies heavily on vegetables for the family support, grows bananas, mangos, papayas, and keeps pigs, goats, and poultry, especially ducks.

In comparison with wet paddy, the drier mixed farming of Thailand is small. Some of the new irrigation projects serve the bench lands, providing water for upland crops such as cotton, tobacco, sesame, and peanuts. The Korat Plateau, which comprises nearly one-third of the kingdom, includes a broad plain a few hundred feet in elevation where considerable rice is grown during the flood season along rivers tributary to the Mekong. Except for these valley paddies, farming throughout the plateau consists of mixed dry land crops. Cheap upland pasturage favors livestock raising, the Korat region producing half the work bullocks and buffaloes used by Thai farmers. These animals are frequently sold to other Southeast Asia countries.

Rubber is grown far south in the peninsula where convection showers bring 75 to 100

*Figure 15-8   Rural house of bamboo and thatch near Ayuthia is raised on stilts above the flood level. Note water storage jar at left corner of the house. (Courtesy of Government of Thailand.)*

inches of well-distributed rainfall. There are few large estates, but many Chinese have small holdings of 2,000 to 3,000 trees; thus rubber is the second most valuable Thai export. The co-conut palm is at home everywhere in coastal Thailand but the largest acreage is in the Kra Peninsula. Land is available for considerable expansion of commercial agriculture.

## THE NEW STATES OF INDOCHINA

East of Thailand, the Indochinese Peninsula includes two great river basins, the Red River (Song Hoi) in the north and the Mekong in the south, connected by the long, narrow coastal plain of Annam. Behind this plain, the Anna-mitic Cordillera forms a continuous mountain range of 5,000 to 8,000 feet in elevation, de-clining on the south and west to a series of pla-teaus which drain westward to the Mekong.

The Cordillera serves as a climatic divide; its western slopes and the Mekong Basin receiving peak rainfall during the southwest monsoon, the eastern slopes getting the rains of the north-east monsoon. Over most of the area summer is rainy, followed, except in the northeast, by a dry season from December through March. Annual rainfall in Saigon is 80 inches, in Hanoi 72, but some of the higher mountains receive over 200 inches.

Within this area, the Tonkinese, Annamese, and Cochinese are of Mongol origin, but the Cambodians are descendants of the ancient Khmers. After a thousand years of independ-ence—with indirect control from China—colo-nialism was introduced in 1863, when Cambo-dia ceded Cochin China to France. This was followed by French protectorates over Cam-bodia, Annam, and Tonkin. In 1887, the three kingdoms were consolidated as the Union of Indochina, with Laos added in 1893.

Following the Japanese occupation, 1941–1945, a republic was proclaimed in the north by Tonkinese opposed to the return of French rule. An eight-year struggle ended in 1954 with a French withdrawal. Indochina became four independent countries—Cambodia, Laos, North Vietnam, and South Vietnam; a line near the 17th parallel divided Annam between the two latter countries. Each of the former Indo-chinese states is trying to perfect its own sepa-rate economy.

### South Vietnam

In South Vietnam, both Cochinese and An-namese occupy the extensive floodplains of the lower Mekong or cluster thickly along the coastal plain between the Cordillera and the South China Sea. With the exception of the Saigon-Cholon area, the population of the re-public is predominantly rural and village-dwell-ing, including small paddy farmers and, to a lesser degree, farm laborers on the large estates. Many hill peoples are scattered thinly through-out the forested plateaus and mountain slopes.

Like the Irrawaddy and the Menam Chao Phraya, the Mekong has built up one of the great floodplains of Southeast Asia. The apex of this delta is in lower Cambodia, but three-fourths of it is in old Cochin China (now Viet-nam), where rice paddies are the basis of the national economy. Most of the occupants are small farmers, but in certain areas sharecrop-pers till rice estates which were drained and reclaimed by French enterprisers. Since the paddy-to-population ratio is large, old Cochin China was a reliable rice exporter, much of the

TABLE 15-1. THE NEW STATES OF INDOCHINA (*Estimates*)

| Country | Area, sq miles | Population |
|---|---|---|
| Republic of South Vietnam | 65,000 | 10,000,000 |
| Communist North Vietnam | 60,000 | 12,000,000 |
| Kingdom of Cambodia | 69,000 | 4,000,000 |
| Kingdom of Laos | 91,000 | 1,300,000 |

surplus going to overcrowded Tonkin in the north. The rice trade is handled by Chinese middlemen; fleets of junks on the delta waterways move the unhusked paddy to the Saigon-Cholon conurbation for milling and shipping.

Introduced in 1897, rubber is planted on a large scale, some holdings reaching 100,000 acres. Most of the plantations are on the red earth uplands between the Mekong and the Cordillera. Young rubber trees are intertilled with tea, coffee, or sugar cane. The estates, most of them within a short radius of Saigon, are well managed and produce crops of high quality. Unlike Malaya, there are few small rubber growers in Vietnam.

Far less productive than rice, corn is grown in paddies as a second crop, but more often in uplands unsuited to rice. The many river banks bordering the watercourses are thickly planted to such nonirrigated crops as tobacco, beans, sugar cane, and cotton which mature during the dry and sunny November-to-April season. Yams are a dietary staple everywhere. Kapok and copra are prepared for the export trade.

Nearly 2 million acres of land are under French management. In addition to the large rubber holdings in the red earth uplands, tobacco, tea, and coffee estates extend into the cooler Moi Plateau at the south end of the Cordillera. Here, small farmers also grow tobacco and tea as cash crops.

Saigon, fifty miles up the Saigon River, is the metropolis, capital, and trade center of South Vietnam. Besides local rice and rubber, most of the Cambodian and the Laotian trade passes through it. Including its nearby rice-milling suburb, Cholon or "Great Market," this conurbation has a population of 1.6 million of which 600,000 are Chinese.

Following the partition of 1954, some 600,-000 refugees from Tonkin and northern Annam fled southward and are now living in temporary camps and villages in the vicinity of Saigon. One of the most pressing problems of the new government is refugee resettlement on upland farms or on newly reclaimed paddy lands in the delta.

## Kingdom of Cambodia

The kingdom of Cambodia, almost encircled by Thailand on the northwest and Vietnam on the southeast, is a basinlike lowland drained by the Mekong River system. With its various tributaries and delta channels, the Mekong virtually dominates the life of Cambodia. The best agricultural land has been built up by silt-laden rivers which enrich the fields annually. The floods provide ample water for paddy irrigation and sufficient moisture for the broad natural levees where most nonirrigated crops are grown. The watercourses determine the agricultural pattern, set the village habitation pattern, and serve as the oldest and best transportation arteries.

The most productive section is southeast Cambodia which includes the upper quarter of the Mekong delta lands with their flooded paddies and extensive areas of river bank cultivation. Two other agricultural regions extend up-country from the apex of the delta. The first follows the Mekong two-thirds of the way to the Laos border; it includes the red soil uplands with their rubber estates. The second extends northwest from the river, two belts of paddy land forming a broad ellipse around Tonle Sap Lake, and almost reaching the Thailand border. Rice-paddy and river-bank farming are similar to Vietnam, but there is almost no double cropping in Cambodia. Despite its 4 million people, the kingdom is not overcrowded. Although the yield per acre is low, large amounts of paddy are grown, one-quarter of it surplus for export. The river-bank farmers plant nonirrigated food crops such as corn, beans, and peanuts; cotton and tobacco are processed locally. Less than 15 per cent of the country is under systematic cultivation, and much of it is in forest and almost uninhabited.

Most farmers in Cambodia are part-time fishermen, gaining a portion of the family livelihood from nearby river or lake. Tonle Sap, in the central plain, is a great shallow lake connected with the Mekong by a 75-mile channel. At low water the lake covers some 1,000 square miles, but when the Mekong is in flood after the monsoon rains, surplus water pushes up the channel into Tonle Sap Lake which frequently inundates an area of 3,500 square miles. During the ensuing dry season the surplus water is slowly disgorged back into the Mekong. This unique lake supports a rich and varied fishing industry, the catching and marketing of fish, fresh, dried, or salted, reaching several million dollars annually.

Phnom Penh, capital and only large city, is situated at the juncture of three rivers, the Mekong, the Bassac which is a major delta channel, and Tonle Sap River. A single line of railway connects the capital with Bangkok, but Cambodia's foreign trade is handled mainly by river to Saigon. Vessels of 16-foot draft, including junks and river steamers, ascend to Phnom Penh to lift rice and other cargo. Plans have been drawn for the development of a new port on the Gulf of Siam.

### Kingdom of Laos

The mountain kingdom of Laos, in the isolated and heavily forested drainage basin of the upper Mekong, has 1.3 million inhabitants, including the ruling Lao group and other indigenous hill peoples. Six hundred and fifty miles long from Yünnan to the Cambodian border, its mountain valleys and dry dissected plateaus support a limited rice-corn-tobacco-cotton economy. Resources for sale are meager, but pigs, cattle, hides, coffee from its southern plateau, teak, stick-lac, and other forest products reach market via the Mekong River to Saigon.

### North Vietnam

Tonkin, in the drainage basin of the Red River (Song Hoi), was the northernmost of the states comprising former French Indochina. Together with the northern half of Annam, it is now North Vietnam and is closely allied with Communist China.

Rice occupies three-fourths of the cultivated land in the Red River delta and Annam coastal plain. When floods rise, a network of dikes and canals diverts water from the river to the paddies which are small, averaging 3 acres to a household. More than half the paddy land grows two crops annually, but flood damage is sometimes extensive. Unlike Cambodia or Cochin China there is seldom rice for export, and frequent shortages must be made up by imports from the less densely populated Mekong delta. Considerable upland rice and other food crops are grown in the plateaus and in the mountain valleys which stretch to the borders of China.

The uplands are well mineralized, most of the active mining being north of the Red River and near the border of China. The best coal measures in Southeast Asia are tributary to Haiphong, a 100-mile field containing rich seams of anthracite and high-grade bituminous coal, easily worked and near the coast. Lode ores of tin-tungsten are an extension of the Yünnan tin field of China.

A coast port in ancient times, the seaward extension of the delta by river silting has left Hanoi some 55 miles inland. Developed by the French as the administrative center for all Indochina, Hanoi has cotton textile factories, and serves as marketing center for the Red River basin. Haiphong has good port facilities for rice trading, coal shipping, and general cargo handling.

## MALAYA AND SINGAPORE

Modern Malaya dates back to the trading activities of the British East India Company which occupied Penang in 1786 and Malacca in 1824. From these two Straits Settlements, Britain extended a protectorate over nine Malay states. In 1948, the Federation of Malaya was formed and, with Kuala Lumpur as capital, it has attained full independence within the British Commonwealth. The island of Singapore still has the status of a Crown Colony. The combined population of 6.5 million includes 3 million Chinese, 2.7 million Malays, and half a million Indians.

The central core of Malaya is a highland 3,000 to 7,000 feet in elevation, which slopes abruptly to a coastal plain, narrow on the east coast, broader on the west along the Strait of Malacca. The short rivers are sluggish in their lower courses, and the coast is fringed by freshwater marshes and mangrove swamps. Situated well within the equatorial belt, Malaya has a precipitation averaging from 75 to 125 inches annually, but reaching 175 inches in the central mountains. As elsewhere in the rainy tropics, the afternoon shower prevails and heat and humidity are high.

The west coast plain from Singapore to the border of Thailand is the most productive part of Malaya. Varying in width from 15 to 50 miles, this 400-mile-long belt encompasses most of the improved land, the main subsistence and export crops, the largest population, and the main cities.

## Agriculture

Two-thirds of all cultivated acreage in Malaya is occupied by rubber, an industry which employs some 500,000 workers and which is the largest single source of income. Soon after its success in Ceylon, *Hevea brasiliensis* was introduced into the older coastal settlements of Malaya. Following the completion of a railway between Singapore and Penang, numerous inland estates were cleared during the rubber boom of 1909–1919.

The large British-owned estates, with thousands of acres in trees, are managed like factories, using work crews of Malays, Chinese, or Tamils. Estates produce 60 per cent of the Federation's export rubber, the rest coming from Malay or Chinese small holders with less than 100 acres each. The 345 acres under *Hevea* trees in 1897 have increased to 3.5 million acres, Malaya becoming the leader in world rubber production, with an annual export of 600,000 tons.

Other cash crops include the coconut, oil palm, and pineapple. An almost unbroken belt of coconut groves, one-half million acres, fringes the west coast and extending up many river valleys. Kiln-dried for market, copra is shipped coastwise to Singapore or Penang where the oil is extracted. Introduced from Africa, the oil palm is best suited to large-scale operation.

British-owned estates employing Indian labor do their own pressing, the oil and palm kernels being marketed through Singapore. Pineapple canning in south Malaya is largely controlled by the Chinese.

Many small farmers cultivate paddies in the lower floodreaches of the rivers. In contrast to Burma and Thailand, with their heavy rice exports, Malaya grows only one-third of its requirements.

## Tin Mining

The great placer tin belt of Asia extends from Yünnan through the Malay Peninsula to Indonesia, its most extensive deposits occurring in Malaya. The richest alluvials are in the valley bottoms and foothills around Kuala Lumpur and in districts farther north. Tin-bearing gravels are worked by two methods, a simple washery operation using a gravel pump, and the more costly but efficient floating dredges. Both pumping and dredging are on the increase, but lode mining in the mountains is still limited. With its rich surface ores and low-cost mining, Malaya has long supplied one-third of the world's tin. The concentrates are consigned to the great smelters in Penang and Singapore.

## Singapore

Because of its crossroad location, Singapore has become one of the great world seaports. Ocean shipping between Europe and the Far East traverses the Strait of Malacca, a narrow sea lane between Sumatra and Malaya, with the island of Singapore at its southern end. Purchased from one of the Malay sultans in 1819, it became a highly profitable trading station for the East India Company and later an outport for the rich tin and rubber trade of Malaya.

The city has some 12 miles of wharves and docks; over them passes a stream of imports and exports, raw, semifinished, or ready for consumption. Commercial activities have two broad bases. The city serves as metropolis and major port for the Federation, rubber, tin concentrates, copra, palm oil, and canned pineapple moving through it. Rice, textiles, and consumer goods needed by upcountry planters are procured through Singapore, which handles nearly 90 per cent of all Malayan foreign trade.

Its second function is that of general entrepôt for the wares of South Asia and the East Indies, Singapore serving as a transit port for Indonesia, Burma, and Thailand. Tin concentrates from Bangka Island, rubber from Sumatra and Borneo, and copra from the South Seas are assembled here. The city deals in pepper, cloves, nutmegs, and curry materials from all over Southeast Asia. Bulk shipments to Singapore are redistributed throughout Australasia.

Industries are mainly restricted to the preparation of raw materials in transit. Tin ores and concentrates are shipped to Singapore for smelting, and the bars and ingots sold to refineries in Britain and America. Copra, rubber, woods, and other tropical materials are also prepared for market.

Singapore's transshipment function includes banking, shipping, and commodity brokerage. As the trade and transfer emporium for much of South Asia it has attracted a diverse population. Chinese of Malayan nationality have increased to 800,000, with the Malays and other Asians in the minority in this city of over one million. Singapore is not a part of the new country of Galaya.

## THE PHILIPPINES

Soon after their discovery by Magellan in 1541, the Philippines became a commercial outpost of Spain, and were ruled by the Spanish for three centuries. This long period of occupation left its cultural imprint upon the religion, language, and customs of the archipelago. Half a century of American control after 1898 also made its contribution to educational, economic, and political development. Self-rule, which began with Commonwealth status in 1935, was interrupted by the Japanese occupation, then followed by full independence, with the establishment of the Republic of the Philippines in 1946.

The archipelago consists of some 7,000 islands. Numerous folded ranges, some reaching

elevations of 10,000 feet, extend in a north-south direction. There are many volcanic peaks, both inactive and active, some having erupted in recent times. Broad interior plains between ranges on the larger islands and narrow coastal plains on the smaller islands contain the best agricultural lands and support the larger part of the 20 million people. Almost half of them live on Luzon.

The larger islands include Luzon on the north, with its many peninsulas and embayments, and rugged Mindanao on the south. These two contain over two-thirds of the 115,-000 square miles in the Philippines. Between them are seven smaller islands or groups known as the Visayan group; Samar and Leyte on the east; Panay, Negros, Cebu, and Bohol on the west. Despite certain similarities throughout the islands, various areas have recognized specialties. The broad Cagayan Valley of northern Luzon is mainly devoted to corn and tobacco. Extending from Manila Bay to the Lingayen Gulf, the central plain of Luzon grows rice, sugar cane, and coconuts. This rich plain is the economic heart of the Philippines. The limited but highly productive coastal plains of Mindanao grow abacá, rubber, and coconuts. With few exceptions, all the better valleys and coasts throughout the Philippines are carefully tilled and densely populated.

With high temperatures and high relative humidity, the climate of the lowlands is oppressive most of the year. The highlands are more pleasant, Baguio at 4,756 feet being 15 degrees cooler than Manila. The summer monsoon brings heavy rain to the western regions, the annual amount varying from 50 to 180 inches. Manila receives more than half its 80 inches during the three midsummer months. Eastern sides of the islands receive their maximum rainfall in winter and have no pronounced dry season. Baguio gets 250 inches a year, most of it during the summer monsoon. North of Mindanao, typhoons frequently damage crops and property.

### Natural Resources

Over one-half the area of the islands is covered with timber, including some 80 species of commercial value. Except for large stands of

*Figure 15-9   Many of the islands of Southeast Asia are either the result of volcanic activity or have volcanoes on them. This one in the southern part of the Philippines is almost a perfect cone. (Courtesy of the Philippine Embassy.)*

*Figure 15-10 The water buffalo is the common work animal of much of Southeast Asia. These are preparing a field for planting. (Courtesy of the Philippine Embassy.)*

pine in the mountains of Luzon, these forests are mainly broad-leaved hardwoods; 1 billion board feet are cut and sold annually. Much of it is used locally, but the finer hardwoods such as narra (Philippine mahogany) are suitable for interior finishing, furniture, and cabinet work, and enter the export trade. Minor forest products include rattans, bamboo, resins, and tanning materials.

Minerals are widely distributed with gold, from the rich mining district near Baguio, taking first rank. Large reserves of iron ore in northern Mindanao and of chromite in both Mindanao and Luzon are near the surface and can be worked by open-pit methods. There are also widely scattered manganese, copper, and silver deposits.

*Agriculture*

Agriculture is predominant, much of the land is carefully tilled, and double cropping is general. The prime food favorite, rice, is most heavily grown in central Luzon and on Panay. Even in the mountains, some steep slopes are terraced for paddy. Farms average less than 5 acres, and the entire family helps transfer the young plants from seedbed to field, and harvest the grain.

Since Spanish times, the Philippines have been a rice deficit area, importing from the surplus countries of Southeast Asia. Under both Spanish and American administration, new lands were cleared for the production of export crops such as abacá, coconuts, sugar, tobacco, and rubber, but little attempt was made to increase the paddy area.

Corn, commonly cultivated on land unsuited to rice, is the second breadstuff of the Philippines. Acreage is largest in the Cagayan Valley where it is frequently a succession crop after tobacco. Cebu and Negros depend heavily on corn, and it is a food staple in most upland areas. Camotes (sweet potatoes), manioc or cassava, taro, peanuts, and bananas supplement rice and corn in the diet. Shifting cultivation is widely practiced in upland areas.

Sugar cane is the major field crop of the Philippines, accounting for over one-half of the total exports. The central plain of Luzon, together with Negros and Cebu, ships a million tons of sugar annually. Despite the long transpacific voyage, preferential entry for Philippine sugar makes the United States the most favored market.

South of Manila, coconuts fringe almost every coast, with high concentrations in certain volcanic areas having favorable slope and drainage. This highly productive tree occupies one-quarter of the cultivated area and is second only to rice in the local economy. The individual grower sun-dries the meat, but on large plantations mechanical dryers prepare copra of higher quality. Small trading vessels circulate through the archipelago buying sacks of copra which they sell to the oil mills. Coconuts are exported in the form of copra, oil, meal, or desiccated coconut, the Philippines supplying one-third of the total entering world trade.

The Philippines long had a virtual monopoly in the production of abacá, a fiber valued for its strength and resiliency. Under the trade name "Manila hemp," it is used chiefly for rope. The tall banana-like plant is cultivated in the Legaspi Peninsula of Luzon, and around the Gulf of Davao in Mindanao. In Luzon, abacá is grown by small farmers or tenants and stripped by hand, but in the newer lands of Davao, where the plantation system has been introduced, the large-scale stripping of fiber is mechanized. Abacá fiber and the cordage made from it in Manila are among the major Philippine exports.

## Cities

Founded in 1571, Manila has been the capital and chief port of the Philippines since early Spanish times. The bay provides commodious anchorage for ocean shipping and the many interisland steamers. The city is more commercial than industrial, since manufacture is mainly processing, coconut oil pressing, sugar refining, rope making, and the preparation of tobacco. Manila has a million inhabitants, the

*Figure 15-11  Manila, the capital of the Philippines, is a large and modern city. (Courtesy of the Philippine Embassy.)*

suburban periphery an additional half million, including 100,000 in nearby Quezon City, the new political capital. Iloilo on Panay, Cebu City on Cebu, Bacolod on Negros, and Zamboanga and Davao on Mindanao serve as regional centers for the provinces.

## INDONESIA

The Indonesian archipelago is the largest in the world, extending some 3,000 miles along the equator and 1,500 miles north-south. Included are large islands with small populations like Borneo and small islands such as Java and Bali that have large populations. Sparsely peopled Borneo (Kalimantan), Celebes (Sulawesi), and New Guinea (Irian) have interiors so mountainous, rugged, and jungle-filled that they have never been completely explored or mapped.

Physically, Indonesia is a continuation of a southward-trending arm of the Himalayas. The folded and volcanic Sunda arc includes Sumatra, Java, the lesser Sundas, and Celebes-Halmahera. The mountain backbone of both Sumatra and Java is mainly volcanic, having 100 or more peaks, 20 of them rising between 8,000 to 10,000 feet. Both Java and Sumatra have many active volcanoes and frequent earthquakes.

Indonesia is generally tropical but has considerable climatic variation because of altitude. Lowland temperatures average 75 to 80°F, with less than 5°F annual range. At higher elevations, the lower temperatures provide better living conditions and permit altitudinal zonation in agriculture. Many lowland cities have nearby hill stations for recreation and for health. Jakarta (Batavia), with an average annual temperature of 79°F, is in contrast to Bandung at 2,500 feet with an average temperature of 72°. Here cooler nights are an attractive feature.

Over much of the archipelago, variations in temperature are less significant than variations in rainfall. Situated between the land masses of Southeast Asia and Australia, western Indonesia is in the direct path of the summer and winter monsoons, Jakarta receiving 75 inches; Medan, 80; Pontianak, 130; Macassar, 115 inches; and stations at higher elevations even more. Relative humidity is generally high.

## People and Politics

The ancient Indian kingdom in Java included both Buddhists and Hindus. Borobudur in central Java, built in the eighth or ninth century, is the most famous of the Buddhist monuments. The Islamic infiltration began in the thirteenth

*Figure 15-12  The new Republic of Indonesia is made up of many islands each of which is, or can probably become, very productive. (Courtesy of Government of Indonesia.)*

*a. Characteristic Javanese landscape showing rice field, water buffalo, and a narrow-gauge railway for transporting sugar cane.*
*b. Pepper picking on the island of Bangka.*
*c. Mining tin-bearing gravels by dragline in Bangka.*

TABLE 15-2.  INDONESIA

| | Area, sq miles | Population census, 1930 | Population per sq mile 1930 | Population estimate, 1955 * |
|---|---|---|---|---|
| Java and Madura | 51,032 | 41,718,364 | 817 | 51,637,572 |
| Sumatra | 182,859 | 8,254,843 | 43 | 11,371,233 |
| Borneo (Kalimantan) | 208,285 | 2,138,691 | 11 | 3,092,206 |
| Celebes (Sulawesi) | 72,986 | 4,231,906 | 56 | 6,065,145 |
| Moluccas (Maluku) | 191,681 | 893,400 † | 5 | 685,704 ‡ |
| Timor Archipelago | 24,449 | 1,657,376 | 68 | 2,183,545 |
| Bali and Lombok | 3,973 | 1,802,683 | 454 | 2,579,187 |
| Total | 735,265 | 60,697,263 | | 77,614,592 |

* Estimate by Election Committee for Parliamentary Election, Government of Indonesia, September, 1955.
† Including Irian (Western New Guinea).
‡ Excluding Irian.

century with the arrival of Arab traders; by 1600 Islam had superseded both Hinduism and Buddhism. Later Portuguese, Dutch, and English companies became active competitors for the trade of the Indies, the Dutch emerging as the dominant power. They absorbed various parts of the Indies; by 1914, most of the archipelago was a colony, the Netherlands East Indies.

Dutch rule was suspended during World War II and the Japanese occupation. In August, 1945, Indonesian patriots proclaimed a republic. After a futile attempt to reestablish Dutch control, the United States of Indonesia was created as part of the Netherlands Union. This agreement was abrogated in 1954, and the Republic of Indonesia attained complete independence, although the Dutch retained western New Guinea.

Through the centuries, migrations from Asia and the Pacific have created a complex social structure. The majority of the people are Moslems, with relatively small groups of animists, Hindus, and Christians. Among the nonindigenous peoples, Chinese are most numerous and control much of the small business and trade. Many different languages and dialects are spoken, but a variant of Malay is the official Indonesian language. In addition to racial, linguistic, and religious diversity, there is great contrast between the highly cultured Javanese and Balinese, and the migratory food-gathering peoples of Borneo and western New Guinea.

*Agriculture*

Like their Arab and Portuguese predecessors, the Dutch in the Indies came in search of spices —cloves, pepper, cinnamon, nutmegs—then cultivated other tropical crops. Coffee was introduced into Java about 1700, the Dutch East India Company making the first large shipment to Amsterdam in 1712.

Under the culture system, 1830–1870, which included compulsory planting, forced native labor, and collection at fixed prices, the coffee gardens expanded into the highlands above Jakarta (Batavia), and the East Indies became the world leader in coffee. Overproduction and price declines broke the market; other crops were substituted and the culture system gave way to long-term plantation leases.

The upland of Java between Buitenzorg, 800 feet, and Bandung, 2,500 feet, was the first area of large estates. Here coffee was superseded by tea and rubber. Most plantations are now in the highlands, the main exceptions being those devoted to sugar cane, tobacco, and sisal. Under Dutch direction, the system spread throughout the island. Tea, rubber, and cinchona predominate in west Java; east Java grows rubber, tea, and coffee; central Java is the major sugar cane region. The island has been a great plant introduction garden where hundreds of possible crops have been tested.

The estate system reached Sumatra about 1865 when large-scale jungle clearing and tobacco planting began near Medan. Tea, abacá, the oil palm, and rubber were gradually added.

The optimum elevation for rubber is about 1,000 feet. *Hevea* saplings, started in nursery beds, are set out in rows, usually with catch crops such as corn, beans, or sweet potatoes, during the six to eight years before tapping begins. Most estates are completely mechanized, some of the largest being on the east coast of Sumatra, now the recognized center of foreign rubber concessions. Considerable latex is exported in liquid form.

Small growers everywhere have increased their holdings, the farmer and his family in Java, Sumatra, or Borneo tapping his trees, coagulating the latex, and processing the sheets of crepe by hand. Growing their own food crops for home use, small holders are not greatly affected by fluctuating world prices. Small-scale rubber now accounts for 75 per cent of the total output. South Sumatra rubber is marketed through Palembang. Growers in southeast Borneo ship down rivers to Benjermasin. Ranking second only to Malaya, Indonesia produces about one-third of the world's natural rubber.

Throughout much of Indonesia, groves of coconuts surround the native villages or kampongs. Together with bananas, papayas, and mangos, coconuts help augment the food supply and are a ready source of cash income. Drying and collecting copra is a year-round business, some 5,000 native vessels (prahaus) cruising the islands as copra traders. In export value, coconut products rank second only to rubber.

Begun by the Dutch under the culture system, tobacco is still a significant estate crop in Java, although little patches on small farms now contribute the larger share of locally used leaf. Door-to-door buyers collect the crop, selling it to the cigarette factories. In Sumatra high-quality tobacco for cigars is grown along the Deli River in the Medan district where Dutch enterprisers secured concessions. Since tobacco can be grown on a field only once in eight or ten years, large acreages are essential. The famous Deli leaf brings high prices from cigar makers.

*Coffea robusta,* a hardy variety introduced from Africa, is cultivated on terraced slopes in east Java, the optimum elevation being 1,500 to 2,000 feet. Estate production has declined, but small cultivators have increased the number of their trees to supply the home demand, Indonesia consuming far more coffee than tea.

Tea from Assam was introduced into the highlands of west Java where volcanic soils and well-distributed rainfall of 100 to 200 inches provide suitable natural conditions. The carefully managed Java estates are between 1,500 and 4,000 feet in elevation. In Sumatra, production is localized in the hills east of Lake Toba. Picking is continuous, and the leaves are processed and packed in factories on the estates. Small growers sell their green leaves to the nearest factory.

The oil palm, a wild forest tree from equatorial Africa, was introduced into Sumatra in 1911. Oil palms in the Medan area are grown on highly mechanized estates of 3,000 to 20,000 acres, employing Javanese or Chinese laborers. Careful selection of trees has raised the oil yield per acre from 500 to approximately 2,000 pounds. After cooking and pressing, most of the oil is shipped in tankers to Europe or the United States. One-third of the world's palm oil comes from Sumatra. In Indonesia, it is used in the manufacture of soaps and edible fats.

Sugar cane is one of the oldest estate crops, large and small growers as well as the sugar factories being concentrated in the lowlands of central and east Java. Stimulated by high prices, sugar output rose to a peak of 3 million tons, 10 per cent of the world crop, in the early 1920s, followed by overproduction and low prices. Since most Java cane is grown on paddy land in rotation with rice, output was readily reduced by substituting more essential food crops.

Spices, original motivation for the East Indies trade, are still cultivated for local use and for export. The Moluccas specialize in nutmegs, cloves, and cardamons. White and black pepper and cinnamon come chiefly from Sumatra and Borneo.

The cinchona tree, successfully transplanted from South America, thrives at altitudes from 4,000 to 6,000 feet. Over 90 per cent of the world's supply of cinchona bark, from which quinine is extracted, was formerly produced in Java, where quinine is also manufactured. Pharmaceutical substitutes, including synthetic quinine, are now in competition with cinchona bark.

Indonesia has the largest rice production per acre of any Southeast Asian country. The area in paddies, called sawahs, almost equals that of all other crops combined, two-thirds of it being in densely populated Java. Water is obtained from simple stream diversion or large reclamation projects built by the government. In Bali and Lombok as well as in Java, many steep slopes have been terraced for sawahs. The growing season is continuous, with planting, cultivation, and harvest going on simultaneously. Seedlings are transplanted to the prepared fields and, after harvest, a second crop is planted. If sufficient water is available, additional rice is preferred; otherwise, the farmer plants a dry crop such as corn, cassava, sweet potatoes, or soybeans. Rice now exceeds prewar production and Indonesia has almost achieved self-sufficiency.

*Figure 15-13 Terraces in southern Bali flooded for wet rice. In the dry season these sawahs will be planted to nonirrigated crops such as sweet potatoes, maize, or beans. (Courtesy of Government of Indonesia.)*

Corn (maize) is grown almost everywhere from sea level to 7,000 feet. Cultivated in the sawahs as a succession crop after paddy, it is also a favorite in the uplands where it is rotated with hill rice. Sweet potatoes, cassava, and bananas grow in almost every garden but lack the prestige of rice. Villages are shaded by trees bearing papayas, tamarinds, coconuts, bananas, and mangos.

Small holders often cultivate cash crops such as tea or cotton. Both peanuts and cassava are grown in excess of local demand, the latter being sold in the form of tapioca. Valuable fibers include sisal, abacá, kapok, and coir. Most of the cacao is purchased by Netherlands chocolate manufacturers.

Largely because of the greater seasonal aridity rice, the dominant crop in western Java, decreases in importance in eastern Java, Madura, Lombok, and other islands to the east. In these areas maize, yams, various taros, and manioc (tapioca) become the staple food crops. Besides the shortage of water which makes the irrigation of rice difficult, the area is also the center of an older native economy which is based upon other staple food products. Rice is an introduction from the mainland, the crop extending eastward into the Indies only about as far as the Hindu and Moslem influences.

## Minerals

The petroleum fields are widely dispersed, extending from northern Sumatra to western New Guinea (Irian). The Sumatran fields are inland from Palembang along the mountain flanks, and along the north coast. Oil is produced near Surabaya and Rembang in east Java, in the Balikpapan and Tarakan fields of east Borneo (Kalimantan), and in the Vogelkop of western New Guinea. Output dropped to zero during World War II, but is again approaching normal. Petroleum is processed in local refineries, gasoline, lubricating oil, and kerosene accounting for one-quarter of Indonesia's exports.

Exploited by the Chinese in the early 1700s, the tin deposits of Bangka, Belitong, and Singkep, islands in the Java Sea, are a continuation of the tin belt of Malaya. On Bangka, the mines are a government monopoly and are worked largely by Chinese labor. Tin ore in placer deposits is worked either by hydraulic pumps or by dredges. Indonesia produces half as much tin as Malaya, ranking third in the world. Most of the ore is smelted in Singapore.

Good steam coal is mined in southern Sumatra, and other islands have workable deposits of bauxite and nickel. Pearls and shell come from eastern Indonesia.

*Figure 15-14   Rubber grown by individual small holders in south Sumatra is smoked and baled for export through Palembang. (Courtesy of Government of Indonesia.)*

*Industry and Cities*

With the exception of cotton textiles and consumer goods such as oleomargarine and soap, most industry has been developed around estate crops. Sugar and rubber mills, coconut-oil plants, cigar and cigarette factories, and petroleum refineries process local materials. Throughout Indonesia, handicrafts are more significant than mechanized industry.

Old Jakarta, at the mouth of the Chilliwong River, was burned by the Dutch in 1620, then rebuilt and named Batavia. Centrally located for the commerce of the Indies, it became a great trading and shipping port. When river silting made the old harbor too shallow, a new deepwater port was developed at Tandjung Priok. With the attainment of Indonesian independence the name Jakarta was restored and, as capital of the republic, the city now has an estimated population of 2.5 million persons.

Surabaya has a well-protected harbor and is the trade center for east Java, Semarang having a similar function for the rich estate lands of mid-Java.

In Sumatra, the upriver port of Palembang handles rubber and other tropical exports as well as petroleum products from the local refineries. Developed by the rubber and tobacco corporations, Medan is more of a planter capital than an Indonesian city; it has a nearby hill station on a 4,500-foot plateau. Bandjermasin is the outlet and trade center for southeast Borneo. Many other regional and insular centers are agglomerations of kampongs or native villages.

Because of its close proximity and crossroad position, Singapore is a natural clearing-house for a large volume of Indonesian trade besides smelting some of its tin ore.

## BRITISH BORNEO

British Borneo, having a population of 1 million and occupying about one-fourth of the island, includes the Crown Colony of British North Borneo, the protectorate of Brunei, and the Crown Colony of Sarawak, located in north and northwest Borneo. The island has a hot, humid climate, and tropical rain forests cover the land. The mountainous interior, from which hardwood timber is exported, has few inhabitants. Among the animals of the forest is the orang-outang, a large ape. Birds of brilliant plumage are abundant. Much of the coast is swampy with a fringe of mangroves growing on the tide flats. Little land is cleared and the native agriculture is of the subsistence type with rice, sago, and bananas being leading crops. Many fruits are grown. Most of the native Malays live in small villages and are less advanced culturally than the Javanese.

British North Borneo was developed by a private trading company. There are plantations of rubber, tobacco, and coconuts. The area is 29,500 square miles and the country has a population of about 335,000, which includes only 1,000 Europeans. The 75,000 Chinese residents handle much of the small business and do much of the plantation work.

Brunei, a small country of 2,226 square miles, has a population of about 46,000. It is governed by a sultan under the advice and protection of Great Britain. Petroleum is the chief export, the Seria oil field producing over 5 million tons a year.

The colony of Sarawak is situated along the China Sea for 450 miles and spreads over 100 miles inland to the mountains. Its 50,000 square miles has a population of about 600,-000. Chief exports are plantation rubber, sago, and pepper. Petroleum is produced near the Brunei fields, and a little gold is recovered from placers. The natives had only a primitive culture before outsiders entered the country. The transition from a condition of savagery to civilization has been gradual, many people in the interior having little contact with the outside world. Even some Europeans live under pioneer conditions without the facilities and comforts of their homelands.

The territory of Sarawak, along with the title of Rajah, was given to an Englishman,

James Brooke, in 1841 as a reward for help given the Sultan of Brunei against pirates. In 1888, both Sarawak and Brunei came under British protection, and in 1946, Rajah Brooke, a descendant of the original, ceded Sarawak to Great Britain and it became a colony.

## PORTUGUESE TIMOR

The Portuguese engaged in the spice trade in the East Indies as early as the sixteenth century. For a time they controlled much of the archipelago, but later were replaced by others. Since 1618, Portugal has controlled the eastern part of the mountainous island of Timor. The western part is Indonesian except for a small enclave belonging to Portugal. The colony has an area of 7,330 square miles and a population of over 450,000. Coffee, tobacco, copra, and sandalwood are the main exports, but total trade is small.

## IN PERSPECTIVE

### Changing Southeast Asia

Extending southward from the borders of India and China, Southeast Asia includes several peninsular countries such as Burma, Thailand, Cambodia, South Vietnam, and Malaya, as well as the archipelagos of Indonesia and the Philippines. Well watered by the tropical monsoon, the great river valleys with their deltas, as well as the richer coastal plains, are devoted in the main to a system of agriculture in which rice is dominant.

Ancient kingdoms with high cultural attainments flourished at various periods, but most of them had declined in power and significance before the advent of Europeans. With the exception of Thailand, all Southeast Asia came under colonial rule. Following the development of large estates, a steady flow of tropical products such as tea, coffee, cacao, coconut oil, palm oil, fibers, drugs, and spices have been exported. Since environmental conditions are especially suitable for the rubber tree, Indonesia and Malaya have become the two greatest world sources of natural rubber. The three great river basins in Burma, Thailand, Cambodia, and South Vietnam produce a surplus of rice, in the export of which the region leads the world.

Under colonialism, mineral resources were developed, transportation improved, and commerce expanded. Cities such as Singapore, Jakarta, and Manila, with strategic locations on trade routes, have become world entrepôts. Up-river delta cities such as Rangoon, Bangkok, and Saigon are more local in function.

Postwar governments are faced with problems of land ownership, population redistribution, and the rehabilitation of factories and transport systems. All the new nations wish to retain the material benefits achieved under colonialism. Except for the Philippines, the new countries lack administrative personnel with experience in government, and they have few skilled technicians. To further complicate the problem, some 12 million Southeast Asians are Chinese. Able and industrious, the Chinese have long been the merchants, middlemen, and moneylenders. With the withdrawal of Europeans, they have become small capitalists. Although long resident in countries such as Malaya, Thailand, and Indonesia, the millions of Chinese, many of whom claim dual nationality, provide an element of political uncertainty.

## EXERCISES

*1.* Which countries of Southeast Asia have gained their independence since 1940? What nations controlled them before independence? How did they gain their independence?

*2.* Which part of the region is dominated by its mountain topography? In which general direction do the ranges extend? How have the mountain ranges influenced cultural development?

*3.* What are the two most important minerals exported from the region? Where is each mined? What countries import the largest amounts of these minerals?

*4.* What is the location of Singapore? Why is it so strategically important? What nation controls Singapore?

*5.* In what way is Vietnam comparable to Korea? Which division of Vietnam has the larger population? Which has the best agricultural potential? Why? What are the principal problems facing Vietnam?

*6.* How does the physical environment influence the economic activities of Burma? What are the chief Burmese exports? In which part of the country are they produced? What are the principal rivers of the country?

*7.* In which part of Thailand do most of the people live? Why? How does the culture of Thailand differ from that of Burma?

*8.* What are the principal islands in the Republic of Indonesia? Which has the greatest population?

What cultural and economic factors cause Java to be better developed than the other islands? What problems face this new nation?

*9.* Why should the nations of Laos and Cambodia be granted independence? What are the physical and economic advantages and handicaps of each?

*10.* How may the Philippine Republic be compared and contrasted to the Republic of Indonesia? What are the chief problems facing the Philippines? What are its principal advantages in its effort to succeed as an independent nation?

*11.* What and where are the largest cities in Southeast Asia? Why is each important? Which are ports? What is the chief type of manufacturing in each? Is manufacturing as important as other functions?

*12.* In which of these countries of Southeast Asia would you prefer to live? Why? What are its chief problems?

*13.* Where are the chief regions of production of Manila hemp, tobacco, sugar, rubber, spices, tea, coffee, and teak?

## SELECTED REFERENCES

Andrus, J. R.: *Burmese Economic Life,* Stanford University Press, Stanford, 1947.

Broek, Jan O. M.: "Resources of the Tropics: III —Southeast Asia," *Focus,* 4(6):1–6, February, 1954.

Cole, Fay-Cooper: *Peoples of Malaysia,* D. Van Nostrand Company, Inc., Princeton, N.J., 1945.

Cutshall, Alden: "Problems of Land Ownership in the Philippine Islands," *Economic Geography,* 28:31–36, January, 1952.

Dobby, E. H. G.: *Southeast Asia,* University of London Press, London, 1950.

Metcalf, J. E.: *The Agricultural Economy of Indonesia,* Washington, 1952.

Mills, Lennox (ed.): *The New World of Southeast Asia,* University of Minnesota Press, Minneapolis, 1949.

Pelzer, Karl J.: *Pioneer Settlement in the Asiatic Tropics,* The American Geographical Society, New York, 1945.

Spencer, J. E.: *Asia, East by South,* John Wiley & Sons, Inc., New York, 1954.

————: *Land and People of the Philippines,* University of California Press, Berkeley, 1952.

Taylor, Alice: "Viet Nam," *Focus,* 1(5):1–6, February, 1951.

Thompson, Warren: *Population and Food Supply in the Pacific,* University of Chicago Press, Chicago, 1946.

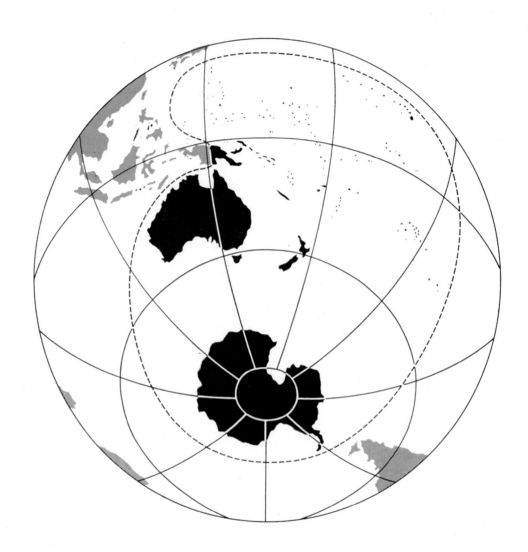

# 16. Australia, Oceania, and Antarctica

BETWEEN the land mass of the Old World continents and the Americas lies
the Pacific Ocean—covering nearly two-fifths of the surface of the globe—an
area larger than all the continents combined. Although so large, it was
long unknown to Europeans and was among the last parts of the world they
explored. Moreover, stories told by voyagers often gave erroneous impressions

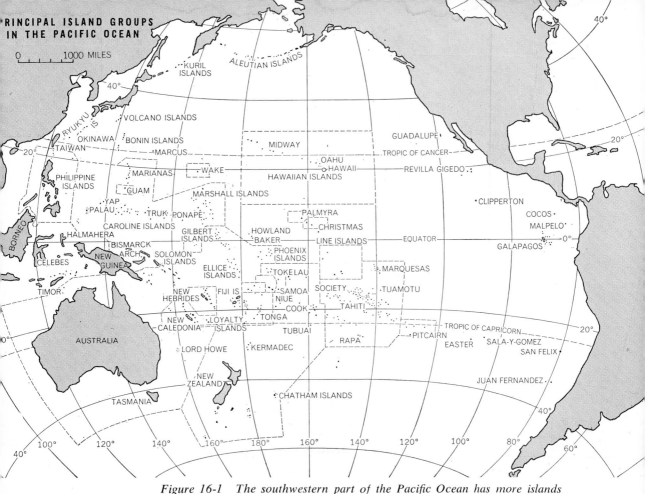

*Figure 16-1   The southwestern part of the Pacific Ocean has more islands than any other equal area. The islands vary in size from New Guinea to mere dots of land. Australia, the smallest of the continents, is also in this area. Note the absence of islands in much of the northeastern Pacific.*

concerning the natives and their customs. Most Americans had small interest in the Pacific until the 1940s when, during World War II, the names of obscure islands were headlined in the newspapers as the armed forces of the United States drove back the Japanese after their invasion had crossed the equator and almost reached Australia.

The regional unity of the Pacific is its vast extent of water. The land areas are very small in comparison; even Australia is only the size of the United States. Stretching southeast from Asia is a series of mountain folds, the tops of which form the elongated islands of Indonesia, New Guinea, the Bismarck Archipelago, and the Solomon group. The folding continues into New Zealand, with New Caledonia, New Hebrides, and other islands partially bridging the

gaps. The Australian continent lies to the south and west of these mountainous islands. Further seaward, east and north, are other folds, almost entirely underneath the waters of the Pacific but having a few peaks, often of volcanic origin, that rise above the open ocean to form small, widely scattered islands. The most remote islands are either of volcanic or coralline origin. The volcanoes generally form high islands; those of coral are low and, except for a limited number of raised coral islands, have a height of only a few feet above sea level. Characteristically, the oceanic islands on a map appear arranged in arclike festoons because, sometimes from great depths, they rise above curving lines of weakness in the earth's crust.

The western Pacific has numerous islands compared to the eastern portion in which is-

Figure 16-2 *Australia is divided into three large regions. Each could be subdivided into many smaller ones. Most of the population of the nation live in the eastern and southern part of the mountain area. Western Australia is very largely a desert region.*

lands are rare (Figure 16-1). The north Pacific between the Aleutian chain and the tropics has practically no islands except near the continents. In the vast southern ocean between New Zealand and Antarctica, only a few isolated volcanoes rise above the boundless appearing sea.

## AUSTRALIA

Australia is called the island-continent because of isolation from the great land masses and because it is the smallest of the populated continents, having an area of about 3 million square miles. Down-under Australia and Antarctica are the only continents wholly south of the equator. Similarity of conditions and problems in some parts of Australia to those of the United States, and the English ancestry of most of the people, make Americans at home in this southern continent.

The Commonwealth of Australia was established on January 1, 1901, by the union of six British colonies. The former colonies, now called states, are New South Wales, Victoria, Queensland, South Australia, Western Australia, and Tasmania. In addition there is a Northern Territory. The capital of the Commonwealth is Canberra. The country is a self-governing member of the British Commonwealth. Australia also governs the eastern half of New Guinea and several smaller islands (Figure 16-2).

Australia has certain outstanding features that affect man and his use of the land. It is a very ancient continent, and old rocks predominate. Australia has the lowest average elevation, hardly 1,000 feet, of any continent. Only 6 per cent of the country has an altitude of over 2,000 feet. Low elevation, combined with its location in the trade winds and under areas of high atmospheric pressure, precludes much rainfall; hence half the continent is arid and a quarter semiarid. From this dry interior no drainage reaches the ocean, and temporary streams and lake basins contain water only after occasional rainstorms. Hardly one-fourth of Australia is blessed with a humid or subhumid climate. Most of the streams in the humid regions are short, but some have been developed for power. In the southeast interior, the Murray-Darling-Murrumbidgee drainage area supplies much water for irrigation. In northern Australia, the rivers vary in volume from flood stages during the rainy season to low or intermittent during the dry season. Australia extends almost 2,600 miles from east to west and 2,000 miles north and south. It is compact and has a coast line with few indentations giving the continent the shortest coast line, compared with its area, of any of the continents. There are few good harbors, no active volcanoes, and the highest peak, Mt. Kosciusko, is only 7,328 feet above the sea.

## Physical Setting

**Regions.** Australia is conveniently divided into the three major regions of the Western Plateau, the Central Basins, and the Eastern Highlands (Figure 16-2).

The Western Plateau occupies three-fifths of the continent. It is composed of very ancient rocks that have been worn down by erosion to a peneplain. Only low knobs and a few ranges rise above the monotonous surface, most of which has an elevation of about 1,200 feet. Around Spencer Gulf, in South Australia, earth movements have resulted in elongated ridges and depressed blocks forming rift valleys. Only in the north and southwest is the rainfall adequate for trees and good pasture for livestock. Wheat and other crops are raised in the southwest.

The Central Basins include the lowlands extending from the Gulf of Carpentaria on the north to the Murray River basin and the Great Australian Bight on the south. From north to south, the Carpentaria, Great Artesian, and Murray Basins together include 800,000 square miles, or over one-fourth of the area of Australia. The basins are underlain by dipping layers of sedimentary rocks, chiefly clay and sandstone. The Carpentaria Basin has generally poor soils and is covered with scrub trees and tall grass. Some cattle are kept by the few settlers living in the region.

In the Great Artesian Basin, water enters the sandstones in high ground along the eastern rim and is held in the previous beds by impervious clay above and below. The water is under pressure and when reached by bores (drilled wells) flows out on the surface. Although most of the water is too salty to be used for irrigation, it is usable for watering livestock and makes possible a cattle industry in grassy areas devoid of surface water. The lower part of the basin is desert, and Lake Eyre, whose elevation is 39 feet below sea level, contains water only after heavy rains. The best grazing coincides with the area of greater rainfall in the eastern part, especially in the Darling Downs of southern Queensland which is drained by the Darling River, a tributary of the Murray.

The Murray Basin has fertile soils and is important for wheat, cattle, and sheep production. It is well watered toward the eastern and southern rims, but the climate becomes drier along the lower course of the river. Here irrigation projects, using the waters of the Murray and Murrumbidgee Rivers, make possible the raising of citrus fruits, grapes, and other crops.

The Eastern Highlands cover about one-sixth of the continent. The region consists of uplifted plateaus, tilted crustal blocks, and folded zones of various rock types, along with small disconnected areas of lowland and coastal plain. Although parts of the Highlands are thinly populated, the region contains two-thirds of Australia's inhabitants, in part because it is the best-watered region of the continent. Elevations are moderate and vary from under 1,000 to over 3,000 feet with summits above 7,000 feet in the southeast. The Highlands continue across Bass Strait to Tasmania, which is a very rugged island composed of two uplands separated by a lowland extending north-south. In southern Victoria a fertile lowland (Gippsland), trending east-west, lies between the Highlands and lower coastal hills. Here live a large majority of the state's population. A remarkable feature off the Queensland coast is the Great Barrier Reef that parallels the mainland for over 1,000 miles.

The Highlands have a rainy climate throughout their length. The temperature changes, however, becoming warmer from south to north. Forests cover most of the region, but there are also well-watered grasslands for grazing. Dairying and livestock industries are important and there are some specialty crops, such as sugar cane in Queensland. The drier inner slopes of the southeast are devoted to wheat and animal industries. The Gippsland area, near Melbourne, and the central lowland of Tasmania support dairying, diversified farms, and temperate fruits.

**Climate.**    The climate of Australia is affected by the continent's location between 10 and 40° south latitude, the general elevation of the land, and the position of the Eastern Highlands (Figure 16-3). The location south of the equator causes the seasons to be reversed from those in the Northern Hemisphere—summer coming from December to February, and winter from June to August. The shifting of the wind belts with the seasons determines the time and location of the rains.

In summer heavy rains drench northern Australia which is then in the tropical calms. Winter is the dry season when the tropical rainy belt shifts equatorward. Throughout the year the temperatures remain generally high. This gives northern Australia a wet-and-dry tropical or savanna climate, except for a small part of northeastern Australia where rains come throughout the year and cause the climate to be classified as rainy tropical.

Rainfall diminishes toward the interior. From central Australia to the west coast is a hot trade wind desert, dry at all seasons. Not only is the

*Figure 16-3    Climate graphs of selected cities.*

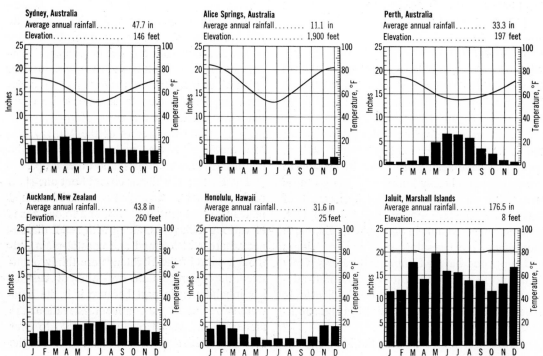

rainfall scant but it is extremely unreliable. The desert touches the south coast at the Nullarbor (treeless) Plains. Between the desert and the savanna and east coast regions is the tropical steppe with rainfall enough for grass and bushes, but not for trees.

Southwestern Australia, the coast of South Australia, and the area near the mouth of the Murray River have a Mediterranean type of climate with mild, rainy winters and hot, dry summers. In winter, the prevailing westerly winds shift north, and the accompanying cyclonic storms furnish the rains. Cyclones downunder whirl opposite to those in the Northern Hemisphere, the winds moving clockwise instead of counterclockwise. Inland, the steppe climate begins at about the 10-inch annual rainfall line—a contrast with northern Australia where the savanna is replaced by steppe at about the 20-inch rainfall line. The difference is accounted for by the higher rate of evaporation toward the equator.

Southeast Australia has a humid subtropical climate with rainfall throughout the year, mild winters, and warm summers. The winter rains are cyclonic; the summer rains are associated with easterly winds from the Pacific.

Tasmania and southern Victoria lie in the westerly winds and have a marine west-coast climate resembling that of western Oregon. Winters are cool and wet. Summers are mild and somewhat less humid. Snow may occur in the highlands in the winter months.

**Natural Vegetation.** Because of its long isolation from other continents, most of the trees are peculiar to Australia and dominantly consist of two types, acacias and eucalypts. There are hundreds of species of each. These have adapted themselves to the various climates along with many unique flowering plants and other vegetation. Patches of rain forest occur in the wet tropical zone; in the savanna regions are tall grasses and stunted woodland. The steppes have grass, usually in clumps, small acacia brush (mulga), and saltbush. The rainier parts in the Mediterranean climate possess excellent commercial forests of eucalypts. With less rainfall, the forests are replaced by shrubs called mallee. In the Eastern Highlands and southeast Australia are forests of eucalypts interspersed with grass and open woods. Forests originally covered most of Tasmania, but Australia proper is not rich in timber; commercially valuable forest trees cover less than 2 per cent of the area. Vegetation in the desert consists of scattered spinifix (a grass), saltbush, and a few stunted mulga bushes. Native trees are hardwoods, except for some misnamed "pines," in Tasmania and the Eastern Highlands.

**Animal Life.** The native animals of Australia are extraordinary in that most of them have no close relatives in other continents. This condition is the result of the long separation of Australia from other lands so that the higher mammals never reached the island country.

*Figure 16-4 Kangaroos, the most characteristic native animals of Australia, at Lake Macquarie near Newcastle, New South Wales. There are several species of kangaroos. They belong to a primitive group of mammals, the marsupials. (Courtesy of Australian News and Information Bureau.)*

Two-thirds of the species of mammals in Australia are marsupials, primitive creatures whose young are carried for some time in an external pouch. Examples include many species of kangaroo, the opossum, koala (tree-bear), and wombat. In Tasmania live two carnivorous marsupials, the Tasmanian wolf and the Tasmanian devil. Australia possesses the only egg-laying mammals in the world. The platypus, or duckbill, has the bill of a duck, the tail of a beaver, is covered with fur, lays eggs, and nurses it young. Closely allied to this is an egg-laying anteater called the echidna. The only higher mammal is a wild dog, the dingo, brought into the country by the early aborigines.

Snakes, lizards, and crocodiles live in Australia. In coastal waters of the tropics are found big sea turtles and the dugong, or sea cow. A curiosity is a lungfish, living in a few streams in droughty interior Queensland, which forms a link between fish and amphibians just as the platypus links reptiles and mammals.

Birds include the emu that resembles an ostrich, a black swan, the lyre bird, many cockatoos, and the kookaburra, a kind of kingfisher with a cry so strange it is called the laughing jackass.

Besides the domestic animals, the British introduced rabbits which throve and multiplied to an estimated five hundred million, eating grass and drinking water needed by sheep and cattle. Rabbits are slaughtered in great numbers in an effort to reduce the pest, and their pelts are exported by the tens of millions, being used for cheap furs. Some rabbits are eaten locally, others exported frozen for consumption, but most of the carcasses are unused. In the 1950s, "myxomatosis," a contagious disease of rabbits, was introduced and has greatly reduced the number of rabbits with resulting benefit to grass and trees. The disease is carried by mosquitos. Since the rabbits that recover from the infection pass along to future generations a resistance to myxomatosis the problem of the rabbit is not completely solved. Another method used in attempts to control the rabbit plague was building rabbit-proof fences, but this has been generally unsuccessful.

## Economic Development

The Commonwealth exports raw materials, or materials partially processed to reduce weight and volume for shipment, and imports much of its needed manufactured goods, lumber, and petroleum products. This is partly because Australia is in an early stage of economic development. Also, because the population is so small, the country cannot afford to manufacture all the varied goods it uses in relatively small amounts. Domestic manufactures are mainly for local consumption. Important exports include wool, wheat, hides and skins, beef and mutton, lead, zinc, and other minerals.

**Pastoral Industries.** Australia is world famous for sheep and important for cattle—the livestock industry being favored by extensive pastures, mild winters that obviate supplemental feeding except during occasional droughts, and absence of natural enemies except a few wild dogs. Since wool, meat, and hides are in demand, ships come from all parts of the world to secure them.

Australia leads all other countries in production and export of wool. Sheep number about 126 million in an average year, a ratio of a dozen sheep for each person in the country, but the number of sheep varies by millions depending on whether a year has drought or adequate rainfall. The large majority of sheep are found in semiarid climates from southern Queensland across interior New South Wales to Victoria and South Australia. Formerly they were handled on huge stations (ranches) leased from the government; now sheep runs have been reduced in size, and flocks usually consist of about 1,000 animals, mostly merinos and mixed breeds. Machines are used for shearing. The wool is delivered to storage warehouses in centers like Sydney and Melbourne. There some wool is scoured, graded, and baled, but a large production is sold in a greasy condition. Australia's wool is of premium quality and totals about 1.4 billion pounds annually, one-fourth of the world's clip. Wool usually accounts for about one-eighth of the domestic income and is

*Figure 16-5   A mob (flock) of sheep at a station (ranch) in New South Wales. (Courtesy of Australian News and Information Bureau.)*

the leading export of Australia, sometimes accounting for over one-third of the country's income from exports. Sales of lambs and mutton often are the greatest of any country, although in some years New Zealand ranks first.

Beef cattle rank next to sheep in number and value of products. About 10 million beef cattle and 5 million dairy cows are kept in Australia. Queensland leads in cattle with over 6 million. Beef cattle are favored over sheep in the tropical savannas and near deserts, but in the cooler areas they generally cannot compete with the more profitable sheep. Packing plants are located in centers convenient to supply, Brisbane being an example. About one-fourth of the beef slaughtered is exported, primarily to England, the business being favored by a reciprocal trade agreement.

Dairying is carried on chiefly in the moist coastal lowlands and lower Eastern Highlands in New South Wales, Victoria, southeast Queensland, and Tasmania. The industry is favored by mild weather and good grazing.

**Agriculture.** Wheat is the most important crop in Australia and occupies well over one-half the acreage tilled. Production of wheat varies from 50 million to more than 200 million bushels annually, the great differences depending on weather conditions and world prices. Ordinarily Australia ships nearly 100 million bushels of wheat, mostly to Great Britain. Wheat farming is highly mechanized. The wheat belt has a crescent shape and is situated where the annual rainfall is 12 to 25 inches, on the inward slopes of the Eastern Highlands in New South Wales and Victoria. South Australia and southwest Australia also produce wheat. Adelaide and Port Lincoln in South Australia are among the chief wheat-exporting ports.

Sugar is raised in Australia, but because white labor is used, costs are high compared with those of most foreign producers; hence the industry is protected by a high tariff. The cane is grown by the plantation method at intervals along the coast of Queensland where fertile soils are available.

Fruits that need a tropical climate, such as

bananas, oranges, pineapples, and papayas, are grown in Queensland and adjacent areas in New South Wales, for marketing in Sydney and other cities. The chief citrus region is along the lower Murray River in South Australia, New South Wales, and northern Victoria as well as near Griffith in the Murrumbidgee Valley. The fruit is raised by irrigation in all these inland localities. Mildura is the chief center for citrus fruits, grapes, currants, and raisins. From vineyards in South Australia, wine is produced, especially near Adelaide. Apples, pears, cherries, and berries are grown in Tasmania, the cool southern coastlands of Victoria and Western Australia, and the uplands in New South Wales. Apples are exported to Europe. Fruits are often canned; they also are made into preserves and marmalade.

**Water Resources.**   Water is stored and used extensively for irrigation in the Murray River basin, where the Hume Dam is especially noteworthy among the other weirs as the dams are called. Burrinjack Dam stores water for the Murrumbidgee Valley. Compared to other continents Australia's potential water power is small because of the lack of large, swift rivers. A few hydroelectric plants are located in southeastern Australia and Tasmania, but big coalfired plants supply 90 per cent of the total electricity. However, the Snowy Development, a multiple-purpose dam for irrigation and power, has one power unit in operation and will eventually add 3 million kilowatts of power and 1.8 million acre-feet of water for irrigation in the Murrumbidgee and Murray Basins.

**Minerals.**   The ancient rocks in West Australia have numerous deposits of gold, the mines at Kalgoorlie being especially productive. During the 1850s gold was discovered in New South Wales and Victoria, and soon the Bendigo and Ballarat deposits in Victoria became great producers. Victoria has mined gold worth over a billion and a half dollars; during the past few years, however, production has been small. Some gold is mined in every state and territory of Australia, the annual output now being worth about 30 million dollars. The Commonwealth is also important for the production of lead, zinc, and silver, the combined value of which is approximately 75 million dollars annually. The greatest center for these metals is Broken Hill, a city of 30,000 in the desert of western New South Wales. Copper and tin are mined in sufficient quantity to supply the domestic demands. Since World War I, Australia has become nearly independent in supplying its needs for iron and steel. Annual production is about 2 million tons. Iron ore is mined in South Australia and Western Australia; most of it is then taken by boat to Newcastle and Port

*Figure 16-6   The 16-mile bore, near Alice Springs, is the last watering point for drovers driving their cattle down the north-south stock route to the railhead for shipment to Adelaide. (Courtesy of Australian News and Information Bureau.)*

*Figure 16-7 Vineyard in South Australia in the Barossa Valley about 40 miles north of Adelaide. Here are cultivated 20,000 acres of wine grapes, half the total for the state. (Courtesy of Australian News and Information Bureau.)*

Kembla, near Sydney, where coking coal is available for smelting. A steel mill is also located at Whyalla in South Australia. Clay products, cement, and limestone are processed for local use. Very beautiful opals and sapphires come from Australia. Uranium is produced at Rum Jungle 60 miles south of Darwin, Northern Territory.

Australia has the largest known coal reserves in the Southern Hemisphere. The annual production is approximately 21 million tons, of which a third is lignite. The best coal underlies the coastal area north and south of Sydney. Coal is also mined from several deposits in Queensland. Victoria has extensive beds of lignite; that at Yallourn, 100 miles east of Melbourne, is nearly 200 feet thick. This deposit is mined by the open-pit method. The lignite is used for generating electric power which is transmitted to Melbourne and other cities in Victoria. Petroleum was discovered in 1953 at Exmouth Gulf, 700 miles north of Perth, but production is small.

**Manufacturing.** Since 1915 manufacturing in Australia has greatly expanded. It was stimulated during both world wars when it was difficult to import finished goods. Heavy manufactures of iron and steel have made notable advances. Light manufactures of textiles, especially woolens, and other consumer goods are supplying much of the domestic market. The processing of raw materials, sugar, metallic ores, oil shale, and wool is characteristic. Meat slaughtering and packing and flour milling are carried on for both export and local sale. Oil refineries at Melbourne, Sydney, and Fremantle operate on imported crude petroleum. A tariff protects many of these developing industries. The cost of goods to consumers is higher, but this is compensated for by increased employment. About one-third of the 2.5 million workers in Australia are employed in manufacturing industries.

**Transportation.** The concentration of population and industries in southeast and southwest Australia, and the great expanse of unpeopled desert, markedly affect location and construction of railroads and highways. Furthermore, until 1900 each state developed its transportation routes independently, focusing on the capitals which were also the chief seaports. This individuality is shown by the fact that three railroad gauges—broad, standard, and narrow—are used. However, conversion of the railroads to standard gauge is planned. Only one railroad, located well to the south, crosses the continent from east to west. A narrow-gauge railroad to Alice Springs, in central Australia, and a highway from there to Port Darwin in Northern Territory is the only well-traveled route across the "Never-Never Land" of the interior from south to north. The government owns and operates about 90 per cent of the 28,000 miles of railroads.

Many of the highways in Australia are un-improved, but 20,000 miles are called improved. The best highways connect the major cities. Nearly a million automobiles, trucks, and motorcycles are licensed in Australia, and the Commonwealth ranks high among the countries of the world in per capita ownership of motor vehicles. Most of the principal cities are on the coast, and exchange of freight among them is largely carried on by coastal ships rather than by trucks or rail.

Airlines connect the principal cities, and air travel in this thinly populated country of large size has proved a great convenience. Overseas airlines connect Australia with Europe, Asia, North America, New Zealand, and many Pacific islands. Doctors and nurses fly to remote ranches when emergencies require them.

## Population

Of about 9.4 million people in Australia, more than 80 per cent are native-born, and the large majority are of British ancestry. In the decade following World War II, nearly a million immigrants came to Australia, among them many Dutch and Italian people. A scant 75,000 aborigines and half-breeds still survive, living mostly in the interior drylands and northern sections.

For a country only partially developed, Australia has a surprisingly large urban population. The six state capitals—Adelaide, Brisbane, Hobart, Melbourne, Perth, and Sydney—contain half the population of the Commonwealth; Sydney and Melbourne together have one-third of the people living on the continent. Except for Port Adelaide, outside the city limits of Adelaide, and Perth, located a few miles

from the port of Freemantle, the capitals are the chief seaports, handle most of the exports and imports of their respective states, are the chief railroad centers, lead in the manufacturing and distribution of goods, and are paramount in business management, government, education, and cultural life. Important for governmental activities is Canberra, the Commonwealth capital. In addition to the six state capitals, there are about 140 smaller cities. Only 30 per cent of the population, less than 3 million people, are classified as rural, and some of these live in villages and not on farms.

Sydney and Melbourne rank fourth and fifth in population among the world cities down under. Each is a modern, well-built metropolis with substantial public buildings, office and business structures, big warehouses on the waterfront, factories, fine residences, theaters, and parks. The other state capitals also present a fine appearance. Sydney ranks with San Francisco in its landlocked harbor which, like its American counterpart, is crossed by a huge bridge at the narrows.

Although widespread aridity reduces its capacity to support great numbers of people, Australia has room for more than double the present population. To be sure, the Eastern Highlands reduce the usefulness to agriculture of the well-watered southeast, and poor soils and tropical climate in northern Australia make that region unattractive to white settlers, who are the only ones acceptable; colored persons are excluded. Even the sugar plantations use white men as field hands. Large areas of good grazing, generally fertile soils in considerable parts of southeast and southwest Australia, important deposits of metals and coal, a healthy and invigorating climate over the southern half of the continent, and a citizenship of a high or-

*Figure 16-8 Sydney, and the great bridge spanning its harbor, seen from the north. The bridge cost 45 million dollars and its arch is 1,650 feet long. Sydney, the largest city in Australia, has one of the finest harbors in the world. (Courtesy of Australian News and Information Bureau.)*

der, are favorable factors in the development of the Commonwealth.

Australia has been in the forefront in social legislation and direct government. The secret ballot, old-age pensions, arbitration of strikes, government loans for housing, social security, the recall of public officials, government own-ership of railroads, the initiative and referendum, and other advanced measures were adopted in Australia before they were accepted in the United States. Education has received universal support and the percentage of illiteracy is very low. Universities are located in each of the state capitals.

## OCEANIA

The term Oceania, as used here, is taken to include New Guinea and other mid-Pacific islands north and east from Australia, south to New Zealand, and north to Hawaii. The islands of the Republic of Indonesia, the Philippine Republic, and Taiwan were discussed with Asiatic areas. It is customary to divide the islands of Oceania into the three areas of Melanesia, Micronesia, and Polynesia (Figure 16-2, inset). The Bismarck Archipelago, the Solomon, New Hebrides, and Fiji groups, New Caledonia, and associated smaller islands are called Melanesia (black-inhabited islands) from the complexion of the natives. Micronesia (small islands) includes the numerous, but usually small, islets of the Caroline, Marianas, and Marshall groups east of the Philippines and generally north of New Guinea and Melanesia. Polynesia (many islands) covers a huge triangular area on both sides of the equator in the middle Pacific from Hawaii on the north to New Zealand on the south and Easter Island on the east.

The native inhabitants are as varied as the islands. Negroid peoples of various types live in New Guinea and Melanesia. Micronesians resemble Malays, being of medium size and having brown skins. Polynesians have a mixed ancestry and are generally a tall, good-looking race of light-brown color.

Native people migrated to the Melanesian and Micronesian islands thousands of years ago. The Polynesians have lived on their islands for a dozen centuries or more. Europeans, however, have known about these land areas for only a few centuries. During the two and a half centuries following the crossing of the Pacific by Magellan in 1521, Dutch, English, Spanish, and French navigators made voyages of discovery. The most renowned explorer of all was Captain James Cook, the Englishman who made three voyages between 1768 and 1780; his maps of the Pacific showed well all essential features of that ocean and its islands.

Europeans of various sorts and occupations followed the explorers. The impact of white whalers, traders, missionaries, merchants, and other settlers was often disastrous to the natives of Oceania. For example, in one hundred and fifty years the number of Polynesians is believed to have been cut by three-fourths. Micronesians and Melanesians have suffered in a similar way.

Control over the Pacific Ocean lands is divided among several powers. Politically, New Zealand is a self-governing member of the British Commonwealth of Nations. England, France, and the United States are now the principal island-governing powers. During the years between the two World Wars, Japan controlled the Marianas, except Guam, and the Caroline and Marshall Islands. Since World War II, however, the United States has governed these islands as a United Nations trust territory. Of the minor powers, Chile owns isolated little Easter Island in Polynesia; the Netherlands controls the western half of New Guinea; and the eastern part of Timor belongs to Portugal. Australia governs part of New Guinea, and, along with New Zealand, rules several Pacific islands under trust agreements.

### Polynesia

Of all the native peoples in Oceania, the Polynesians were most admired by the European navigators. They were a large, fine-looking race of mixed ancestry and high intelligence, although culturally they were still in the stone age. Scientists believe that the Polynesians were derived from intermarriage of many peoples including those of Asiatic, Melanesian, and Caucasian origin. Although declining in numbers after the arrival of Europeans in islands like Hawaii and New Zealand, the Polynesians have freely married with the English, American, and other nationalities. These new mixtures now constitute an important element in the population. In most of Polynesia the scenery is exceedingly attractive to tourists and other visitors, for it is often spectacular, with startlingly steep cliffs covered with tropical verdure, clean beaches shaded by waving palm trees, active volcanoes, and in New Zealand, snow-capped peaks and glaciers. Paintings, photographs, moving pictures, plays, books, and stories about Polynesia, although popularizing the islands, have sometimes resulted in odd and exaggerated notions about the ease and pleasures of tropical living and the relationships to be expected from the natives.

Polynesia covers a huge triangular area from Hawaii on the north to New Zealand on the south, and from the Samoan and Tonga Islands on the west to lonely Easter Island on the east. Except for New Zealand, Polynesia lies in the tropics on both sides of the equator. There are dozens of groups and hundreds of islands scattered around this part of the Pacific, some are quite large and populous, but the greater number are small, and many are uninhabited. Always the extent of ocean vastly exceeds the area of land.

**New Zealand.** By far the largest area of land in Polynesia is New Zealand. Americans feel at home here, for the people speak English. Both the climate and landscape resemble parts of Europe and the United States. The industries of the country are familiar and many of its economic problems are similar to those in certain parts of the United States.

The Dominion of New Zealand is situated about 1,200 miles southeast of Australia and consists of two large islands and several smaller ones, having an area of about 104,000 square miles and a population of nearly 2 million. In contrast with Australia, New Zealand is mountainous, and has a generally rainy climate. It possesses many fine harbors and has active volcanoes as well as numerous geysers and glaciers. Its native Maoris were intelligent and culturally far in advance of Australia's aborigines.

The natural environment of the islands varies greatly. With a latitudinal extent approaching a thousand miles, New Zealand has a generally humid marine west-coast climate, with temperatures modified by the surrounding ocean but getting progressively colder toward the south. North of Auckland, snow is unknown and the climate is subtropical. Snow and frost are rare on the lowlands of all of North Island. The southern end of South Island has cold winters. The west coast is very cloudy with heavy precipitation, and snow piles up in the high mountains to feed numerous glaciers. The eastern side of South Island, leeward of the high mountains, has less rainfall and most of it has a subhumid climate with a fairly large range of temperatures. New Zealand lies in the belt of prevailing westerlies, thus cyclones provide much of the rainfall. Mountains cause large local differences in rainfall and temperature.

The backbone of South Island is a high and rugged mountain chain, culminating in Mt. Cook or Aorangi (cloud piercer) 12,349 feet above sea level. Some seventeen peaks reach elevations of 10,000 feet or more. The southwest coast, called fiordland, is indented by a score of fiords that were scoured out by prehistoric glaciers. Beautiful lakes, snow fields for skiing, glaciers, serrated peaks, and the fiords are tourist attractions in South Island. Both islands offer the tourist excellent fishing, sandy beaches, and protected harbors. North Island mountains are not so high as those in South Island, but central North Island has active volcanoes and also many hot springs and geysers, those of Rotorua being world famous.

Like Australia, New Zealand was long isolated from other land masses, and this isolation greatly affected the native flora and fauna. Many plants are peculiar to the islands. Southern pines and beeches, tree ferns, ferns, and laurels are characteristic. Tussock and other grasses supply excellent grazing on the semi-arid slopes and plains. Notable is the Canterbury Plain, famous for sheep and wheat, in the east South Island. In both North and South Islands, much of the original "bush" has been cleared and planted to grasses on which the dairy industry is based.

Except for marine animals and the bat, native mammals are lacking. Flightless birds were common; one of these, the extinct moa, stood twelve feet tall. The nearly wingless kiwi and the kea, a type of parrot, are unique. The tuatara, one of the lizards present, has a rudimentary third eye. Some introduced animals, like rabbits and deer, have become pests.

The economic resources of the country are varied. Coal easily leads in value among the minerals although proven resources total under a billion tons, of which only a third is bituminous. It is mined in several localities, but the best coal and chief mines are located on the west coast of South Island near Greymouth and Westport. The coal output is 2.5 million tons annually, but small amounts are imported, chiefly from Australia, to supply the country's needs. Clay products, cement, and lime are manufactured for local consumption. Gold is the principal metal, but the once large output is now small.

Streams in New Zealand are short. Many are swift and have enough volume of water to make considerable potential water power, but only a small amount has been developed.

The forests which originally covered much of New Zealand have been damaged by careless grazing, logging, and fire. There remain about 17 million acres of forest. The annual production of lumber exceeds 500 million board feet. Although the cut of rimu (red pine) is the largest, other softwoods and beech are important sources of lumber for constructions and furniture. Kauri, one of the tallest trees in the world, is a superior timber, but most of the stands of this fine tree have been logged. Kauri gum is valuable for varnish manufacture. Much fossil gum is dug from marshes in which it has been preserved.

Animal industries form the chief economic base in New Zealand. The generally mild, rainy climate favors both native grasses and the introduced species which give the grasslands a high carrying capacity. Animal products such as wool, meat, hides, and dairy products comprise over 90 per cent of the exports from the Dominion.

The dairy industry is the leading source of income for a majority of the farmers of North Island. Many also raise pigs, sheep, and beef. Farmland is mostly devoted to grazing. Even most crops are feed for livestock; of 20 million acres of improved land, only 1.5 million acres are in field crops.

Neither dairy cows nor sheep require shelter, and but little supplemental feeding is need-

*Figure 16-9  A rural scene from the New Plymouth–Stratford highway, New Zealand. Note the fine dairy cattle. (Courtesy of New Zealand Embassy.)*

ed. Purebred animals predominate. Dairying methods are sanitary and efficient, and New Zealand dairy products have a good reputation. Cheese, butter, and dried and canned milk are exported, in particular to Great Britain.

Sheep are raised extensively on both islands, North Island having 55 per cent and South Island 45 per cent of New Zealand's 38 million sheep, which exceed the human population in the ratio of 18 to 1. New Zealand follows Australia in exports of wool but leads all countries in exports of mutton.

Most of the wheat is raised on the Canterbury Plain which has a subhumid climate. Production is adequate to supply local demands. Oats, potatoes, and apples are among the other crops grown.

Aside from the processing of dairy products and meat slaughtering, New Zealand is unimportant in manufactures for export. Clothing, flour, woolens, lumber, and other products are manufactured for the local market.

The population of New Zealand is slightly less than 2 million. The native Maoris, who originally inhabited the islands, lived in villages, cultivated the sweet potato and some other crops, built canoes, caught fish, and wove cloth from the fiber in the long leaves of New Zealand flax. They were a tall, kindly, fine-looking, and intelligent people. Clever carvers of woods, the Maoris had no knowledge of metals or of pottery. Although reduced in numbers—perhaps fifty-six thousand survive—many natives have intermarried with Europeans and form a self-respecting integral part of New Zealand's population.

The great majority of the settlers came from the British Isles. They introduced new plants and animals and thereby changed the entire economy of the country. Social changes were equally important. Education is universal and universities are located in the chief cities. Women can vote. Social legislation is advanced, and the people pride themselves on the absence of poverty and on the fact that equal opportunities are open to all. Life in New Zealand resembles life in rural regions of the United States. Farmers have trucks, automobiles, milking ma-

*Figure 16-10   Auckland is the largest city in New Zealand. The street shown here is Queen Street which extends from the business center to the wharves. (Courtesy of New Zealand Embassy.)*

chines, tractors, and a variety of other equipment along with telephones and mail delivery. Many farms are electrified. Principal highways are graded and paved.

Large cities are few in New Zealand. Auckland is the largest city and ranks first among the seaports. Wellington is the Dominion's capital and is located on a good harbor on Cook Strait. On South Island, Christchurch and Dunedin are the largest cities.

New Zealand governs western Samoa, the Cook Islands, Niue, and the Tokelau group. Control is also exercised over several nearby unpopulated islands in the far south Pacific.

**Hawaii.** The Territory of Hawaii, once a kingdom and then for a few years an independent republic, joined the United States in 1898.

Figure 16-11   *Aerial view showing the geometrical pattern of planted pine-apple fields in the Hawaiian Islands. Hawaii's output of canned pineapple exceeds that of all other regions of the world combined. (Courtesy of North-west Orient Airlines.)*

To most Americans it is the best known part of Polynesia. Tens of thousands of soldiers, sailors, marines, and aviators were based there during World War II, and the islands are annually visited by thousands of mainland vacationers.

The main Hawaiian Islands are Hawaii, Maui, Molokai, Oahu, Kauai, Lanai, Niihau, and uninhabited Kahoolawe, all of which are volcanic in origin. Volcanoes on Hawaii that are frequently in eruption include Mauna Loa, bearing Kilauea, the world's largest active volcano, and Hualalai. Except for certain peaks on New Guinea, Mauna Kea, 13,784 feet, an extinct volcano, is the highest summit in Oceania.

The Hawaiian chain is nearly 2,000 miles long, continuing to the northwest beyond the main islands as coral reefs, atolls, shoals, and a few pinnacles of lava, the last remainder of former sizable islands. The eight main islands have an area of 6,435 square miles, but the island of Hawaii accounts for 4,030 square miles of this. With an area of only 604 square miles, Oahu is the most populous island in the group; it has three-fourths of the more than half-million people in the territory. On Oahu is Honolulu, the largest city in Oceania, with the great naval base of Pearl Harbor, major airfields, and army bases, besides world-famous resorts. The islands lying beyond the main group total only 7.5 square miles in area. Most important of these is Midway, an atoll of 2,000 acres with a maximum elevation of 40 feet, that is used as an air base.

Situated in the northeast trade winds, the Hawaiian Islands have elevations so great that considerable differences in rainfall occur, up to 300 inches and more falling on the windward slopes and only 10 to 20 inches on the leeward side of the mountains. Frost is unknown except in the higher mountains. The mountains and rainy coasts were originally covered with a dense forest, and the mountains are still mostly wooded. The lava bedrock decomposes to form fertile soil; thus most of the lowlands and gentler slopes of old lava are in crops. Nevertheless, only about a sixth of the land area is classified as tillable, although some uplands make good grazing land.

The economy of Hawaii is based on sugar cane and pineapples. Together these crops annually bring 100 to 150 million dollars from mainland buyers. About 200,000 acres are planted in cane. From 800,000 to 900,000 tons of sugar are produced annually on some 28 plantations which employ about 27,000 men. Giant machines plow the fields and harvest the cane with great economy of labor. Much nitrate fertilizer is applied to maintain yields. On the windward slopes, there is more than sufficient rainfall to support agriculture; elsewhere, the fields are irrigated. Great attention is paid to control of pests and diseases of cane and to the development of improved varieties.

Pineapples are grown on about 70,000 acres by the plantation method. The fruit is processed in canneries, the largest being in Honolulu on Oahu. The total annual pack is about 20 million cases. Applied science in raising and processing pineapples, good management, and salesmanship account for the development of this industry, with Hawaii marketing more pineapples than all the rest of the world combined.

Crops of minor importance include coffee, bananas, vegetables, taro, rice, macadamia nuts, papaya, and various other fruits. Although some cattle are raised on Hawaii, dairy cows, poultry, and pigs are insufficient in numbers, and much butter and eggs are imported from the mainland. One ranch, located on the island of Hawaii, covers an area of some 500,-000 acres. It is one of the largest ranches in the world and supplies most of the fresh beef consumed in the islands.

The third industry of Hawaii is tourism. Each year nearly 50,000 tourists visit the islands and spend about 35 million dollars. The climate, beaches, volcanoes, and people are among the attractions. Honolulu, with its Waikiki beach, is the center of the tourist business.

The army, navy, and air force all have installations in Hawaii. The military establishments employ thousands of civilians in addition to enlisted personnel, and their expenditures are very important in the Territory.

The population of Hawaii, over half a million, is made up of many peoples with varied cultural backgrounds. Hawaiians and part-Hawaiians form about one-seventh of the popula-

*Figure 16-12 View of Waikiki beach, famous tourist center, with Diamond Head, an extinct volcano, in the background, at Honolulu. (Courtesy of Northwest Orient Airlines.)*

tion, Japanese approximately one-third, Caucasians over one-fourth, Filipinos about one-sixth, and Chinese, Koreans, and others the remainder. The various races have intermarried to a considerable degree, and Hawaii is often pointed out as a successful racial melting pot. American culture predominates, partly because the children attend school together; and all born in Hawaii pride themselves on being American citizens.

Honolulu contains nearly half the population of the territory. Sprawled between mountains and the sea, it is the largest city in Oceania. It is the focus of air and steamship lines as well as the center of the tourist trade. Through the port passes most of the 300-million-dollar annual trade of the islands. Pearl Harbor, 7 miles northwest of Honolulu, is one of the major naval bases in the world.

**Smaller Islands of Polynesia.** Except for New Zealand, most of the islands of Polynesia, including the Hawaiian group, are divisible into two types—high volcanic islands and low islands built of coral. A few of the coral islands have been elevated, some others are made of a combination of volcanic and coralline material, and there are examples of volcanoes surrounded by coral reefs and islets.

The high islands generally are larger, and have greater rainfall, better soil, and a greater variation of vegetation than the low islands. Having more resources, the volcanic islands can support more people and provide a greater variety of goods than the flat strips of coral thinly covered by sand and only a few feet above sea level. Some of the high islands include the Hawaiian, Samoan, Society (Tahiti), and Marquesas groups. In contrast, the Tuamotu Archipelago, Ellice, Phoenix, Tokelau, Line, and most of the Tonga (Friendly) Islands, except for some active volcanoes, consist of numerous coral islets. The Cook Islands include some that are of elevated coral and the Tubuai (Austral) Islands are of both volcanic and coral origin. Remote Pitcairn and Easter Islands are volcanic.

Hundreds of the coral islands in the tropical Pacific are atolls. These are low, narrow strips of coral, usually of an oval shape, surrounding a lagoon. The coral ring may be continuous, but more often is broken into numerous motus (parts). Sometimes an atoll has a score or more of these islets. Atolls vary in size from a diameter of a few miles to a few of a hundred miles or more. They are often built on platforms that rise from great ocean depths. Many geologists believe atolls were once fringing reefs around volcanoes which have disappeared, leaving only the coral strands.

Coconut palms, pandanus, and a variety of bushes constitute the principal native plants on the coral islands. Sea birds that resort to some of the low islands for nesting are everywhere. With the exception of bats, land mammals are lacking except those later introduced by man. The people have a saying that the sea is the poor man's garden. They catch fish and turtles, gather shellfish and certain seaweeds, and sometimes obtain the porpoise or other sea mammals for food. The coconut supplies a great variety of products. The meat is eaten fresh, the milk of immature nuts is a refreshing drink, a fermented drink is made from the sap, the living crown makes a delicious salad, and from the dried meat, called copra, is pressed oil for cooking, skin lotion, and other purposes. The trunk serves as posts for huts; the leaves are used for roofing material and fuel; the fiber, for ropes, fish nets, mats, and sails; the shells, for dishes—in fact, every part of the coconut is put to some use. Pandanus leaves are also woven into mats and clothing, and the fruit, resembling a pineapple in looks but not in flavor, is eaten. Coral sand is poor soil; hence if gardens are desired, pits are dug in which various wastes are allowed to rot. It then becomes possible to raise vegetables and fruits on these places, which, although small in size, supply the chief food crops like taro. Coral atolls support limited numbers of people, ranging from a few hundred down to a few families. The natives live in villages. They build excellent sailing canoes, often equipped with outriggers for stability, and in the old days, they lived without using money and with little trade. A limiting factor of life on some low islands was the small supply, or even absence, of drinking water.

Before the arrival of Europeans, the natives on the high islands raised taro, a starchy root planted in an artificial swamp, breadfruit, sweet potatoes, and several other crops. A few pigs and chickens were kept. Sea food was gathered, fish were caught, and mullet was sometimes raised in fishponds. Cooking bananas grew in the mountains, and oily nuts were used for seasoning along with sea salt. Hardwood timber was carved into many useful objects. Birds' feathers were used for decorative costumes. Villages were usually built near the sea, and long voyages were made in sturdy outrigger canoes.

Today, after contact with Europeans, the number of natives in Polynesia has declined greatly. Tuberculosis and other diseases, wars, and the destruction of the old ways of life wrought havoc with the Polynesians. Only in a few places, for example the Tonga Islands, are the natives as numerous as in the past.

The United States owns several isolated little islands, south and west of Hawaii. These include Wake, Johnston, Baker, Howland, Palmyra, Kingman Reef, and Jarvis. Most of these islands are used for air bases. By mutual agreement, the United States and the United Kingdom maintain a joint administration and use of most of the Line Islands and the Phoenix Islands that are south of the equator. These tiny low atolls also have strategic value as air bases. Canton Island has been developed as a major fueling stop on flights between Hawaii and Australia or New Zealand.

The Samoan Islands, like the Hawaiian chain, are high islands. The rock structure is largely volcanic. Savaii, Upolu, and Tutuila are the three principal islands. Tutuila and a few small islands in the eastern end of the group are owned by the United States. The landlocked harbor of Pago Pago, on Tutuila, is a superior strategic base for ships and aircraft. Western Samoa is a trust territory of New Zealand. The village of Apia, on Upolu, is the chief supply center for that area.

French Polynesia includes the Society Islands, largest of which is Tahiti, the Tuamotu Archipelago, the Marquesas Islands, and the Tubuai Islands. Tahiti grows vanilla for export in addition to copra, which is produced on most of the islands. Pearls are secured by divers in the lagoons of the Tuamotus. Pearl shell, tortoise shell, and dried trepang or *bêche-de-mer,* a sort of sea slug, are other exports. The little city of Papeete on Tahiti is the chief center for trade in eastern Polynesia. Artists and writers have given the world an enticing view of the attractive people, the lush tropical vegetation, and the steep-walled mountains of Tahiti.

## Melanesia

The land area included in Melanesia is large, but except for Fiji, the islands are little developed economically and most natives have a primitive culture. The white population is small.

**New Guinea.**    The second largest island in the world is New Guinea. It has an area of 312,000 square miles, being nearly 1,500 miles long by 500 miles at its greatest width. The western half is controlled by the Netherlands; the eastern half is governed by Australia. The northeastern section, with the Bismarck Archipelago and Bougainville Island of the Solomons group, is part of an Australian United Nations trusteeship; the southeastern section, called Papua, is directly administered by the Commonwealth.

Very high ranges, over 12,000 feet in elevation, extend the length of New Guinea. Peaks reach 15,000 to 16,500 feet, high enough to be snow-capped all or part of the year. The mountains are a great barrier to ground travel, but do provide man with cooler sites for villages. From the mountains descend large rivers that could provide millions of horsepower in hydroelectric energy.

New Guinea has a rainy tropical climate and most of the island is covered with jungle growth or a dense rain forest. Much of the coastal areas and river floodplains is mangrove swamp, very difficult to traverse. Groves of sago palm, which flourish in some of the swamplands, are a source of starchy food for the natives. Important deposits of gold have been found on the is-

*Figure 16-13   Chief's house, Fiji, built of local material in the native style.*

land, and the placers yield about 10 million dollars per year.

Both the flora and fauna of New Guinea are mixtures of Asiatic and Australian types. Among the fauna is a species of kangaroo. Birds are in great abundance and singular variety, including birds of paradise, cockatoos, and the flightless cassowary.

Among the natives are pygmies, living in remote mountain areas; Papuans, tall Negroes with woolly hair; and Melanesians, who have dark skins, frizzly hair, and a somewhat higher culture than the Papuans. The natives live in villages, plant gardens, process sago palms for food, raise pigs, and make a variety of stone implements and other articles. They build large houses without nails. The dwellers by the sea construct big seagoing canoes. New Guinea is little developed, and most of the natives continue to live in a self-sufficient way as they have done for centuries.

Comparatively few whites have yet settled in New Guinea. Those that have engage in trading, gold mining, and managing coconut plantations.

**Bismarck Archipelago.**   New Britain, New Ireland, and many smaller islands form the Bismarck Archipelago. These, together, have the shape of a horseshoe. The two principal islands are narrow and mountainous. Active volcanoes are located around the fine harbor of Rabaul, the chief trading center. Lowlands are small but contain most of the scattered native villages. Copra is the chief export.

**Eastern Melanesia.**   Fiji, Santa Cruz, and the Solomons, except for Bougainville Island, are governed by Great Britain. New Caledonia is French and the New Hebrides are under a condominium (joint government) by France and England. Generally the large islands are very mountainous and several contain active volcanoes. There are many coral reefs and coral islets. Volcanic rocks predominate, but there are also occurrences of older rocks especially in New Caledonia and Fiji where they are associated with deposits of metals. These include nickel, chrome, cobalt, and iron in New Caledonia, and gold in Fiji. The Melanesian islands all have a rainy tropical climate, and except for grasslands in part of New Caledonia, dense rain forests prevail. The Solomons are little developed except for plantations producing copra.

Fiji consists of two large islands, Viti Levu and Vanua Levu, and over 250 small ones. Some gold, hardwood timber, and kauri pine are exported, but the chief products are agricultural. Sugar plantations export about 200,000 tons annually. Bananas, rice, cacao, and coconut are among other products of the land. Indians, mainly Hindus, were brought in as plantation laborers and now equal the native Fijians in numbers. Many Indians now run small businesses or operate little farms. The chief port and capital is Suva. It is an important communications center by air and sea.

New Caledonia is 250 miles long by about 30 wide and is the largest French territory in the Pacific, having an area of 8,548 square miles. Offshore are barrier reefs and coral islets. Besides nickel and chrome, the island exports copra, coffee, and beef cattle. The population of 62,000 includes about 18,000 natives, nearly 19,000 French, and many Asiatics. Noumea, the capital and chief seaport, is an important supply and communications center by both sea and air. Its industries include a nickel smelter.

*Micronesia*

At present most of Micronesia is controlled by the United States. Spain established control over the Micronesian islands in the sixteenth century and continued as governing power un-

**TABLE 16-1. MICRONESIAN ISLANDS**

| Island | Number | Area, sq miles | Population |
|---|---|---|---|
| Guam | 1 island | 215.5 | 59,500 |
| Marianas, except Guam | 14 islands | 184 | 6,721 |
| Caroline Islands | 936 islands | 461.5 | 33,000 |
| Marshall Islands | 34 atolls | 70 | 10,550 |
| Gilbert Islands | 16 atolls | 144 | 27,700 |
| Ocean Island | 1 island | 2.3 | 1,800 |
| Nauru | 1 island | 8.2 | 1,545 |

til the Spanish-American War. In 1898, Spain ceded Guam to the United States and sold the rest of the islands to Germany. During World War I, the islands were taken by Japan. In World War II, the islands were captured by the United States which now governs them, excluding Guam, as the Pacific Trust Territory, under trusteeship from the United Nations. Included are the Marianas (Ladrones) Islands, except Guam, the Caroline Islands, and the Marshall Islands. The Gilbert Islands and Ocean Island are controlled by Great Britain, and Nauru is a trust territory of Australia.

**Marianas.** The largest island of the Marianas, Guam, is an important United States naval and air base. On the west coast is Apra Harbor, with Agana, the capital, a few miles away. Many of the native Guamanians (Chamorros) work for the government or are supported indirectly from government funds. Most families have a plot of ground on which corn, vegetables, and fruit are raised. Copra is exported, cattle are kept both for draft purposes and food supply, and a little fishing is done.

Saipan, Tinian, and Rota in the Marianas were economically developed by the Japanese, who planted sugar cane, manioc (tapioca), vegetables, coffee, bananas, and other fruits. A sugar mill on Saipan was destroyed during World War II and the Japanese were removed from the islands after the war. No sugar is produced at present and farming has declined, with only subsistence crops now being raised.

**Carolines.** The Caroline Islands, situated just north of the equator, are scattered over an ocean area half the size of the United States. The Carolines include more than 900 atolls and several volcanic islands, but their land area totals only 461 square miles. The population is approximately 33,000 and consists mostly of natives. The principal volcanic islands are the Palau and Yap groups toward the west, the Truk Islands near the center, and the islands of Ponape and Kusaie at the eastern side. These five islands or groups account for about 430 square miles of the Carolines and support 25,000 of the inhabitants. The volcanic soil is fertile and there is greater variety of resources than on the atolls. Hundreds of the atolls are unpopulated, and those that are inhabited support populations ranging from a few families up to a few hundred persons. People make their living by subsistence agriculture and fishing. They live in villages in huts built of native materials. Life is slow, but the natives are happy and satisfied with simple things. Some copra is exported and native handicrafts are made for sale in America.

Palau consists of eight islands and scores of islets, together with a large lagoon surrounded by coral reefs. Phosphate rock is exported for fertilizer, especially from Angaur, an island at the south of the group.

Yap is a cable base and consists of closely adjacent islands. The Yapese have retained traditional customs and have rejected Western dress as too warm. They continue to value their unique stone money, some specimens having the shape and size of millstones.

Truk is a group of half-submerged hills that are the eroded remnants of a large volcanic dome rising from a submarine platform. There are six sizable islands, and many small ones, in the midst of a lagoon about 25 miles across. The area is surrounded by an irregular coral reef. Truk was once a major Japanese military base. Ponape and Kusaie are high, compact islands with a tropical climate and forest-covered mountains. Both islands are sites of ruins of ancient dikes and stone walls.

**Eastern Micronesia.** The Marshall and Gilbert groups and Nauru and Ocean Island constitute the chief land areas of eastern Micronesia. The atolls forming the Marshalls are in two chains, an eastern and a western. The land area is only 70 square miles compared with 4,500 square miles for the enclosed lagoons. The population is about 11,000. A few of the islands are large enough for good air bases. Some of these islands, especially Bikini, have served as sites for atomic bomb experiments.

British islands include the Gilberts, low islands situated on both sides of the equator, and Nauru and Ocean Island, located just south of the equator. Tarawa is the capital and chief port of the Gilbert group. Nauru is a trust territory of Australia. Ocean Island is governed by the British. Both of these islands have valuable deposits of phosphate rock which is exported.

## ANTARCTICA

Surrounding the South Pole is Antarctica, an unpeopled continent almost completely covered with mile-thick ice. The land mass has an estimated area of 5 million square miles. It is the coldest of all continents, temperatures seldom rising above freezing. Antarctica is essentially lifeless, save for the penguins that resort to the shore ice. The Weddell seal is abundant but rarely hunted. Whales are taken in the adjacent seas during the summer, and sea mammals resort to the shores of storm-swept South Orkney, South Georgia, and other islands where man may slaughter them for their fat. From Antarctica great icebergs break off and float away to melt. The interior is a white, monotonous plateau surface, whose elevation at the South Pole

is nearly 10,000 feet. Through the snow and ice, mountain ridges sometimes emerge, especially near the ocean margin. Coal has been reported and other minerals may exist beneath the ice. There is an active volcano, Mt. Erebus. Shelf ice is lodged on the continental shallows.

## IN PERSPECTIVE

### The Pacific Area

Throughout the Pacific's vast extent its islands, both large and small, and its peoples of varied ancestry, are of increasing importance in their world setting as they emerge from obscurity to play a part in global strategy. Islands so insignificant or remote that formerly months and even years elapsed between visits by outsiders have become landing fields and fueling stations on airlanes between North America, Asia, and Australia. Some islands are the sites of great supply depots and strong defense bases for naval, army, and air forces. The beauty and unique life on South Sea islands attract increasing numbers of pleasure seekers. To care for this expanding tourist industry, many new hotels and other facilities have been constructed, and additional plane and ship transportation has been provided. Many inhabited islands of the Pacific now have radio communication and keep in daily contact with the world news.

In Australia, New Guinea, and other islands which contain ancient crystalline rocks new occurrences of metals are being found, and from the sedimentary rocks petroleum is being produced in New Guinea and coal in Australia and New Zealand. Deposits of phosphates are developed on several islands that are built of coral limestone. Such discoveries are bound to increase in number and variety with more thorough geological exploration, and large expansion in the exploitation of the mineral industry is a certainty for the future.

Fish resources are inadequately developed. The use of radar and sonic devices to detect swarms of fish in the depths and of helicopters to locate schools near the surface and areas of floating plankton on which fish feed, are applications of science that are assisting the growth

*Figure 16-14   Coastal vegetation, Koror, Palau Islands, a group in the Caroline Islands. (Courtesy of United States Navy.)*

of the fishing industry. Quick-freezing and packaging of the catch along with the operation of floating canneries are among other ways that will aid in marketing fish caught in waters remote from world markets.

Science applied to agriculture will increase production of food crops and export staples, especially in the underdeveloped regions of Australia, New Guinea, and many oceanic islands. Medical science is improving the health of native peoples, although much remains to be done in this connection in some of the island groups. With increased education and knowledge about the world there will be improvements in culture, health, and self-government among many native groups that now live in a primitive manner. The advance made in a century by the Maoris of New Zealand and the Fijian and Tongan people are examples of what can be expected to happen even more rapidly in coming years. With improvements in knowledge the lands and waters of the Pacific will become more and more useful to the nations and peoples of the world. Even parts of icebound Antarctica are claimed by several nations and that continent may become a source of coal and of other minerals as well as the whales now taken near its coasts.

Scientific studies in Antarctica, as were made during the Geophysical Year of 1957–1958, may improve our knowledge of atmospheric circulation and the origin of cyclonic storms.

## EXERCISES

*1.* How does the area and population of Australia compare with that of the United States? How is the cultural background of these two nations similar?

*2.* Is climate or topography the dominating influence in land utilization in Australia? What are the principal economic activities? In which part of the country is each most important?

*3.* What European countries formerly controlled Pacific islands? What is the Trust Territory? What islands and island groups make up this Territory? Why was the United States placed in control of the group?

*4.* Into what three large groups are most Pacific islands placed? What does the name of each group mean? Which is the most important group? Why?

*5.* How large in area is Antarctica? What is the chief value of the continent? What nations claim at least a part of it? Why is Antarctica undeveloped?

*6.* What are the principal divisions of New Zealand? Who were the native people of these islands? How did their culture compare with that of the natives of Australia? What are New Zealand's chief economic activities? How are these related to the physical environment?

*7.* What are the political divisions of Australia? Which are best developed? Why? In which are the largest cities? What are the principal problems facing the Australian nation?

*8.* Why are the Hawaiian Islands more highly developed than most other Pacific islands? What are the two chief islands of this group? Which is the largest? Which has the greatest population? What are the principal economic activities? Should Hawaii become a state in the United States? Why?

*9.* How advanced culturally are the natives of most island groups? In what ways has progress of these natives been handicapped? What do these people contribute to world trade? How has life on many of these islands been changed since 1940?

*10.* Is the importance of the Pacific Ocean increasing each year? Why? If China should become an influential world leader, would life on the islands be affected? Why? Could these islands serve as possible settlement areas for a growing world population? Why?

*11.* Besides Hawaii, which Pacific islands are owned by the United States? What is a trusteeship? Which islands are controlled by the United States for the United Nations?

*12.* What Pacific islands or island groups are controlled by the British? French?

## SELECTED REFERENCES

Coulter, John W.: *Fiji, Little India of the Pacific,* University of Chicago Press, Chicago, 1942.

————: *The Pacific Dependencies of the United States,* The Macmillan Company, New York, 1957.

Cumberland, K. B.: *Southwest Pacific,* McGraw-Hill Book Co., Inc., New York, 1956.

Davis, Charles M.: "Merino Sheep on the Australian Riverina," *Geographical Review,* 44:475–495, October, 1954.

Department of Internal Affairs: *Introduction to New Zealand,* Whitcombe and Tombs, Ltd., Wellington, New Zealand, 1945.

Dobson, R.H.T.: "Antarctica," *Focus,* 6(5):1–6, January, 1956.

Freeman, Otis W. (ed.): *Geography of the Pacific,* John Wiley & Sons, Inc., New York, 1951.

Gould, Laurence M.: "Antarctic Prospect," *Geographical Review,* 47:1–28, January, 1957.

Johnston, W. B.: "Pacific Island Agriculture: The Contemporary Position in Western Samoa and Some Wider Implications," *Economic Geography,* 29:26–38, January, 1953.

Kreiger, Herbert W.: *Island Peoples of the Western Pacific: Micronesia and Melanesia,"* Smithsonian Institution, Washington, 1943.

Osborn, Fairfield (ed.): *The Pacific World,* W. W. Norton & Company, Inc., New York, 1944.

Pownall, L. L.: "The Functions of New Zealand Towns," *Annals of the Association of American Geographers,* 43:332–350, December, 1950.

Taylor, Griffith: *Australia,* Methuen & Co., Ltd., London, 1949.

————: "Fiji: A Study of Tropical Settlements," *Economic Geography,* 27:148–162, April, 1951.

Wreckler, Jr., J. E.: *Polynesians—Explorers of the Pacific,* Smithsonian Institution, Washington, 1943.

# Conclusion:

# People in the Changing World

IN the preceding chapters, the authors have sketched the geographical environment of the various regions of the world and pointed out the principal geographic relationships of each. Thus this study may be considered a background against which to view current happenings and possible future developments.

In many ways the modern world is dynamic, a place of rapid change; in others, however, changes are so slow that conditions are almost static. Since 1910, two major world wars, as well as several minor engagements, have affected every country to such an extent that it can now be said that no nation is so independent as to be unaffected by events outside. During the past fifty years, wars have raged and brought numerous political changes. Old empires—Serbia, Austria-Hungary, Russia, Germany—have disappeared. Several old nations which had been absorbed—Latvia, Lithuania, Ukraine, Hejaz—were revived, existed for a brief period, and were then again absorbed by a neighboring larger or stronger power. Several countries—Poland, Finland, Czechoslovakia, Hungary, South Korea, Burma, and others—

regained their independence and survive as independent or semi-independent nations, although they have had to make numerous boundary adjustments. Still others—Saudi Arabia, the Soviet Union, the Philippines, Yugoslavia, the Republic of Indonesia, Israel—have come into existence as new nations, each exerting much influence, if not on a world-wide basis at least regionally. War and the consequences of economic change have forced many nations, long thought of as world leaders—United Kingdom, France, Germany, Italy, Japan—to shrink their national boundaries and yield parts of their former colonial empires. The latest surge of nationalism which has created, or re-created, such countries as Vietnam, Libya, the Sudan, Malaya, Laos, and Cambodia, is but a continuation of the search for political freedom. Every nation, even the United States because of its additional world responsibilities, has been affected by the continually changing political geography of the world.

Despite the changes in the political boundaries of nations, be they large or small, much of the geography of the world remains the same.

592

Whoever controls them, the mountains still have their heights and barrier effects; the major rivers and streams continue to flow in the same directions; the winds continue to move in the same general patterns and bring their life-sustaining rains; and the soils of the plains remain the principal producers of food. The earth continues to revolve and rotate so that man may depend on a succession of seasons and day following night. However, man has modified his environment in many ways. Some of these effects such as the reclamation of land, the harnessing of water power, and the extraction of metals from ores are beneficial. Other effects are harmful as, for example, when man's activities cause soil erosion, forest fires, and the spread of pests and diseases. Natural changes are usually very slow, but those resulting from human activity may be quite rapid. Man, more than nature, is the real variable in the geography of the world.

## PROBLEMS OF DISTRIBUTION

World conflict is the result of the great differences existing in the natural environment. The uneven distribution of minerals, fertile soils, and life-giving water makes for an equally uneven distribution of population and resource utilization. Man can utilize these resources to better his standard of living through work, peace, and prosperity, or eventually to destroy himself completely by war and famine. In the previous chapters, "have" and "have not" regions have been discussed. What, then, is the world point of view?

### Population

The total area of the earth is 197 million square miles. Of this area, 140 million square miles are covered by oceans, seas, and lakes; another 10 million square miles are either too cold, too dry, or too rough for permanent settlement by large numbers of people. This leaves an area of 45 million square miles in which man does live; but of this, approximately half is subhumid or semiarid. Thus, more than 2.5 billion persons are confined largely to 23 million square miles of the earth's surface.

Not only is the world's total population increasing more rapidly than ever before, but the normal span of life is also longer. Between 1900 and 1950, the increase in world population was approximately 800 million persons, or an average of 43,000 per day. Since 1950, the average daily increase has approximated 63,-000. The population of India alone is now being increased by about 15,000 living births per day, that of the United States by about 5,000. Because of lower infant mortality, increasing medical knowledge, and a somewhat better distribution of food, the expected life span in the United States has increased by more than 20 years since 1900. In 1950, there were 12,364,-000 persons in the United States 65 years of age and over. By 1960, it is estimated that there will be 15,701,000 in this age group, and by 1980, it will number 18,885,000. Life expectancy, although increasing in other countries, has not risen as much in most places as in the United States.

The countries with the largest total populations are China and India. People, however, are not evenly distributed throughout their areas. Because of various physical factors, the people of China are concentrated on the narrow southeastern coastal plains, along the valleys of such rivers as the Hsi, Yangtze, Yellow River, the many smaller stream valleys, and in some instances on the sides of terraced highlands. Large parts of the interior are too dry and far too elevated to support many people. In India the situation is similar; the Ganges Valley and the narrow coastal plains are densely populated, but the rougher parts of the Deccan Plateau and drier interior areas are less densely settled. When applied to the country as a whole, population density means little; when considered for the areas of arable land, it is significant. For example, the density for all of China is 123 persons per square mile. Since the different parts of the country vary greatly in their ability to produce, however, the density ranges from 0 in the deserts to more than 2,000 per square mile in the arable areas. This is a density of three persons per acre—probably twice the number who could be fed by agriculture alone. In the United States, at least 2.5 acres of arable land per person are needed to maintain the present standard of living. In many ways, India and China are typical since they emphasize the problem of too many people for too small an amount of arable land.

Part of the Northeastern United States, much of West Central Europe, and sections of South Asia, Southeastern Asia, and Central Eastern Asia have large areas in which the density of population exceeds 250 persons per square mile. In each of these areas, there is not only a considerable amount of productive land, but other factors such as minerals, suitable climates for particular crops, and sufficient water supply are also favorable. People in some areas do not take as much advantage of these factors as they might. Nevertheless, the potentiality for development is theirs.

Advancing scientific knowledge will, perhaps at a date not too far in the future, enable man to use large areas of land not now in production. If, by using atomic power, it becomes feasible to process sea water and pipe it to desert areas, vast amounts of unproductive land could be put to work. New methods of cultivation, new and improved plants, better methods of processing and preserving, all will aid in caring for the increasing world population to a certain point. Population pressure upon the land is, then, world problem number one.

## Natural Resources

**Minerals.** Minerals are one of the principal bases of modern civilization, or of the modern standard of living. Iron, copper, uranium, coal, and petroleum are the most important of the major mineral resources. Many of the minor minerals—minor only in the sense that they are not produced in such large quantities—help make the basic minerals far more usable than they would be otherwise. Thus vanadium, limestone, and other minerals are as essential to pro-

ducing certain kinds of steel as are iron ore and coke.

Some nations because of their large areas—Soviet Union, United States, Canada—have a variety of minerals; others because of smallness and location—Italy, Egypt, Bulgaria, Thailand—have only a few, if any, minerals in significant amounts. Several nations produce one or two minerals—Malaya, tin; Sweden, iron ore; Union of South Africa, gold and diamonds; Saudi Arabia, petroleum—but, because they lack other substances necessary for their processing, they export vast quantities as raw material.

Minerals are of little if any value, until put to work. Since much of the modern standard of living is based on minerals, nations often have attempted to gain control of the properties of their neighbors. Thus, the unequal geographic distribution of minerals is a problem to be solved if the world is to remain at peace.

**Water.** Most essential of all the natural resources is water. Without water, plants cannot grow even in fertile soil; man dies in a few days unless he has water to drink. Yet overabundance can be just as disastrous to an area as a scarcity of water. The Amazon Valley is no more densely populated than large areas of the Sahara. Not all plants need the same amount of water to thrive. Some, such as the great forests of the selvas, need at least 70 to 80 inches of rainfall fairly evenly distributed throughout the year; others, like numerous desert plants, can thrive on 5 inches or less of moisture per year. Corn does best in a region having long, warm summer days wherein the moisture is supplied by afternoon thundershowers. Wheat produces well if it has about 20 inches of rainfall, provided that it occurs at the right time. Other plants also have their peculiar water needs which in many respects are adjustment to their environment. Where a surplus of fresh water is available and irrigation can be practiced, most crops can be produced and the problem of food production partly settled.

Water is as essential in the life of cities as in rural areas. In the United States, where urban population is rapidly increasing, the function limitations of several major cities are determined by the amount of water available. Cities throughout the world attempt to solve their water problems in diverse ways. Gibraltar has cemented sides of the Rock, creating catchment basins; Los Angeles pipes water completely across southern California; and Athens rations its supply. New York is constantly searching for new places to build dams and thus insure a permanent supply. Until the water problem is solved, approximately 9 million square miles of the earth's surface will be of little value to mankind.

**Soils.**   Those soils which are capable of producing the most abundant crops are, like minerals and water, also unevenly distributed. Poor management and constant utilization have put hundreds of thousands of acres out of production, some permanently. Large areas in northern China, parts of North Africa, especially near Carthage, and sections of Italy were in ages past good producers of food. Many farms in the southern part of the United States are so badly gullied that the land is no longer usable. Dust storms in the subhumid parts of the Soviet Union, China, and the United States are but warning signals that grasslands are being put to improper use.

Man has gone far in solving some of his current soil problems. Rotation of crops, contour plowing, strip cropping, gully control, and fertilization are but a few of the conservation measures that have been developed. To carry out such a program is costly, in most instances requiring government aid in addition to what the owner contributes. Frequently, land must be taken out of production for a short period of time. In areas where food production is at a subsistence level, such a program might mean starvation. Thus to help solve its soils problem, the world needs a better distribution of foods and a closer unity among nations.

## Food Production

Each part of the world specializes in some crop or crops. The principal agricultural products of an area are usually the crops that do best in that particular environment. Thus farming in most parts of the world is an adjustment to the natural environment of soil, water, and climate. Irrigation and other specialized types of agriculture are, of course, exceptions.

The two great food crops of the world, wheat and rice, are basic foods for more than 90 per cent of the world's people. Rice is intensively cultivated in the monsoon lands of Asia, most of which are densely populated. Wheat is an extensively cultivated plant of the semiarid and subhumid lands of Central Eurasia, central North America, southeastern South America, and northern China. Most of the rice produces four or five times as many bushels of grain per acre as wheat. The per capita consumption of wheat for the world as a whole is 184 pounds, for rice, 155 pounds. In general, the standard of living in wheat-producing and wheat-consuming lands is considerably higher than in the rice areas. The areas producing rice depend much more upon the current crop than do the wheat-producing areas. In some parts of the United States and Canada, beef has replaced wheat as the chief staple food. If the rice crop in an area fails, famine and starvation are common since there is no surplus from previous years, nor is there money to buy the surplus from other regions. Most wheat areas have a surplus from previous years or have some means of securing grain from another region.

Rye, corn, barley, and oats are also important grain food crops. Potatoes form the principal part of the diet in certain sections of Europe and the Americas. Supplementary foods such as vegetables and fruits vary with the locality.

Animals which are suitable for meat live in most parts of the world. In areas having the highest standard of living in the Western world, beef, mutton, pork, and poultry are essential items of diet. The consumption of meat products varies greatly from region to region depending upon the amount of land available for pasture, the religion of the people, and the general prosperity of the area. The average consumption of meat per capita for the world is 53 pounds, ranging from 20 pounds per person in Asia to 219 pounds in Australia and New Zealand. The per capita consumption in Anglo-America is 155 pounds.

Usually enough food is produced each year to feed the people of the world if it were evenly distributed. Should production be low in some area there is generally enough surplus in another to make up the deficiency, but wars and lack of transportation or money to buy food may prevent needed shipments. Food production in each part of the world can be increased by more efficient land utilization, improved methods of harvesting, and plant betterment, but improvement in transportation and in the economy of poverty-stricken peoples is also needed.

## Manufacturing

The processing of goods, in some form or other, is carried on in every part of the world. Complex manufacturing, however, is confined primarily to the Northeastern United States and the most densely populated section of Western and Central Europe. Each of these areas has, or did have at one time, large quantities of coal and iron ore, water power, access to rivers, lakes, or oceans for cheap water transportation, fairly level topography or gaps through inland barriers so that land transportation was not handicapped, access to sufficient quantities of food and necessary raw materials, and a reputation for skilled workmanship. Outside these two principal areas there are numerous smaller developments such as the Texas Gulf Coast and Los Angeles areas of the United States, the Donets and Ural areas of the Soviet Union, the Jamshedpur and Calcutta areas of India, and the Sydney area of Australia. Many of the smaller centers are areas of specialization.

In most instances, the nations having the highest standard of living are those having the easiest access to manufactured goods. Machines used in producing a specific item decrease the amount of labor required for making that item. Ultimately, however, mechanization creates more new jobs. The worker has more time for educational and recreational activities. Each nation attempts to increase its output of manufactured goods for sale in foreign countries, since the sale of these goods adds purchasing power. Simultaneously, however, each nation develops protective tariffs to encourage its own industries and to discourage the sale of foreign goods within its own boundaries. Many nations could use their resources to better advantage by developing agriculture, mining, or other activities, than by trying to compete in the market for manufactured goods. If such was the case, manufactured goods could flow more freely to the areas where needed, and by so doing aid both the producer and consumer.

## WORLD LEADERS

The two most important and influential nations today are the United States and the Soviet Union. Each is a giant in area—the Soviet Union, with 8.6 million square miles, ranking first in size, the United States, with 3 million, ranking fifth. Each has a large population—the Soviet Union with 200 million persons ranking third, the United States with 170 million ranking fourth. Neither country is densely populated. Both have large areas for agricultural production, and each has great mineral wealth and vast industrial activities. Each is the leader in its sphere of influence. There, however, most of the likenesses end, for in political activity and political thought the two nations are diametrically opposed.

The Soviet Union, in building its sphere of influence, has brought many of the nations that border it partly or completely into the Communist block. China, which is one of the most important conquests, has more than twice the population of the U.S.S.R. and is larger than the United States in area. Yugoslavia has been the only adjoining country to throw off the domination of the Soviet Union. Beyond the adjacent areas, the Communist doctrine has been successfully spread in parts of Africa, Asia, and South America. This particular block of nations actually controls more land area and a larger population than any other group.

The United States has attempted to build its sphere of influence by working with other nations through mutual-aid programs. The British Empire, France, Greece, the Philippine Republic, and other countries have worked with the United States in the development of these programs. In addition to building a joint armed force, there has been economic aid in an attempt to better agricultural and industrial development. The United States has borne most of the cost; most of the immediate benefits have gone to the countries assisted by improving the standard of living and increasing the educational opportunities.

The third block of nations of special importance is known as the Islamic world. With the exception of the Republic of Indonesia, Malaya, and Eastern Pakistan, these 16 nations form a compact group in North Africa and the Near East. The population of 290 million is held together largely by common religious belief, since more than 90 per cent of the people are Moslems. Approximately 178 million or 62 per cent of the inhabitants of the area live in Turkey, Pakistan, and Indonesia. In these three countries there is a variety of agricultural activities as well as some complex industrial development. In the remaining countries, the standard of living is low; most of the people eke out a living by farming near an oasis or in an area where irrigation is possible. In some countries, many lead a nomadic life by following their flocks. The Near East area is the location of large oil developments and reserves. The Islamic world as a whole is not aligned with either the Communist world or the Free World. Turkey is a member of the North Atlantic Treaty Organization, and Pakistan belongs to the Southeast Asia Treaty Organization, both groups being anti-Communist. Lebanon, Syria, Iraq, Egypt, the Sudan, Yemen, Jordan, and Saudi Arabia have organized themselves into the Arab League to gain mutual objectives.

The fourth large block of nations is joined together in the Pan-American Union. This group is made up of the 20 Latin-American Republics and the United States. Its primary purpose is to encourage peaceful development of the area through the betterment of economic conditions.

## PLACE OF GEOGRAPHY

What, then, is the place of geography in this world of unequally distributed natural resources and unsettled peoples? Study of the many facets of human activity must not be regarded as a study of uncorrelated facts. To understand the activities of mankind, one must have knowledge of the various factors, physical and cultural, that make up man's environment. These factors may or may not determine what man will do in or about a specific area. They will of necessity, however, influence both his thinking and actions about the problems at hand.

The study of geography will aid individuals in our region of the world to understand better the people and problems of other regions. Only through sincere and sympathetic mutual understanding of each other can the people of the world hope for lasting peace. An understanding of geography will definitely contribute toward this goal of good international relationships throughout the world.

# Glossary

*Alluvium*     Material deposited by water such as a floodplain or a delta.

*Anticline*     An upfold in the earth's crust.

*Arable*     Land is suitable for cultivation by plowing or tillage.

*Archipelago*     A group of islands, or an area of ocean or sea interspersed with islands.

*Arroyo*     A stream-cut valley in dry lands. Usually it will have water in it only during and immediately after rains.

*Artesian*     Underground water supply, usually under enough pressure to cause the water to rise to the surface in a well.

*Barrens*     Areas of poor soil that are covered by scant or scrubby vegetation.

*Basalt*     A dark-colored and heavy rock of volcanic origin.

*Benches*     Elevated areas of flat land, a topographic terrace or shelf.

*Bora*     Violent, cold, northerly wind of the Alps and Adriatic area.

*Braided stream*     A stream or river in which there are many joining and rejoining channels of water and in which sediments are usually being deposited.

*Browse*     Low tree growth or bushy growth eaten by animals.

*Campos*     Wet-and-dry tropical region in central Brazil covered with scrub and grass vegetation.

*Chernozem*     Class of soils found along the dry margins of black prairie lands, originally covered with a thick mat of grass roots at the surface, rich soils.

*Chinook*     Warm, dry wind that moves with high speed down the leeward side of mountains, especially the east slope of the Rocky and Cascade Mountains.

*Cirque*     An amphitheater-shaped, steep-walled head of a glaciated valley in mountains.

*Combine*     A machine which harvests, threshes, and cleans grain while moving over the field.

*Condominium*     A country or region governed by two or more powers, joint dominion or sovereignty.

*Coniferous*     Cone-bearing, like the pine tree.

*Conurbation*     Cities and towns near enough together that they form a large and almost continuous urban area.

*Convection*     A process of heating the atmosphere, rapid uplift or masses of moist air in a vertical or nearly vertical stream which may result in convectional heating and thunderstorms.

*Cordillera*     Combination of mountain ranges or system that form a large unit such as the Andes or Himalayas.

*Currents, ocean*     Movement in a definite path of large quantities of ocean water such as the Gulf Stream or the Japanese Current.

*Cyclone*     Region of low atmospheric pressure about which the winds blow counterclockwise in the Northern Hemisphere or clockwise in the Southern.

*Deciduous*     Shedding leaves during the winter or dry season, as the oak or hickory does.

*Delta*     Deposit of sediment at the mouth of a river caused by decreasing velocity of the stream.

598

*Diurnal*   Daily, recurring every day.

*Diversified farming*   Farming in which two or more crops are produced each year, a combination of stock and crop farming.

*Doldrums*   Transition zone between the trade-wind belts characterized by calms and weak winds.

*Drifts, ocean*   Slower movement of oceanic circulation than a current such as the North Atlantic Drift.

*Elevation*   Height above the level of the sea.

*Escarpment*   A long, high, steep face of rock, steep cliffs such as the "Break of the Plains."

*Estancia*   A large stock ranch in Latin America.

*Estuary*   Drowned mouth of a river, a river mouth where the tide meets the river current.

*Extensive agriculture*   Use of land with a minimum of labor and outlay, such as wheat farming on the Great Plains.

*Fallow*   Land tilled but not planted for a season or two; weeds and insects are destroyed and water is conserved so that one crop may be produced every two or three years.

*Fathom*   Depth measurement of water; one fathom equals six feet.

*Faulting*   Slipping or breaking of rock structure under pressure; many faults form scarps or steep cliffs.

*Fazenda*   A plantation in Brazil, for example, a coffee fazenda.

*Finca*   A farm in Latin America, for example, a coffee farm in Colombia.

*Fiord*   A narrow inlet of the sea between high banks or mountains which has been gouged out by glaciers as along the coast of Norway or southern Alaska.

*Floodplain*   Area along the sides of a river where the river overflows and deposits its sediments.

*Foehn winds*   A relatively warm, dry wind which descends a mountain front when a cyclonic storm causes air to cross the range from the opposite side of the divide.

*Gallery forest*   Forest along the banks of rivers that flow through grasslands, tree crowns meeting over the stream give the impression of going through a green tunnel.

*Ghee*   A semifluid type of butter used in India.

*Growing season*   The period of plant growth between the last killing frost in spring and the first killing frost in fall.

*Hogan*   Earth-covered lodge of the Navaho Indians.

*Humus*   Partly decayed plant and animal matter in the soil, the organic portion of the soil.

*Hurricane*   Tropical cyclone.

*Hydrophyte*   A plant that grows in wet situations.

*Hydrosphere*   The liquid sphere of the earth, chiefly water such as the oceans, seas, bays, and lakes.

*Igneous*   Formed by solidification of molten material into rocks such as granite and lava.

*Intensive agriculture*   Use of the land to produce as much as possible in a given area and period of time by the expenditure of much labor and capital upon it.

*Isobar*   Line on a map connecting places of equal atmospheric pressure.

*Isohyet*   Line on a map connecting places of equal amounts of rainfall.

*Isotherm*   Line on a map connecting places of equal temperature.

*Jungle*   Dense undergrowth or second growth in the rainy tropical forests.

*Kampongs*   Native villages of Indonesia.

*Karroo*   Dry tableland of South Africa.

*Karst*   Land surface formed by the solution or underground erosion of limestone rocks such as in the Highland Rim or the Karst area of Yugoslavia.

*Lacustrine*   Formed by or in a lake such as a plain formed by deposition in an old lake bed.

*Laterite soil*   Reddish clay soil of the subtropics and tropics where the process of laterization is dominant.

*Leaching*   The removal of calcium and other elements frcm the soil by water seeping through it.

*Lithosphere*   The solid part of the earth.

*Llanos*   Tropical plains covered with tall grass, located in the interior Orinoco Basin of Colombia and Venezuela.

*Loess*    Deposits of windblown soils, usually found in the zone between dry and humid areas or in front of the former limits of glaciation.

*Meltwater*    Water from the great ice-age glaciers.

*Metamorphic rocks*    Rocks changed and formed by heat and pressure.

*Metropolitan area*    Densely populated area around a large city such as the Greater New York or greater London areas.

*Migratory agriculture*    Primitive agriculture, usually in the tropics, where the larger trees are killed and the brush burned, with only a few crops grown on one field before the field is abandoned.

*Milpa*    Term applied to plot under migratory agriculture especially in Africa and the Americas.

*Monsoon*    Seasonal winds that reverse their direction. For example, the summer monsoon blows toward Asia, but the winter monsoon blows away from Asia.

*Moraine*    An accumulation of unassorted clay, earth, stones, and other materials deposited by a glacier.

*Muskeg*    Swampy area in the subarctic or Arctic regions, usually has spruce and sphagnum moss.

*Nagana*    African name of trypanosomiasis, a cattle disease transmitted by the tsetse fly.

*Naval stores*    Pitch, tar, and turpentine which are extracted from the pine forests of the middle latitudes.

*Oblast*    A province within one of the states of the Soviet Union.

*Okrug*    District or circuit within a state of the Soviet Union.

*Orographic*    Precipitation caused when moist air is forced to move over mountains.

*Outcrop*    A series of rocks exposed at the surface of the earth.

*Outwash*    Material carried from a glacier by meltwater. Laid down in stratified deposits.

*Paddy*    Field in which rice is grown; unmilled or rough rice whether growing or cut.

*Pampa*    Grassland of South America especially in Argentina.

*Paramo*    Cold, treeless zone above tree line in highlands of tropical Americas.

*Paramos*    High, bleak plateaus or similar areas in mountains.

*Pedalfer*    Class of leached soils in which many chemical elements except aluminum and iron have been removed.

*Pedocal*    Soils of dry areas in which little leaching has taken place; much calcium still present in a zone of accumulation in the subsoil.

*Peneplain*    An old land surface worn down by erosion to almost a plain.

*Permafrost*    Permanently frozen layer of the earth beneath the surface as in the Polar or subpolar regions.

*Placer mining*    Removal of minerals from an alluvial, wind, or glacier deposit by the use of water.

*Podsol*    Leached soils developed in humid and usually cool regions especially under cover of conifers.

*Polder*    A tract of lowland reclaimed from the sea by dikes and dams as in the Netherlands.

*Polyes*    Basin meadows or large sinkholes.

*Pulses*    Edible seeds of legumes, usually beans and peas.

*Raion*    An area or division of an oblast.

*Residual soil*    Soil that is covering the bed rock from which it was formed.

*Retting*    Process of soaking or exposing to moisture of certain fibers such as flax or jute.

*Rift valley*    Valley formed by faulting in contrast to one formed by erosion.

*Sawahs*    Term used in place of paddy in Indonesia.

*Scablands*    An extremely desolate region north of the Palouse Country which is made up of wide, steep-sided, interlacing, dry channels.

*Scarp*    Steep slope caused by faulting or erosion.

*Scrub*    Vegetation chiefly of dwarf or stunted trees and shrubs as the "bush" area of Australia.

*Sedimentary*    Formed from the accumulation of sediments deposited in water; a class of rock.

*Selva*    Rain forest in Brazil.

*Sensible temperature*    The combination of temperature and humidity as it feels to the body.

*Sericulture*    Production of raw silk by the raising of silkworms.

*Sirocco*    Hot, dry wind blowing from Sahara.

*Skerry*   A rocky isle, a reef.

*Steppe*   Usually a plains area in a semiarid or subhumid region that is covered with short grass.

*Subsistence agriculture*   Producing for immediate needs of the family, very little, if anything, to sell.

*Syncline*   A downfold in the earth's crust.

*Synclinorium*   Folds of strata dipping toward a common line; series of folds that create a trough.

*Taiga*   Extensive northern forests predominantly of conifers in North America, Europe, and Asia.

*Tierra caliente*   Hot lands in tropical highlands of Americas up to elevations of 2,500 feet.

*Tierra fría*   Cool lands in tropical highlands of Americas, elevation about 6,500 to 12,000 feet.

*Tierra templada*   Temperate lands in tropical highlands of Americas, elevation approximately 2,500 to 6,500 feet.

*Till*   Unsorted and unstratified glacial drift deposited directly by melting of ice, with sand, gravel, clay, and boulders mixed.

*Timber line*   Elevation on a mountain above which trees do not grow, varies with latitude and exposure. A lower tree line may result from deficiency in rainfall.

*Trade winds*   Winds blowing toward the equatorial area from the subtropical high-pressure belts.

*Transhumance*   Movement of herds between upland and lowland pastures with the seasons.

*Troposphere*   Layer of the atmosphere next to the earth.

*Tundra*   Area poleward of the taiga, vegetation composed of lichens, mosses, and low bushes.

*Typhoon*   A hurricane near Asia.

*Velds*   Semiarid grasslands in which there may be scattered trees as in the Union of South Africa.

*Wadi*   Channel or bed of a watercourse which is dry except during or immediately after a rain as in desert or semidesert areas.

*Xerophytes*   Plants that are adapted to growth in areas of drought.

# Index

# Index